The Bacteria

VOLUME V: HEREDITY

THE BACTERIA

A TREATISE

The Bacteria

A TREATISE ON STRUCTURE AND FUNCTION

edited by

I. C. Gunsalus

Department of Chemistry
University of Illinois
Urbana, Illinois

Roger Y. Stanier

Department of Molecular Biology
University of California
Berkeley, California

VOLUME V: HEREDITY

1964

ACADEMIC PRESS • *NEW YORK AND LONDON*

ACADEMIC PRESS INC.
111 Fifth Avenue, New York, New York 10003

United Kingdom Edition published by
ACADEMIC PRESS INC. (LONDON) LTD.
Berkeley Square House, London W.1

LIBRARY OF CONGRESS CATALOG CARD NUMBER: 59-13831

First Printing, 1964
Second Printing, 1966

PRINTED IN THE UNITED STATES OF AMERICA

CONTRIBUTORS TO VOLUME V

Numbers in parentheses indicate pages on which the
authors' contributions begin.

ROBERT L. BALDWIN, *Department of Biochemistry, Stanford University School of Medicine, Palo Alto, California* (327)

ALLAN CAMPBELL, *Department of Biology, University of Rochester, Rochester, New York* (49)

ROYSTON C. CLOWES, *Medical Research Council, Microbial Genetics Research Unit, London, England* (253)

PATRICE DRISKELL-ZAMENHOF, *Department of Biochemistry, Columbia University, College of Physicians and Surgeons, New York, New York* (155)

JULIAN D. GROSS, *Medical Research Council, Microbial Genetics Research Unit, Hammersmith Hospital, London, England* (1)

D. A. HOPWOOD, *Department of Genetics, University of Glasgow, Glasgow, Scotland* (233)

PIERRE SCHAEFFER, *Physiologie Microbienne, Institut Pasteur, Paris, France* (87)

G. SERMONTI, *Research Unit for Microbial Genetics, Istituto Superiore di Sanità, Rome, Italy* (223)

ROGER Y. STANIER, *Department of Molecular Biology, University of California, Berkeley, California* (445)

N. SUEOKA, *Department of Biology, Princeton University, Princeton, New Jersey* (419)

CHARLES YANOFSKY, *Department of Biological Sciences, Stanford University, Stanford, California* (373)

PREFACE

Only seventeen years have passed since Luria, in the first modern review of bacterial genetics,* stigmatized bacteriology as "one of the last strongholds of Lamarckism," and stated that "scant knowledge and lack of agreement have until recently prevailed even in the most elementary facts of reproduction and character transmission in bacteria." The winds of change had begun to blow, however. Two germinal discoveries—the chemical identity of pneumococcal transforming principle as DNA, and the existence of genetic recombination in *Escherichia coli*—had recently been reported, and led Luria to suggest that "we may find ourselves on the threshold of a deep change in our ideas of bacterial heredity." The amplitude with which this cautious prognostication has been fulfilled is evidenced by many of the contributions contained in the present volume. In 1947, the dominant role that bacterial genetics would soon play in the formulation of our general concepts of heredity could scarcely have been foreseen by the most farsighted or optimistic exponent of this new branch of genetics; yet the connection has been so intimate that chapters on genetic fine structure, genetic replication mechanisms, and gene-enzyme relationships find a natural place in a volume devoted to the consideration of bacterial genetics.

The Editors wish to thank the contributors for their cooperation in the preparation of this, the final volume of "The Bacteria." As in the past we are deeply grateful for the expert help furnished so unfailingly by the publishers and the members of their staff.

March 1964

I. C. GUNSALUS

R. Y. STANIER

* *Bacteriol. Revs.* **11**, 1 (1947).

CONTENTS OF VOLUME V

The Bacteria

A TREATISE ON STRUCTURE AND FUNCTION

VOLUME I: STRUCTURE

VOLUME II: METABOLISM

VOLUME III: BIOSYNTHESIS

VOLUME IV: THE PHYSIOLOGY OF GROWTH

CHAPTER 1

Conjugation in Bacteria

JULIAN D. GROSS

I. Introduction

Three mechanisms of genetic exchange are known in bacteria: transformation, transduction, and conjugation. In each, a portion of the genetic material of one cell is introduced into another, giving rise to a partially diploid zygote.[1] The genetic material introduced from the donor cell cannot generally be maintained as an independently multiplying entity. However, genetic recombinants, i.e., clones of cells having characteristics of both the donor and the recipient cell, may arise from the zygotes as a result of genetic exchange between homologous regions of the two parental genomes.

In transformation the agent of transfer is purified DNA (deoxyribonucleic acid) extracted from the donor cell; in transduction bacteriophages act as vectors of genetic material. Both processes involve the transfer of relatively small amounts of genetic material, and their study has been of great importance in elucidating the chemical nature and fine structure of the genetic material. However, knowledge of the over-all organization of the genetic material in bacteria has been derived mainly from the study of conjugation, in which large amounts of genetic material, occasionally even a complete genome, may be transferred.

The outstanding studies of Lederberg and his collaborators,[1, 2] followed by those of Jacob and Wollman[3] and of Hayes,[4] have established that the genetic determinants of the characteristics of *E. coli* K12 are arranged in linear fashion on a single structure, or chromosome. The analysis of conjugation in other species suggests that the same is probably true of all Enterobacteriaceae. Evidence has been obtained that the chromosome of *E. coli* K12 is a closed or circular structure, that is, one having no ends.[3]

The ability to conjugate is conferred upon cells by the presence of discrete genetic determinants, which may exist independently of the bacterial chromosome and be transferred with high frequency during conjugation. They are closely allied to certain other determinants such as prophages and determinants of bacteriocin production.[5] The application of conjugation to analysis of the nature of these determinants has demonstrated that some, if not all, are capable of existing in two alternative states: an "autonomous" state, in which they are transferred independently of the bacterial chromosome, and an "integrated" state where they are transferred along with it.[5] Such determinants, known as episomes, are the subject of a separate chapter and will be considered here only when relevant to an understanding of conjugation. Conjugation in *E. coli* has been the subject of a number of excellent reviews.[1, 3, 6-8]

II. Conjugation in *Escherichia coli* K12

A. Determination of Mating Type

In 1946 Lederberg and Tatum observed the formation of prototrophic recombinants in mixtures of different multiple auxotrophic derivatives of *Escherichia coli* K12. The prototrophs arose at frequencies of about 1 per

10^7 parental cells and appeared as isolated colonies on solid medium on which neither of the two parental types of auxotrophic cells could grow.[9, 10] Recombinant formation was later shown to require direct contact between cells of the parental strains, since supernatants or filtrates of cultures of either strain were incapable of yielding recombinants when mixed with cells of the other strain.[10] Furthermore, no recombinants were formed when cultures of the two parental strains were placed in the separate arms of a U-tube divided by a sintered glass filter which prevented passage of intact cells from one arm to the other, but allowed thorough mixing of the culture fluids.[11]

The parental strains employed in some of the early crosses differed in characters other than their auxotrophic requirements and the important observation was made that these unselected characters did not assort at random among recombinants selected for prototrophy.[2, 9, 10] This indicated that the genetic determinants (markers) controlling these characters were physically associated in some precise manner. At that time genetic recombinants in bacteria were believed to arise by a process similar to meiosis in zygotes formed by the fusion of complete parental genomes. However, data obtained in further studies were difficult to reconcile with this assumption.

The first evidence that the parental cells do not play identical roles in conjugation was provided by Hayes, who showed that the cells of one of the parents could be pretreated with streptomycin and their viability drastically reduced without markedly affecting the yield of recombinants, whereas treatment of cells of the other parent prevented recombinant formation.[12] In addition, ultraviolet irradiation of the former strain stimulated recombinant formation while irradiation of the latter led to reduction in yield parallel with loss of viability.[13] These observations were interpreted as showing that cells of one of the parents serve as donors of genetic material, while those of the other act as recipients and give rise eventually to the recombinant clones.

The division of strains into donors and recipients was confirmed by the chance discovery of derivatives of a "donor" strain which were no longer fertile when mixed with cells of a "recipient" strain.[14-16] Systematic study indicated that combinations of donor and recipient cultures were generally about 10 times more fertile than mixtures of two donor strains and that crosses of two recipient strains were always sterile. Prior to this time all the combinations of strains which had been examined had evidently involved either mixtures of two donors strains or of a donor and a recipient strain. Cells of recipient type were found to be converted with high efficiency to donors by conjugation with donor cells.[14-16] The ability to act as donor appeared therefore to depend on the presence of a determinant, termed F,[14] which was transmitted with high frequency from donor (F^+)

to recipient (F⁻) during conjugation, in marked contrast to the low efficiency of transfer of chromosomal determinants (see Table I).

It was observed that recombinants tended to inherit most of their unselected markers from the F⁻ parent.[4, 15, 16] This led to the suggestion that the donor usually transfers only a part of its genome to the recipient cell, so that recombinants are derived from incomplete zygotes.[4, 16, 17] An alternative explanation involving the elimination of part of the donor genome after its transfer was also proposed[1, 15, 18] but was abandoned as a result of studies which will be considered below.

TABLE I

PROPERTIES OF HFR AND F⁺ DONOR CELLS[a]

Property	F⁺ donor	Hfr donor
Frequency of transfer of chromosomal determinants	Very low (10^{-4}–10^{-6}) for all determinants	Ranging from high (10^{-1}) to low (10^{-4}) for different determinants
Frequency of transfer of donor ability	Very high (0.5–10^{-1})	Low (10^{-3}–10^{-4})
Type of donor ability transferred	F⁺	Hfr
Linkage of donor ability to chromosomal determinants	Unlinked	Linked to determinants transferred with lowest frequency
Susceptibility of donor ability to acridines	Susceptible	Not susceptible

[a] See text for references.

The key to an understanding of the role of the *F* factor was provided by crosses involving a new type of donor cell, which originated from an F⁺ strain, and is referred to as Hfr[4, 19] (high frequency of recombination). In such crosses the yield of recombinants depends on the selected donor marker. With some markers the yield is up to 10^4 or 10^5 fold greater than in F⁺ crosses while with others it is not much more than in F⁺ crosses.[4] Jacob and Wollman have shown that the markers of any Hfr strain can in fact be arranged in a continuous gradient with respect to their frequency of transmission to recombinants.[3, 20] This gradient is due to the fact that transfer is a slow oriented process which starts at the same point of the chromosome or "origin," in all the cells of any one Hfr strain, and is interrupted by random spontaneous breakage of the chromosome as transfer progresses. As a result recipient cells receive fragments all of which start at the same point but have variable lengths.[3, 20] By contrast populations of F^+ cells give rise to approximately the same number of recombinants irrespective of the particular marker selected.

Comparison of the inheritance of donor ability in F^+ and Hfr crosses provides strong evidence that the F factor is in an autonomous state in F^+ cells, whereas it is attached to the bacterial chromosome in Hfr cells. A summary of the relevant observations is given in Table I. F^+ cells transfer donor ability with high frequency and independently of the bacterial chromosome whereas Hfr cells only rarely transfer the ability to act as donor[14, 15]; only those recombinants that inherit donor markers which are located at the furthest extremity of the chromosome and are thus transferred with lowest frequency may be donors and those that are donors are invariably of Hfr and not F^+ type.[4, 21, 22] The Hfr character thus behaves

Hfr strain	
HfrH	O —— Thr — Leu — T6 —— Try — His — Str —— Met — Thi —
HfrC	O —— T6 — Leu — Thr —— Thi — Met — Str —— His — Try —
J4	O —— Thi — Met — Str —— His — Try — T6 —— Leu — Thr —
G10	O —— Met — Thi — Thr — Leu — T6 —— Try — His —— Str —
AB-311	O —— His — Try — T6 —— Leu — Thr — Thi — Met — Str —

FIG. 1. The order of transfer of various chromosomal markers by different Hfr strains. O stands for the origin, the chromosomal extremity which first enters the recipient cell during transfer. The meaning of the symbols is given in the legend for Fig. 6.

as a chromosomal determinant linked to the terminal region of the Hfr chromosome. Further evidence for the chromosomal attachment of the F factor in Hfr cells is provided by the finding that their donor ability is not affected by growth in acridine orange, which is known to act upon various types of cytoplasmic particle, whereas after similar treatment a large proportion of F^+ cells are converted to F^-.[23] That the F factor is actually present in Hfr cells is indicated by the fact that Hfr cells can only arise from F^+ strains and that they can revert to the F^+ state.[4, 14] The transition from F^+ to Hfr and vice versa thus corresponds to chromosomal attachment and detachment of the F factor.

Jacob and Wollman have compared the orientation of chromosome transfer in a group of Hfr strains isolated from the same F^+ parent.[22] Interrupted mating experiments (see Section V, A) showed that all the cells of a given strain transfer their determinants in a precise sequence but that the order of transfer is different for each Hfr strain. The order of transfer of several Hfr strains is shown in Fig. 1. It may be seen that despite the difference in order of transfer the relative position of the markers does not change at all.[22] This observation provides convincing evidence that the determinants of *E. coli* K12 are located on a single chromosome. It is apparent that although the chromosomal structure transferred by the cells of any one Hfr strain has definite ends and may therefore be represented as a straight line the chromosome of the F$^+$ strain from which the various Hfr strains arose cannot be represented in this way. For, no matter in which linear sequence the markers are written, Hfr strains can be found which transfer the markers at opposite ends of the sequence in immediate succession. If, however, the F$^+$ chromosome is represented by a circle then the sequence of transfer by a given Hfr may be derived by

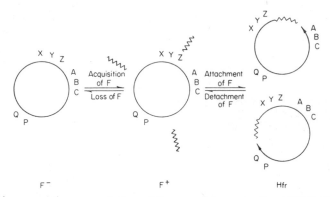

FIG. 2. Diagrammatic representation of the sexual types in *E. coli* K12. The *F* factor is indicated by a short zigzag line. The letters represent hypothetical chromosomal markers and the arrows the leading extremities (origins) of two possible Hfr types. From Jacob and Wollman (ref. 3, p. 187).

opening it at the appropriate point and reading the sequence of markers in one or the other direction from that point.[22]

Figure 2 contains a diagrammatic representation of the hypothesis concerning the determination of sexual types that has been developed by Jacob and Wollman.[3, 22, 24] The F$^-$ cell has a closed chromosome and no sex factor, while the F$^+$ cell also has a closed chromosome but contains autonomous *F* factors which enable it to conjugate with F$^-$ cells. The *F* factors are transmitted with high frequency during conjugation so that recombinants from F$^+$ × F$^-$ crosses are generally F$^+$. The transition from F$^+$ to a given Hfr type is due to attachment of an *F* factor at some point on the F$^+$ chromosome followed by actual or potential rupture of the chromosome at the point of attachment to give a linear structure. The extremity to which the *F* factor remains attached upon rupture corresponds to the distal extremity of the Hfr chromosome and the other to the leading extremity in transfer.

When the F factor becomes integrated to the chromosome a mechanism is set up which represses the multiplication of autonomous F factors.[25, 26] Consequently Hfr cells do not harbor any autonomous F factors, and recombinants from Hfr $\times$ F$^-$ crosses are F$^-$ except for the few which inherit the terminal chromosomal extremity and are Hfr. The integrated sex factor of Hfr cells very occasionally reverts to the autonomous F$^+$ state; sometimes, as discussed below, it carries with it a fragment of the bacterial chromosome adjacent to its site of attachment, giving rise to an intermediate donor strain in which the autonomous sex factor has a high affinity for its original site of attachment.

B. The Origin of the Fertile Cells in F$^+$ Populations

The fact that F$^+$ cells transfer the autonomous F factor efficiently but give rise to very few genetic recombinants, whereas cells in which F is integrated initiate chromosome transfer with extremely high efficiency suggests that F$^+$ cells as such, i.e., cells in which F is not associated with the chromosome, are unable to bring about chromosome transfer.[6, 27] The rare recombinants formed in mixtures of F$^+$ and F$^-$ cells are thought to be due to the presence in F$^+$ cultures of a small number of cells in which F has become attached to the chromosome. Since the F factor can become integrated at different sites the gradients of marker transfer corresponding to each particular site of attachment tend to cancel one another out, so that, among the population as a whole, all markers are transferred at approximately the same frequency.[6, 27]

It is not clear whether the association between F and the chromosome in the fertile cells of an F$^+$ population is invariably similar in its stability to that observed in the known Hfr strains or whether the latter represents only one extreme of a wide spectrum of stability. The attachment in an Hfr strain must be quite stable if it is to be isolated and maintained in the laboratory and even among the known Hfr strains the frequency of reversion to the F$^+$ state does vary somewhat.[28]

Jacob and Wollman have observed that the variation in fertility between small independent cultures of F$^+$ cells is considerably greater than between samples from the same culture.[27] This result indicates that fertility can be clonally inherited and therefore that a considerable proportion of the fertile cells which arise have some degree of stability. The same workers were able to isolate stable Hfr cells from most of the fertile cells detected in an F$^+$ population.[27] However, this does not necessarily mean that most of the fertile cells are typical Hfr's since the technique used in detecting the fertile cells involved indirect selection by replica plating and would be biased in favor of more stable donor types.

There is, in fact, some evidence that the fertile cells in F$^+$ populations may not be quite like typical Hfr cells. For example the majority of recombinants from $F^+ \times F^-$ crosses are F^+, and reconstruction experiments have shown that they must have acquired F from the cell which contributed the chromosomal marker to the recombinant.[29-31] The fertile cells in F^+ populations must therefore possess and be able to transfer F, unlike established Hfr cells. However, this difference is of doubtful significance, since irrespective of their stability a sizable proportion of the fertile cells present at any one time in an F^+ population must be of recent origin. They would therefore be expected to continue to harbor and transfer F pending its elimination as a result of repression of its multiplication. The existence of unstable donor cells is also indicated by experiments on the stimulation of the fertility of F^+ populations by ultraviolet (UV) irradiation.[4] It was found that the fertility of F^+ cultures reached a maximum about 1 hour after irradiation and then gradually fell off, indicating that most, if not all, of the increased fertility is due to unstable donor cells.

Work with conjugation systems other than that of *E. coli* K12 supports the idea that fertility can result from unstable interactions between F and chromosome. Zinder has reported that the fertile cells present in cultures of *Salmonella typhimurium* which have acquired the F factor by conjugation with *E. coli* K12, show some clonal stability. However, he was unable to isolate stable Hfr derivatives except after heavy UV irradiation of the donor cells.[32] In addition it has not proved possible to isolate any stable Hfr derivatives from P^+ strains of *Pseudomonas* which have donor properties similar to those of F^+ cells[33] (see Section III, I).

It appears, therefore, that the F factor can bring about transfer of the bacterial chromosome by becoming transiently attached to it. While there is no doubt that Hfr cells contribute to the fertility of F^+ populations the frequency of transfer of individual markers may be accounted for by assuming that the majority of fertile cells represent those in which the F factor has become transiently attached to one of an indefinite number of chromosomal sites.[8] Preliminary mapping of the origins of a number of Hfr strains (Fig. 7, p. 31) suggests that the number of sites of stable attachment is restricted.

C. Intermediate Donor Strains

Adelberg and Burns[34] have studied a derivative of an Hfr strain, which transfers its chromosome with high frequency and with the same orientation as the parent strain, but gives rise to recombinants which are themselves high frequency donors and transfer donor ability to cells with which they conjugate. This aberrant strain thus combines the infective properties of an F^+ with the high frequency chromosome transfer of an Hfr, and has been referred to as an intermediate donor. It appears to harbor a sex factor which has incorporated a segment of the bacterial chromosome near its site of attachment in the parent Hfr strain, and thus possesses a region of homology with the chromosome at the point where it had originally been attached. As a result it frequently becomes integrated at that point and brings about high frequency chromosome transfer with the same orientation as in the original Hfr parent.[34]

The chromosomal segment thought to be incorporated in this hybrid sex factor does not carry any known determinant. However, if the explanation of the behavior of the aberrant donor strain is correct, it should be possible to isolate cells harboring hybrid sex factors which carry known bacterial markers, provided that the F factor in the Hfr strain which one uses as source is located close to a convenient marker. Factors of this kind (called F') have been isolated from several different Hfr strains.[28, 35, 36] The segment of bacterial chromosome in the F' factors is variable in size but always corresponds to the distal end of the Hfr chromosome from which they originated. In addition, these factors invariably bring about high frequency chromosome transfer with the same orientation as in the parent Hfr strains.[28, 35] Their properties thus provide additional proof of the role of attachment of sex factor to chromosome in transfer of the latter.

A different type of intermediate donor strain has been described. Its properties may be illustrated by further observations made by Adelberg and Burns. They found that when the hybrid sex factor was eliminated from the original intermediate donor strain by acridine orange treatment and the resulting F^- cells infected with F the derivatives obtained were again intermediate donors, despite the fact that they now only harbored and transmitted a normal F factor. This remarkable observation suggested that the intermediate donor strain had originated in an event which not only gave rise to the hybrid sex factor but also left a piece of F at the initial point of attachment. This piece of F would not by itself be able to bring about chromosome transfer but would provide a region of homology for attachment of autonomous sex factors. Consequently, cells of this type harboring a normal F factor should mediate chromosome transfer with high frequency owing to the frequent association between F and the inserted material, which is referred to as a "sex factor affinity" (sfa) locus.[34]

Richter has studied a strain which carries an sfa locus at a different location.[37] It was isolated as a mutant incapable of fermenting maltose, after UV irradiation of an F^+ culture, and transfers its chromosome with high frequency and with constant orientation. Analysis of the inheritance of the intermediate donor property of this strain has provided direct proof of the presence of the sfa locus. Intermediate donor activity is transferred as a distal character during oriented chromosome transfer, just as is donor ability in Hfr cells. A further point of interest is that the sfa locus and the mal^- mutation are inseparable, showing that they must have arisen in one and the same event.

Intermediate donor strains thus fall into two categories: one possessing an *sfa* locus and normal *F* factor, and the other a hybrid *F* factor and a chromosome without any *sfa* locus. In each the high frequency of oriented chromosome transfer is due to homology between the sex factor and a specific point on the bacterial chromosome.

Cells harboring an *sfa* locus and normal *F* can exist in alternative states corresponding in all essentials to the F+ and Hfr states of normal K12 strains. Owing to frequent transition from one state to the other cultures grown from cells with *F* in the autonomous state contain about 1% of cells in which *F* is in the integrated state. Such populations therefore transfer chromosomal markers at moderately high frequency as well as being highly infective for *F*. Similarly, cultures grown from cells with *F* in the

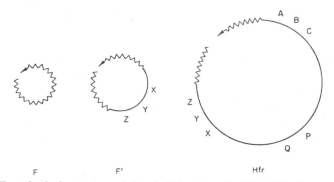

F   F'   Hfr

FIG. 3. Hypothetical structure of *F* and *F'* factors and of the Hfr chromosome. The genetic material of the *F* factor is represented by a zigzag line and that of the bacterial chromosome by a straight line. The arrows indicate the extremity of each structure which first penetrates the recipient cell and the letters represent hypothetical chromosomal markers.

integrated state contain about 1% of cells in which the sex factor has reverted to the autonomous state.[37] In intermediate donor strains of the other category the frequency of transition of the hybrid sex factor from autonomous to integrated states, and vice versa, appears to be so great that cultures in which one or the other state predominates cannot be obtained.[34]

D. The Mode of Attachment of the Sex Factor to the Chromosome

A general hypothesis for the mode of attachment of the sex factor is illustrated in Fig. 3. It is based on the idea that chromosome transfer is a special case of transfer of the sex factor itself, and on the fact that attachment of the sex factor not only determines the point at which the chromosome opens, but also specifies the direction of its transfer. It is assumed that transfer of *F* is itself an oriented process, and that the orientation of chromosome transfer is a direct result of this basic orientation. It is possible that the F factor is a closed structure which opens at a specified break point during conjugation. If so, this scheme would suggest that the Hfr chromosome is also closed except during its transfer, which is in accord with results obtained by Taylor and Adelberg.[37a] The scheme also allows for the possibility that in addition to the distal piece of F whose transfer is necessary for the inheritance of the Hfr character, there is also a piece located at the leading end of the chromosome.[34, 38]

The major feature of the scheme in Fig. 3 is the colinearity of F and the chromosome in Hfr cells. It has two advantages. The first is that, as already discussed, it could account well for the opening of the F^+ chromosome in the mutation to the Hfr state and for the imposition of a unique direction of chromosome transfer. Secondly, a single genetic exchange between a circular F or F' factor and the bacterial chromosome would give rise to a chromosomal structure like that in Fig. 3. The scheme would thus explain the ability of F' factors to bring about chromosome transfer. For further discussion the reader is referred to the stimulating review by Campbell.[39]

III. Other Systems of Conjugation

All systems of conjugation which have been studied in detail are controlled by episomal elements which are similar to the F factor. These elements will be referred to as conjugation factors. The only known properties conferred upon the cell by some conjugation factors are those directly connected with the ability to conjugate. Others carry, in addition, determinants of properties such as resistance to antibiotics or ability to ferment sugars. The main features of the conjugation systems known in Eubacteria are listed in Table II. Genetic exchange in actinomycetes is considered separately in Chapter 5.

A. Crosses between Strains of *Escherichia coli*

Lederberg and his co-workers have performed crosses between an F^+ strain of *E. coli* K12 and auxotrophic derivatives of a large number of other *E. coli* strains. Only about one in twenty of the combinations was fertile.[14] Ørskov and Ørskov examined 200 independent strains and detected recombinants in 18% of the crosses with an F^+ donor, and in 30% with Hfr donors.[40] The somewhat higher degree of interfertility observed by the latter workers is probably due to greater homogeneity of the strains examined. The infertility of most of these crosses is presumably due either to inability to form a cellular union, or to poor homology between the genetic material of the participating strains which would interfere with genetic recombination. In addition, other factors such as colicin production

JULIAN D. GROSS

TABLE II
Distribution and Major Features of Conjugation Systems[a]

Bacterial species in which conjugation was originally observed	Transmissible conjugation factor	Determinants associated with conjugation factor	Transfer of chromosomal determinants	Species to which conjugation factor has been transferred
Escherichia coli K12	F	None	+	*S. typhimurium, Shigella* sp.
E. coli K12	F'	Segments of the bacterial chromosome	+	*V. cholerae, S. marcescens, Salmonella* sp.
E. coli	Unnamed factors	None reported	+	*E. coli* K12
*Salmonella typhimurium** *E. coli* K12†	col I (col B)	Bacteriocin production	+	Various enterobacteria
E. coli *Shigella sonnei* *Shigella flexneri*	R	Antibiotic resistance	+	Various enterobacteria, *V. comma*
Salmonella typhosa	F^0-*lac*	Lactose fermentation	None detected	Various enterobacteria, *V. cholerae*
E. coli	Mutator transfer factor	Instability at streptomycin locus	Not examined	*E. coli* K12
Pseudomonas aeruginosa	FP	None	+	Not examined
Vibrio cholerae	P	Bacteriocin production (?)	+	Not examined
Serratia marcescens	None yet detected	—	+	—

[a] References concerning the various systems are given in the appropriate part of the text.

* *col I* was introduced from *Shigella sonnei* by mixed culture.[60]

† *col I* was introduced from *Salmonella typhimurium* by mixed culture.[63]

or the presence in the donor of prophages or other determinants may prevent the formation of recombinant clones.[41]

The *F* factor of *E. coli* K12 has been transferred to several other strains of *E. coli* as shown by the recovery of cells able to transmit it back to the donor or to act as donors of genetic material themselves; the fragmentary data available indicate that these F⁺ strains are generally infertile in crosses with *E. coli* K12.[14, 42, 43] The infertility is probably not due to inability of the *F* factor to bring about chromosome transfer in these hosts but rather to the same causes as the infertility observed in interstrain crosses in which *E. coli* K12 cells are the donors. Bernstein has in fact studied an F⁺ strain which was infertile when crossed with recipients of strain K12 but fertile in combination with derivatives of its own strain.[42] However, other strains were fertile as recipients in crosses with donors of strain K12 but could not be made fertile with K12 recipients by infection with F.[42] F⁺ strains of *E. coli* B can be produced and are fertile both with other derivatives of *E. coli* B and with F⁻ strains of K12.[44-47]

A large number of *E. coli* strains have been tested for ability to yield recombinants in crosses with an auxotrophic F⁻ derivative of strain K12. About one in forty was found to be fertile,[49] it is possible that a considerably higher proportion are fertile within themselves.[49] Some of the fertile strains must harbor transmissible conjugation factors since they are able to transfer fertility to an F⁻ strain of *E. coli* K12.[14, 15] These factors are not identical to *F* since some of them give rise to unstable donor strains when introduced into K12,[14] and there is evidence from examination of the segregation of unselected markers that the affinity of these factors for chromosomal sites is different.[49] The inability of certain other fertile strains to transfer fertility to *E. coli* K12 may be due to an even greater instability of their conjugation factor in the K12 host.

One interesting strain showed low fertility in crosses with K12 recipients and was unable to transfer fertility to the latter. It could be infected with *F* and the derivative obtained showed similar fertility to F⁺ strains of K12 but reverted with high frequency to the original donor type.[42] Other strains have been found which show little or no fertility in crosses with K12 recipients but can transmit to them conjugation factors which render them fertile.[49]

B. Crosses between *Escherichia coli* and Other Enterobacteriaceae

Crosses between donor strains of *E. coli* K12 and strains of *Salmonella* are generally infertile, but a few *Salmonella* strains do give rise to a low yield of recombinants.[50-53] If these recombinants are used as recipients in further crosses the yield of recombinants is considerably increased and analysis of such crosses has demonstrated over-all similarity in the sequence of chromosomal determinants in the two species.[53, 54] It has been suggested that the majority of cells of *Salmonella* strains are unable to act as recipients in crosses with *E. coli* K12 and that the few recombinants that are produced are derived from rare fertile mutants and consequently act as efficient recipients in further crosses. Such mutants can in fact be isolated by replica plating.[55] The mutation involved seems likely to affect the efficiency of cellular union with the donor cell rather than the acquisition of increased genetic homology with the *E. coli* chromosome since mutants with a greatly improved ability to act as recipients of F' factors from *E. coli* have been isolated in *Serratia marcescens*.[56]

The importance of genetic homology in the formation of recombinants is indicated by the fact that some *Salmonella* strains which do not yield any detectable genetic recombinants can act as recipients of autonomous determinants such as F' factors.[57] Moreover, crosses between *E. coli* K12 donors and strains of *Shigella* as recipients are fertile but the yield of recombinants is a hundred to a thousand times lower than when F$^-$ strains of *E. coli* K12 are used as recipients. The low yield is due to low recombination efficiency, since the chromosomal segment carrying lambda prophage has been shown to be transferred with high efficiency.[58]

The F factor has been transferred from *E. coli* K12 to *Salmonella typhimurium*[32] and to strains of *Shigella*.[58] The F$^+$ strains obtained are able to transfer F back to *E. coli*, but with considerably lower efficiency than to cells of their own species.

C. Crosses within Other Species of Enterobacteriaceae

Zinder has studied the fertility of crosses involving derivatives of *Salmonella typhimurium* which have received the F factor by conjugation with *E. coli*. The yield of recombinants in F$^+$ × F$^-$ crosses in *Salmonella* is similar to that in *E. coli*, and the frequency of inheritance of unselected markers indicates that the chromosomal segments transferred are also of about the same size in the two systems.[32]

Analysis of the fluctuation in yield of recombinants from independent F$^+$ cultures indicates that recombinants are derived from a small minority of fertile cells which have some degree of clonal stability, as in F$^+$ cultures of *E. coli* K12. Attempts to isolate stable Hfr strains by indirect selection were unsuccessful although an initial increase in the proportion of fertile cells was obtained. Hfr strains could, however, be isolated after irradiating the F$^+$ cells with large doses of ultraviolet light.[32] The Hfr character has been transferred from *E. coli* to *Salmonella* by selecting for recombinants inheriting a marker close to the distal chromosomal extremity of the Hfr strain used as donor.[54]

The properties of F+ strains of *Shigella* are strikingly different from those of F+ strains of *Salmonella*; none of them gave any recombinants in crosses either with other *Shigella* derivatives or with F− strains of *E. coli* K12 despite repeated attempts with a variety of selected markers.[58] This infertility may perhaps result from inability of the F factor to mobilize the *Shigella* chromosome for transfer due to the absence of any chromosomal site for its attachment.

D. CONJUGATION MEDIATED BY COLICINOGENY FACTORS

Fredericq and other workers have shown that the production of colicines and related substances is under the control of autonomous determinants which may be transferred during conjugation (see Chapter 4). It has been shown recently that certain determinants of colicine production, notably *col I* and *col B*, are able to mediate their own conjugal transfer as well as transfer of other colicinogeny determinants.[59, 60] Cells of established colicinogenic strains transfer the *col I* or *col B* determinant with only low efficiency. However, cells which have recently acquired the determinant transmit it with very high efficiency. This difference appears to be due to a difference in the efficiency with which they form contact with recipient cells.[61]

Ozeki and Howarth have shown that cells of *S. typhimurium* which have recently acquired *col I* can bring about transfer of chromosomal determinants with very low frequency.[62] Similar low frequency chromosome transfer has been observed in *E. coli* K12.[63] If the cells of *S. typhimurium* harbor *col E1* in addition to *col I* the frequency of chromosome transfer is increased approximately 100-fold.[62] The mechanism of this stimulation is unknown.

Chromosome transfer is unidirectional from *col+* to *col−* cells and appears to involve chromosome segments similar in size to those in F-mediated transfer.[63, 64] The study of *col*-mediated recombination adds further support to the evidence that the genetic determinants of *Salmonella* are arranged on a single chromosome and in the same sequence as in *E. coli* K12.[64] Moreover, it is not possible to ascribe any ends to the chromosome since all adjacent pairs of markers show a high frequency of joint transfer. It may therefore be concluded that the chromosome of *S. typhimurium* like that of *E. coli* K12 is a closed structure.[64]

E. TRANSMISSIBLE DRUG RESISTANCE

Since 1955 numerous drug resistant strains of *Shigella* and *E. coli* have been isolated from patients with bacillary dysentery in Japan (for review see ref. 65). Most strains are resistant to streptomycin, chloramphenicol, tetracycline, and sulfonamide, but others are only resistant to certain combinations of these four drugs. The determinants of drug resistance are located on an episomal structure, termed an R factor, which is capable of bringing about its own transfer by conjugation.[65-67] Multiple drug resistance can be transferred between *Shigella* and *E. coli*, and to most other species of Enterobacteria[65] and to *Vibrio cholerae*.[68] As in *col I*-mediated transfer, cells which have recently acquired an R factor transmit it with much higher efficiency than do cells of established resistant strains.[65] Transfer of R factors is stimulated by ultraviolet irradiation, which in addition renders the R factor very sensitive to elimination by acridine dyes.[69]

R factors are capable of bringing about transfer of chromosomal determinants at low frequency.[70] The frequency of chromosome transfer is increased 100-fold by the presence of the sex factor affinity locus *sfa* which, as discussed above, is believed to be a piece of the F factor inserted in the bacterial chromosome. Moreover, this transfer has the same orientation as that found by Richter in a strain harboring *sfa* and F factor.[70] These observations point to the existence of homology between F and R factors, and also support the general validity of the idea that chromosome transfer results from physical association between conjugation factor and chromosome.

Most R factors which have been examined have the interesting property of almost completely suppressing transfer of F or of the chromosome when introduced into F^+ or Hfr cells of *E. coli* K12.[65] This effect is associated with suppression of the characteristic surface component associated with the F factor (see Section IV,A) which is almost certainly required for contact formation.[71] The mechanism of this suppression will be considered below.

F. F^0-*lac* FACTOR OF *Salmonella typhosa*

Strain ST-2 of *Salmonella typhosa*, which was isolated from a hospital patient, is similar to other strains of typhoid bacteria except for its ability to ferment lactose. It is able to transfer this ability with varying efficiency to a wide variety of Enterobacteriaceae.[72, 73] The lactose fermenters so obtained are in turn able to transfer this character. It was at first thought that strain ST-2 was an Hfr strain with the exceptional property of transferring the Hfr character to all recombinants.[72] However, further analysis has shown that the determinant of lactose fermentation is located on an autonomous structure, termed F^0-*lac*, which is capable of mediating its own conjugal transfer as a single unit, independently of the bacterial chromosome.[73] Small doses of UV stimulate F^0-*lac* transfer 10- to 50-fold; stimulation reaches a maximum about an hour after irradiation and then decreases. A variety of strains harboring F^0-*lac* have been tested for ability to transfer several different chromosomal markers, with negative results.

The *lac* determinant of F^0-*lac* and the *lac* segment of *E. coli* K12 may be at least partially homologous since they can undergo genetic recombination. In addition, the F^0 determinant appears to be related to the *F* factor since cells harboring F^0-*lac* exhibit a weak but definite cross-reaction with antisera to the antigen of F$^+$ cells (see below). Also F^0-*lac*, like *F* or *F'* factors, is transferred more than a hundred times less efficiently to F$^+$ or Hfr strains of *E. coli* K12 than to F$^-$ strains.

G. Bacteriophage τ

A system of genetic transfer involving phage τ has been described briefly in a Japanese abstract[74] and in the review of multiple drug resistance.[65] Phage τ is a temperate phage which can lysogenize F$^-$ cells of *E. coli* K12. It adsorbs to F$^+$ cells but cannot establish lysogeny or multiply in them. It was initially thought that the transfer of genetic material mediated by τ required cellular contact. However, recent evidence indicates that the system involves transduction by free phage.

H. Streptomycin-Mutability Transfer Factor

Strains of *E. coli* exhibiting a high rate of mutability at the streptomycin locus have been isolated from hospital patients. These strains show a normal rate of mutation at all other loci tested. Evidence has been obtained that the instability at the streptomycin locus is due to a determinant of episomal nature.[75] Cells harboring the mutator episome transfer it at low frequency to *E. coli* K12. The frequency of transfer of the mutator episome is increased if the cells are made F$^+$ by infection from K12, but not by irradiation of the donor cells with ultraviolet light.

I. Conjugation in *Pseudomonas aeruginosa*

Conjugation in *Pseudomonas* was discovered by Holloway.[76] It is controlled by a transmissible factor which has been termed *FP*.[78] Crosses between FP$^+$ and FP$^-$ strains yield about 1 recombinant per 10^7 parental cells; those between two FP$^+$ strains yield somewhat fewer recombinants; while mixtures of FP$^-$ strains are sterile.[77] The production of recombinants has been shown to require cellular contact.[76]

Of four independent strains of *P. aeruginosa* which were studied three were found to act as donors of genetic material. Donor ability was not affected by treatment with acridines and consequently infection experiments could not be performed between derivatives of the same strain. However, both the donor strains that were tested were able to transfer fertility to the fourth strain. The efficiency of transfer in the two cases was different and the fertile derivatives resulting from acquisition of the *FP* factor from one of these donor strains were unstable.[33] Both these observations suggest that the donor strains harbor different conjugation factors.

There is good evidence that the production of recombinants results from unidirectional transfer of genetic material from FP$^+$ to FP$^-$ cells. Thus if FP$^+$ and FP$^-$ cells are first incubated together for half an hour, destruction of the FP$^+$ parent with virulent phages does not markedly reduce the number of recombinants formed, whereas destruction of the FP$^-$ abolishes recombinant formation. Furthermore, transfer is incomplete since the unselected markers of the recombinants tend to be derived mainly from the FP$^-$ parent.[33]

Attempts to clarify the origin of the small number of fertile cells in FP$^+$ populations gave inconclusive results although there appeared to be some variation in the fertility of independent FP$^+$ cultures. One culture gave an unusually high number of recombinants. Its fertility was found to decrease progressively on further subculturing and attempts to isolate stable Hfr strains by indirect selection either from this culture or from other FP$^+$ populations with or without prior UV irradiation were entirely unsuccessful. It thus appears that the capacity to initiate chromosome transfer, which may be supposed to result from chromosomal attachment of the *FP* factor, is always unstable.

The pattern of inheritance of seven markers has been examined in crosses involving various types of selection. The results indicate that all seven are located on a single physical structure, and are consistent with a linear arrangement of the markers. This result suggests that the genetic material of *Pseudomonas aeruginosa*, like that of *E. coli* and *S. typhimurium*, is organized as a single chromosome.[33]

J. CONJUGATION IN *Vibrio cholerae*

While screening pairs of strains of *Vibrio cholerae* for recombinant formation, one particular strain was observed to give rise to about 1 recombinant per 10^6 cells in mixtures with various other strains and to produce a lytic agent which was active on other *V. cholerae* strains.[79] Lysis was at first thought to be due to production of bacteriophage but it now seems more likely that a bacteriocin is involved.[80, 81] The ability to produce the lytic substance could be transferred to other strains, and its transfer was invariably accompanied by acquisition of fertility. The determinant *P*, responsible for the synthesis of the lytic substance, thus appears to play the role of a conjugation factor. As in the conjugation systems already considered, mixtures of P$^+$ strains are less fertile than combinations of P$^+$ and P$^-$, while P$^-$ mixtures are of course sterile.[79, 81]

Transfer appears to be unidirectional from P$^+$ to P$^-$ cells and is incomplete. Transfer of unselected markers has been detected but it is rare, suggesting that the segments of chromosome transferred are smaller in size than in *F*-mediated conjugation. Alternatively, the genetic determinants of *V. cholerae* may not be organized in a single chromosome.

K. CONJUGATION IN *Serratia marcescens*

Belser and Bunting have detected the formation of prototrophic recombinants in mixtures of auxotrophic derivatives of a strain of *Serratia marcescens*.[82] Recombinant formation requires cellular contact, and neither DNase (deoxyribonuclease) nor trypsin has any effect on the yield of recombinants. The various derivatives of the single *S. marcescens* strain which was examined could be divided into two groups, members of one of the groups being infertile with each other but fertile with members of the other group. This suggested that cells of the former group can act only as recipients while those of the other may act as donors of genetic material.

This interpretation was only partially substantiated by further observations. UV irradiation of cells of the group of "donor" strains leads to a very striking increase in fertility, just like similar treatment of F^+ cells of *E. coli* K12. However, irradiation of cells of the "recipient" strain also increases the yield of the cross. With the exception of one pair of markers no joint transfer of more than one marker was ever detected even when sensitive selective techniques were employed. These observations suggest that the segments of genetic material transferred during conjugation in this system are much smaller than in F-mediated chromosome transfer, and more analogous to those transferred in transduction or transformation.

Analysis of the inheritance of unselected markers indicated that cells of both groups of strains are able to act as donors. Although in most experiments the recombinants tended to inherit the unselected markers of the recipient strain there were generally some which inherited those from the donor strain; occasionally the proportion of these was very high.[82]

In summary, it appears that the genetic recombinants formed in *S. marcescens* result from the transfer during conjugation of very small segments of genetic material. The derivatives of the one strain which has been examined can be divided into two groups, which are in some ways very similar to F^+ and F^- types, on the basis of interfertility and with respect to the effect of UV irradiation on their fertility. However, cells of both groups show some ability to act as donors.

IV. Union between Donor and Recipient Cells

The capacity to conjugate may be regarded as a specific differentiation of the donor cell which makes possible infective transfer of the conjugation factor. From this point of view the process of conjugation is comparable with the infective transmission of bacteriophage particles. Transfer of phages takes place by means of free extracellular particles each possessing its own apparatus for attaching and injecting into a new host cell, whereas in conjugation it occurs by the formation of a temporary intercellular connection.

A. Surface Properties of Male Cells

The first demonstration of a physiological difference between donor and recipient cells of *E. coli* K12 was provided by Maccacaro, who showed that F+ cells have a greater affinity for acidic dyes than female cells, and precipitate out of suspension in less acid media. He also observed that F+ cells have a greater tendency to autoagglutinate.[83, 84] The inference that the surface of F+ cell is less negatively charged than that of F− cells has recently been confirmed by electrophoresis of intact cells.[85] F+ cells have also been found to be less motile than F− cells,[86] and there is evidence that male and female cells can be separated by countercurrent distribution.[87]

A characteristic surface antigen, termed $f+$, has been detected in strains which have acquired the *F* factor.[88] Antibody to the $f+$ antigen cross-reacts weakly with the surface of cells harboring the F^0-*lac* factor of *Salmonella typhosa*,[73] indicating that this factor controls the production of an analogous and related antigen. In addition, the presence of a surface antigen which is serologically unrelated to $f+$ has been demonstrated in cells of a wild strain of *E. coli* harboring a conjugation factor different from *F*.[89]

Phages which adsorb to F+ or Hfr cells of *E. coli* but not to F− cells have been isolated by several workers. Surprisingly the genetic material of these male-specific phages is RNA (ribonucleic acid) rather than DNA.[90-93] Phages which multiply in F− cells but are unable to multiply in male cells have also been isolated. One of them has been shown to adsorb less efficiently to male cells, presumably because its adsorption site is covered by the male-specific surface component(s).[92] Another adsorbs equally well to male and female cells of *S. typhimurium* but cannot multiply in the male.[94]

B. Modification of the Ability of Male Cells to Conjugate

The evidence that the surface component(s) responsible for the specific properties of male cells play a direct role in conjugation is derived from various instances of phenotypic or genetic modification of the ability of male cells to conjugate.

1. The Ability of Male Cells to Act as Recipients

Extensive pairing and clumping of cells may be observed microscopically in mixtures of male and female cells.[95, 96] Such interactions are virtually absent from cultures of male or female cells alone, indicating that specific pairing can only take place between cells of opposite mating type. The same conclusion is suggested by the low fertility of crosses between male strains observed in several conjugation systems; those recombinants which do arise in mixtures of male strains are believed to result from conjugation involving as the recipient a male cell in which the specific surface component is transitorily absent.

The role of surface components in specific pairing is strongly supported by the properties of so-called "F⁻ phenocopy cultures." These are cultures of cells of male genotype which have temporarily lost their ability to act as donors as a result of being grown to maximum cell density with aeration.[14] Such F⁻ phenocopy cultures have a markedly increased ability to act as recipients in crosses with normal donor cells.[14] Their behavior is just what would be expected if synthesis of the male surface component were temporarily suppressed. This interpretation is supported by the demonstration that aerated F⁺ cultures adsorb male-specific phage much less efficiently than nonaerated cultures.[92]

2. DEVIRILIZING ACTION OF PERIODATE TREATMENT

Further evidence that a surface component plays a role in conjugation is provided by the demonstration that brief exposure of male cells of *E. coli* K12 to periodate markedly reduces their ability to pair with female cells.[97] The treated cells regain their mating ability after 1 or 2 hours' growth in broth. The identity of the periodate reactive surface component with that responsible for the adsorption of male-specific phages has been demonstrated by the observation that periodate-treated cells have reduced ability to adsorb male-specific phages.[92] Transfer of *R* factors has also been shown to be temporarily suppressed by periodate treatment,[65] indicating that *R* factor-mediated conjugation also involves a periodate-sensitive surface component.

3. SUPPRESSION OF CONJUGATION IN ESTABLISHED STRAINS

Cells which have recently acquired certain types of conjugation factor conjugate with very high frequency but lose the ability to conjugate after a few generations.[61, 65] In the case of *col I*-mediated conjugation it has been conclusively shown that loss of ability to conjugate is due to inability to form contacts with recipient cells; this observation again points to the importance of some surface component in conjugation.[61] Preliminary experiments have not revealed the presence of any specific surface antigen on cells recently infected with *col I*.[61]

4. SUPPRESSION OF *F*-MEDIATED CONJUGATION BY *R* FACTORS

Several groups of workers (see ref. 65) have observed that transfer of *F* or *F'* factors is virtually eliminated and chromosome transfer by Hfr cells markedly reduced by the introduction of *R* factors into male strains of *E. coli* K12. This effect is not due to elimination of the *F* factor since the cells regain their original properties when the *R* factor is lost. It appears instead

to be due to suppression of the synthesis of the surface substance controlled by the F factor, since cells harboring F and R factors have been
shown to lack the sites for adsorption of F-specific male phages.[41] Moreover, some R factors have been isolated which do not suppress the ability
of the F+ or Hfr cells to adsorb male-specific phages and they also do not
suppress their fertility.[41]

Watanabe and Fukasawa have proposed that suppression is due to synthesis, under the control of the R factor, of a surface component which
replaces or covers the corresponding component synthesized by the F
factor.[98] This explanation would imply that F-mediated transfer cannot
take place through intracellular connections formed as a result of specific
pairing involving the R factor surface component. An alternative which
avoids this implication is suggested by the fact that R factor-mediated
conjugation is one of the systems which is suppressed in cells in which the
conjugation factor has become established. If this is due to production of
a repressor which inhibits synthesis of a surface component by the R
factor,[8] this repressor might also act on the F factor, inhibiting its functional activity. This explanation gains some support from the evidence of
homology between F and R factors indicated by the affinity of the latter
for the sfa locus of Richter's strain.[40] If it is correct, then F-mediated
transfer should not be inhibited in cells newly infected with R factor. Furthermore, transfer of those R factors which do not supress F-mediated
transfer may perhaps itself not be suppressed in established strains.

It may be noted that all the instances of suppression of fertility in $E.$
$coli$ K12 have been found to involve loss of the the component responsible
for adsorption of the male-specific phage. It therefore seems probable that
one and the same component is responsible for all the specific surface properties of male cells. The periodate sensitivity of this component suggests
that it is a polysaccharide. Strains of $E.\ coli$ K12 harboring either F[99, 100] or
R factors[65] retain their ability to conjugate when converted to spheroplasts,
indicating that the male component is located in that part of the cell wall
which is retained by the spheroplast.

Nothing is known about the nature and degree of specificity of the surface structure of recipient cells. No treatment has yet been found which
impairs ability to act as recipient. However, the low efficiency of conjugation in most interstrain or interspecies crosses is possibly due in part to
poor complementarity with the male component, and mutations leading to
increased ability to act as recipient may well involve alterations in surface
structure.

Various male strains which exibit a heritable alteration of fertility have
been isolated; in some cases the mutation has been unambiguously shown
to be located on the F factor. Some of the mutations probably result in al-

terations or absence of the surface component(s). For example, Clark[101] has isolated a mutant strain from an Hfr culture by selecting for resistance to a male-specific phage. It adsorbs the phage with reduced efficiency and has much lower fertility than the parent strain. Similar mutants have been described by Cuzin.[102] Another case is the so-called F-refractory strain,[23, 43] isolated from an Hfr by selection for high motility.[86] It has very low fertility and perhaps harbors a mutant F factor in the integrated state.

A different type of alteration is probably involved in the mutant clones isolated by Jacob and Wollman[103] and by Cuzin[102] after UV irradiation of cells harboring an F-lac factor. These derivatives still segrated lac⁻ cells by loss of the F-lac⁺ factor but were incapable of transferring either the F′ itself or chromosomal makers, or did so very inefficiently. They appear to have retained the ability to synthesize the surface component(s) since they exhibit the poor ability to act as recipients characteristic of male strains, and are presumably blocked in some function involved either in the formation of the intracellular connection or in active transfer.

C. THE KINETICS OF CELLULAR UNION

The formation of cellular union may be taken to include the sequence of events which culminates in the formation of an intercellular connection between mating cells. These events include random collision between male and female cells, and pairing by means of the surface structures considered above. In addition, there must occur a localized breakdown of the cell walls and membranes of the participating cells and the formation of some connecting structure. Three procedures are available for studying these various steps.

1. Microscopic observation, which gives an indication of the frequency and rapidity of visible interactions between donor and recipient cells.

2. Measurement of effective contact formation. This may be defined as the formation of a connection between conjugating cells which is sufficiently strong to prevent their being separated by gentle dilution.[6, 104] It is evident that the formation of effective contact need not correspond to the completion of cellular union. Indeed, there is ample evidence for a variable delay between effective contact formation and initiation of transfer; this delay may correspond to the time required for completion of cellular union.[104, 105]

3. Measurement of the amount of transfer which has taken place at successive times by stopping further transfer. This should give a precise indication of the kinetics of cellular union, provided transfer is initiated immediately after completion of cellular union and proceeds at constant rate. Allowance must, of course, be made for the time taken for actual transfer.

From an examination of these three procedures it should be evident that there is at present no way of distinguishing experimentally between hypothetical steps involved in the completion of cellular union, and those involved in the initiation of transfer.

The formation of pairs and clumps of male and female cells has been observed with the light microscope by several authors[95, 96, 106] and occurs with equal frequency whether the male is F+ or Hfr. The occurrence of clumps of various sizes demonstrates that mating is not restricted to individual pairs. In fact pairs are only present in large numbers during the first few minutes after mixing donor and recipient cells. Thereafter they give way to groups of cells of varying degrees of complexity[96] whose biological significance is shown by the efficiency with which triparental recombinants are formed in appropriate mixtures.[107, 108]

Conjugation has also been studied with the electron microscope.[109] A micrograph of a mating pair in which the connection between the mating cells is clearly visible is reproduced in Fig. 4. Examination both in the light microscope and in the electron microscope has shown that pairing is not restricted to any particular area of the cell surface.

Since the formation of effective contact is only detected genetically if it is followed by some type of transfer, it is important to interfere as little as possible with transfer. Donor and recipient cells are mixed and samples removed at intervals and diluted to prevent further contact formation. After a period of incubation to allow transfer the samples are plated on selective medium. It is important to use an excess of female cells in the mating mixture since at higher donor concentration the yield of recombinants may cease to be a linear function of the extent of contact formation owing to cell clumping and associated physiological effects.[108]

Effective contact formation commences immediately after mixing Hfr and F− cells of *E. coli* K12 and proceeds at a rate which is proportional to the product of the initial parental densities. An experiment in which transfer of prophage λ was measured by observing the extent of zygotic induction is presented in Fig. 5. It may be seen that contact formation (curve A) is essentially complete by 30 minutes after mixing. Figure 5 also contains the data obtained when the actual extent of transfer of λ prophage was measured in successive samples by deliberately breaking apart the mating cells. The curve obtained (curve B) parallels fairly closely the curve for effective contact formation and is separated from it by the time required for transfer of the segment of chromosome between the origin and the prophage locus. The kinetics of contact formation in high-frequency, *col I*-mediated conjugation appears to be quite similar.[61]

The role of specific pairing in the formation of effective contact is well illustrated by the observations of Fisher, who has shown that zygote formation in defined medium is pH dependent; he has interpreted this dependence

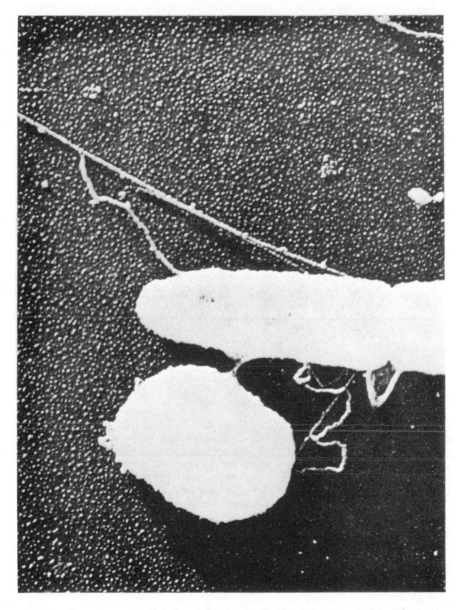

FIG. 4. Electron micrograph of conjugating bacteria. The elongated flagellate cell which is undergoing division is an Hfr cell of *E. coli* K12. The plump cell belongs to *E. coli* C. The conjugating cells are connected by a clearly visible bridge. From Anderson *et al.*[16c]

as being due to alteration in the efficiency of pairing as a result of changes in the distribution of ionized groups on the bacterial surface.[110, 111] The presence of streptomycin was also found to reduce the efficiency of contact formation even when both parents are streptomycin resistant. The streptomycin probably acts by complexing with groups involved in pairing.[112] It has been shown recently that extracts of the cell walls of male or female

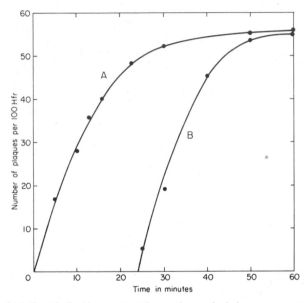

Fig. 5. The kinetics of effective contact formation and of chromosome transfer. Streptomycin-sensitive, λ-lysogenic HfrH cells were mixed with an excess of streptomycin-resistant nonlysogenic F⁻ cells, and the mixture shaken gently at 37°C. Samples were taken at intervals and either diluted carefully in one-tenth normal strength nutrient broth (curve A) or treated in a blendor to stop further transfer (curve B). The blended samples were plated immediately with streptomycin-resistant indicator bacteria on to nutrient agar plates containing streptomycin. The untreated samples were kept at 37°C. without agitation and plated 60 minutes after the beginning of the experiment. From Wollman and Jacob.[20]

cells of *E. coli* K12 or *E. coli* B interfere with an early step in zygote formation, presumably contact formation.[113] As the activity of extracts of male cells as well as of female cells is unaffected by periodate the interference is probably due in each case to the F⁻ surface component, or to some non-specific substance.

D. Energy Requirement for Cellular Union

The transfer of material during conjugation requires not only specific pairing between donor and recipient cells but also removal of the barriers to transfer constituted by their cell walls and cytoplasmic membranes. This is achieved by the formation of a direct cytoplasmic connection or "bridge" between the cells, which may be triggered off by pairing with the female cell.

The formation of cellular union appears to be an energy-dependent, temperature-sensitive process which utilizes the high-energy bonds generated by oxidative phosphorylation. It cannot take place under anaerobic conditions and is severely inhibited by dinitrophenol.[110, 114, 115] Numerous other observations have been made on the effect of various agents on conjugation but it is generally not possible to determine whether the effects are on the formation of cellular union or on transfer, which is itself an energy-requiring process.[115]

There is evidence that a source of carbon is required by the donor but not by the recipient cell for the formation of effective contact and for transfer.[110] The energy-dependent process in the formation of cellular union may involve synthesis by the donor cell of a specific structure connecting it with the female. If so its synthesis in E. coli K12 must be highly resistant to streptomycin.[12, 36] On the other hand, streptomycin treatment of sensitive donor cells of Pseudomonas completely destroys their ability to conjugate.[33]

E. THE MAINTENANCE OF CELLULAR UNION

The extent of transfer depends not only upon the efficiency with which cellular union is established but also upon the length of time that it is maintained. The latter factor is of particular importance in the case of chromosome transfer; the less stable union is, the more pronounced will be the gradient in the extent of transfer of successive markers. The stability of union is affected by mechanical agitation during aeration or plating[116] and is greater when mating takes place on solid rather than in liquid medium.[117] In addition, it has been found that the gradient of transfer is greatly increased in the case of certain Hfr strains, but not others, by the presence of a complete mixture of amino acids.[104] The choice of recipient appears to have no effect, thus supporting the idea that the donor alone is responsible for the formation and maintenance of cellular union.[104]

Taylor and Adelberg have isolated several Hfr derivatives of an F+ strain and all appear to have a lower gradient of marker transfer than usual Hfr strains. Their stability is perhaps due to the formation of unusually stable connections with the recipient cells.[118]

F. PHYSIOLOGICAL EFFECTS OF CELLULAR UNION

Observation of the multiplication of exconjugant cells isolated by micromanipulation has shown that in general both donor and recipient cells remain viable.[95, 96, 106] The high efficiency of triparental recombinant formation indicates, moreover, that mating with more than one Hfr cell need have no lethal effect on the F⁻ cell.[107, 108] However, experiments in which the ratio of donor to recipient cells was varied have revealed that with certain combinations of strains mating may lead to inhibition of multiplication of the F⁻ or even loss of F⁻ viability. Hfr strains may be divided into two groups. Cells of one group have a marked effect on the growth of their F⁻ mates, while those of the other have little or no effect. Furthermore, F⁻ strains differ in their sensitivity; one F⁻ strain, in particular, which is very sensitive to the inhibitory effects of mating has been found. The extent of the effect is a function of the ratio of donor to recipient cells; matings between an excess of Hfr cells of the first type and cells of the sensitive F⁻ strain lead to a marked loss of F⁻ viability and a correspondingly low yield of recombinants, while at lower Hfr concentrations inhibition of the multiplication of the F⁻ exconjugants is only temporary.[108]

The loss of viability has been shown to be due to mating of recipient cells with several Hfr cells. Killing does not occur at the time of contact formation but rather over a period of up to about 20 minutes thereafter. This period may correspond to the interval between contact formation and the completion of cellular union. It is tempting to suppose that the loss of viability is due to a phenomenon similar to lysis-from-without which occurs after the adsorption of many particles of bacteriophage onto a bacterial cell.[119]

A characteristic staining reaction has been found to take place when male cells of *E. coli* K12 are cross-streaked against F⁻ cells of *S. typhimurium* on an acid indicator medium. It is thought to result from a surface interaction between the cells which causes sufficient damage to allow dye to enter the acid cytoplasm but apparently does not lead to loss of viability. It is not observed in cross-streaks of male and female cells of the same species, *S. typhimurium* or *E. coli*.[32]

V. Chromosome Transfer during Conjugation

A. ORIENTED TRANSFER

The concept of unidirectional transfer of genetic material originated from observations of the effect of streptomycin treatment and of ultraviolet irradiation on the fertility of crosses.[12, 13] Later, micromanipulation experiments showed that recombinants are derived solely from F⁻ exconjugants.[95, 96, 106] Moreover, once transfer has taken place the male parent can be killed with virulent phage without affecting the yield of recombinants.[33, 111] The unidirectional nature of transfer follows from the fact that transfer of the bacterial chromosome is dependent upon association between the chromosome and the conjugation factor so that only cells harboring a conjugation factor are able to act as chromosome donors.

The incomplete nature of the chromosomal contribution of the donor cell to zygotes was deduced from the study of F^+ by F^- matings. Recombinants from such matings were found to derive most unselected markers from the F^- parent.[14, 15, 16] The reason for the incomplete donor contribution became clear when crosses involving Hfr males were analyzed. These led to the discovery that chromosome transfer is an oriented progressive process which may be interrupted spontaneously, giving rise to incomplete zygotes containing variable segments of the donor chromosome.[20, 111, 120]

The evidence for oriented transfer comes principally from interrupted mating experiments. In such experiments samples are withdrawn at intervals from a mixture of Hfr and F^- cells and further transfer prevented by separating the mating cells by violent mechanical agitation[120] or by killing the donor cells selectively with virulent bacteriophage, generally T6.[111] The extent of transfer of different markers is measured either (a) by plating the treated samples on different selective media to determine the number of recombinants which inherit various donor markers, or (b) by plating on to a single type of selective medium and scoring the recombinants for inheritance of each of a group of unselected markers. An example of the latter type of experiment is presented in Fig. 6.

By these means it has been shown that each Hfr marker is transferred at a definite and characteristic time by a given strain of Hfr.[111, 120] Transfer of all the donor markers beginning with the origin of the chromosome and ending with the terminally attached sex factor requires approximately 120 minutes.[20, 118] As described in Section II,A, the origin and direction of chromosome transfer depends upon the Hfr strain but the relative position of chromosome markers is constant. Figure 7 contains a schematic representation of the chromosome of *E. coli* K12 based upon interrupted mating experiments. It also gives an indication of the time interval between penetration of pairs of markers and the order of marker transfer in different Hfr strains.

The evidence for oriented transfer of the bacterial chromosome is supported by the results of uninterrupted matings; it is found that the number of recombinants which receive a particular Hfr marker depends on the length of time required for its transfer.[20, 120] This correlation, which is illustrated in Fig. 8, may be accounted for by spontaneous interruption of oriented transfer. Correspondence between the extent of transfer and distance from the origin is observed in all Hfr strains and would be difficult to account for it it were due to elimination of segments of the donor chromosome after their transfer, as was at one time proposed.[1, 15] The idea of partial transfer is strongly supported by observations on the transfer of prophages located at widely different positions on the chromosome. Multiplication of each of these prophages is known to be initiated immediately they are introduced into the recipient cell, so that the number of lytic centers is a direct measure of the frequency of their transfer. The number of lytic centers is, in fact, found to depend on the distance of the particular prophage locus from the origin of the Hfr chromosome.[116, 121] Furthermore,

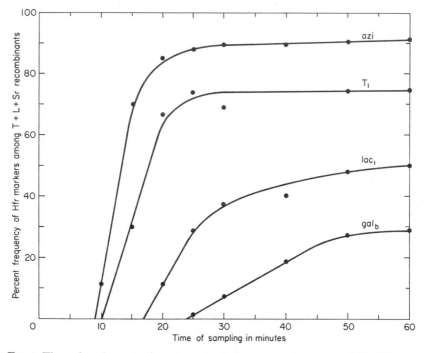

FIG. 6. The order of penetration of proximal chromosomal markers of HfrH bacteria during conjugation. Samples were taken at intervals from a mixture of str[s] HfrH and str[r] F- bacteria and blended to stop further transfer. The treated samples were then plated to select for $TL^+ str^r$ recombinants, and the recombinants analyzed as to their genetic constitution. From Wollman and Jacob.[20]

Wollman and Jacob have shown that in crosses in which transfer and consequent zygotic induction of prophage λ occurs with high frequency virtually no recombinants inherit markers which are closely linked to the prophage site, whereas a considerable number inherit markers which are transferred some time before the prophage.[122, 123] These recombinants are derived from zygotes which, owing to spontaneous interruption of transfer, do not receive λ and are therefore able to give rise to recombinants.

Further confirmation of the idea of progressive transfer of a single linear chromosome is provided by experiments in which P[32] is incorporated

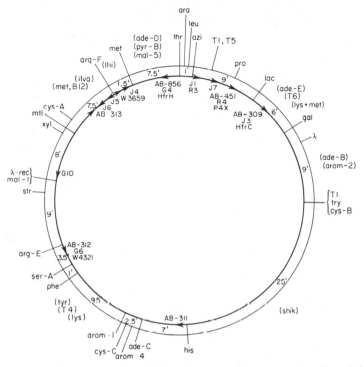

Fig. 7. The linkage group of *E. coli* K12. The outer line shows the order of chromosomal markers. The map is based upon a diagram prepared by Dr. A. L. Taylor (*Genetics*, in press). The interval between markers shown by darker lines extending to the inner circle represents the time between penetration of the successive markers. The inner circle represents the order of chromosome transfer by various Hfr strains. The data on the origin and direction of transfer of the various Hfr strains is derived from the work of Dr. A. L. Taylor and several other authors. Each arrow corresponds to the origin of the corresponding Hfr strain. The disposition of the chromosomal markers and of the origins of the Hfr strains is approximate, and the correspondence between the origins of various Hfr strains is tentative.

The symbols correspond to: requirement for threonine (*thr*), arginine (*arg*), leucine (*leu*), vitamin B$_{12}$ (*B$_{12}$*), proline (*pro*), adenine (*ade*), lysine (*lys*), methionine (*met*), various combinations of aromatic amino acids or aromatic vitamins (*arom*), pyrimidine (*pyr*), tryptophan (*try*), cysteine (*cys*), shikimic acid (*shik*), histidine (*his*), tyrosine (*tyr*), phenylalanine (*phe*), serine, or serine or glycine (*ser*), isoleucine plus valine (*ilva*), thiamine (*thi*); fermentation of arabinose (*ara*), lactose (*lac*), galactose (*gal*), maltose (*mal*), xylose (*xyl*), mannitol (*mtl*); resistance to sodium azide (*azi*), phages T1 and T5 (*T1,T5*), phage T6 (*T6*), phage T1 (*T1*), phage T4 (*T4*), streptomycin (*str*); lysogenicity for phage λ (λ) and synthesis of surface receptor substance for phage λ (λ-*rec*). Capital letters refer to loci, and numbers to independent mutant isolates. Brackets indicate that the location of the marker with respect to neighboring markers has not been exactly determined.

The Hfr strains were isolated by: Jacob and Wollman (J) and (P), Lederberg (W), Hayes (H), Adelberg (AB), Reeves (R), Cavalli (C), Goldschmidt (G).

into the genetic material of the donor cells which are then stored prior to mating, to allow radioactive decay to occur. P^{32} decay reduces the transfer of donor markers to an extent dependent on the time required for their transfer. Its effect is therefore to increase the gradient of transfer, presumably by causing random breaks in the bacterial chromosome and preventing transfer of markers beyond the point of breakage.[124, 125]

By assuming that P^{32} decay breaks the chromosome with the same efficiency with which it kills phage or bacteria it is possible to estimate that 1 minute of chromosome transfer corresponds to the penetration of 10^5 nucleotide pairs of DNA. This calculation is consistent with chemical estimates of 10^7 nucleotides for the DNA content of the bacterial nucleus, since the chromosome requires just over 100 minutes to be transferred in its entirety.[24, 125]

	Thr	Lac	Gal	Try	His	Str	Met
Gradient of transmission (% Hfr input)	46	36	30	18	6	1	0.1
Time of transfer (min)	8-8½	18	24	33	59	90	115

FIG. 8. The correlation between the time of transfer of chromosomal markers and the frequency of their transmission to genetic recombinants. These data refer to transfer by HfrH bacteria. From Hayes et al.[7]

B. KINETIC ANALYSIS OF TRANSFER

1. ASYNCHRONY OF TRANSFER

In the experiments of the type just described the formation of mating pairs can take place during the entire period of the mating. As a result there is great variation in the time at which transfer is initiated, which tends to obscure the finer details of the transfer process; the slope of the curve representing the increase in the numbers of recombinants of a given type in successive blended samples reflects primarily the rate of cellular collision and union and only secondarily the kinetics of transfer itself. The spread in time of mating can be reduced by allowing contact formation for only a brief period, then diluting the mating mixture to prevent further collisions, and studying the kinetics of transfer in the pairs present at the time of dilution. By this means it has been possible to demonstrate the existence of two types of asynchrony in the transfer process.[104]

First, a variable interval elapses between the time of effective contact formation and the initiation of chromosome transfer. In some pairs there is a delay of up of to 15 minutes before transfer is initiated.[104] A similar delay has also been observed in the case of transfer of F' factors[105] and colicinogeny determinants.[61] It may be due to variation in the time required for the completion of cellular union or for mobilization of the material for transfer. Second, in some Hfr strains but not others the rate of chromosomal transfer by individual cells varies. This is shown by the fact that the spread in the time taken for transfer of a given marker to be completed in all mating pairs increases with increasing distance of the marker from the origin of the Hfr chromosome.[104] Nothing is yet known of the reason for the variable rate of chromosome transfer nor why it occurs in some Hfr strains only. An additional source of asynchrony exists in the case of chromosome transfer by cells harboring an F' factor. As already mentioned, the F' is not stably attached to the chromosome as is the F factor in Hfr cells, but instead alternates between autonomous and integrated states. Consequently, the spread in the time between contact formation and initiation of transfer is considerably greater than in Hfr cells; the number of cells which can initiate transfer is small at first and increases progressively as the F' becomes attached in additional cells.[34]

2. CHROMOSOME WITHDRAWAL

Experiments in which the period of contact formation is limited by dilution of the mating mixture have brought to light an additional phenomenon. Under such conditions the number of recombinants in successive blended samples rises rapidly after an interval corresponding to the minimum time required to transfer the selected marker and then decreases over a period of about 30 minutes to a value which may be as low as half the maximum. The evidence suggests that this reduction is due to withdrawal in some of the mating pairs of the segment of donor chromosome which has penetrated the F^- cell. When the cells are mechanically separated before withdrawal has occurred the donor segment remains in the F^- and can participate in recombination. Withdrawal is thought to occur when mating cells separate provided the chromosome has not been broken before or at the time of separation.[104, 104a]

C. PHYSICAL DETECTION OF CHROMOSOME TRANSFER

The effect of P^{32} decay on chromosome transfer[124] indicates that the chromosome contains nucleic acid, presumably DNA, and that the nucleic acid is responsible for maintaining the structural continuity of the chromosome. Several successful attempts have been made to detect the transfer of nucleic acid from donor to recipient cells. Garen and Skaar[126] grew donor cells in P^{32}-containing medium and obtained evidence that

P^{32}-containing material corresponding to about 10% of the DNA of the donor cells was transferred to the F^- in 1 hour. Silver[127] has performed experiments using labeled thymidine which demonstrate progressive transfer of DNA-containing material from Hfr to F^- cells. The total amount of tranfer corresponds to about 9% of the DNA content of the donor cells, or an average of one-fourth to one-sixth of a chromosome per cell, assuming that the cells have an average of three nuclei. Study of the chemical nature of the material transferred by Hfr cells during conjugation may provide an answer to the important question whether the bacterial chromosome consists of DNA alone or also contains other material. No transfer of RNA or protein has been detected but the resolution of the methods of anaylsis used was not sufficient to exclude transfer of small amounts of these substances associated with the bacterial chromosome.[127] It is not yet known whether the chromosome transferred during conjugation is one of those present in the donor cell before the onset of mating or whether it represents a newly synthesized replica. Experiments with inhibitors of DNA synthesis should provide an answer.

VI. Transfer of Nonchromosomal Material during Conjugation

A. Transfer of Conjugation Factors

Interrupted transfer experiments provide a rough indication of the minimum time required to transfer a given conjugation factor. The minimum time for transfer of the F factor appears to be 4–5 minutes at $37°$,[97, 128] whereas various F' factors which have been examined require somewhat longer.[28, 105] Some transfer of $col\ I$ has been reported to occur within 2.5 minutes of mixing the cells[61] while transfer of F^0-lac[73] and R factors[65] has been observed within 5 minutes of mixing. An interesting fact which emerges from interrupted mating experiments is that transfer of F' factors is an oriented process, with the determinant of maleness penetrating the recipient cell last just as in transfer of the bacterial chromosome by an Hfr donor.[28] Oriented transfer of the F^0-lac factor and R factors has not yet been demonstrated.

A special case is provided by the transfer of conjugation factors in cells which are simultaneously transferring their chromosome. The fact that in Hfr cells of $E.\ coli$ K12 the F factor is not transferred as an autonomous determinant but only in association with the terminal extremity of the chromosome is probably due simply to the absence of any autonomous F factors.[26] Prototrophic recombinants derived from F^+ by F^- matings,[29-31] and recombinants receiving chromosomal markers from cells harboring an F' factor[34] almost always receive the F or F' factor as well, indicating that it is transferred with high efficiency at the same time as the bacterial chromosome. It would seem, therefore, that autonomous conjugation factors can be transferred efficiently at the same time as the bacterial chromosome.

B. Transfer of Determinants Other Than Conjugation Factors

The determinants of *col E_1* and *col V* are transferred efficiently by both F+ and Hfr cells of *E. coli* K12.[129-131] It was at first believed that transfer of *col E_1* by Hfr cells took place when it was attached to the bacterial chromosome,[130] but recently Clowes has shown that it is in fact transferred independently of the bacterial chromosome in all of several Hfr strains examined as well as in F+ strains.[132] Other determinants, such as *col E_2* ,[131] *P1* prophage,[133, 134] and *F^0-lac*,[73] are transferred with much lower efficiency. The reason for this lower efficiency of transfer is unknown, but in these cases too the efficiency of transfer by F+ and Hfr cells appears to be essentially the same. Both *col E_1* and *col E_2* are transferred with very high efficiency in the high-frequency colicinogeny transfer system constituted by cells newly infected with *col I* or *col B*.[59, 61, 64] An unexplained difference in the behavior of *col E_2* in *F*- and *col I*-mediated conjugation may be noted. In the former, *col E_2* is transferred with low frequency,[131] while in the latter it is transferred with high frequency.[59, 61, 64] *Col E_1* , on the other hand, is transferred with high frequency in both systems.

Autonomous determinants appear to be transferred only from the male to the female cell, like the bacterial chromosome and the conjugation factor itself. Thus Clowes[132] failed to detect any transfer of *col E_1* from F− to F+ cells although it is transferred very efficiently from F+ to F−. This behavior does not seem to be due to physical association of the colicinogeny determinant with *F* since interrupted mating experiments indicate that they are transferred independently. Similar experiments have shown that the different colicinogeny determinants are not physically associated during their transfer in *col I*-mediated conjugation.[59]

C. Physical Detection of Transfer of Nonchromosomal Material

F and its derivatives have been shown to contain nucleic acid by labeling donors with P^{32} and demonstrating inactivation of the transferred factor as a result of P^{32} disintegration.[135, 136] The *R* factor has also been shown to be sensitive to P^{32} disintegration.[65] Transfer of DNA, presumably associated with transfer of the *F* factor, has been demonstrated by radioautography of microcolonies formed by recipient cells after mating with F+ cells labeled with tritiated thymine.[137] In addition, cesium chloride centrifugation of the DNA isolated from cells of a strain of *Serratia* which had received an *F′* factor by conjugation with *E. coli* K12, demonstrated the presence of a DNA component absent from uninfected *Serratia* cells.[138] Silver and Ozeki have detected transfer of C^{14}-labeled thymidine associated with certain colicinogeny determinants in *col I*-mediated conjugation.[139]

D. Transfer of Cytoplasmic Material

There is evidence from the study of *F*-mediated conjugation that small amounts of low-molecular-weight substances which are presumably dispersed throughout the cytoplasm may be transferred during conjugation, and that this transfer is exclusively unidirectional. Borek and Ryan have shown that an unstable product of UV irradiation which causes induction of λ prophage can be transferred with remarkably high efficiency from irradiated F^+ or Hfr cells to unirradiated F^- cells, but not in the opposite direction.[140] The fact that transfer of this irradiation product, like that of the *col E_1* determinant, is unidirectional suggests that movement of all material across the connection between male and female cell is brought about by a mechanism which ensures unidirectional passage. The nature of this mechanism is a most challenging problem.

Fisher has shown that a substance which represses multiplication of phage λ can be transferred by conjugation from a lysogenic F^+ cell to a nonlysogenic recipient. No similar transfer was detected with Hfr instead of F^+ cells as donors, indicating that the flow of cytoplasmic material may be more restricted in cells which are in process of transferring their chromosome.[141] However, Borek and Ryan detected transfer of the UV irradiation product by Hfr cells, though to a somewhat lesser extent than by F^+ cells.[140] The apparent difference in the extent of transfer of the two types of substances may be due to differences in their stability or in the amount required to produce induction and repression respectively. Pardee *et al.*[142] have detected passage of lactose from Hfr to F^- cells but they found, like Fisher,[141] that there was little or no transfer of a cytoplasmic repressor, in this case the repressor of β-galactosidase synthesis. Experiments with isotopically labeled donor cells have shown that the amounts of RNA and protein transferred during *col I*-mediated conjugation cannot be greater than 0.5% of the total cellular content of these substances.[139]

VII. Genetic Recombination

We have seen that owing to spontaneous interruption of chromosome transfer, the zygotes formed in conjugation are generally incompletely diploid. Zygote formation is thus quite different from fusion of complete haploid nuclei in higher organisms. The occasional occurrence of repeated recombination events[96] indicates that the donor fragment can persist for quite long periods in the zygotes. In certain instances the fragment even appears to multiply quite extensively;[58, 80, 143] chromosomal abnormalities or other causes of poor homology between donor fragment and recipient chromosome may impede genetic exchange and thus favor detection of such rare persistent diploids.

However, zygotes generally have a transitory existence and donor characteristics can only be perpetuated if genetic recombination occurs, i.e., if exchange takes place between the donor fragment and the host chromosome in such a way that the relevant genes are incorporated into the recipient chromosome and thereafter replicate as an integral part of it. The formation of a complete recombinant chromosome requires an even number of exchanges between donor fragment and recipient chromosome, since an odd number of exchanges would give rise only to chromosome fragments. Moreover, if exchange in bacteria is reciprocal, as is generally the case in higher organisms, the reciprocal product of recombination could not be detected since it too would be an incomplete structure. Thus the only recombinant product which can be directly studied in bacteria is the intact recombinant chromosome resulting from an even number of exchanges between the genetic material of donor and recipient cells.

A. The Efficiency of Recombination

The efficiency of integration of a marker is defined as the probability that it will be incorporated into a genetic recombinant when introduced into a recipient cell. It has a value of about 0.5 in crosses between Hfr and F'− cells of *E. coli* K12 performed under optimal conditions, and appears to be independent of the distance of the marker from the origin of the Hfr.[104, 144] In interstrain or interspecies crosses, such as those between *E. coli* and *Salmonella* or *Shigella*, the efficiency of recombination may be much lower, due, at least in part, to poor homology between the recombining structures, and consequent interference with specific pairing.

The efficiency of recombinant formation has been found to be affected by various treatments which act more or less directly on the DNA of the donor fragment. UV irradiation of donor cells or of zygotes reduces the efficiency of integration of individual markers and has a pronounced effect on the simultaneous incorporation of two or more markers.[24, 128] Similar effects are observed if P[32] incorporated in the donor cells before mating is allowed to decay after transfer, or after growth of donor bacteria in bromodeoxyuridine.[145] These treatments are thought to exert their effect by causing localized damage or breaks in the DNA which either prevent genetic exchange or lead to inviability of the recombinant products.

When zygotes which have been formed in broth are shifted to a synthetic medium the number of recombinants produced may be less than 20% of the number formed in a medium containing small amounts of broth enrichment. The low yield of recombinants is not due to insufficient residual growth of the zygotes but probably results from temporary inhibition of some step in recombinant formation as a result of the change in cellular environment.[108] The donor fragment must be destroyed or otherwise made unable to participate in recombination after a limited time has elapsed, since otherwise recombination would occur when the cells eventually resume normal growth.

B. THE TIME OF RECOMBINATION

Two general approaches have been employed in attempts to gain insight into the nature of the recombination process. The first involves isolating the individual progeny of exconjugant cells over several generations by micromanipulation and analyzing the distribution and genotypes of the recombinant clones which are produced. The other involves studying the kinetics of the formation of recombinant cells in large populations of zygotes derived from crosses in which the period of mating is deliberately restricted.

The time after zygote formation at which recombination occurs has been estimated by determining when treatments which alter the yield or types of recombinants cease to have any effect. Examination of the effect of UV irradiation and P^{32} decay at various times after zygote formation shows that these agents cease to have any detectable effect after about an hour at 37°C., indicating that recombination has taken place by then.[24] Similarly, it has been shown that by an hour after zygote formation the yield of recombinants is no longer affected by a shift from broth to minimal medium.[108]

These results are on the whole supported by determination of the time at which genetically pure recombinant cells are formed and begin to increase in number. Tomizawa has shown that essentially all cells giving rise to lac^+ recombinant progeny are genetically pure by about 90 minutes after zygote formation, and increase in number at the same rate as the total F^- population very soon after.[146] Since cells of *E. coli* are multinucleate, this sets an upper limit on the time elapsing between zygote formation and recombination. Similarly, Hayes[111] showed that the number of recombinants increased exponentially from about 100 minutes after zygote formation, and Lederberg[147] found in pedigree analysis of F^- exconjugants that recombinants became pure at the third or fourth division after mating. By contrast, Anderson has observed a delay in the formation of pure recombinant cells of nine generations or more from the time of mating.[96, 106] It is possible that this delay is related to the divisional abnormalities and frequent inviability observed by Anderson among the exconjugant cells of the recipient strain employed by him.

The difference between Anderson's observations and those of other workers is also reflected in the degree of purity of the recombinant clones obtained. Thus Lederberg[147] found that of 75 exconjugant cells which yielded recombinants 55 gave rise to cells of only one recombinant genotype and none to cells of more than four, whereas Anderson[96] found an average of more than 2.5 different recombinant genotypes in each recombinant clone. The results of Tomizawa[146] agree with those of Lederberg in indicating that there is generally only one recombination event per zygote.

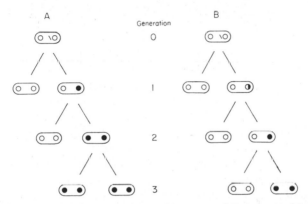

Fig. 9. The alternative patterns of segregation expected if the recombinant chromosome is genetically pure (model A) and if it is genetically impure (model B). The cells present at generation 0 are lac⁻ recipient cells which have received a donor chromosomal fragment carrying the lac⁺ marker. Each bacterial cell is depicted as possessing two chromosomes (circles) consisting of two subunits (half-circles). The chromosome fragment derived from the donor is omitted after the first generation. Subunits carrying the lac⁺ marker are shown black; those carrying the lac⁻ marker are shown white. The descendants of genetically pure lac⁻ chromosomes are omitted after the second generation.

C. THE MECHANISM OF RECOMBINATION

The information which is available concerning the mechanism of recombination after conjugation is unfortunately too limited to allow any but the sketchiest conclusions. It is, however, reasonably well established that the chromosome which is the immediate product of the recombination event is genetically pure.[146] The evidence for this conclusion may be best understood by reference to Fig. 9, which depicts the sequence of events in successive generations after zygote formation according to two alternative models of the structure of the recombinant chromosome. Both models start with a lac⁻ recipient cell which has two chromosomes, each consisting of genetically identical subunits. The cell has received a donor fragment carrying the *lac+* marker. In model A both subunits of the chromosome formed as a result of the recombination event are recombinant, whereas in model B only one of the subunits is recombinant and the other parental. A third model in which recombination results in the formation of two recombinant chromosomes has been excluded by the observation that the number of cells giving rise to *lac+* progeny does not increase until after genetically pure recombinant cells have been formed.

Models A and B may be experimentally distinguished by determining the time at which the segregation of pure recombinant cells occurs since, according to the former, segregation should take place in the second generation after recombination whereas, according to the latter, it should take place in the third. Tomizawa[146] has studied the kinetics of appearance of pure *lac+* recombinant cells and obtained results which are in agreement with model A rather than model B. It should be emphasized that these results do not exclude the possible existence of localized regions of heterozygosity such as have been detected in bacteriophage particles.[148]

The fact that the chromosome formed in the recombination event is genetically pure indicates that the interaction between recipient chromosome and donor fragment which gives rise to the recombinant structure does not involve the same type of semiconservative duplication process as is thought to occur in chromosome replication (see Chapter 9). If it did the recombinant chromosome would contain one parental nonrecombinant subunit, and one new recombinant subunit as in model B. Recombination must therefore occur either by physical exchange of material between recombining structures (breakage reunion) or by copying information first from one parental structure and then from the other (copy choice) with association of two newly synthesized replicas in the recombinant structure. The same inference as to the mechanism of recombination may be drawn from studies of bacterial transformation and from data obtained with higher organisms.

Observations of the effect of various agents on the recombination process do not appear to permit a decision between breakage-reunion and copy-choice models of recombination. The effect of UV irradiation in reducing the frequency of joint incorporation of neighboring donor markers has been explained in terms of the copy-choice model by supposing that lesions produced in the DNA cause the replica to switch to the undamaged template.[24] However, it would be equally well accounted for by the breakage-reunion model if incorporation of a lesion by recombination resulted in inviability. Jacob and Wollman[24] have found that the yield of recombinants is no longer sensitive to decay of P^{32} incorporated into the donor chromosome by about 100 minutes after the initiation of mating. However, the available data are not sufficiently precise to tell whether the stabilization to P[32] decay occurs at the time of recombination or only at a later generation, i.e., whether or not P[32]-containing material is incorporated into the recombinant chromosome.

Recent studies of recombination in phage T4[149, 150] and in bacterial transformation[151, 152] indicate that recombination involves physical exchange of material, and that it can take place in the absence of DNA synthesis, and therefore favor the breakage-reunion model. Although the same may well be true of recombination after conjugation, some caution appears advisable in extrapolating from these other systems in view of the evidence that repeated mating events can occur within the progeny of individual zygotes. The breakage-reunion model, at least in its simplest form, implies that the incorporated donor material should not be able to participate in any further recombination. However, pedigrees containing different recombinant types could result from limited multiplication of the donor fragment, formation of reciprocal recombinant products able to participate in further matings, or genetic exchange between sister chromosomes.*

D. ANALYSIS OF LINKAGE

In the early studies of recombination in *E. coli* K12 zygotes were assumed to result from fusion of complete parental genomes. Consequently, when the alternative alleles of a given unselected marker appeared with unequal frequencies among the selected recombinants that marker was thought to be "linked" to the selected marker of the parent whose allele predominated.[2] The fact that the donor contribution is not complete alters this situation greatly, since the probability that two donor markers will appear together among recombinants of a given type depends on the frequency of their joint transfer to zygotes as well as on the frequency of their joint incorporation into recombinants. Consequently, a donor marker may appear in a minority of the recombinants without its being linked to the selected recipient marker, simply because it is far from the selected donor marker and therefore rarely transferred to the zygotes.

Thus chromosome maps based upon the frequencies of joint inheritance of donor markers[17, 21] are not comparable to linkage maps in higher organisms. Instead they are similar to maps derived from interrupted mating experiments or from relative extents of transfer in Hfr crosses and depend ultimately on the oriented partial nature of chromosome transfer, a feature unique to bacterial conjugation. True linkage data can, however, be obtained in crosses employing Hfr strains as donors provided one examines

---

* Siddiqi has recently demonstrated by an ingenious experiment that recombination after conjugation does occur by physical exchange of material (O. H. Siddiqi, *Proc. Natl. Acad. Sci. U. S.* **49,** 589, 1963).

the segregation of markers which are proximal to the selected donor marker and are therefore transferred to all zygotes giving rise to recombinants of the selected type. Analyses of this kind are useful in estimating the distances between closely linked markers but for more distant markers the alternative methods are more practicable. Figure 10 presents the results of an analysis of recombination in the *lac-ade* region of *E. coli* K12. Comparison of the frequencies of recombination between neighboring markers with estimates of the distance between them based on interrupted mating experiments indicates that a segment of chromosome transferred in 1 minute corresponds to about 20 recombination units.[153]

The interpretation of data on segregation in Hfr crosses depends on the relative position of the selected markers of the donor and recipient cells (see Fig. 11). In crosses of type A the selected donor marker is distal to the selected recipient marker and the position of the latter affects the inheritance of proximal unselected donor markers. In the other type of

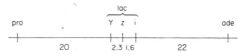

Fig. 10. Genetic distances in the *lac-ade* region of the chromosome of *E. coli* K12. Recombinants inheriting the *ade*[+] marker from HfrH were selected in crosses with appropriate F[-] cells and scored for inheritance of other characters. From Jacob and Wollman (ref. 3, p. 230).

cross (type B) the selected recipient marker is distal to the selected donor marker and its position generally has no effect on the segregation of proximal unselected donor markers. However, if it is close to the selected donor marker an exchange must occur just distal to the latter and the observed frequency of exchanges in the proximal region may be affected by negative interference.

Negative interference may be illustrated by further reference to Fig. 10; as indicated, the fraction of *ade*[+] recombinants with an exchange between z and y was found to be 2.3%, among those which had no detectable exchange between *ade* and z; however, among those in which an exchange had occurred between *ade* and z, the corresponding fraction was increased to 7.3%, and where the exchange had taken place in the small interval between z and i it was 14%. Thus, the nearer the exchange on one side of a marker the higher is the probability of an exchange on the other side. This effect, which has been observed in several other organisms, is probably due, at least in part, to clustering of exchanges within small regions of "effective pairing."[154, 155]

There is evidence that negative interference in bacteria extends over a greater portion of the chromosome than in other organisms, perhaps due to interaction between separate regions of effective pairing.[156] The existence of this extended negative interference underlines the possibility that estimates of recombination in small intervals such as those reproduced in Fig. 10 may give an exaggerated impression of the average frequency of exchanges along the chromosome. This idea is supported by the results of a cross of type B (Fig. 11) in which the selected donor marker was a considerable distance from the origin of the Hfr strain (Hfr H) used as donor.[153] The recombinants obtained appeared to inherit large "blocks" of donor markers as would be expected if the frequency of exchange was

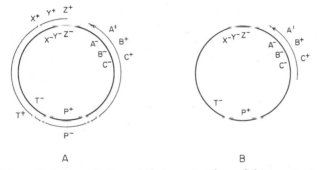

A   B

Fig. 11. Schematic representation of the zygotes formed in two types of genetic cross in *E. coli* K12. The inner (closed) line represents the chromosome of the recipient cell and the outer line the segment of the Hfr chromosome transferred to the zygote. The letters represent hypothetical chromosomal markers, and the arrow the leading extremity of the Hfr chromosome. In cross A the selected donor marker (Z^+) is distal to the selected recipient marker (P^+): in cross B the selected donor marker (C^+) is proximal to the selected recipient marker (P^+). The average size of the chromosomal segment transferred to zygotes depends on the position of the selected donor marker.

low. Data obtained from F^+ crosses and from study of *col I*-mediated recombination also show that recombinants inherit blocks of donor markers.[63, 64]

In the cross involving HfrH just alluded to the various proximal unselected donor markers were each inherited by a considerable proportion of the recombinants; however, in some other crosses virtually complete exclusion of proximal donor markers has been observed.[37, 157] This exclusion may be due to very restricted pairing between the genetic material of donor and recipient within the zygote; alternately some sort of postzygotic elimination of the proximal segment of the Hfr chromosomal fragment may occur, perhaps as a result of a prior recombination event. In other crosses involving recombination in smaller regions of the chromosome just the contrary type of observation has been reported; all proximal donor markers appeared in about 80% of the recombinants irrespective of their distance from the selected Hfr marker. However, this peculiarity has not been observed in crosses reported more recently.[153]

Crosses of type A (Fig. 11) have been of importance in demonstrating the terminal attachment of the F factor in Hfr cells; when selection is exerted for inheritance of, say, the Z^+ marker from the donor and the P^+ marker from the recipient a higher proportion of the recombinants are Hfr than if selection is exerted for any less distal donor marker.[4, 21, 22] The same crosses provide evidence that the chromosome of the F^- cell is circular; the proportion of Z^+P^+ recombinants which inherit proximal markers close to the origin, such as A^+ or B^+, may be as great as the proportion which inherit distal ones, such as X^+ or Y^+, and greater than the proportion which inherit, say, T^+. Pairing of the intact Hfr and F^- chromosomes thus re-established linkage between the extremities of the Hfr chromosome broken by the insertion of F in the transition from F^+ to Hfr. This result is most easily accounted for if the chromosome of the F^-, like that of the F^+, is circular.

ACKNOWLEDGMENT

The author is very grateful to Dr. W. Hayes, Dr. S. Silver, and Mr. J. Scaife for their help in the preparation of this chapter. He would also like to thank Drs. A. L. Taylor, T. S. Matney, and E. P. Goldschmidt for permission to include unpublished material, and Drs. F. Jacob and E. L. Wollman and the copyright owners for permission to include several published illustrations.

REFERENCES

[1] J. Lederberg, *J. Cellular Comp. Physiol.* **45,** Suppl. 2, 75 (1955).
[2] J. Lederberg, *Genetics* **32,** 505 (1947).
[3] F. Jacob and E. L. Wollman, "Sexuality and the Genetics of Bacteria," Academic Press, New York, 1961.
[4] W. Hayes, *Cold Spring Harbor Symposia Quant. Biol.* **18,** 75 (1953).
[5] F. Jacob and E. L. Wollman, *Compt. rend. acad. sci.* **247,** 154 (1958).
[6] E. L. Wollman, F. Jacob, and W. Hayes, *Cold Spring Harbor Symposia Quant. Biol.* **21,** 141 (1956).
[7] W. Hayes, F. Jacob, and E. L. Wollman, *in* "Methodology in Basic Genetics" (W. J. Burdette, ed.). Holden-Day, San Francisco, California, 1963.
[8] A. J. Clark and E. A. Adelberg, *Ann. Rev. Microbiol.* **16,** 289 (1962).
[9] J. Lederberg and E. L. Tatum, *Cold Spring Harbor Symposia Quant. Biol.* **11,** 113 (1946).
[10] E. L. Tatum and J. Lederberg, *J. Bacteriol.* **53,** 673 (1947).
[11] B. D. Davis, *J. Bacteriol.* **60,** 507 (1950).
[12] W. Hayes, *Nature* **169,** 118 (1952).
[13] W. Hayes, *Nature* **169,** 1017 (1952).
[14] J. Lederberg, L. L. Cavalli, and E. M. Lederberg, *Genetics* **37,** 720 (1952).
[15] L. L. Cavalli, J. Lederberg, and E. M. Lederberg, *J. Gen. Microbiol.* **8,** 89 (1953).

[16] W. Hayes, *J. Gen. Microbiol.* **8**, 72 (1952).

[17] R. C. Clowes and D. Rowley, *J. Gen. Microbiol.* **11**, 250 (1954).

[18] T. C. Nelson and J. Lederberg, *Proc. Natl. Acad. Sci. U.S.* **40**, 415 (1954).

[19] L. L. Cavalli, *Boll. ist.sieroterap. milan.* **29**, 281 (1950).

[20] E. L. Wollman and F. Jacob, *Ann. inst. Pasteur* **95**, 641 (1958).

[21] L. L. Cavalli and J. L. Jinks, *J. Genet.* **54**, 87 (1956).

[22] F. Jacob and E. L. Wollman, *Compt. rend. acad. sci.* **245**, 1840 (1957).

[23] Y. Hirota, *Proc. Natl. Acad. Sci. U.S.* **46**, 57 (1960).

[24] F. Jacob and E. L. Wollman, *Symposia Soc. Exptl. Biol.* **No. 12**, 75 (1958).

[25] F. Jacob, P. Schaeffer, and E. L. Wollman, *Symposium Soc. Gen. Microbiol.* **10**, 67 (1960).

[26] J. Scaife and J. D. Gross, *Biochem. Biophys. Research Communs.* **7**, 403 (1962).

[27] F. Jacob and E. L. Wollman, *Compt. rend. acad. sci.* **242**, 303 (1956).

[28] Y. Hirota and P. H. A. Sneath, *Japan J. Genetics* **36**, 307 (1961).

[29] P. Reeves, *Nature* **185**, 265 (1960).

[30] L. L. Cavalli, in "Recent Progress in Microbiology" (G. Tunevall, ed.), 7th Intern. Congr. Microbiol., Stockholm, 1958, pp. 40–50. Almqvist & Wiksells, Stockholm, 1959.

[31] J. Lederberg, *Abstr. Communs. 7th Intern. Congr. Microbiol., Stockholm, 1958*, pp. 59–60, Almqvist & Wiksells, Stockholm.

[32] N. D. Zinder, *Science* **131**, 924 (1960).

[33] B. W. Holloway and B. Fargie, *J. Bacteriol.* **80**, 362 (1960).

[34] E. A. Adelberg and S. N. Burns, *J. Bacteriol.* **79**, 321 (1960).

[35] F. Jacob and E. A. Adelberg, *Compt. rend. acad. sci.* **249**, 189 (1959).

[36] P. H. A. Sneath, *Brit. Med. Bull.* **18**, 41 (1962).

[37] A. Richter, *Genet. Research Cambridge* **2**, 333 (1960).

[37a] A. L. Taylor and E. A. Adelberg, *Biochem. Biophys. Research Communs.* **5**, 400 (1961).

[38] E. L. Wollman and F. Jacob, *Compt. rend. acad. sci.* **247**, 536 (1958).

[39] A. Campbell, *Advances in Genet.* **11**, 101 (1962).

[40] F. Ørskov and I. Ørskov, *Acta Pathol. Microbiol. Scand.* **51**, 280 (1961).

[41] D. Dussoix and W. Arber, *J. Mol. Biol.* **5**, 37 (1962).

[42] H. L. Bernstein. *Symposia Soc. Exptl. Biol.* **No. 12**, 93 (1958).

[43] J. Lederberg and E. M. Lederberg, in "Cellular Mechanisms of Differentiation and Growth" (D. Rudnick, ed.), pp. 101–124. Princeton Univ. Press, Princeton, New Jersey, 1965.

[44] E. Calef and L. L. Cavalli, *Ricerca sci.* **25**, Suppl. 123 (1955).

[45] P. G. de Haan, *Genetica* **27**, 293 (1954).

[46] P. G. de Haan, *Genetica* **27**, 300 (1954).

[47] P. G. de Haan, *Genetica* **27**, 364 (1955).

[48] J. Lederberg, *Science* **114**, 68 (1951).

[49] G. Furness and D. Rowley, *J. Gen. Microbiol.* **17**, 550 (1957).

[50] L. S. Baron, W. M. Spilman, and W. F. Carey, *Science* **130**, 566 (1959).

[51] L. S. Baron, W. F. Carey, and W. M. Spilman, *Proc. Natl. Acad. Sci. U.S.* **45**, 976 (1959).

[52] T. Miyake and M. Demerec, *Nature* **183**, 1586 (1959).

[53] N. D. Zinder, *Science* **131**, 813 (1960).

[54] T. Miyake, *Genetics* **47**, 1043 (1962).

[55] T. Miyake, *Nature* **184**, 657 (1959).

[56] S. Falkow, J. Marmur, W. F. Carey, W. M. Spilman, and L. S. Baron, *Genetics* **46**, 703 (1961).

[57] F. Ørskov, I. Ørskov, and F. Kaufmann, *Acta Pathol. Microbiol. Scand.* **51**, 291 (1961).

[58] S. E. Luria and J. W. Burrous, *J. Bacteriol.* **74**, 461 (1957).

[59] H. Ozeki, "Colicinogeny in *Salmonella*; genetic and other studies." Ph.D. Thesis, Univ. London, 1960.

[60] H. Ozeki, B. A. D. Stocker, and S. M. Smith, *J. Gen. Microbiol.* **28**, 671 (1962).

[61] B. A. D. Stocker, S. M. Smith, and H. Ozeki, *J. Gen. Microbiol.* **30**, 201 (1963).

[62] H. Ozeki and S. Howarth, *Nature* **190**, 986 (1961).

[63] R. C. Clowes, *Nature* **190**, 989 (1961).

[64] S. M. Smith and B. A. D. Stocker, *Brit. Med. Bull.* **18**, 46 (1962).

[65] T. Watanabe, *Bacteriol. Revs.* **27**, 87 (1963).

[66] R. Nakaya, A. Nakamura, and Y. Murata, *Biochem. Biophys. Research Communs.* **3**, 660 (1960).

[67] T. Watanabe and T. Fukasawa, *J. Bacteriol.* **81**, 669 (1961).

[68] L. S. Baron and S. Falkow, *Genetics* **46**, 849 (1961).

[69] T. Watanabe and T. Fukasawa, *J. Bacteriol.* **81**, 679 (1961).

[70] Y. Sugino and Y. Hirota, *J. Bacteriol.* In press.

[71] T. Watanabe, T. Fukasawa, and T. Takano, *Virology* **17**, 218 (1962).

[72] L. S. Baron, W. F. Carey, and W. M. Spilman, *Proc. Natl. Acad. Sci. U.S.* **45**, 1752 (1959).

[73] S. Falkow and L. S. Baron, *J. Bacteriol.* **84**, 581 (1962).

[74] A. Hakura and Y. Hirota, see T. Watanabe, *Bacteriol. Revs.* **27**, 87 (1963).

[75] W. B. Gunderson, K. Jyssum, and S. Lie, *J. Bacteriol.* **83**, 616 (1962).

[76] B. W. Holloway, *J. Gen. Microbiol.* **13**, 571 (1955).

[77] B. W. Holloway, *J. Gen. Microbiol.* **15**, 221 (1956).

[78] B. W. Holloway and P. A. Jennings, *Nature* **181**, 855 (1958).

[79] K. Bhaskaran, *J. Gen. Microbiol.* **19**, 71 (1958).

[80] K. Bhaskaran, *Indian J. Med. Research* **47**. 253 (1959).

[81] K. Bhaskaran, *J. Gen. Microbiol.* **23**, 47 (1960).

[82] W. L. Belser and M. I. Bunting, *J. Bacteriol.* **72**, 582 (1956).

[83] G. A. Maccacaro, *Nature* **176**, 125 (1955).

[84] G. A. Maccacaro and R. Comolli, *J. Gen. Microbiol.* **15**, 121 (1956).

[85] M. Turri and G. A. Maccacaro, *Giorn. microbiol.* **8**, 1 (1960).

[86] P. D. Skaar, A. Richter, and J. Lederberg, *Proc. Natl. Acad. Sci. U.S.* **43**, 329 (1957).

[87] G. D. Baird, P. A. Albertson, and B. V. Hofsten, *Nature* **192**, 236 (1961).

[88] I. Ørskov and F. Ørskov, *Acta Pathol. Microbiol. Scand.* **48**, 37 (1960).

[89] I. Ørskov, F. Ørskov, W. J. Sojka, and J. M. Leach, *Acta Pathol. Microbiol. Scand.* **53**, 404 (1961).

[90] T. Loeb, *Science* **131**, 932 (1960).

[91] T. Loeb and N. D. Zinder, *Proc. Natl. Acad. Sci. U.S.* **47**, 282 (1961).

[92] R. Dettori, G. A. Maccacaro, and G. L. Piccinin, *Giorn. microbiol.* **9**, 141 (1961).

[93] J. S. Davis, J. H. Strauss, Jr., and R. L. Sinsheimer, *Science* **134**, 1427 (1961).

[94] N. D. Zinder, *Science* **133**, 2069 (1961).

[95] J. Lederberg, *J. Bacteriol.* **71**, 497 (1956).

[96] T. F. Anderson, *Cold Spring Harbor Symposia Quant. Biol.* **23**, 47 (1958).

[97] P. H. A. Sneath and J. Lederberg, *Proc. Natl. Acad. Sci. U.S.* **47**, 86 (1961).

[98] T. Watanabe and T. Fukasawa, *J. Bacteriol.* **83**, 727 (1962).

[99] J. Lederberg and J. St. Clair, *J. Bacteriol.* **75**, 143 (1958).

[100] A. Hagiwara, *Nature* **182**, 456 (1958).

[101] A. J. Clark, see A. J. Clark and E. A. Adelberg, *Ann. Rev. Microbiol.* **16**, 289 (1962).

[102] F. Cuzin, *Compt. rend. acad. sci.* **255**, 1149 (1962).

[103] F. Jacob and E. L. Wollman, "Sexuality and the Genetics of Bacteria," p. 196. Academic Press, New York, 1961.

[104] P. G. de Haan and J. D. Gross, *Genet. Research Cambridge* **3**, 251 (1962).

[104a] N. Symonds, *Genet. Research Cambridge* **3**, 273 (1962).

[105] P. G. de Haan and A. H. Stouthamer, *Genet. Research Cambridge.* **4**, 30 (1963).

[106] T. F. Anderson and R. Mazé, *Ann. inst. Pasteur* **93**, 194 (1957).

[107] L. Fischer-Fantuzzi and M. diGirolamo, *Genetics* **46**, 1305 (1961).

[108] J. D. Gross, *Genet. Research Cambridge.* In press.

[109] T. F. Anderson, E. L. Wollman, and F. Jacob, *Ann. inst. Pasteur* **93**, 450 (1957).

[110] K. W. Fisher, *J. Gen. Microbiol.* **16**, 136 (1957).

[111] W. Hayes, *J. Gen. Microbiol.* **16**, 97 (1957).

[112] K. W. Fisher, personal communication.

[113] M. Kern, *Biochem. Biophys. Research Communs.* **6**, 151 (1962).

[114] K. W. Fisher, *J. Gen. Microbiol.* **16**, 120 (1957).

[115] K. W. Fisher, *Symposium Soc. Gen. Microbiol.* **11**, 272 (1961).

[116] F. Jacob and E. L. Wollman, *Ann. inst. Pasteur* **95**, 497 (1958).

[117] T. S. Matney and N. E. Achenbach, *J. Bacteriol.* **84**, 874 (1962).

[118] A. L. Taylor and E. A. Adelberg, *Genetics* **45**, 1233 (1960).

[119] M. Delbrück, *J. Gen. Physiol.* **23**, 643 (1940).

[120] E. L. Wollman and F. Jacob, *Compt. rend. acad. sci.* **240**, 2449 (1955).

[121] F. Jacob and E. L. Wollman, *Ann. inst. Pasteur* **91**, 486 (1956).

[122] E. L. Wollman and F. Jacob, *Compt. rend. acad. sci.* **239**, 455 (1954).

[123] E. L. Wollman and F. Jacob, *Ann. inst. Pasteur* **93**, 323 (1957).

[124] C. R. Fuerst, F. Jacob, and E. L. Wollman, *Compt. rend. acad. sci.* **243**, 2162 (1956).

[125] W. Hayes, *Symposium Soc. Gen. Microbiol.* **10**, 12 (1960).

[126] A. Garen and P. D. Skaar, *Biochim. et Biophys. Acta* **27**, 457 (1958).

[127] S. D. Silver, *J. Mol. Biol.* **6**, 349 (1963).

[128] F. Jacob and E. L. Wollman, *Compt. rend. acad. sci.* **240**, 2566 (1955).

[129] P. Frédéricq and M. Betz-Bareau, *Compt. rend. soc. biol.* **147**, 2043 (1953).

[130] L. Alfoldi, F. Jacob, E. L. Wollman, and R. Mazé, *Compt. rend. acad. sci.* **246**, 3531 (1958).

[131] R. N. de Zwaig, D. N. Anton, and J. Puig, *J. Gen. Microbiol.* **29**, 473 (1962).

[132] R. C. Clowes, personal communication.

[133] L. Boice and S. E. Luria, *Bacteriol. Proc.* (*Soc. Am. Bacteriologists*) (V 80a), 197 (1961).

[134] L. Boice, "Transfer of Pl-dl factors during conjugation." Ph.D. Thesis, Univ. of Illinois. Urbana, Illinois, 1961.

[135] P. J. Driskell and E. A. Adelberg, *Bacteriol. Proc.* (*Soc. Am. Bacteriologists*) (p. 81). 186 (1961).

[136] R. Lavallé and F. Jacob, *Compt. rend. acad. sci.* **252**, 1678 (1961).

[137] R. K. Hermann and F. Forro, quoted in A. J. Clark and E. A. Adelberg, *Ann. Rev. Microbiol.* **16**, 289 (1962).

[138] J. Marmur, R. Rownd, S. Falkow, L. S. Baron, C. Schildkraut, and P. Doty, *Proc. Natl. Acad. Sci. U. S.* **47**, 972 (1961).

[139] S. Silver and H. Ozeki, *Nature* **195**, 873 (1962).

[140] E. Borek and A. Ryan, *Biochim. et Biophys. Acta* **41**, 67 (1960).

[141] K. W. Fisher, *J. Gen. Microbiol.* **287**, 711 (1962).

[142] A. B. Pardee, F. Jacob, and J. Monod. *J. Mol. Biol.* **1,** 165 (1959).

[143] J. Lederberg, *Proc. Natl. Acad. Sci. U.S.* **35,** 178 (1949).

[144] F. Jacob and E. L. Wollman, "Sexuality and the Genetics of Bacteria," pp. 152–153. Academic Press, New York, 1961.

[145] C. E. Folsome, *Genetics* **45,** 1111 (1960).

[146] J. Tomizawa, *Proc. Natl. Acad. Sci. U.S.* **46,** 91 (1960).

[147] J. Lederberg, *Proc. Natl. Acad. Sci. U.S.* **43,** 1060 (1957).

[148] A. D. Hershey and M. Chase, *Cold Spring Harbor Symposia Quant. Biol.* **16,** 471 (1951).

[149] M. Meselson and J. J. Weigle, *Proc. Natl. Acad. Sci. U.S.* **47,** 857 (1961).

[150] G. Kellenberger, M. L. Zichichi, and J. J. Weigle, *Proc. Natl. Acad. Sci. U.S.* **47,** 869 (1961).

[151] M. S. Fox and R. D. Hotchkiss, *Nature* **187,** 1002 (1960).

[152] M. J. Voll and S. H. Goodgal, *Proc. Natl. Acad. Sci. U.S.* **47,** 505 (1961).

[153] F. Jacob and E. L. Wollman, "Sexuality and the Genetics of Bacteria," pp. 223–234, Academic Press, New York, 1961.

[154] R. H. Pritchard, *Heredity* **9,** 343 (1955).

[155] M. Chase and A. H. Doermann, *Genetics* **43,** 332 (1958).

[156] G. A. Maccacaro and W. Hayes, *Genet. Research Cambridge* **2,** 406 (1961).

[157] R. Weinberg, *J. Bacteriol.* **79,** 558 (1960).

CHAPTER 2

Transduction

ALLAN CAMPBELL

I. Discovery and General Features

In 1952, Zinder and Lederberg[1] reported that certain temperate bacterial viruses could act as vectors in the transfer of bacterial genes from one cell line to another. The phenomenon was first observed with phage PLT22 in *Salmonella*. It has now been extensively studied with several phages of the Enterobacteriaceae but has also been observed in such diverse genera as *Pseudomonas*,[2] *Bacillus*,[3] and *Micrococcus*,[4] and probably is of as general occurrence among bacteria as is phage itself.

Zinder and Lederberg introduced at that time the term "genetic transduction" to denote not only the virus-mediated transfer that they had observed, but any recombinational process involving intercellular transmission of a genetic fragment, rather than of a complete genome. Their discovery constituted a new example of such fragmentary recombination. Their very

49

logical terminology has not gained wide currency, however. The other well-documented example of fragmentary recombination—transformation by free DNA (deoxyribonucleic acid)—already had a name of its own, and the word "transduction" has therefore frequently come to be used to refer only to the phage-mediated transduction which Zinder and Lederberg discovered.

We have no strong preference for one usage or the other. As the subject matter of this chapter will be solely transduction by phage, it will be more convenient for our purposes to use the term in the restricted sense popular usage has given it.

Like transformation with free DNA, transduction involves the entrance into a cell of a small piece of genetic material which is homologous to some portion of the genome already present and which can in some fraction of the recipient cells replace its homolog totally or partially. Transduction provides, therefore, a method of high resolution for recombination analysis of small regions of the bacterial genome. This property has been extensively exploited, and much of our knowledge of fine structure genetics of bacteria is derived from transduction data.[5] It is also possible to do transductions in many genera in which a conjugational mating system has not yet been demonstrated. In some genera, transduction represents the only method for studying genetic recombination. Until recently, this was the case for *Salmonella*.

A survey of the literature on transduction reveals immediately that the bulk of experimental work has been limited to such uses of transduction as a tool for finding out something about the genetics of the bacterial host. The concepts employed have been reasonably simple and obvious, and we do not intend to dedicate an amount of space here commensurate with the volume of this work. We shall rather concern ourselves primarily with a limited number of investigations which have specifically clarified certain aspects of the mechanism of transduction itself.

II. Nature of the Transducing Particle

The basic experimental result of Zinder and Lederberg was that a lysate which contains bacteriophage has also some transducing activity for each of the genes of the host on which it was grown. The frequency is usually low, and surprisingly variable from one lysate to another. For a typical gene, one finds on the order of 1 transduction per 10^5 plaque-forming particles. One of the first points which had to be understood was whether the transducing activity was associated with the phage particles themselves rather than with something else in the lysate. Zinder[6] found that the transducing ability and the plaque-producing ability fractionated in the same way on centrifugation and ultrafiltration, had the same specificity of attachment to particular bacterial strains, and showed identical kinetics of inactivation by antiserum, heat, and ultrasonic irradiation. Therefore the two activities must be located on particles of similar size and surface properties.

The most reasonable picture to draw was that the transducing activity resides in particles which contain a small piece of bacterial DNA surrounded by an ordinary phage coat with a tail. Later chemical and microscopic work, which we will describe presently, has verified this interpretation in certain cases. The question which remained unanswered for a long time was how different these transducing particles might be from the average phage particle in the lysate. In particular, does the transducing particle contain an ordinary phage genome in addition to some pieces of bacterial DNA? If so, does every phage particle contain some such extra DNA, or is this restricted to a rare abnormal class of particles? Finally, if both phage and bacterial DNA occur within the same particle, is there some enduring intimate genetic association between the two, or are they merely accidental bedfellows who later can go their separate ways?

The direct study of transduction by phage PLT22 has not provided a definitive answer to these questions. What evidence we do have for this phage has come subsequent to the study of some specialized systems of transduction by other phages which happened to be technically well suited for investigations of the mechanism of transduction. In these cases, it is clear that transduction is performed by a special class of particles within the lysate which differ both physically and genetically from the phage particles themselves and whose genetic behavior indicates that phage and bacterial DNA have become permanently connected into a new genetic structure.

The system most thoroughly studied in this respect is the transduction of the galactose genes of *Escherichia coli* K12 by bacteriophage λ. We will therefore describe in some detail the properties of this system and the history of the development of our knowledge of it.

III. Transduction of the Galactose Genes by Bacteriophage λ

A. Properties of Bacteriophage λ

In 1953, Lederberg and Lederberg[7] described some of the properties of a new bacteriophage (λ), for which the wild-type strain of *Escherichia coli* K12 was lysogenic. This phage had escaped attention for many years simply because no one had tested the strain for lysogenicity on any indicator which was sensitive to it. Phage λ is generally now propagated on derivatives of *E. coli* K12 which have been cured of the λ prophage by exposure to heavy doses of ultraviolet irradiation. Its utility in transduction studies derives partly from the special character of the transduction it performs but equally to the large background of information which has been accumulated both on the characteristics of the phage and on the genetics of the host.

The genetic map of bacteriophage λ has been carefully worked out by Kaiser.[8] Most of the known mutants either affect plaque size, host range,[9] or ability to lysogenize. In addition, Jacob et al.[10] have identified numerous defective mutants of λ. These are lethal mutants which have lost the ability to carry out properly some step in the normal lytic cycle.

As with any temperate phage, infection of a sensitive cell by bacteriophage λ has at least two possible outcomes. (1) The cell lyses and liberates

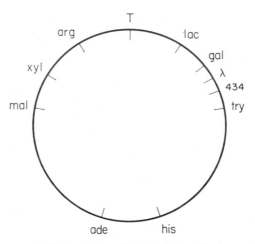

FIG. 1. Genetic map of *Escherichia coli* K12. (After Taylor and Adelberg.[55]) T, threonine-requiring; *lac*, unable to ferment lactose; *gal*, unable to ferment galactose; *try*, tryptophan-requiring; *his*, histidine-requiring; *ade*, adenine-requiring; *mal*, unable to ferment maltose; *xyl*, unable to ferment xylose; *arg*, arginine requiring. The phages λ and 434 are located according to the work of Jacob and Wollman.[56]

phage (lytic pathway). In this pathway, the synthetic capacities of the cell are diverted from the synthesis of cellular material to that of phage material. The blueprints for the phage material, as well as for the catalysts affecting the diversion and those causing the ultimate destruction of the cell, seem to be carried in the phage genome. A genetic defect in any of these functions will cause a lethal mutation, the bearer of which would quickly perish in the following cycles of lytic growth. (2) The cell does not lyse, but survives as a lysogenic complex. The phage is converted into a latent form called prophage and reproduces as such. In the case of bacteriophage λ, the prophage is located at a particular point on the bacterial chromosome, as shown in Fig. 1. As long as the lysogenic complex is multiplying as such, the prophage is reproduced like any other component of the bacterial genome. As far as we know, none of the specific phage-directed syntheses of the lytic cycle occurs in the lysogenic cell. The prophage is replicated by the same machinery which replicates the rest of the host material. A mutation altering any of these phage-specific syntheses is therefore not deleterious to the prophage. The prophage state resembles diploidy in higher organisms in that it creates a shelter under which genetic variability can accumulate. The appearance of defective mutants in the lytic cycle and in the prophage state is diagrammed in Fig. 2.

A phage mutant which is unable to carry out some function or functions of the lytic cycle is called a defective phage. A nondefective phage is called

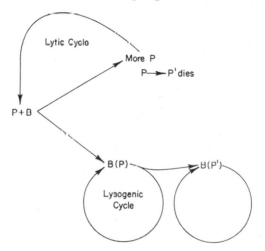

Fig. 2. Diagrammatic representation of the origin and fate of deleterious mutants in lytic and lysogenic cycles. P, phage; B, bacterium; P′, deleterious phage mutant, B(P), bacterium lysogenic for prophage P.

active. A defective phage in the prophage state is a defective prophage. A bacterial strain carrying a defective prophage is called a defective lysogen.

Active lysogens are recognized by the production of phage. This occurs spontaneously by the rare sporadic lysis of occasional cells in the culture. With some phages, including λ, lysis can be induced in almost all the cells of the population by a variety of treatments, the simplest of which is exposure to small doses of ultraviolet (UV) irradiation. Defective lysogens are distinguished from active lysogens by their failure to produce phage, either spontaneously or following ultraviolet induction. They are distinguishable from nonlysogenic cells by two means. (1) They retain the specific immunity to superinfection by the homologous phage which characterizes nonlysogenic strains. (2) If they are induced with UV (to destroy the immunity) and then superinfected with genetically marked active phage, genetic recombinants between the defective prophage and the superinfecting phage can be isolated.

For example, suppose we start with an active lysogen carrying wild-type λ and isolate a defective lysogen from it. We superinfect the defective lysogen with the double mutant λhc, where h and c are two mutations (host range and clear plaque, respectively), each of which leads, under proper conditions, to a type of plaque visibly different from that of wild type. Qualitatively, this is equivalent to making the cross $\lambda h^+ c^+ i \times \lambda h c i^+$, where i stands for the lethal mutation causing the defect. All eight possible recombinant types will be produced in such a cross, but those carrying the i gene will be lethal and unable to form plaques. The fact that, among the active phages, one finds individuals of the genotypes $h^+ c^+ i^+$, $h^+ c i^+$, and $h c^+ i^+$, proves that the h and c genes were present in the defective phage, although they cannot be directly detected there. The defect is therefore localized. Other genetic markers can recombine away from it. The frequency of such recombination depends on the distance between the marker in question and the i gene studied. From a study of such frequencies one can arrive at a consistent approximate location of each defect.

Since many different steps are necessary for the proper functioning of the lytic cycle, one expects the existence of many different types of defective phage in which the mutation has blocked different steps. This is indeed found, and various defective mutants are also located at different points on the linkage map of the phage.

Analogous to the defective mutants are the conditionally lethal or sensitive mutants, which manifest some specific block in the lytic cycle only if grown under certain conditions.[11] Some of these, for example, are blocked at high temperatures or extreme pH's at which the wild-type phage can grow. Others respond to the action of particular suppressor genes in the bacterial host and are able to grow only on those hosts carrying the appropriate suppressor gene. These have been called host-dependent (hd) or suppressor-sensitive (sus) mutants. The bacterial strain carrying the suppressor gene that allows the mutants to grow is called a permissive (pm^+) strain; strains lacking the suppressor are nonpermissive (pm^-). As with the true defectives, sensitive mutants occur at numerous places on the phage genetic map and apparently cause blocks in many distinct functions.

The host-dependent mutants especially have been handy tools for studying transduction, for reasons which we shall discuss later. For many purposes, they are more convenient to use than the "true" defectives, because it is possible to prepare lysates, perform phage crosses, etc., on the strain on which they grow. Thus, the localization of these mutants on the genetic map of λ can be based on ordinary phage crosses and does not require superinfection of defective lysogens.

The superinfection immunity of lysogenic strains is itself under the genetic control of the phage. This is clearly demonstrated by crosses between
λ and other related phages, independently isolated from nature, which can
recombine genetically with λ, but whose immunity specificity is different.
The specificity has been localized in that part of the chromosome in which
are found clear plaque mutants, which are unable to lysogenize. According
to current theory, the immunity region should contain both a regulator
gene, which synthesizes a specific repressor, and an operator gene, which
responds to the same repressor by shutting off, directly or indirectly, all the
synthetic activities of the phage particle of which it comprises a part.[12] A
stock in which the immunity determinant from such a related phage has
been introduced into an otherwise λ genome[13] has been very useful in transduction studies.

B. Discovery of Transduction by λ

Whereas bacteriophages such as PLT22 will transduce any marker of
their host, this is not true for all temperate phages. Indeed, out of 13 different temperate coliphages independently isolated from nature, only one was
shown to have this property[14] In particular, such generalized transduction
is not shown by λ. Bacteriophage λ can transduce a cluster of loci which
determine the synthesis of some enzymes concerned with the metabolism
of galactose, but no other genes of E. coli are known to be transduced by
it.[15]

Morse found that this "specialized" transduction has many features
which distinguish it from the generalized transduction carried out by phage
PLT22. In the first place, if λ is grown lytically on gal+ bacteria (the standard procedure in generalized transduction), no transducing activity is obtained. Transducing activity appears only if one starts with a culture of
gal+ bacteria lysogenic for λ. Active lysates can then be prepared by inducing this culture to lyse with ultraviolet irradiation. When a gal− E. coli culture is infected with such a lysate, about one gal+ colony is obtained per
10^6 phage particles added.

When many such gal+ colonies are isolated and purified by restreaking,
one finds two classes. About one third have been stably converted from
gal− to gal+. If one induces these strains (which are almost always lysogenized by the infection), they give rise again to lysates whose activity in transduction is similar to that of the lysates derived from the original parent
strain. Everything happens as though the gal+ genes transferred by the
phage had substituted and replaced their homologs in the chromosome of
the recipient. This is the type of result one would expect in generalized
transduction.

The other two thirds of the transductants, however, have much different and more interesting properties. They are persistently unstable and segregate gal^- progeny at a rate of about 10^{-3} per bacterium per division. The gal^+ genes, instead of replacing their homologs, have been added to the chromosomal complement so that the resulting cell is diploid for this small region of genetic material. The hypothesis of diploidy was confirmed by the use of different gal^- mutants which are recombinationally and/or physiologically distinct from each other.[16] One always finds among the segregants of such unstable strains only those gal^- types that one used in synthesizing the stock in the first place.

For example, suppose we use the mutants gal_1 and gal_2. These two were each isolated as gal^- mutants of *E. coli* K12. Further examination showed that they were recombinationally distinct, i.e., a cross between a gal_1 and a gal_2 strain produced some gal^+ recombinants. They are also physiologically distinct, and have been shown each to lack a different enzyme of galactose metabolism. If a strain of K12 gal_1 (λ) is induced, the resulting lysate will convert recipient cells of K12 gal_2 to gal^+ at the usual rate of 10^{-6}. It is devoid of transducing activity on a gal_1 recipient. We can isolate the unstable transductants produced from a gal_1 donor and a gal_2 recipient and study the gal^- segregants which they produce. What is found is that most of these are gal_2. The added fragment of genetic material which came from the donor has been lost, and we are back with the original recipient strain. Less frequently, somatic recombination between the added fragment and the gal region of the recipient results in the production of segregants which are gal_1 or the double mutant gal_1 gal_2.

There is therefore no doubt that partial diploidy is indeed involved. Morse *et al.*[16] called such strains which are diploid for a very limited region of genetic material syngenotes. If the two gal regions of an individual are nonidentical genetically, it is a heterogenote; if identical, a homogenote. They also called the added fragment of genetic material the exogenote, and its homolog in the recipient the endogenote. They found that the heterogenotes produce, on induction, lysates which can give, under optimal conditions, almost one transduction per plaque-forming particle present. This was called high frequency transduction (Hft) in contrast to the low frequency transduction (Lft) seen with the original donor strain.

If we start with a heterogenote such as the one described above, in which the exogenote is gal_1^+ gal_2 and the endogenote is gal_1 gal_2^+, a variety of segregational and recombinational events is possible. For example, the gal^- segregants found in cultures of such a strain might in principle be one of two things: haploid segregants, which have lost the exogenote, or gal^- homogenotes produced by somatic recombination between exo- and endogenote. In fact, both types are found, but haploid segregants are about ten times more frequent than homogenotes. They are most easily distinguishable by the fact that homogenotes and not haploids produce lysates which are Hft when tested on recipients carrying other gal^- alleles. To equate this property with diploidy requires a more complete understanding of the system than was possible at the time, but this interpretation was verified in some cases by the behavior of gal^+ reverse mutants isolated from these strains. Revertants from a haploid should be stable gal^+ and those from a homogenote should (in the absence of further segregational or recombinational events) be unstable, since the gene is perpetuated in two independent lines of descent and the mutation will have occurred in either one or the other. This is a very direct test for diploidy and correlates completely with the ability to produce Hft lysates.

C. IDENTIFICATION OF DEFECTIVE PHAGE AS THE TRANSDUCTION VECTOR

It seemed obvious, whatever these complex findings might mean, that high frequency transduction was a very good system for studying the properties of transducing particles, as they must constitute a fairly high proportion of the total number of visible particles in the lysate. Convincing evidence was soon obtained that the transductions are carried out by a special class of particles which contain some genetic material derived from the phage but do not have a complete phage genome and are unable to form plaques.[17-19]

If one performs transduction with an Hft lysate at a phage/bacterium ratio sufficiently low so that one is looking at the result of infection of cells by a single transducing particle, one finds that almost all of the transductions are heterogenotes. Unlike those produced at higher phage/bacterium ratios, however, these heterogenotes are defective rather than active lysogens. They are immune to superinfection by λ, they lyse beautifully after UV induction, but no infectious particles are liberated during such lysate. The rather inexact term "defective heterogenote" is used to denote these strains which, as a consequence of being lysogenic for the transducing phage, are both heterogenotic and defectively lysogenic.

If one superinfects these defective heterogenotes with genetically marked active phage, the results are somewhat different from that obtained with an ordinary defective lysogen. For example, suppose a defective heterogenote made from $\lambda h\ c^+$ is superinfected with $\lambda h^+\ c$. Among the active phage liberated, one finds some $\lambda h^+\ c$ and some $\lambda h^+\ c^+$ but no $\lambda h\ c$ or $\lambda h\ c^+$. Since the h gene is a selective marker, if one particle in 10^8 were λh it could easily be detected. It is as though the h gene had disappeared completely from the phage. The c gene, on the other hand, is obviously still there. If one performs superinfection experiments with various other mutants of λ, one finds the expected recombinant types for most markers, except for those in one region of the map (*dg* region) which includes the *h* locus and which comprises about 25 % of the known genetic map of λ.[17]

Figure 3 shows the result of such superinfection experiments for a number of markers. It is seen that a continuous section of genetic material, taken from the middle of the genetic map, is missing. The acquisition of the galactose genes seems to require a concomitant loss of phage genes. The *c* genes, which control superinfection immunity, are present, which explains the immunity of the defective heterogenotes and probably accounts also for the ability of the defective phage to lysogenize at all.

An Hft lysate would then be a mixture of two types of particles: (*a*) ordinary phage particles, which do not transduce, and (*b*) transducing particles, which do not form plaques. A cell infected with a transducing particle in single infection might be lysogenized, giving rise to a transduction, or it might lyse without liberating anything, like a defective heterogenote induced by ultraviolet. If a population of cells is infected with an Hft lysate at a multiplicity of about 0.4 phage per cell and individual lysing cells local-

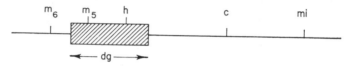

Fig. 3. Genetic map of λ, showing the *dg* region. (After Arber.[17])

ized on a fixed grid and observed in the electron microscope, one sees that roughly half of the cells which lyse fail to liberate any visible particle similar to phage.[17] Arber has called the transducing phage λ*dg* (for *défectif, galactose-transducteur*). That region of the phage chromosome which is missing from the transducing phage is referred to as the *dg* region.

Since λ*dg* cannot multiply in single infection, it follows that the phage yield from a population of cells infected with an Hft lysate at very low multiplicity will contain very little transducing activity, because most of the λ*dg* enter cells which are not simultaneously infected with active λ phage. If the infection is done at high multiplicity, however, the transducing activity is multiplied about to the same extent as the active phage.[17]

Whereas one can infer from these observations that the lysate is a mixture of two types of particles, they do not rigorously exclude the possibility that all particles in the lysate are really identical and that the defect arises in a fraction of the individuals after the time of infection. Additional experiments somewhat more elaborate than those described here made this possibility unlikely, but a complete proof required the physical separation of the two types of particles from the Hft lysate.

Such a separation was simply and beautifully achieved by the use of density gradient centrifugation.[20] Whereas an ordinary λ lysate gives only one sharp band in the ultracentrifuge, an Hft lysate gives two, as shown in Fig. 4. The plaque-forming particles are concentrated in one band and the

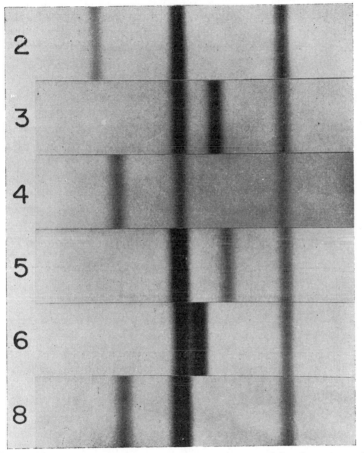

FIG. 4. Banding of normal phage and transducing particles from several independent Hft lysates. The dark band to the right is N[15]-labeled λ which was added to all lysates as a density marker and was used to align the photographs. The central band is normal λ. The transducing particles band either to its left or to its right, depending on the density. Reproduced from the *J. Mol. Biol.*[20] with permission of the publishers.

transducing particles in another. Whereas the transducing particles from any one Hft lysate have a uniform density, those from different lysates may band at quite different densities. We shall return to this point later.

The absence of a connected region of genetic material which characterizes the transducing phage has not yet been found among any of the defective mutants of λ which have been isolated as such. Among bacterial and phage mutants in general, multisite mutations, which cover a region rather than a point, are common, although less frequent than point mutations. Such mutations have been attributed to small deletions or other structural aberrations, and, in one case, the genetic distance across such a "deletion" has been shown to be much less than that across the material normally present there.[21] From the results of λ transduction, however, we can say that some unknown fraction of all multisite mutants in phage must represent not simple deletions but rather replacements of phage genes by genes from the host. As we shall discuss later (see Section III,G), it is not necessary to suppose that the host genes have actually gone where the phage genes were, but at least the loss of the phage genes was accompanied by the gain of some extraneous genetic material. The important point is that, by all the operations of phage genetics, the *dg* region behaves as a deletion. If λ*dg* had first turned up in a stock unmarked at the *gal* locus, it would have been classified simply as a deletion defective. The methods used for studying λ*dg* genetically have borrowed heavily from the techniques and concepts developed from studying deletions in other systems.[22]

D. NATURE OF THE ASSOCIATION BETWEEN PHAGE AND BACTERIAL GENES

The transducing particles thus contain some bacterial genes and some phage genes. What is the connection between the two? Is there a genuine physical association, such as we suppose occurs between any two genes of the phage? Or do the defective phage just leave a convenient empty space within their shells into which a galactose gene can be neatly accommodated? This question has been answered first from biological evidence, which is highly indicative, and more recently by chemical evidence, which is quite conclusive. The biological evidence is worth recounting first because it shows us some interesting features of the system.

In the first place, if the association between defective phage and transduced genes were a loose one, they should be easily separated from each other. Thus, a defective heterogenote might be expected to lose only the *gal* genes but retain the defective prophage or vice versa. What is observed, instead, is that, when the *gal* genes are lost, the defective prophage is usually lost, too. If one picks a number of independent *gal⁻* segregants from a defective heterogenote, one finds that about 90 % have lost the immunity which indicates the presence of the defective phage.

What about the other 10 %? Do these show that the genes can really become detached from the defective phage? As we mentioned earlier, in the discussion of lysogenic heterogenotes, a *gal⁻* segregant can in principle arise from a heterogenote in two ways: either through loss, to give a haploid strain, or through internal recombination, to give a still diploid homogenote. One expects that the haploids should have lost the immunity and the homogenotes should have retained it. The homogenotes can be independently distinguished by the study of reverse mutants, or by their ability to give Hft lysates following induction and superinfection. Thus far, all the individuals examined which were *gal⁻* but still immune have proven to be homogenotes.

All the results on segregation from defective heterogenotes are compatible with the formation of a permanent stable association between the genes from the bacterium and those of the defective phage. Those types which would constitute obvious exceptions (e.g., a cell which was still segregating *gal⁻* but had lost the immunity) have never been observed. One might, however, still maintain that a cell can carry a variety of such loose fragments and shed them all at once because of some special state that the cell occasionally enters rather than because of a physical connection between the various fragments.

The segregation patterns of lysogenic heterogenotes are also in accord with the idea of an indissoluble union of phage and bacterial genes in the transducing particle. If lysogenic *gal⁻* cells are infected with an Hft lysate, most of the transductants are doubly lysogenic, carrying both λ*dg* and λ prophage. If both phages are genetically marked, such cells on induction liberate transducing particles and a mixture of active phages with genetic markers from the two parents, although never from the *dg* region of the λ*dg* parent. *Gal⁻* segregants from such strains are usually singly lysogenic, and have lost most frequently the phage alleles with which the *gal⁺* genes entered the cell.[23] This was taken to indicate linkage between the *gal* genes and the transducing parent; but alternatively one could say it means merely that both the λ*dg* prophage and the *gal* genes remain separate from, and more easily dislodgeable than, the prophage of active λ.

The real proof has come from transformation studies. Kaiser and Hogness[24] have shown that DNA prepared from free transducing particles can transform *gal⁻* cells into *gal⁺*. This transformation is really a lysogenization of the bacterial recipient by the DNA of the transducing phage and results mainly in the formation of heterogenotic rather than haploid transformants. The number of transformants is directly proportional to the amount of DNA added. The transformation requires the presence of added "helper" phage, but, even at multiplicities of 0.1 phage DNA equivalents per bacterium, most of the transformants have acquired some genetic markers from the transducing phage.

This implies that the phage genes and the galactose genes remain associated on a single physical structure through the extraction and isolation of the DNA. Thus, the λ*dg* particle, like active λ, consists of a single DNA molecule covered by a protein coat. The biological experiments, furthermore, indicate strongly that this DNA molecule retains its unity during intracellular growth, both in the vegetative and in the prophage state. The problem to which attention must next be addressed is the origin of this new type of DNA molecule which contains components from two diverse sources.

E. Effect of Nontransducing Phage in Transduction

Before discussing the origin of λ*dg*, we shall complete our description of the experiments mentioned thus far by returning to a point we have deliberately glossed over. When we recounted the characterization of the transducing phage as defective, we specified that the multiplicity of infection (i.e., the phage/bacterium ratio in the transduction) must be sufficiently low that we are sure to be looking at the results of single infection by the transducing particle. This seems such an obvious requirement that the reader unacquainted with this work may wonder why the defectivity was not discovered immediately, or even in low frequency transduction.

The reason is purely technical. In single infection, λ*dg* lysogenizes very poorly. If the same cell is simultaneously infected with an active phage particle, the lysogenization is greatly increased. We say that the active phage helps its defective relative to lysogenize, and therefore to transduce. An Hft lysate is a mixture of active λ and λ*dg*. When a population of cells is infected with such a lysate, a certain fraction of those cells receiving λ*dg* phage will receive an active λ as well. At multiplicities of infection much less than one, this fraction is approximately equal to the multiplicity. However, because of the helping effect, this fraction will account for the majority of transductions down to quite low multiplicities.

For example, suppose that a cell infected with one active phage and one transducing phage has a probability of giving rise to a recoverable transductant colony which is 40 times that of a cell infected with a transducing phage alone. Consider a population of *gal*− cells infected with an Hft lysate in the proportion of 1 active phage : 10 bacterial cells (multiplicity of infection, 0.1). Of every 100 cells which receive a transducing particle at all, approximately 90 will receive only the λ*dg*, whereas 10 will be simultaneously infected with an active λ phage. However, each of these 10 cells has 40 times the probability of giving rise to a transduction which the other 90 have. Among the recovered transductions, then, a fraction 400/490, or 82%, will arise by multiple infection, even at a multiplicity where only 10% of the cells were multiply infected.

Figure 5 shows the type of data from which such conclusions are drawn.[18] On the ordinate is plotted the number of transductions per active phage particle added (T/P) as the multiplicity of infection is varied. At very low multiplicities this quantity equals the product of the number of transducing particles per active phage in the lysate by the probability of transduction in single infection. As multiplicities are raised from 0.01 to 1, the T/P value rises some 20- to 40-fold. That this is due to a helping effect is verified by a control experiment in which all the cells are infected at a multiplicity of 2 with a λ lysate obtained from a *gal⁻* bacterium which has no transducing activity whatsoever, and only the multiplicity of transducing phage is varied. The T/P is then independent of multiplicity, and some 20- to 40-fold greater than that obtained in single infection.

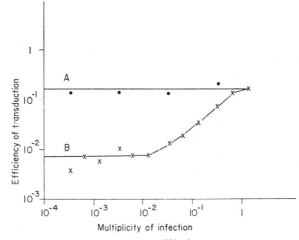

FIG. 5. Efficiency of transduction by an Hft lysate as a function of the multiplicity of infection. Curve B: high frequency transducing lysate alone. Curve A: same lysate with constant background multiplicity (1.7) of nontransducing phage. Reproduced from *Virology*[18] with the permission of the publishers.

All of the transductants arising from mixedly infected cells seem to become lysogenized by the active phage as well as by the transducing phage. They are thus double lysogens, which is easily verified by the use of a genetically marked helping phage. The lysogenic heterogenotes originating from Lft have properties identical with these double lysogens and presumably arise in the same way. It is technically difficult to perform low frequency transduction at very low multiplicities, but it is possible to demonstrate the presence of defective phage in Lft lysates by density gradient centrifugation.[25]

The mechanism of the helping effect is not understood. It has been suggested that the main effect is to permit vegetative multiplication of the transducing phage, thereby increasing the number of copies available to lysogenize and thus augmenting the frequency of lysogenization.[26] We know that help is blocked whenever the recipient cell carries a prophage of the same immunity specificity as the helping phage.[23] We know also that some of those cells singly infected with a transducing phage are lost through lysis,[17] but it is not clear whether the fraction of cells lysing is changed by the helping phage. The main interest of the whole phenomenon at the moment is that it creates a technical difficulty which has confused the interpretation of results in the past and might do so in other systems in the future.

F. Genetic and Physical Variability of the Transducing Phage

The model of transduction arrived at by the experiments described thus far can now be recapitulated briefly. When one prepares a lysate of λ by inducing a lysogenic strain, there are produced, in addition to ordinary λ phage particles, very rare abnormal phage (about 1 in 10^5) which have picked up the galactose genes from nearby on the host chromosome and have lost a block of their own phage genetic material. These are ordinarily detected by transduction and recovered in the form of lysogenic strains which carry a normal λ prophage in addition to the prophage form of the abnormal (λdg) phage. The normal phage is present in these strains for the technical reason that low frequency transduction cannot be performed at very low multiplicities with the expectation of any recovery at all, and at higher multiplicities the helping effect occurs. Among the phage liberated by such strains, the abnormal type is no longer very rare. It is produced in an amount about equal to that of the normal phage. This information is summarized in Table I. Table II shows the relationship between the symbolic and verbal descriptions of the various types of strains involved.

Such an Hft lysate contains two discrete classes of particles—normal phages which produce plaques, and abnormal phages which mediate transduction. If we consider that an Hft lysate can be prepared from a culture of a lysogenic heterogenote which has been grown from a single cell, we see that the two classes of particles are lineally derived from the two prophages carried by this heterogenote. We therefore expect that, except for the intervention of additional rare events, all the transducing particles in this lysate will be identical.

On the other hand, in the case of low frequency transduction, the lysate is prepared from a culture ultimately descended from a single cell which carried one λ prophage in the normal, active form. The transductions one sees have resulted from rare events which have occurred sometime after this single cell was isolated, and different isolates may have resulted from different events. There is therefore no *a priori* expectation as to whether or not the transducing phage derived from different events in low frequency transduction should be identical.

The problem has been attacked by physical as well as genetic methods. We have mentioned the result of the physical studies already. Whereas

TABLE I

COMPARISON OF LOW FREQUENCY TRANSDUCTION WITH HIGH
FREQUENCY TRANSDUCTION

Type of trans- duction	Donor	Approximate composition of lysate	Transductants	
			High m.o.i.	Low m.o.i.
Lft	$gal^+(\lambda)$	$10^5 \lambda{:}1 \lambda dg$	$\frac{2}{3} gal^+(\lambda)(\lambda dg)$ $\frac{1}{3} gal^+(\lambda)$	Not feasible[a]
Hft	$gal^-(\lambda)(\lambda dg)$	$1 \lambda{:}\lambda dg$	$gal^-(\lambda)(\lambda dg)$ $gal^+(\lambda)$ (rare)	$gal^-(\lambda dg)$ gal^+ (rare)

[a] Low frequency transduction is not feasible at really low multiplicities, although by special methods one can show that some of the transductants are $gal^-(\lambda dg)$.[25]

TABLE II

RELATION BETWEEN TERMS AND SYMBOLS IN λ TRANSDUCTION

Symbol	Term
gal^+ gal^-	Sensitive bacteria
$gal^+(\lambda)$ $gal_1(\lambda)$	Active lysogens or lysogenic strains
$gal^+(\lambda dg\ gal^+)$	Defective gal^+ homogenote
$gal_1(\lambda dg\ gal^+)$ $gal^+(\lambda dg\ gal_1)$ $gal_1(\lambda dg\ gal_2)$	Defective heterogenotes
$gal_1(\lambda dg\ gal_1)$	Defective gal_1 homogenote
$gal_1(\lambda)(\lambda dg\ gal^+)$	Lysogenic heterogenote

there is no detectable density heterogeneity among the transducing particles within any one Hft lysate, there is almost invariably some difference between the density seen in one Hft lysate and that in any other which was derived from a different Lft event.[20] Some kinds of λdg particles are denser than ordinary λ. Others are lighter. The density of a particle probably depends on the ratio of DNA to protein. If the protein content of all the particles is the same, the density depends directly on the DNA content. It would thus seem that some λdg phages have more DNA than active λ and that others have less. Of 10 independent lysogenic heterogenotes studied, a different density was found for each; therefore the total number of possible density classes must be very large.

Genetic methods have yielded concordant results.[27] One transducing particle might in principle differ from another either in the extent of bacterial genetic material picked up, or in that of the phage genetic material lost. Differences of the former type have not yet been found, but the latter have been studied rather extensively with the aid of the *sus* mutants of λ. As explained earlier, these are mutants which can form plaques on some strains of *E. coli* K12 (pm^+) and not on others (pm^-) (see Table III). The

TABLE III

PLATING PROPERTIES OF ACTIVE AND DEFECTIVE λ

Phage types		Bacterial strain[a]	
Name	Symbol	pm^+	pm^-
Wild-type λ	λ^+	+	+
Host-dependent (suppressor-sensitive) mutant	λhd_n or λsus_n	+	−
Defective mutant of λ	λi_n	−	−
Transducing λ	λdg	−	−

[a] Key: +, forms plaques; −, does not form plaques.

pm^- strains provide an absolute selection for any wild-type recombinants which may be produced in a cross between two *sus* mutants, or between one *sus* mutant and one true defective. If a defective heterogenote carrying λdg is induced and then superinfected with a *sus* mutant, wild-type recombinants will appear if the *sus* mutation lies outside of the *dg* region. None will appear if it lies inside. By making such crosses between a particular heterogenote and a collection of *sus* mutants, one can define the extent of the *dg* region in that heterogenote.

In practice, many such crosses can be performed on the surface of a single Petri plate (Fig. 6). On a background of pm^- cells, drops of various defective heterogenotes, various *sus* mutants, and paired combinations of the two are placed. After drying, the plates are irradiated briefly to induce the heterogenotes. The appearance of plaques in the spot in excess of those produced by reverse mutants in the phage lysate itself shows that wild-type recombinants are formed. Since we are asking only whether or not a given genetic site is contained in the transducing phage, we are not concerned with how many such recombinants are produced, but only with their presence or absence.

Such studies have shown, first, that all of the transducing particles

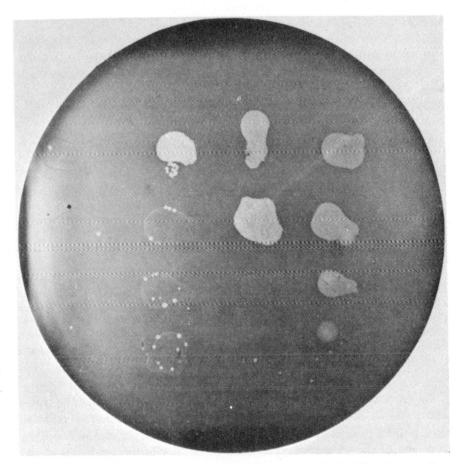

FIG. 6. Crosses between suppressor sensitive mutants and λdg. The plate was first seeded with a background of pm⁻ cells, and then in the center of each square was placed a loopful from a culture of a defective heterogenote (the same one for all the squares of a row) and from a lysate of an sus mutant (the same one for all the squares of a column). After an inducing dose of ultraviolet light, they were incubated overnight. Formation of plaques on the pm⁻ background shows the ability of the λdg to produce wild-type recombinants when crossed with the sus mutant in question.

derived from the same Lft event are genetically as well as physically identical. Second, particles derived from separate events are frequently different. The differences thus far revealed have all involved the position of the left end point, which generally falls within a region of the chromosome especially rich in *sus* mutants. Figure 7 shows the different classes of transducing particles which have been revealed by this technique. Figure 8 is a diagrammatic representation of the origin of the various types of defective phages shown in Table III.

One sees, first of all, that there is a "common core" to all the *dg* regions— a group of genes which are missing from every transducing λ thus far examined. This core region covers a group of *sus* mutants and also the *h* locus. The *dg* regions of various λ*dg*'s penetrate to different extents the section of the genome to the left of the common core.

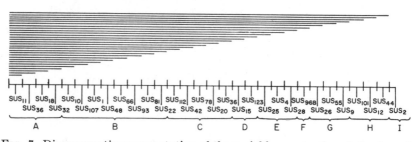

FIG. 7. Diagrammatic representation of the variable penetration of the *dg* region into a section of the phage chromosome. The entire section shown is to the left of the *h* gene in Fig. 3. Each solid line represents that portion of the phage chromosome which is present in a particular transducing phage. The mutants are all of the suppressor sensitive (*sus*) type. For simplicity, only one mutant has been shown in each region, and the regions have been equally spaced. The capital letters represent complementation classes into which the mutants can be grouped.

The results of the crosses between all of the mutants and all of the transducing phages constitute, by themselves, an adequate system for ordering along a linear linkage map both the *sus* mutations and the end points of the *dg* regions of the transducing phages. The validity of the method is shown by the fact that one can make a diagram such as that of Fig. 7 where every *dg* region is represented as an uninterrupted segment of the linear structure. The order of some of the *sus* mutants has also been corroborated by standard two- or three-factor crosses. The results shown in Fig. 7 indicate that the end point of the *dg* region can occur at a great many points, perhaps any point, within a certain part of the phage chromosome. They indicate definitely that it can fall within a genetic locus as well as between loci.

For some transducing phages, both physical and genetic measurements have been made. The results show a general correlation between DNA content and number of phage genes present. The longer the *dg* region, the less dense the transducing phage. The correlation is not perfect, however, which means that there are other variables which can change independently of this end point of the *dg* region.

From all of these results, it is obvious that an Lft lysate differs from an Hft lysate not only in the ratio of transducing particles to active phages, but also in the spectrum of types of transducing particles formed. An Hft lysate contains only the one type which is a copy of the particular λ*dg* prophage carried by the heterogenote from which the lysate was made. Other types presumably can occur at the same level as in an Lft lysate, but

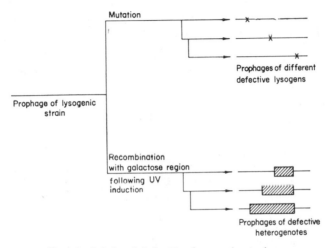

FIG. 8. Origin of defective lysogenic strains.

they are hidden by the 10^5 times greater amount of identical transducing particles present.

One might therefore wonder whether an Lft lysate contains an even wider range of transducing particles than are recovered among the prophages of heterogenotes. It is quite possible that this is so. Lft lysates give a higher proportion of stable nonheterogenotic transductions than do Hft lysates.[15] This probably reflects the presence of a class of transducing particles which lysogenize poorly, if at all, and therefore rarely, if ever, form heterogenotes. Special methods will be required to obtain any information as to the nature of these particles. Most people have preferred to study the heterogenotes because it is easier. Any generalizations about transduction at the present moment must be tempered with an understanding of the bias introduced by studying a limited class of objects which happen to be convenient to work with.

G. Mechanism of the Recombinational Event

The transducing phage can be considered as a genetic recombinant between the host bacterium and the bacteriophage. We are using "recombination" in a very broad sense to cover any process in which two or more (parent) individuals with different genetic characters interact to produce a new individual, some of whose genetic specificity is derived from each of the parents.

Recombination as thus defined can be of two basically different types, which we can call equal and unequal, respectively. In equal recombination, the genetic elements of the two parents can be put in a one-to-one correspondence with each other, and the rule is that each offspring must receive a complete set of genetic elements. Recombination which is not equal is unequal.

In organisms where a sexual process constitutes an essential part of the reproductive cycle, equal recombination is far more common than unequal recombination. This is necessary because the products of unequal recombination are likely to be lethal due to duplications or deficiencies of genetic material. Unequal recombination certainly does occur, though, giving rise to chromosomal aberrations. Equal recombination is probably the rule also in bacteria and phages. Otherwise, multisite mutations would occur with a far higher frequency than is observed.[22]

The physical bases of equal recombination are, first, the mitotic apparatus, and, second, the precise pairing of homologous regions within the chromosome. Such an exact matching of homologous parts of the parent structure is essential for equal recombination within the chromosome, regardless of whether the mechanism is by chromosome breakage or by copy choice, and irrespective of whether the individual recombinational event is reciprocal or nonreciprocal. Unequal recombination, on the other hand, does not require any genetic homology between the two parent structures.

In transduction, the λ phage loses a specific region of its own genome concomitantly with picking up a specific portion of the bacterial genome. This could be the result of equal recombination. Certain regions of the phage DNA might match corresponding regions in the bacterial DNA, and within these regions crossing over or miscopying might occur. The facts that the same "common core" of the *dg* region is absent from all the transducing phages, and that the deletion of phage genes is interstitial rather than terminal gives superficial plausibility to such a scheme. The simplest model for an origin by equal recombination is shown in Fig. 9.

However, equal recombination of this type should give rise to recombinants containing the same amount of DNA as the parents in the region of homology. According to Fig. 9, the transducing phage might contain more or less DNA than the λ phage itself, but all transducing phages should have the same DNA content. Insofar as DNA content can be deduced from density, this is contrary to experimental fact.

The argument is supported also by genetic evidence. Suppose that there were a region (such as $A_L A_R$ of Fig. 9) in which the λ chromosome matched perfectly the bacterial chromosome, and that the transducing phage originated by equal recombination in this region. Then the active λ phage and the transducing phage would likewise match each other in this region. Since the transducing phage can only mature in the presence of active phage, every λ*dg* particle has had some opportunity to recombine with active λ, and one product of such recombination should be a transducing phage which now contains a larger amount of phage material than it had

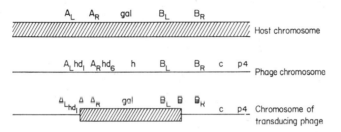

FIG. 9. Simplest model for origin of the transducing phage by equal recombination. It is assumed that the chromosomes of the phage and the bacterium are homologous between A_L and A_R and between B_L and B_R and that a transducing phage can be produced by recombination at any points A and B within these regions. The suppressor-sensitive mutants are denoted by their old name of host-dependent (*hd*₁ and *hd*₆). The mutation p_4 is at the same place as *mi* of Fig. 3. Reproduced from *Virology*[28] with the permission of the publishers.

previously. We can recognize the point at which recombination has taken place as the end point of the *dg* region, determined genetically by crosses with the *sus* mutants.

Now, the fact is that the end point of the *dg* region has never been observed to change after primary isolation among many hundreds of individuals examined. More important, if we select among transducing phages those which have recombined with an active phage and have acquired from it a genetic marker at the extreme left-hand end of the linkage group, we still do not detect any change in the end point of the *dg* region.[28] We conclude that such recombinants arise by equal recombination within the region of λ*dg* which was derived from λ and never in that derived from the bacterium.

Likewise, if one selects for individual λ*dg* prophages in which the *gal⁻* allele from the bacterial chromosome has substituted for the *gal⁺* allele of λ*dg* (giving a defective homogenote), we find no change in the end point of the *dg* region. The transducing phage thus contains some genetic material derived from the phage and able to undergo equal recombination with the homologous regions of the phage, and other genes derived from the bacterium which can recombine with the bacterial chromosome. What is absent in the picture is any common ground, any portion of the structure which falls into both categories at once.

Both physical and genetic methods therefore agree in ruling out equal recombination between two perfectly matched regions. Unfortunately, they cannot eliminate the possibility of matching which, though imperfect, is sufficient to serve as a basis for precise pairing. We do not expect the matching to be completely perfect anyway. Perfect matching occurs only between truly identical structures. In equal recombination between identical parents, no record is left of where or whether the recombinational event has occurred. One can study this only by introducing genetic markers, thereby destroying identity. The success of classical recombinational genetics depends on the fact that the individual markers generally have negligible effects on the mechanics of the recombination process. This assumption is not necessarily valid in molecular genetics at the level studied here. If the end point of the *dg* region does represent a point of equal recombination, the matching regions of phage and bacterial chromosome must differ at least enough so that the wild-type allele of the *sus* mutants studied cannot be recovered by recombination from λ*dg* at a detectable frequency.

We conclude that there is no direct evidence favoring equal recombination, and that, if genetic homologies between phage and host are involved, these homologies are very imperfect. It must be mentioned also that, whereas we know that an interstitial region of the phage chromosome is missing, there is no real evidence that the galactose genes have replaced them rather than adding to some other part of the structure. It is thus quite feasible to entertain models for the origin of transducing λ in which the *gal* genes add to the end of the phage chromosome rather than to the middle.

H. Mechanism of Low Frequency Transduction

All of this work says that, once the primary transductional event has occurred, a new stable genetic structure is formed which rarely, if ever, changes its properties. The fixed character of this primary change throughout the introduction and exchange of genes into various parts of the structure by ordinary recombination is reminiscent of inversions or translocations in higher organisms and suggests that some alteration more far reaching than equal recombination between homologous regions has transpired. At any rate, since nothing very interesting happens after the primary event, one is forced to delve backwards and try to study the event itself.

From what we have said thus far, the primary determination of the transducing particle occurs sometime before the isolation of the lysogenic heterogenotes produced by low frequency transduction. It could therefore happen at one of several times: (1) during growth of the original lysogenic donor strain, while the phage is still a prophage; (2) at induction; (3) during vegetative growth following induction; or (4) during transduction of the primary recipient.

Possibility (4) is made unlikely by the results of fractionation of Lft lysates in a density gradient.[25] The transducing phages already exist in the Lft lysate as particles of the characteristic density their descendants will have. In some fractions there is a sufficient concentration of transducing particles relative to active phage particles so that the direct production of defective heterogenotes by the Lft lysate can be shown.

There is no direct evidence against possibility (3). It seems unlikely because lytically grown λ does not transduce, and we know of no difference between vegetative growth following infection and that following induction of a lysogen. If possibility (1) were true, the transducing particles should be clonally distributed among lysates prepared by inducing parallel lysogenic cultures each grown from small inocula. This clonal distribution should manifest itself not only as an inequality of transduction titers between different Lft lysates but, more crucially, in a nonrandom distribution among lysates of the types of transducing phage, as distinguished by density or by genetic measurements. The experiments thus far conducted have failed to yield any evidence of such a clonal distribution of genetic types.[28a]

It therefore seems most likely that the transducing phage originates as a genetic structure at or immediately following induction. This conclusion is still tentative, and experiments in progress in several laboratories at the time of writing should shed further light on this important question.[28b, c]

IV. General Transduction

A. RELATION TO SPECIAL TRANSDUCTION

We have discussed transduction by λ in such detail, despite its special nature and limited range, because it is one of the rather few systems for which we have some information about the mechanism of transduction. It remains to be justified that this system is not entirely special and that it has any pertinence to a discussion of generalized transduction of the type carried out by phage PLT22.

In answering such a question, one must first separate the fundamental features of the mechanism from the incidental or trivial ones. Such a separation is always somewhat arbitrary, but, in our opinion, the most important new fact coming from the study of λ transduction is that bacterial genes can become a part of the phage genetic structure, that some kind of hybridization process is possible which produces the kind of DNA molecule in λ*dg*. To generalize the λ*dg* model would then be to say that such a hybrid structure occurs in other transductions, if not as an end product, at least as an intermediate. We shall call this the "hybrid intermediate" model of transduction. The λ*dg* genome can be considered an intermediate rather than a final product, in that it can undergo further recombination with the recipient chromosome to yield a stable *gal*+ cell. The two steps (formation of the hybrid structure and later recombination between it and the recipient chromosome) are, for this system, easily separable.

The properties of all transductional systems involving hybrid intermediates need not be very similar to those observed with λ. Depending on which and how many of the phage genes have been eliminated from the hybrid, one might expect the intermediate to range anywhere from an active phage which could now "convert" bacteria for the transduced character, down to something which was utterly incapable of lysogenizing, multiplying, or maturing, even in the presence of an active phage. Because of this great flexibility, with the operations now performable, it is easy enough in some cases to obtain positive evidence in favor of a hybrid intermediate, but there is no way of proving that in any given case an intermediate is absent. It is therefore scientifically improper at this time to pose the question of whether all transductions involve such intermediates. The available evidence is sufficient, however, to indicate that this is a rather general process which intervenes in many transductions by various phages.

Before we turn to specific cases, one fact about general transduction is quite pertinent. Both for phage P1[29] and for phage PLT22,[30] it has been shown that the transducing particle is abnormal in that it either fails to contain or fails to inject properly a normal phage genome. Whenever sufficient precautions are taken to avoid accidental superinfection of transductants by stray phage in the system (precautions which were almost never taken during the first few years of transduction work!) one finds that the transductants are nonlysogenic. If these cells had been infected with a normal phage genome, one would expect a high frequency of lysogenization among the survivors, particularly with a phage such as P1 where all the progeny of an infected cell become lysogenic. When these precautions are taken, also, transduction can be performed even with lysates of virulent mutants which are completely unable to lysogenize.

The most straightforward conclusion is that most transducing particles do not contain a whole phage genome in addition to the bacterial genes. A corollary (the argument for which will be given in more detail later; see

Section IV,C) is that most of the active phage particles in the lysate do not carry extra bacterial genes effective in transduction. Transduction is performed by a few abnormal particles in the lysate. The only remaining questions to be asked in each particular case are (1) What is the proportion of such abnormal particles to normal phage? (2) Do these abnormal particles contain any phage genes? (3) If so, are the phage and bacterial genes connected on a single DNA molecule?

B. Transduction of the Lactose Genes by Phage P1

Of the many examples now available, the most illuminating come from the experiments of Luria and collaborators on the transduction of the lactose gene by phage P1.[31] This work was actually begun before the mechanism of λ transduction had been worked out, and the general concordance of results in the two systems has been very encouraging to further generalization of the concepts emerging from them. Phage P1 is like PLT22 (and unlike λ) in carrying out general, rather than special, transduction. Any genetic marker from the donor can be transferred by the phage, and the lysate can be prepared by infection rather than by induction of a lysogenic strain.

If a *lac⁻* mutant of *E. coli* is infected with a lysate of P1 grown on *lac⁺* *E. coli*, the transductants are stable *lac⁺* and seem to resemble in every way the original donor strain. The *lac⁺* gene has substituted for its *lac⁻* allele, and there is no indication that phage is ever intimately associated with the transduced gene. This is the customary superficial result of general transduction.

However, if we use now the same donor strain and employ instead the permanently *lac⁻* species *Shigella dysenteriae* as recipient, a different result is obtained. Probably because of the poor homology of the *lac* region in the two genera, the *lac⁺* gene is unable to substitute for its homolog in the *Shigella* chromosome. Transduction occurs, but the transductants are persistently unstable. Like the heterogenotes found in λ transduction, they segregate *lac⁻* individuals at a constant rate per generation. Also, like the heterogenotes, they are immune but nonlysogenic. Lysates prepared by superinfecting these strains with active P1 phage will transduce with high frequency on both *Shigella* and *E. coli* recipients. The transductants on *E. coli* are again stable and nonlysogenic.

The idea that this behavior of *Shigella* is due to the absence of a *lac* region with good homology to the donor was verified by using as recipient an *E. coli* strain which has a large apparent deletion covering most of the *lac* region. Likewise in that case, by minimizing transduction by substitution one can see instead transduction by lysogenization. The important homologies apparently are not only these within the *lac* region but also those of adjacent regions. Another strain (＃60) of *Shigella* has been shown to contain the entire *lac* region, although the permease gene is not in a functional state. Transductions between this strain and *E. coli*, in either direction, frequently result in heterogenote formation. Once the heterogenote is formed, recombination between the *lac* regions of the exogenote and the endogenote take place rather easily.[32]

The experiment illustrates well how easily the intermediate in transduction can be overlooked. There is nothing in the transduction from a *lac+* *E. coli* to a *lac−* *E. coli* which implicates anything more than a fragment of bacterial chromosome as the transduction vector. Only when we set a deliberate trap to select for lysogenization by the intermediate do we find that it is indeed there. The name P1*dl* has been given to the transducing element in this system.

Another interesting result is the great variety of types of P1*dl* which are found—showing a much wider range of properties than do, for instance, the various λ*dg* types. The difference between the two systems may reflect nothing more fundamental than the method of selection of transductants. At any rate, in *lac* transduction by P1 the transducing elements demonstrated range from types which can produce mature particles by themselves without help from an active phage, down through those which do not cause immunity and contain no known phage genes. The latter differ from a fragment of bacterial chromosome only in their ability to persist and replicate in the nonintegrated state. The whole spectrum of types expected from a hybrid intermediate model are found here with one phage transducing one gene.

C. Proportion of Transducing Particles in Ordinary Phage Lysates

Having concluded that transduction is performed by a few abnormal particles in the lysate, we must try to estimate what fraction of the total these abnormal particles comprise. The fraction can be measured directly (by electron microscope counts of visible particles) only for lysates exhibiting high frequency transduction.[17] If one assumes that the transductional efficiency of the Lft particles is the same as that of the Hft, we can estimate that an ordinary λ lysate prepared by induction has about 1 transducing particle per 10^5 active phage particles.

For general transduction, one must have some measure of the transfer frequency of the average gene and divide this by the fraction of the total bacterial genome which the average transducing particle carries. This calculation has been made for P1 by Arber.[33] The transfer frequency of a gene (i.e., the proportion of the total number of phage particles in the lysate which both carry the gene and inject it into the recipient) is higher by a factor of about 10 than the frequency of recovery of complete transductions. The transfer frequency can be estimated by extrapolating the ultraviolet (UV) inactivation curve of the transducing particles to zero dose, or by measuring the frequency of "transfer induction." When phage P1 is grown on a strain lysogenic for λ, the λ prophage is transducible like any other group of genes; however, if the recipient is nonlysogenic, the prophage is induced to multiply vegetatively upon entering the nonimmune cytoplasm, and the cell lyses and liberates phage. The frequency of transfer induction of λ is higher than its frequency of complete transduction into an immune recipient. The methods agree that the transfer frequency of most genes is around 10^{-4}. This is a minimal estimate, as both transfer induction and incorporation at high UV doses may be less than completely efficient.

The average amount of genetic material transferred by one transducing particle of P1 has been estimated as 1–2 % of the total bacterial chromosome. So one expects that there is one transducing particle for every 100 or 200 active P1 particles in an ordinary lysate. This is a minimal estimate in that one can never eliminate the possibility of a large class of phage particles which have a low efficiency of transfer. Even our conclusion that transduction is performed by a few abnormal particles cannot be taken in an absolute sense. Strictly speaking, all that can be concluded from the observations is that some members of the population are better transducers than others; and that the best transducers are usually abnormal with respect to their function as phage.

D. Abortive Transduction

The fact that the transfer frequency is higher than the frequency of recovered transductions raises the question of the fate of the unsuccessful transducing particles and of the cells which they have infected. It has now been shown for a number of genetic markers that, for every complete transduction, there are many more (on the order of 10×) abortive transductions. Abortive transductions are characterized by unilinear inheritance of the transduced material. Only one cell is altered by the transduction; when it divides, the alteration does not pass to both daughter cells but only to one. It is as though something had been transferred which, like a gene, imparts a new specificity of synthesis to the recipient, but does not multiply at all and at each cell division passes to one daughter or the other.

Abortive transductions were first observed in the case of transduction for motility.[34] If nonmotile bacteria are seeded on fairly soft agar, any motile transductants which are produced will swim outward from the margin of the growth zone into the agar. Complete transduction of motility results in a swarm of bacteria coming out from the margin. About 10 times more common than the swarms, however are "trails" of colonies which result from abortive transduction. The trail marks the path of a single motile cell, and each colony shows where its nonmotile sister was produced by cell division. Abortive transductions of nutritional markers manifest themselves as very small colonies visible under the microscope, all of whose properties are compatible with the idea that growth is proceeding linearly from the one cell which has received the transferred material.[35]

Direct microscopic examination of population transduced for motility has shown that the situation is more complex than was originally supposed. [36, 37] Stocker has shown that the motile cells produced by transduction fall into three categories: (1) the cell and all its descendants are motile; (2) the cell and some of its descendants (20–100 after 10–15 generations) are motile; (3) the cell and a few of its descendants (0–12 after 10–15 generations) are motile. Class (1) is obviously the result of complete transduction. Class (2) is apparently the result of abortive transduction. Within each clone of class (2), there is never more than one cell of class (2). Individuals of class (3) appear in clones of class (2), especially among the close relatives of the one class (2) cell present. Individuals of class (3) may initially produce several motile offspring, but after a few generations, only one offspring from each division is motile.

The property of belonging to class (3), like that of belonging to class (2), thus ultimately shows unilinear inheritance. Stocker's interpretation is that the class (2) cell (called "E" for "exceptional") is carrying the transferred fragment (supernumerary gene) from the donor, and that the class (3) cell carries one or more copies of some product of the supernumerary gene. This product (called "MC" for "motility conferring factor") might be, for example, the basal granule which produces the flagellum. A single MC particle is enough to render a cell motile in broth, but several are necessary to impart motility through agar; thus the observed trails are generated by E cells and not be cells of class (3).

Stocker's designation of the transferred fragment carried by the E cell as a supernumerary gene was simply for economy of hypotheses. We know that genes are transferred from cell to cell by phage; if something which is gene specific has been transferred, maybe it is a gene. A direct demonstration of this would require that the gene be revived at some later time by incorporation into the recipient chromosome, which would produce a complete transduction from an abortive one. This has never been unequivocally observed. The best evidence that abortive transduction does involve a transfer of genes is that genetic linkage between functionally unrelated loci is preserved.[38] Not only do the determinants for the two loci enter the recipient cell together, but likewise they must segregate together at every cell division and therefore presumably are located on one physical structure.

Abortive transduction has been observed for fermentation markers[39] as well as for nutritional characters and flagellation. Unilinear inheritance of a certain fraction of the transferred genes is therefore probably a very general phenomenon. Biochemical determinations on cultures infected with P1dl indicate that, following infection, there is a period of several hours during which β-galactosidose synthesis proceeds linearly, at a rate which is several fold greater than expected on the basis of the number of cells which ultimately will give rise to complete transduction.[40]

E. UNIFORMITY OF THE TRANSDUCED FRAGMENTS

In special transduction of *gal* by λ, we have shown that the transducing particles are heterogeneous with respect to density and number of phage genes carried. Thus far, there is no good evidence on their uniformity with respect to the amount of bacterial genetic material included. With P1, it is possible to find rare individuals which carry only part of the *lac* region in the transducing particle.

In general transduction, most pairs of genes are transferred completely independently. Linkage is the rare exception. A small fraction of the bacterial genome is effectively transferred by a single transducing particle, and the total amount of genetic information in a bacterium precludes that a particle the size of a phage could contain it all. As the entire bacterial genome seems to be carried in the ensemble of particles within the lysate, it is obvious that different kinds of transducing particles can occur which carry different parts of the genome. Fixing our attention on a particular marker, we can ask whether all the particles which carry this marker might carry identical pieces of the bacterial genome. This depends on whether transduction involves chopping out pieces of the genome which terminate at certain prespecified end points, or whether instead the end points are picked at random.

A completely random choice of end points is made unlikely by Ozeki's observation that the frequency of joint abortive transduction for linked markers is the same as that for either of the markers individually.[38] This could mean, alternatively, that the transduced region is much longer than the distance between the two genes used; but the fact that they are usually incorporated singly in complete transduction argues against this. It has also frequently been observed that reciprocal crosses do not give equal yield, whereas if transductional fragments are chosen at random, they should. The unequal yields could be explained in other ways (e.g., specific marker effects on crosses),[41] but most of these alternatives are eliminated by Ozeki's finding that the frequency of joint incorporation of two markers is the same in reciprocal crosses, as it should be regardless of the uniformity or heterogeneity of the transducing particles. This experiment must be repeated in other systems before a general conclusion can be drawn.

Complete uniformity of the transducing particles for each member would of course preclude ever mapping the whole genome of a bacterium by transduction alone. The bacterium in this case would simply appear to have many independent "linkage groups." Ozeki's results do not prove that the situation is this extreme, but only that the transducing fragments are not chosen completely at random.

F. MATERIAL ORIGIN OF TRANSDUCED GENES

Depending on which of the mechanisms of low frequency transduction discussed in Section III, H is correct, one might or might not expect the transducing particle to multiply as such within the phage-infected donor cell. If one extends the hybrid intermediate model to general transduction, the same alternatives exist.

One consequence of multiplication would be that the DNA of the transducing particle should be composed mainly of atoms assimilated by the cell subsequent to infection, as is the case for the phage DNA. If, on the other hand, the transducing particle is formed directly from pre-existing bacterial DNA without further multiplication, it should be composed of atoms already in the bacterial host before infection.

The question has been investigated for phage P22 by studying the rate of suicide of transducing activity during phosphorus decay.[41a] The results show that much and perhaps all of the transducing activity is in DNA formed from pre-assimilated material. The transducing particle therefore cannot have multiplied extensively in the donor.

Unfortunately, the same experiment has yet to be done either in λ or in P1.

V. Effects of Irradiation on Transduction

We have alluded at several points to experiments in which a lysate with transducing activity was exposed to ultraviolet irradiation. This experiment was first done by Zinder,[42] who found that the transducing activity behaved very differently from the plaque-forming ability of the lysates. Whereas the number of plaque-formers decreased exponentially from zero dose, the transducing activity was actually increased several fold by low doses of irradiation and fell off at higher doses with a sensitivity less than that of the plaque-forming particles.

The same properties have been found with many systems, including λdg. In the absence of helper phage, low doses of UV increase the probability of transduction by a factor of 10 or 20—in other words, about to the level obtainable with helper phage. Whereas most of the transductants produced by unirradiated phage are heterogenotes, the irradiated phage give rise almost exclusively to stable transductions. The sensitivity to irradiation at high doses is about one third as great for transduction as for plaque-forming ability.[17]

The easiest interpretation is that a UV "hit" anywhere on the λdg "chromosome" will destroy its ability to lysogenize, and therefore it can transduce only by the recombination of a small region from λdg into the bacterial chromosome. It is hard to give a detailed explanation as to why the number increases, because we do not know the fate of those cells infected with unirradiated λdg which fail to produce transductants. What is rather interesting is that if another unirradiated phage is introduced into the system—by using either a lysogenic or an infected recipient—one gets again the formation of heterogenotes. The undamaged phage apparently somehow "rescues" the irradiated transducing phage and allows it to lysogenize. In some cases, this rescue is accompanied by a donation of genetic markers from the phage to the λdg.

Irradiation of the lysate thus eliminates the possibility of transduction by lysogenization, and destroys the intermediate in transduction, thus making transduction by integration appear to be a one-step process.

VI. Uses of Transduction

We indicated at the outset that the bulk of the work on transduction has been in using transduction as a tool to investigate bacterial genetics, and that we would not dwell on the details of the methods nor on the results obtained. However, we shall list and discuss briefly here some of the problems in which transduction techniques have been of some help.

A. MAPPING OF MUTATIONS

The methodology here is similar to that used in mapping mutations by transformation. One performs two- and three-factor crosses, the interpretation of which is complicated only by the fact that the parents of the cross are of unequal size and one is selecting for incorporation of genes from one parent into another. One is really therefore looking always at the result of a double crossover within a limited region of genetic material.

Because of large variations in transduction titer from one lysate to another, little reliance can by placed on crosses involving only selected markers. Regardless of how many genetic factors are involved in the cross, at least one should be unselected. One tabulates the frequency of the unselected marker(s) among the selected class. Inasmuch as most closely linked markers occur either within the same gene or in genes controlling steps of the same metabolic pathway,[41] this is sometimes difficult but frequently possible.

In practice, one of the most useful methods has been the so-called "three-point test," in which one selects for marker A from the donor and marker B from the recipient and looks for the assortment of marker C among these individuals. Because the cross itself is asymmetrical, one must compare reciprocal crosses. Marker C from the donor will show more frequent joint incorporation with whichever of the two markers A and B is closer to it. The principle is illustrated in Fig. 10. In the first cross, ABc and ABC both result from double crossovers. However, in the second case ABC can only arise by a quadruple crossover, and consequently will be relatively less frequent. An unambiguous linear ordering of mutants can be made by this method.[39]

Another very handy method is the use of multisite mutants.[41] These mutants behave as though they had a deletion of genetic material, and, as we discussed earlier in connection with the phage genes missing from λdg, it is possible to locate a given mutation by purely qualitative tests either within or outside of the region covered by a given multisite mutation. For determining order (without regard to distance) the method is more direct than three-point tests and avoids any problems created by effects of the

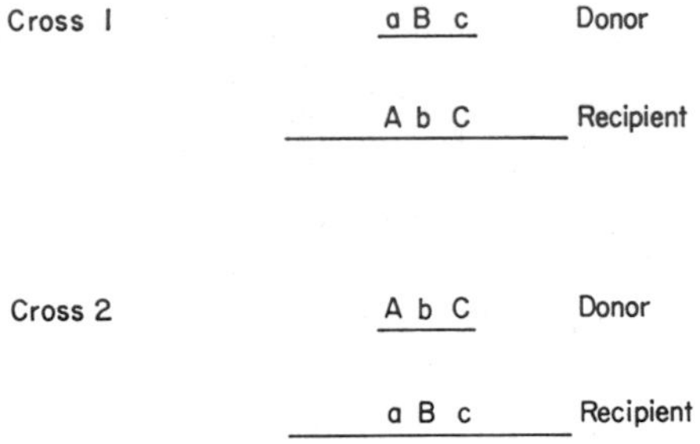

	Cross I		a B c	Donor
			A b C	Recipient

	Cross 2		A b C	Donor
			a B c	Recipient

Fig. 10. The principle of the three-point test.

mutations themselves on crossover frequencies. It also constitutes the simplest and most direct test for linearity of the genetic material.[22]

B. Complementation Tests

It is frequently useful to know whether two phenotypically similar mutants will give a wild-type phenotype in the *trans*-configuration of a diploid. Since bacteria are not ordinarily diploid, methods such as transduction by which partial diploids can be created are useful in this regard. The λdg heterogenotes have been much used for assigning galactose mutants to different cistrons.[43] If two mutations are in different cistrons, the heterogenote will be *gal+*. If they are in the same cistron, it will be *gal−* and produce rare occasional *gal+* segregants.

In general transduction, the presence of abortive transductants indicates that the mutations carried by donor and recipient are in different cistrons.[44] Their absence indicates that the mutations are in the same cistron, provided that abortive transductants can be seen in the same system when a wild-type donor is used. Frequently the locus determining a single enzyme comprises more than one cistron as determined by this test.

C. Biochemical Genetics

High frequency transduction offers an opportunity of studying what happens following the introduction of a gene into a cell. Both λdg[45] and $P1dl$[39, 46, 47] have been (and are currently) the object of such investigations. This method is technically simpler than to introduce these genes by bacterial mating, since in that case the donor cell must be present in the system, and one is therefore restricted to combinations in which the donor cannot perform the syntheses one is looking for in the recipient.

VII. Evolutionary Implications

The finding that pieces of bacterial DNA can become incorporated into the chromosome of what is still mainly a phage raises the questions of how often this may have happened in the past, and to what extent existing phages constitute a potpourri of fragments picked up at various times from diverse hosts. It seems unlikely that any phage is solely such a collection of bacterial genes. Especially in the larger phages, the number of specifically viral functions which have been identified, as well as the structural complexity of the phage particle itself, argue that much of the phage genome must comprise blueprints for phage growth, and that the genes controlling viral functions are the product of a long period of evolution in association with each other. However, in addition to these genes, the average phage may well contain other genes which have originated from the bacterium and have become accidentally but intimately associated with the phage. One can make quite plausible arguments that the potentiality for mediating bacterial recombination, either by transduction or by conversion, is the main factor which allows phage to survive in nature without eliminating its host.[48]

If this be so, the average phage should have genetic homologies with at least some parts of the host genome, and these homologies should manifest themselves genetically. Such homologies have often been postulated on other grounds, but there is still no clear-cut evidence for them. We have tentatively concluded that the formation of at least one transducing phage does not require such genetic homology but reflects some kind of rearrangement which places phage genes and bacterial genes on the same DNA molecule. The same process should also create occasionally the reverse case in which genes from a phage (controlling either "bacterial" or "phage" functions) should become attached to and integrated into the bacterial chromosome, not by replacement of a homologous piece, but as a genuine addition to the genome.

Evolution proceeds by the constant interplay of mutation, selection, and recombination. Recombination can include not only the interchange of genetically similar elements between closely related individuals, but also the building up of the genome by the confluence of initially diverse genetic lines. The second process is always limited by incompatibility at some level, but very rare events may sometimes be the decisive ones in evolution. At any rate, it seems that phage can play an important role in both types of recombination.

VIII. Review Articles on Transduction

In addition to the research and symposium papers we have referred to in the text, some valuable reviews of the transduction field have appeared. Hartman's paper[49] gives a complete account of the earlier literature on transduction and related subjects. It is still quite useful although, because of the rapid progress of the field, many of the models and ideas discussed there have been superseded by new data. A good concise summary of the area is given by Adelberg[50] in the introduction to his volume of collected reprints on microbial genetics. The reviews by Hartman and Goodgal[51] and Hartman[52] should be consulted for additional factual support for the "hybrid intermediate" model in generalized transduction, as well as for a critical discussion of some of its implications. The review by Stocker[53] and the book of Jacob and Wollman[54] are also highly recommended.

REFERENCES

[1] N. D. Zinder and J. Lederberg, *J. Bacteriol.* **64,** 679 (1952).

[2] B. W. Holloway and M. Monk, *Nature* **184,** 1426 (1959).

[3] C. B. Thorne, *J. Bacteriol.* **83,** 106 (1962).

[4] M. Morse, *Proc. Natl. Acad. Sci. U.S.* **45,** 722 (1959).

[5] M. Demerec, *in* "The Molecular Control of Cellular Activity" (J. M. Allen, ed.), Chapter 5, p. 167. McGraw-Hill, New York, 1962.

[6] N. D. Zinder, *J. Cellular Comp. Physiol.* **45** (Suppl. 2), 23 (1955).

[7] E. M. Lederberg and J. Lederberg, *Genetics* **38,** 51 (1953).

[8] A. D. Kaiser, *Virology* **1,** 424 (1955).

[9] R. K. Appleyard, J. F. McGregor, and K. M. Baird, *Virology* **2,** 565 (1956).

[10] F. Jacob, C. R. Fuerst, and E. L. Wollman, *Ann. inst. Pasteur* **93,** 724 (1957).

[11] A. Campbell, *Virology* **14,** 22 (1961).

[12] F. Jacob and J. Monod, *J. Mol. Biol.* **3,** 31 (1961).

[13] A. D. Kaiser and F. Jacob, *Virology* **4,** 509 (1957).

[14] F. Jacob and E. Wollman, *in* "Recent Progress in Microbiology" (G. Tunevall, ed.), *Intern. Congr. Microbiol. Symposium* **No. 7,** p. 15. Almquist & Wiksells, Stockholm, 1958.

[15] M. L. Morse, E. M. Lederberg, and J. Lederberg, *Genetics* **41,** 142 (1956).

[16] M. L. Morse, E. M. Lederberg, and J. Lederberg, *Genetics* **41,** 758 (1956).

[17] W. Arber, *Arch. sci. (Geneva)* **11,** 259 (1958).

[18] A. Campbell, *Virology* **4,** 366 (1957).

[19] W. Arber, G. Kellenberger, and J. Weigle, *Schweiz. Z. allgem. Pathol. u. Bakteriol.* **20,** 659 (1957).

[20] J. Weigle, M. Meselson, and K. Paigen, *J. Mol. Biol.* **1,** 379 (1959).

[21] M. Nomura and S. Benzer, *J. Mol. Biol.* **3,** 684 (1961).

[22] S. Benzer, *Proc. Natl. Acad. Sci. U.S.* **45**, 1607 (1959).
[23] A. Campbell and E. Balbinder, *Genetics* **44**, 309 (1959).
[24] A. D. Kaiser and D. S. Hogness, *J. Mol. Biol.* **2**, 392 (1960).
[25] J. Weigle, *J. Mol. Biol.* **3**, 393 (1961).
[26] E. Six, *Virology*, **14**, 220 (1961).
[27] A. Campbell, *Virology* **9**, 293 (1959).
[28] A. Campbell, *Virology* **11**, 339 (1960).
[28a] A. Campbell, *Genetics* **48**, 409 (1963).
[28b] D. K. Fraser, *Virology* **17**, 397 (1962).
[28c] M. L. Morse, *Genetics* **47**, 255 (1962).
[29] J. N. Adams and S. E. Luria, *Proc. Natl. Acad. Sci. U.S.* **44**, 590 (1958).
[30] P. Starlinger, *Z. Naturforsch.* **13b**, 489 (1958).
[31] S. E. Luria, J. N. Adams, and R. C. Ting, *Virology* **12**, 348 (1960).
[32] N. Franklin and S. E. Luria, *Virology* **15**, 299 (1961).
[33] W. Arber, *Virology* **11**, 273 (1960).
[34] B. A. D. Stocker, N. D. Zinder, and J. Lederberg, *J. Gen. Microbiol.* **9**, 410 (1953).
[35] H. Ozeki, *in* "Genetic Studies with Bacteria." *Carnegie Inst. Wash. Publ.* **612**, 96 (1956).
[36] J. Lederberg, *Genetics* **41**, 845 (1956).
[37] B. A. D. Stocker, *J. Gen. Microbiol.* **15**, 575 (1956).
[38] H. Ozeki, *Genetics* **44**, 457 (1959).
[39] J. Gross and E. Englesberg, *Virology* **9**, 314 (1959).
[40] H. R. Revel, S. E. Luria, and B. Rotman, *Proc. Natl. Acad. Sci. U.S.* **47**, 1956 (1961).
[41] P. E. Hartman, J. C. Loper, and D. Šerman, *J. Gen. Microbiol.* **22**, 323 (1960).
[41a] P. Starlinger, *Z. Naturforsch.* **14b**, 523 (1959).
[42] N. D. Zinder, *Cold Spring Harbor Symposia Quant. Biol.* **18**, 261 (1953).
[43] E. M. Lederberg, *in* "Microbiol Genetics." *Symposium Soc. Gen. Microbiol.* **10**, 115 (1960).
[44] P. E. Hartman, Z. Hartman, and D. Šerman, *J. Gen. Microbiol.* **22**, 354 (1960).
[45] G. Buttin, F. Jacob, and J. Monod. *Compt. rend. acad. sci.* **250**, 2471 (1960).
[46] H. R. Revel and S. E. Luria, *Proc. Natl. Acad. Sci. U.S.* **47**, 1968 (1961).
[47] H. R. Revel, S. E. Luria, and N. L. Young, *Proc. Natl. Acad. Sci. U.S.* **47**, 1974 (1961).
[48] A. Campbell, *Evolution* **15**, 153 (1961).
[49] P. E. Hartman, *in* "The Chemical Basis of Heredity" (W. D. McElroy and B. Glass, eds.), p. 408. Johns Hopkins Press, Baltimore, Maryland, 1957.
[50] E. A. Adelberg, "Papers on Bacterial Genetics." Little, Brown, Boston, Massachussets, 1960.
[51] P. E. Hartman and S. H. Goodgal, *Ann. Rev. Microbiol.* **13**, 465 (1959).
[52] P. E. Hartman, *in* "Symposium on Methodology in Basic Genetics" (in press).
[53] B. A. D. Stocker, *in* "Recent Progress in Microbiology" (G. Tunevall, ed.), *Intern. Congr. Microbiol. Symposium* No. 7, p. 31. Almquist & Wiksell, Stockholm, 1958.
[54] F. Jacob and E. L. Wollman, "Sexuality and the Genetics of Bacteria." Academic Press, New York, 1961.
[55] A. Taylor and E. Adelberg, *Genetics* **45**, 1233 (1960).
[56] F. Jacob and E. L. Wollman, *in* "The Chemical Basis of Heredity" (W. D. McElroy and B. Glass, eds.), p. 468. Johns Hopkins Press, Baltimore, Maryland, 1957.

CHAPTER 3

Transformation*

PIERRE SCHAEFFER

I. The Definition of Transformation and the Facts on Which It Stands

A. DEFINITION

Bacterial transformation today can be defined as the integration with the genome of a recipient cell of a small piece of exogenous genetic mate-

* Note added in proof: this Chapter was written in the fall of 1962.

rial, extracted from a donor cell and introduced into the receptor as part of a free DNA particle.

Many years of intensive study were necessary before this definition could be given. Several points are worth emphasizing:

1. The definition implies that the genetic material of bacteria is identified with DNA (deoxyribonucleic acid); this is precisely the fundamental notion introduced by the study of transformation. The fact that in bacteria genetic information can also be transferred by more complex structures, such as a chromosome, an episome, or a virus (see Chapters 1, 2, and 4, respectively, this volume), makes the specification that in transformation the carrier is free DNA, an essential part of the definition.

2. By *integration* is meant some sort of permanent association between the reacting genetic materials, such that the exogenous piece will be replicated in pace with the rest of the genome and have its genetic capabilities normally expressed in the phenotype of the transformed cell. This association is generally believed to establish itself by a substitution of the exogenous segment for its counterpart in the original genome (see Section V,D,2,e, for a discussion).

3. The contribution of the donor strain is limited to a short segment of genetic material. While the same can be said of the other bacterial recombination processes, the fact is of such significance for understanding the mechanism of transformation that its inclusion in the definition seems justified.

4. Two parental strains participate in the phenomenon; as their qualification as donor and receptor illustrates, the roles they play are essentially different. But in principle at least, they can be freely interchanged, the phenomenon requiring no sexual differentiation of the reacting strains.

5. Although new genetic factors may be created in the process of transformation, they arise by recombination between preexisting genetic structures, a mechanism incompatible with transformation being referred to as a mutation.

Those studies on transformation that permitted the above definition to be arrived at will be reviewed in this section.

B. Previous Reviews

A landmark in the development of bacterial transformation and molecular biology, the classical paper of Avery *et al.*,[1] may be quoted as the first review on the subject; the most complete and up-to-date is by Ravin.[2] The successive advances and the various points of view may be followed along the years with the reviews of McCarty,[3] Austrian,[4] Hotchkiss,[5, 6] Ephrussi-Taylor,[7, 8] Zamenhof,[9, 10] and Thomas.[11]

C. Discovery

The phenomenon was discovered by Griffith,[12] as he was studying immunity to pneumococcal infections. While mice will die in two days of bacteriema, when injected subcutaneously with a few encapsulated, smooth pneumococci, they will survive infection with enormous numbers of nonencapsulated, rough mutants. But if the latter are injected together with heat-killed smooth organisms (the "vaccine"), a fatal infection again develops, with the invading pneumococcus being encapsulated and of the same serological type as the vaccine. It was then believed that the type-specific capsular polysaccharide of the vaccine was responsible for the observed transformation of the rough inoculum. That this was not so was recognized by Sia and Dawson,[13] who were able to obtain transformation in *in vitro* cultures.[14] The preparation of heat-stable, cell-free transforming agent was described by Alloway.[15]

D. DNA as the Transforming Substance

With the active "principle" available in solution, its chemical identification was achieved by Avery and his collaborators. It was observed that trace amounts of the transforming agent (1 mμg./ml.) produced transformed bacteria, but that any desired amount of it could subsequently be extracted from a transformed clone: obviously the agent was being synthesized by the transformed cells, which had therefore simultaneously acquired two new biosynthetic abilities, one leading to the capsular polysaccharide, the other to the transforming substance, both abilities being regularly transmitted to the progeny.[1]

The transforming agent was shown to be DNA. A wealth of arguments was produced in support of this conclusion: chemical, physical, enzymic, and serological tests all agreed in indicating that activity is associated with DNA alone. Among the best pieces of evidence was the fact that crystalline proteases and RNase (ribonuclease) leave the activity unimpaired, while traces of DNase (deoxyribonuclease), whatever its origin, destroy it readily. Crystalline DNase was not available at that time, but tests made later[16-18] confirmed the results entirely. Overwhelming as it was, the evidence still met with skepticism,[19] the reasons for which are instructive to consider briefly.

At least half a dozen capsular transformation reactions were already known,[20] which meant that the transforming substance had to exist in a large number of specific forms. As the progress of enzymology and immunology had already demonstrated, proteins did display such specificity and therefore could conceivably be the transforming substance, while DNA, still believed to be a monotonous polymer of a tetranucleotide unit,[21] was considered to be lacking in specificity. Considering the primitive state of knowledge of DNA composition, Avery's conclusion came too early to make sense. Hotchkiss spent much effort in reducing the maximal protein content of the transforming substance to 0.02%[22] and eventually proposed that anyone who again suggested proteins as the active factor of transforming extracts would have to buttress the argument with new experimental evidence. The challenge was not taken up, and did not need to be, since meanwhile the supposedly uniform composition of DNA was disproved by Chargaff.[21] Polysaccharides could no longer be suspected of activity, when transformation reactions were extended to characters in the expression of which they were not involved.[23] Early additional reasons for identifying the "transforming principle" with DNA deal with resistance to inactivation by physical agents,[10, 17] purification by electrophoresis[1, 24] and electron microscopy.[22]

E. DNA as the Genetic Substance

The meaning of Avery's discovery was at first far from obvious. The notion slowly emerged that DNA is the genetic substance, and that recombination can occur between the genome of a living bacterium and the dissolved genome from a dead one. For the sake of clarity and at the risk of disregarding their chronology, the facts which contributed to the elaboration of this notion will now be presented under three headings.

1. Reciprocal Transformations

From smooth strains of pneumococcus, rough mutants are isolated, which in turn produce a second-step mutant, with an "extreme rough" colonial appearance. Like its parental rough form, the latter is unable to produce any capsular substance. With the symbols originally in use provisionally adopted, the three strains are referred to as S, R, and ER, respectively. The following reactions were shown by Taylor[25] to occur*:

$$ER + (R) \rightarrow R \tag{1}$$

$$R + (ER) \rightarrow ER \tag{2}$$

The possibility of a reciprocal transformation reaction was thereby established. That this reciprocality was the rule rather than the exception was later demonstrated by studies on other systems: $S_b \rightleftharpoons S_d$, between the serological types b and d, in smooth strains of *Hemophilus influenzae*[26]; $S_{III_1} \rightleftharpoons S_{III_2}$, between type III mutants of pneumococcus, producing

* In describing transformation reactions, the following convention is adopted: the recipient strain is written first, the donor second, parentheses indicating DNA preparation; the designation of the transformants obtained follows an arrow.

various subnormal amounts of capsular material[27]; $Sp^+ \rightleftharpoons Sp^-$, between sporogenous and asporogenous forms of *Bacillus subtilis*,[28, 29] etc.

Whenever the reciprocality of transformation cannot be demonstrated, the difficulty is one of selection only. Any $X^s \rightleftharpoons X^r$ system, between the sensitive and the resistant forms to an antibacterial agent X, can be taken as an illustration: the only transformants difficult to select for are the sensitive ones. But even in such cases, the reciprocality of transformation can be demonstrated, as shown by Hotchkiss and Marmur,[30] if a selectable marker, linked to the X marker, is available*:

$Mtl^-Sm^r \times (Mtl^+Sm^s) \rightarrow$ selected Mtl^+ transformants, 20 % of which are also Sm^s.

The same demonstration was also given by Goodgal[31] in *Hemophilus*, where the Sm and Cm (cathomycin) markers are linked:

$Sm^s Cm^r \times (Sm^r Cm^s) \rightarrow$ selected Sm^r transformants, many of which are also Cm^s.

Reciprocality therefore is the rule and excludes the possibility that one of the strains might have lost a determinant present in the other.[25] The following interpretation was suggested: different forms of a gene are present in the two strains, each strain having one, and transformation consists in an exchange reaction of the allelic form present in the recipient genome for the one present in the exogenous DNA (MacLeod and Krauss[32]; Taylor[25]).

2. INDEPENDENT TRANSMISSION OF CHARACTERS

In Avery's laboratory, capsular transformation only was tried, and with this one marker being followed, the transformed cells appeared identical with the donor cells. A demonstration that this was not the case can be found in Langvad-Nielsen's work.[33] Still following Griffith's procedure of transformation *in vivo* by heat-killed "vaccine," this author was concerned with the sterility of the vaccine, and for this reason differentiated the interacting strains with a sulfonamide (Sf) marker. His results can be summarized in the following way:

$$R\ Sf^s \times (S_{II}\ Sf^r) \rightarrow S_{II}\ Sf^s \qquad (3)$$

$$R\ Sf^r \times (S_{II}\ Sf^s) \rightarrow S_{II}\ Sf^r \qquad (4)$$

With phagocytosis in the mouse selecting for smooth transformants, it can be seen that the latter retained the Sf marker present in the receptor: they differed from both parental strains, having acquired only one of the two markers present in the DNA and being in fact *recombinants*. (Double transformants, identical with the donor, were presumably also present, but

* Mtl for growth behavior on mannitol, Sm for behavior in streptomycin; the two characters are linked in pneumococcus.[30]

being rare were overlooked.) While the recombinational nature of transformation had been demonstrated, the author only concluded, too modestly, that the occurrence of transformation had been confirmed, and his demonstration went unnoticed for some time.

The next illustration of the one-by-one transmission of characters is found in the stepwise transformation of an ER into an S strain (Taylor[34]). A description of the relations existing between these two strains must first be given. The peculiar colonial appearance of ER mutants results from both their inability to produce any capsular substance and their tendency to grow in the form of long filaments (Austrian[35]). These two characters, capsule production (S^+) and filament formation (Fil^+), were shown by Austrian to mutate independently.[36] Thus, an ordinary smooth strain of serological type III is $Fil^- S_{III}^+$, a rough mutant derived from it is $Fil^- S_{III}^-$, and an extreme rough mutant, isolated from the latter, $Fil^+ S_{III}^-$. (The Fil character only was changed in the reactions 1 and 2 described above).

Now the two following reactions were obtained in succession by Taylor[34]:

$$Fil^+ S_{II}^- \times (Fil^- S_{III}^+) \rightarrow Fil^- S_{II}^- \tag{5}$$

$$Fil^- S_{II}^- \text{ (from reaction 5)} \times (Fil^- S_{III}^+) \rightarrow Fil^- S_{III}^+ \tag{6}$$

Here is a case where one and the same DNA preparation is shown to contain two distinct genetic determinants $(Fil^-$ and $S_{III}^+)$ which, in transformation, are transmitted singly. The same is shown also in Austrian and MacLeod's case: the ability of pneumococcus to produce a somatic, type-specific protein and a capsular polysaccharide can be independently lost by mutation and acquired by transformation.[23, 37]

A clear formulation, however, that characters are, as a rule, transferred independently, was only given by Hotchkiss,[38] studying simultaneous transformation for both encapsulation and penicillin resistance (Pen^r), i.e., two physiologically unrelated markers, of which the latter is easily selected and quantitatively recovered. In the reaction: $S^- Pen^s \times (S^+ Pen^r)$, transformation occurred for both markers, but most individual transformants had acquired one of them only; a very few doubly transformed clones could be detected in this case.

Another important point was made. A high level of penicillin resistance, obtained by selection of successive mutations, had been attained in some strains. When the sensitive wild type was given DNA from such a strain, it acquired, by transformation, the increments in resistance one by one, just as it had by mutation (although not necessarily in the same order). The point here is that with DNA so similar in all its potentialities with the genome of the organism from which it was extracted, another powerful argument is given in favor of the view that DNA is the genome itself in solution.[38]

3. Heteroallelic Transforming Agents

Still other arguments supporting the above conclusion had in fact already been produced in studies following quite a different line: the transformation analysis of mutants producing reduced amounts of an otherwise normal capsular polysaccharide, and appearing thereby as intermediary between the rough (S^-) and the normal smooth (S_N^+) conditions.

With such an intermediary mutant of type II ($S_{II_i}^+$), MacLeod and Krauss[32] observed the following reactions:

$$S_{II}^- \times (S_{II_i}^+) \to S_{II_i}^+ \tag{7}$$

$$S_{II}^- \times (S_{IIN}^+) \to S_{IIN}^+ \tag{8}$$

$$S_{II_i}^+ \times (S_{IIN}^+) \to S_{IIN}^+ \tag{9}$$

The results were those to be expected, if the two DNA's employed were carrying distinct allelic forms of a gene for type II polysaccharide synthesis, the third and extreme form of which would be present in the rough strain. Under the assumptions made, transformation again would consist in an exchange reaction.

A similar situation in type III was exploited further by Ephrussi-Taylor.[34, 39, 40] For the sake of simplicity, only two of her intermediary mutants will be mentioned, $S_{III_1}^+$ and $S_{III_2}^+$. Here again, stepwise intratype transformation was observed, as appears in the following reactions:

$$S_{II}^- \times (S_{III_1}^+) \to S_{III_1}^+ \text{ (exclusively)} \tag{10}$$

$$S_{II}^- \times (S_{III_2}^+) \to S_{III_2}^+ \text{ (exclusively)} \tag{11}$$

$$S_{III_1}^+ \text{ [from reaction (10)]} \times (S_{III_2}^+) \to S_{III_2}^+ \tag{12}$$

$$\text{[not exclusively, however; see reaction (12a)]}$$

Several important additional observations were made.

a. Loss of the Replaced Segment. Transformants in reaction (12) have at the same time acquired the $S_{III_2}^+$ determinant and lost the $S_{III_1}^+$ factor they posessed originally. This was shown in the reaction:

$$S_{II}^- \times [S_{III_2}^+, \text{ a transformant from reaction (12)}] \to S_{III_2}^+ \text{ (exclusively)} \tag{13}$$

(Had $S_{III_1}^+$ transformants been formed, they would have been detected.) Replacement of one determinant by another is directly demonstrated here, together, incidentally, with the haploidy of the organism. That the chromosomal marker, allelic to the one introduced by transformation, is not only displaced, but actually lost at integration, has been confirmed by many authors.[31, 41-43]

b. Test for Allelism. While the $S_{III_1}^+$ and $S_{III_2}^+$ agents are mutually exclusive, this is not true of other pairs of determinants, like Fil^- and S_{III}^+, the coexistence of which has been demonstrated [reactions (5) and (6)]. The reason for this difference in behavior was assumed to be an allelic relation existing between the members of the former pair only, an assumption supported by the similar function and the common gene of origin of the two intermediary S_{III}^+ genes. A new kind of *test for allelism* was thereby provided, ample use of which was made later.

c. Allogenic Transformations. Reaction (12), as written, is incomplete, since in addition to the $S_{III_2}^+$ transformants mentioned, another class of (rare) transformants, $S_{III_N}^+$ (N for normal), is formed. The correct reaction is therefore:

$$S_{III_1}^+ \times (S_{III_2}^+) \rightarrow S_{III_2}^+ + S_{III_N}^+ \tag{12a}$$

It shows that more than one kind of reaction is possible, when a given pair of genomes is reacting. The $S_{III_2}^+$ transformants, with their acquired character already present in the donor, are said to result from an "autogenic" reaction, and are expected; but the $S_{III_N}^+$ transformants unexpectedly display a character, absent from both parents, which must have arisen by intragenic recombination.[39, 40] Such transformants, said to be "allogenic," are detected from the normal-looking smoothness of their colonies. Having arisen by recombination, their genotype might be either $S_{III_1}^+ S_{III_2}^+$ (with the simultaneous presence of the two mutated determinants leading, by summation of their synthetic abilities, to a normal polysaccharide production), or $S_{III_N}^+$ (with elimination of both mutated sites and reconstitution of a wild capsular gene). That the latter event alone is responsible for the formation of the normal smooth transformants is shown by the following reaction:

$$S_{II}^- \times [S_{III_N}^+ \text{, from reaction (12a)}] \rightarrow S_{III_N}^+ \text{ (exclusively)} \tag{13}$$

The $S_{III_1}^+ S_{III_2}^+$ recombinants, therefore, if they are formed, do not contribute to the normal smooth class, the defects, rather than the abilities, of their determinants being additive. The following interpretation was proposed[39, 40] to account for the creation, by transformation, of genetic factors absent from both "parental" strains.

One linear genetic region exists in type III pneumococcus, responsible for its specific encapsulation. At different sites along this region, mutation is possible, the various capsular mutants observed corresponding to various mutational sites. Essentially a recombination between two genetic structures, transformation requires, when carried out with two heteroallelic mutants, that their mutated sites do not overlap exactly. Transformation may be of two types, autogenic and allogenic, both types of transformants arising by replacement of one segment of the host's genome by another, carried in with the DNA. As illustrated by Fig. 1, replacement implies the occurrence of two events, formally analogous to crossing over. The capsular reactions studied imply that the site homologous to the one mutated in the bacterium always be included in the replaced segment; whether a transformation turns out to be autogenic or allogenic depends simply on whether the location of the second "crossing-over" is such that the mutated site of the donor is included in, or excluded from, the replaced segment.[39, 40]

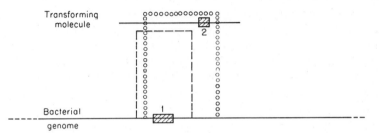

FIG. 1. Autogenic and allogenic transformations (after Ephrussi-Taylor[39, 40]). The transforming molecule, mutated at site 2, is shown synapsed with the homologous region, mutated at site 1, of the capsular genome of the cell. O O O, autogenic transformation; – – –, allogenic transformation.

4. EVIDENCE FROM OTHER FIELDS

The notion that the genetic substance is DNA, established by the study of bacterial transformation, was soon found to fit admirably a large number of observations (cf. ref. 6 for a review), some of which will now be mentioned.

a. In higher organisms DNA, like genes, is confined to chromosomes[0, 44]; with due recognition of the peculiarities of the bacterial "nucleus",[45] this is also true of bacteria.[46, 47]

b. Variable with the species, the amount of DNA per cell within a species is constant, but follows the degree of ploidy whenever the latter varies, as is the case in gametogenesis.[48]

c. DNA alone is endowed with the metabolic stability that is to be expected of the genetic substance[6]; its genetic (transforming) activity was found to be independent of whether the physiological function under its control is expressed in the cell or not.[49]

d. A number of agents altering the structure of DNA are powerful mutagens at the same time: ultraviolet (UV) light, mustard gas, acridine dyes (see ref. 6), heat,[50] nitrous acid,[51] base analogs, etc.

e. Recent biochemical studies have come very close to demonstrating directly that DNA is endowed with both the autocatalytic and the specific heterocatalytic activities, upon which the definition of the gene is based. DNA is required as a primer, and most likely as a specific template, for its own enzymic synthesis.[52, 53] It is also required as a specific template for the synthesis of enzymes, or more precisely, of the messenger RNA's which confer their specificity to the proteins being synthesized in the cytoplasm (see Chapter 8).

f. The situation in viruses will break the monotony of this accumulation of unfailingly concording data. Viruses differ from cells in having one kind of nucleic acids only, DNA or RNA as the case may be, wrapped in a protective coat of specific viral proteins. Whatever its nature, however, the nucleic acid alone is infectious; once introduced into the host cell, it is able by itself to give rise to mature, infective particles.[54-56] While the secondary role played by proteins is thereby confirmed, the results demonstrate that RNA may in some cases be the primary source of genetic specificity. Although this apparent oddity may have some bearing upon the cellular origin of some viruses, it casts no more doubt on the genetic nature of DNA than do the known cases of extrachromosomal heredity on the existence of Mendelian heredity.

F. Genetic Heterogeneity of DNA Extracts

DNA extracts from a single clone contain more than one genetic factor, and these are as a rule transmitted singly. In *Bacillus subtilis* transformation, for instance, just as many transforming activities can be detected in wild-type DNA as auxotrophic markers have been introduced in the recipient strains: the entire genome of the donor organism is present in solution in the extract. The rule of unit factor transmission still generally applies.

If to every bacterial character, whether recognized or not, there corresponds one specific gene, thousands of genes must be present in the extract, either as specific segments along one linear DNA structure, or as discrete DNA particles, each containing one gene or more. Indeed, it is now known that a conventional DNA extract contains some fifty molecular species, with probably a few tens of genes accommodated in each of them. Suffice it here to point out (*1*) that a gene (and *a fortiori* a marker, which may be a mere mutated site in a gene) is smaller than the usual DNA particle, and (*2*) that the heterogeneity of DNA particles in extracts, first deduced from genetic considerations, prompted chemical and physical studies which fully confirmed it.

With the definition of transformation now fully justified, particular aspects of the phenomenon will be described.

II. The Quantitative Study of Transformation

In the experience of early workers, transformation was a rare and poorly reproducible phenomenon, affecting a fraction of the population that was hard to estimate, but very small. The main difficulty was with competence, a property to be dealt with in another section. But the choice of the recipient strain, of the character transferred, the quality of the DNA preparation, and the time course of the reaction also are of importance and will now be considered.

A. CHOICE OF THE SYSTEM

Not all strains of a species can be transformed. Unlike *competence*, a physiological state, *transformability* is a genetically determined property. In pneumococcus, the amount of capsular substance that a strain is able to produce seems to bear an inverse relation to its transformability.[27] Avery *et al.* reported that the rough strain R36 was exceptional, among a number of rough clones, in being highly transformable[1]; so are the strain Rd of *H. influenzae*,[57, 58] some strains of streptococci,[59, 60] the mutant ✕168 of *B. subtilis* Marburg,[61] the rough strain C of *Rhizobium lupini*,[62] the strain Ne-11 of *Neisseria catarrhalis*.[63] No ways are known of selecting for highly transformable clones, a rare transformant from a poorly transformable strain retaining the original low level of transformability. Since the search for good transformable strains must be conducted blindly, and in general brings poor rewards, it is not surprising that a few selected strains are being used the world over in studies on transformation. Since serial transfers of a transformable strain may lead to a loss of transformability, early lyophilization of such strains is recommended.

The choice of the character to be transferred may be dictated by the subject under study (see Section VI); as a rule, preference will be given to characters easily selected for, permitting a quantitative recovery of the transformants.[38] In that respect, capsular characters are well known as unsuitable,[64, 65] their expression apparently requiring a restricted dispersion of the cells,[66] usually obtained by adding an antiserum. But transformants are trapped in the aggregates, and in some cases the antiserum may even be inhibitory to the desired reaction.[66] Anti-R antibodies are not required for the appearance of competence, and can be dispensed with in the study of transformations other than capsular ones.[38, 66] Even with an accurate count of the transformants, transformation frequencies are not the same for all characters, the probability of integration being an innate property that varies with each marker.

B. Preparation of DNA

Although transformation may be obtained with DNA directly liberated from the donor in the presence of the receptor cells,[38, 67] quantitative work demands that a purified extract of known DNA content be used. The classical method of pneumococcal DNA preparation, involving deoxycholate-induced lysis of the cells, deproteinization by chloroform, and ethanol precipitation, has been described and improved many times.[15, 32, 39, 68, 69] RNA is usually removed by RNase treatment, but removal of the inert polysaccharides is today seldom carried out. Deproteinization, a tedious step requiring many treatments when chloroform is used, is obtained more rapidly with detergents, or by phenol treatment.[61, 70] Direct phenol extraction of DNA[71] has also been used in transformation studies.[72, 73]

With other bacterial species, the classical method is generally applicable only after the DNA has been solubilized, cell lysis requiring special treatments.[70] Mechanical or sonic disruption of the cells should be avoided; even pipetting of the solutions should be performed as gently as possible and kept to a minimum (see Section IV,F,2).

Sterilization of the extract is most simply obtained by the last ethanol precipitation (filtration should be avoided). This procedure is inadequate, however, with DNA that contains spores. In the case of spore-formers, DNA extraction should be made only from cultures growing exponentially in a rich medium, or, when possible, from asporogenous mutants. Contaminated preparations can be rid of spores, however, by inducing germination with alanine and glucose before alcohol treatment, or by killing the spores directly with phenol.[74]

Stock solutions of DNA will keep for years in saline, or better sometimes in 2 M NaCl.[75] Since molecular aggregation occurs and increases with age,[69, 76] applying a chloroform treatment to old solutions before use may be good practice.[69] Titration of DNA may be chemical,[77] spectrophometric, or biological.[65, 78]

C. Time Course of an Experiment

The general principles upon which an experiment is to be scheduled, laid down by Hotchkiss,[65, 78] can be summarized as follows. The number of transformants become meaningful only when expressed relative to the number of viable cells exposed to treatment; detemination of the ratio (i.e., the frequency of transformation) requires two bacterial counts. An accurate count of the transformants demands not only that they be quantitatively selected for, but also that their progeny cannot disperse before selection is applied; this can be insured either by timely plating on a solid medium, or by adding the proper agglutinins to a liquid one.[65] An accurate count of the viable population during treatment requires: (a) a sharp end of the exposure to DNA (terminated by treatment with DNase), and (b) a treatment that is short, relative to the generation time of the organism. With exposure thus necessarily short, use of a highly competent culture is all the more important.

How these principles apply in actual practice partly depends on the system being used. The cultural conditions have first to be empirically adjusted, as described in Section V,A,1. The time at which competence is maximal is then determined in kinetic experiments of the kind described by Hotchkiss[287] and by Thomas.[79] Needless to say, reproducible kinetics will not be obtained until all cultural conditions are strictly standardized.

DNA then can be added, at a precisely known time, and DNase 5–10 minutes later. What is next to be done depends on the character being transferred. With the acquisition of a resistance to a bactericidal drug, like streptomycin, exposure to the drug will have to be postponed until resistance is expressed, otherwise even the transformants will be killed.[80] Time alone is of no avail, however, when nutrients for syntheses are lacking; with competence often appearing at the end of exponential growth, in a medium approaching exhaustion, it is good practice to dilute the culture with fresh medium before incubating for expression.[81] If the diluted culture is plated at various time intervals directly onto a drug containing agar medium ("immediate challenge"), an expression curve is obtained, giving the number of transformants expressed at the time of plating (Fig. 2, curve A).[5, 79]

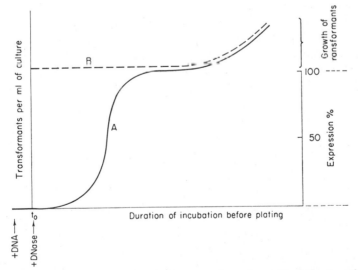

Fig. 2. Expression of resistance to streptomycin and growth of the transformants (after Ephrussi-Taylor[82]). DNase is added at t_0, the time zero of expression (the duration of contact with DNA, ca. 5 minutes, is negligible). The procedures followed for obtaining curves A and B are described in the text. In a complete medium, at 37°C., 60 to 75 minutes are required for complete expression.

Alternatively, the DNase-treated culture may at once be incorporated into a plain agar medium and incubated for 2 hours, a drug-containing agar layer being then poured on top. This second procedure ("belated challenge") simply gives the total number of transformants.[65] The two procedures may also be combined into a third, whereby samples of the treated liquid culture, taken out at various times after addition of DNase, are submitted to a belated challenge.[82] This leads to curve B of Fig. 2, representing the multiplication of the transformed cells; the two curves superimpose when expression is completed.[82]

When the drug does not kill the sensitive cells at once, as is the case with sulfonamides, or when a new biosynthetic ability has been acquired by transformation, immediate challenge can be used after DNase addition, since expression takes place during residual growth on the plate. Other selective methods may have to be devised for special cases, like acquisition of motility, ability to sporulate, etc.

Fox and Hotchkiss[83] have introduced a very useful modification of the standard procedure just described, which consists in storing at deep-freeze temperatures aliquots of a competent culture to which 10–15% glycerol has been added.

D. DOSE-RESPONSE CURVE

When the transformants counted are expressed as a function of DNA concentration, a saturation curve is obtained similar to the one in Fig. 3.[58, 64, 65, 79] It shows a linear part, at low DNA concentrations, and a horizontal part at higher, saturating ones. Minor deviations from the curve have occasionally been observed in the plateau region.[76]

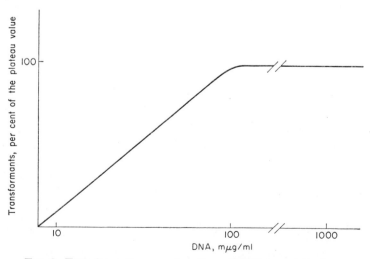

FIG. 3. Transformation as a function of DNA concentration.

The linear part, extrapolated down to zero concentration, goes through the origin, as expected if one DNA particle is enough to transform one bacterium. This important point has been stressed by many authors.[64, 65, 79, 84] Formally, the treatment of a bimolecular reaction can be applied to the reaction of a bacterium with DNA.[79, 83, 85-88]

The proportional response part of the curve lends itself to, and should be exclusively used in, biological titration of transforming DNA, the concentration of which is measured by the slope of the linear part; information of another, qualitative sort is obtained by studying the plateau region.[65, 78]

III. The Present Extent of Transformation

A. TRANSFORMABLE SPECIES

That ability to transform is not a unique attribute of the pneumococcus first became apparent with the discovery by Alexander *et al.* of transformation in *Hemophilus*[89] and *Neisseria*.[90] Since then, transformation has been reported to occur in a number of bacterial species (bibliography in Ravin[2]; see also Jarai,[91] Wacker and Laschet,[92] Perry and Slade,[93] who recently reported on transformation in streptomyces, *Escherichia coli*, and streptococci, respectively).

A new transformable species nowadays raises interest mostly as a material making some new bacterial function accessible to genetic analysis (see Section VI). *Bacillus subtilis* Marburg deserves special mention in this respect. This strain can be grown and transformed in chemically defined media,[61, 75, 94] and with the practically unlimited number of genetic markers that can be obtained, some precise genetic mapping has already been done.[95-97] In addition, the organism produces spores, pigments, flagella, mesosomes,[98] extracellular enzymes, at least one antibiotic,[74] and probably bacteriocins; moreover, phages,[99] some of them transducing,[100-103] are known in this strain, which itself carries an inducible prophage.[74]

B. TRANSFERABLE CHARACTERS

In transformable strains, all characters that can be recognized can also be transferred by DNA (an enumeration of specific examples may be found in ref. 2). This may mean either that cytoplasmic mutations do not occur in bacteria, or that most of them are lethal.

However, two preliminary reports have recently appeared, claiming that stable genetic transformation had been induced by RNA. In one of them, the ability to produce a constitutive penicillinase was transferred from a penicillin-resistant mutant to a sensitive strain of *B. subtilis*[104]; in the other, a pyrimidineless mutant of *Neurospora* was said to be restored to prototrophy by RNA.[105] In both cases, RNase inactivated the extracts, while DNase had no action. Independent confirmation of these unexpected results is highly desirable.

A potentiation of DNA-induced transformation by an RNA fraction "closely associated with DNA" has been described by Spizizen in *B. subtilis*[61, 106]; it seems, however, to be detectable only when special markers are being transferred.[75, 106] No genetic effect was attributed in this case to RNA, which was believed to help with the expression, and therefore the scoring, of the transformants. If any one of these specific activities of RNA is confirmed, a more detailed characterization of the active RNA will be needed, since the same activity would not be expected for messenger RNA[107] and for DNA-RNA hybrids,[108] particularly with respect to genetic effects.

C. NATURAL OCCURRENCE OF TRANSFORMATION

Since transformation in the laboratory requires the preparation of cell extracts, the question arises of its natural occurrence.[109] Penicillin lysis[38] need not be invoked as a way of liberating genetically active DNA in nature, since this liberation takes place spontaneously, either by autolysis[110, 111] or even by a nonspecified mechanism, during exponential growth[67]; the fact is that transformation does occur in untreated mixed cultures.[67] Transformation may well occur in nature, but its actual contribution to gene flow is hard to evaluate.

D. INTERSPECIFIC TRANSFORMATIONS

Transformation is not a strictly intraspecific phenomenon. Leidy *et al.*[112] and Schaeffer[81, 113] simultaneously observed interspecific transformations in *Hemophilus*. The first mention of their occurrence, however, is found in papers by Balassa, working with *Rhizobium*.[114, 115] These reactions were later found to be widespread, occurring between pneumococcus and streptococcus[59, 116] and among species of *Neisseria*[63, 117] and *Bacillus*.[118] Cases of interspecific recombination by transduction or conjugation are also steadily increasing. Genetic compatibility being one of the best criteria upon which species are defined, a classification of bacteria which took into account the recent genetic evidence would end up with a smaller number of highly polytypic species[119, 120] (see also Chapter 9).

Interspecific recombination, as a rule, is rare, when compared with the corresponding intraspecific reaction; the suggestion has been made that transformation frequencies might reflect the degree of kinship existing between the reacting strains.[81, 112] Exceptions to the rule have been observed, indicating that genetic factors other than kinship may affect transformation frequencies.[59, 121] Genetic factors influencing these frequencies are known to exist, even in intraspecific transformation.[112, 122]

The meaning of the low frequencies usually obtained in interspecific transformation reactions and the way in which these reactions can be used to recognize steps in the transformation process[121] will be discussed in a later section.

E. TRANSFORMATIONS OTHER THAN BACTERIAL

Transformation has not yet been found in any microbial group other than bacteria. A good deal of effort has been spent trying to detect its occurrence in genetically well-known microorganisms, like *Neurospora*, *Penicillium*, and yeast, with only failure as the result. It is not known to the writer whether Cyanophyceae have been tried.

Infection of cells by viral DNA is outside the scope of this review, except in cases where acquisition by the cell of a stable new trait, rather than cell death, results from the infection. DNA from a temperate phage can lysogenize an infected bacterium; and with special transducing phages as the DNA source, this lysogenization, leading to the integration of bacterial genes, complies with the definition of transformation.[73] It seems quite plausible that lysogenization and immunity can also be obtained with DNA from a lysogenic bacterium ("prophage DNA"), the only data pertaining to this point[123] do not seem very convincing.

On condition that free viral DNA can enter the host cell, viruses themselves, as genetic entities, are transformable during their vegetative stage. This has only recently been established (Kaiser[124]), and had long been the accepted interpretation of the well-known Berry-Dedrick phenomenon, in which an animal virus is "transformed" into another, serologically related one.[125-128] Twenty-five years after the initial observations, however, not only is good characterization of the active material as free DNA still lacking, but the possibility for a heated virus to be reactivated by a mechanism other than genetic has been established.[128a]

Reaction of DNA with bacteria can be demonstrated at the physical, the physiological, and the genetic level by measuring uptake of a labeled DNA, synthesis of a specific enzyme or product, and recombination, respectively. With bacterial transformation serving as a model, reaction of DNA with animal cells begins to be investigated. Uptake has been demonstrated by using DNA's labeled with tritiated thymidine,[129-132] radiophosphorus,[133] or acridine orange.[130] Addition of unlabeled DNA in excess or of DNase being inhibitory, the label must be incorporated as a polymerized molecule[129, 133]; indeed, it is found in the DNA fraction of the cells[129] and may be localized in the nucleus by autoradiography.[130-132] With some cells, uptake requires that DNA-protein particles be made for the cells to phagocytize.[130]

The physiological and genetic demonstrations, requiring genetic markers, are much more difficult to obtain; but Kraus was recently able to show that the ability to produce the β^A polypeptidic chain of hemoglobin, absent from the bone marrow cells of a patient with sickle cell anemia, was conferred on these cells *in vitro* by DNA from the bone marrow of a man homozygous for hemoglobin A.[132] The physiological evidence seems thereby provided. Experiments providing genetic evidence, which would require active multiplication of the animal cells into clones and a marker lending itself to selection, have not yet been feasible (see Section V,E, however).

IV. The Required Background Knowledge on DNA

As a result of the identification of DNA as the bearer of genetic information, research on its physical, chemical, and biological properties has lately been progressing at an ever-increasing pace. Much of the newly accumulated knowledge is essential for an understanding of the processes involved in transformation. While no attempt is made to cover these divergent fields (some aspects of which are developed in Chapters 7 to 9), the minimal relevant information will now be given.

A. STRUCTURE OF THE DNA MOLECULE

The structure of DNA proposed by Watson and Crick in 1953[136, 137] (see Chapter 7), which integrated existing chemical[21] and physical[134, 135] evidence into an illuminating model, has ever since been recognized as the one that fits best all facts. This structure has been observed in all preparations of native DNA, whether deproteinized or not, and even *in situ* in cells.[138] Suffice it here to recall that two levels of structure are considered. The primary structure is that of the chains or strands of nucleotides. The secondary structure results from the molecule being double-stranded, hydrogen bonds maintaining together specific pairs of nucleotides.

B. SIZE OF THE MOLECULE

The question of the size of the DNA molecule is complex and has been "solved" only recently. The DNA preparations obtained by the usual methods have molecular weights of the order of 1×10^7 (see 140, 141 for references; this is a mean value, DNA being polydisperse). Since the amount of DNA per bacterial cell is close to 2×10^{-15} g.,[17, 142] or 1×10^{-15} g. per nucleus,[143] it follows that some 50 molecules are liberated per nucleus upon cell lysis (a figure leading to 20 genes per molecule, if there are 1000 genes in a bacterial genome).

The question then arises of whether these "molecules" are preexisting in the chromosome (in which case "linkers" are required to connect them together), or are artifacts, being produced, at the time of cell lysis, from a continuous double-stranded structure. The assumed difficulties of unwinding too long a duplex at replication at one time seemed to make the linker hypothesis more likely.[144]

The situation was changed, however, when it was found that shearing forces, such as are applied to DNA in solution by mere pipetting, are capable of breaking long molecules near their center.[145-148] It was found that carefully extracted DNA from phage T2 had a molecular weight as high as 1.3×10^8, representing the total DNA of the phage chromosome.[149-151] The following conclusions were drawn from the results:

1. Even DNA from the chromosome of a bacterium or of an animal cell might also be a single enormous molecule, much too long to be possibly studied intact in solution.

2. There is no longer any need to assume the existence of linkers, since the unwinding difficulties are not so serious after all.

A word must be said of the techniques employed for measuring the molecular weight of DNA. The usual ones (involving light-scattering or sedimentation measurements) cease being reliable for weights above 16×10^6 [152, 153]; this is not true, however, of the autoradiographic method.[154] Electron microscopy is another powerful tool, permitting an estimation of length distribution among the molecules.[155] When these more appropriate techniques were applied to bacterial DNA, liberated from the cells by specially mild procedures, a minimal molecular weight of 1×10^9 was obtained[156] and the electron micrographs were consistent with DNA being present as one continuous thread.[157] If one also remembers that the best-known bacterial genome, that of *E. coli*, behaves genetically as one linear structure,[158] the presumption becomes very strong that the 50 molecular species one is dealing with in transformation are an artifact. The fragility of the native chromosomal DNA in solution is such, however, that artifact cannot be avoided.

C. BASE COMPOSITION AND ITS DISTRIBUTION AMONG INDIVIDUAL DNA MOLECULES

As a result of the amounts of adenine and thymine and of guanine and cytosine (A, T, G, and C, respectively) being equimolar,[21, 137] one base content is enough to characterize the mean composition of DNA. (The latter is often expressed as per cent of G + C, i.e., 2 G%). In bacteria the G-C content is found to vary widely (from 25 to 75%) with the species and may reflect phylogenetic relations[159-161]; see Chapter 9). Several physical constants, such as the density[162-164] and the melting temperature,

T_m ,[165] were shown to vary linearly with the guanine content; these observations made it possible to estimate the composition of a DNA sample from its T_m value,[166] or from a density determination[167] requiring merely an equilibrium sedimentation of the solution in a CsCl density gradient.[168] Additional information can be obtained with these physical methods: the sharpness of the melting reflects the compositional heterogeneity of the DNA preparation and the width of the DNA band in the gradient, its polydispersity. Although bacterial DNA's show a relatively small dispersion of the G-C content among their molecules, it has been possible to establish by centrifugation that DNA particles of different densities carry distinct markers.[169, 170] While the physical heterogeneity of DNA was thereby clearly demonstrated, no clean separation of specific molecules could be obtained. Similar conclusions had already been reached in studies in which fractionation of transforming DNA had been attempted by chromatographic techniques.[171, 172] Better results were claimed by Bendich et al.,[173, 174] obtained by a procedure that has not been adopted by other workers. Lerman's columns (kieselguhr impregnated with methylated albumin), as employed by Hershey et al.,[145, 175] and by Sueoka and Cheng,[176] do fractionate DNA according to size, composition, and secondary structure, however. The DNA of the defective, transducing phage λdg is a case of a homogenous transforming DNA,[73] but this is only so because no fractionation is required in this case.

A similarity in mean composition of the DNA's of the two parental strains has generally been recognized to be a minimal requirement for transformation[63, 118, 139] and more generally for genetic recombination.[177] The same is true for the formation of hybrid molecules by renaturation,[178-180] but no correlation was found to exist between the composition of a DNA and its activity as an inhibitor of transformation.[139]

D. DNA REPLICATION

1. THE FORMAL ASPECT

The complementarity of the strands in the Watson-Crick structure led these authors to propose that each strand might function as a template for the synthesis of the other (see Chapter 7). The strand separation implied in such a model seemed at first to run into topological and energetic difficulties, which may be more apparent than real, however.[148] Also, as pointed out by Delbrück and Stent, the proposed replication mechanism leads to the prediction that the single strands of the parental DNA duplex will become separated from each other at the first replication, while conserving their atomic identity in this and the subsequent replication; in others words, replication is predicted to be semiconservative with respect to the distribution of the atoms of the parental to the daughter molecules.[181]

The experimental verification of this prediction, achieved by Meselson and Stahl[182] and by Levinthal and Thomas,[183] strengthened the hypothesis considerably; complete demonstration, however, would require the identification of the conserved subunits with single nucleotide chains, and this has not been done.[182] These subunits (shown by Rolfe to be associated laterally,[184] as assumed in the model), were claimed by Cavalieri et al. to consist of two chains rather than one, the parental molecule itself being four-stranded.[185-187] This claim has far-reaching implications, since it leads to the rejection of the concept that base-pairing plays a role in duplication, but it also has physical implications which seem to be already disproved.[188, 189] The following points in Cavalieri's work seem more likely to be generally accepted: (1) DNA is in different physical states, depending on whether the cells from which it was extracted were actively dividing or not; (2) heat treatment of DNA in concentrated CsCl solution differentiates the two states; (3) DNA goes through the nondividing state during a small fraction of the division cycle, as can be shown with synchronized cultures[185]; (see also Ephrussi-Taylor[190]).

2. THE BIOCHEMICAL ASPECT

As is well known, in vitro synthesis of DNA has been obtained in Kornberg's laboratory[52] and shown to correspond to the following reaction:

$$\left.\begin{matrix} \text{TTP} \\ \text{dGTP} \\ \text{dATP} \\ \text{dCTP} \end{matrix}\right\} \xrightarrow[\substack{+ \text{ primer DNA} \\ + \text{Mg}^{++}}]{\text{DNA polymerase}} \text{Dna} + \text{inorganic pyrophosphate}$$

in which dXTP is a deoxynucleoside triphosphate.

In this enzymic reaction DNA is required as a primer,[53, 191] both strands of which are copied. No increase in activity has so far been obtained, when a transforming DNA is supplied as primer.* Single DNA chains are endowed with priming activity and there are reasons to believe that a double-stranded DNA will be active only if it has first somehow been denatured.[191, 192] Synthesis does not stop, when an amount of DNA equal to the primer has been made.

In conclusion, any participation in DNA replication of RNA, or of a specific protein other than an enzyme, seems excluded by the biochemical studies; the biosynthetic reaction described is compatible with the semiconservative model of Watson and Crick.

3. DNA SYNTHESIS AND THE DIVISION CYCLE

While in cells from higher organisms DNA synthesis is restricted to the early prophase, it has been found in bacteria to extend over most, and possibly all, of the division cycle. This has been shown in a variety of

---

* Note added on proof: See Chapter 7, however.

ways.[193-195] Once started in a cell, DNA replication, according to Maaløe, is independent of protein (and RNA) synthesis; but some protein synthesis must have taken place, before the next replication cycle can start again. The proposed interpretation is, that DNA replication starts at one point and proceeds from there on, all along the chromosome.[196]

E. HETEROCATALYTIC ACTIVITY OF DNA

The transfer and recombination of genetic information and the functioning of this information are two distinct fields of study. Transformation proper can be considered terminated with genetic integration, the only borderline problem being whether integration of a newly introduced piece of DNA is a prerequisite to its function. For the mechanism and specificity of protein synthesis, the reader is referred to Chapter 8.

F. ALTERATIONS OF THE DNA MOLECULE

It has long been realized that transformation offered the unique advantage of the possibility of altering the structure of the DNA molecule by various agents, and of then relating the nature and extent of the lesion with biological activity. Nevertheless, such experiments involve considerable difficulties. In the first place, the agents applied may cause more than one type of lesion. The precise determination of the nature and extent of the various lesions and the complexity of the biological test, transformation, in which different steps may be sensitive to different types of structural alterations, pose additional problems.

1. HEAT TREATMENT

To quote an early work, the transforming activity of pneumococcus extracts is unaffected by heating 30 minutes at 60°C., reduced abruptly at 80°C., and some residual activity remains even after 10 minutes at 90°C. This unexpectedly high thermoresistance had first been reported by Alloway in 1933,[15] but it is only recently that the facts could be interpreted in terms of molecular changes. Today, largely as a result of the outstanding contributions of Meselson and Stahl,[182] Doty et al. (cf. ref. 152), Lerman and Tolmach,[197] Roger and Hotchkiss,[198] etc., two distinct types of heat inactivation have been recognized. Their description requires that the notion of denaturation be first introduced.

a. Denaturation. When DNA solutions are heated for a short time at temperatures close to boiling and cooled rapidly, all their properties have changed. The transforming activity is reduced to a few per cent (residual activity[198]), the viscosity drops,[17, 199] the relative absorbance at 260 mμ increases (hyperchromic effect),[200, 201] the buoyant density increases,[182, 202] the reactivity to certain chemical and physical agents (formaldehyde, UV) is changed. These spectacular changes have been shown to reflect a disruption of hydrogen bonds, with unwinding and physical separation of the strands, whenever disruption is complete; the nature of the change has been studied by sedimentation,[182] molecular weight* determinations,[182, 185, 202] and electron microscopy.[202] Surprisingly, some rigidity of the strands is conserved.[203] This collapse of the secondary structure of DNA has been variously named denaturation,[200] helix-coil transition,[199] or melting. The mid-point in the temperature range where this transition takes place is known as the melting or critical temperature (T_m).

The T_m of a DNA has been found to be linearly related to its G-C content[165] and this, together with the compositional heterogencity of DNA, accounts for the spread of the transition over a range of a few degrees. The more homogeneous a DNA, the sharper its transition; but for an individual molecule, the transition seems to be an all-or-none change.[164] However, evidence for the existence of partially denatured molecules, with some segments only denatured, has been produced.[204, 205] Temperature can be so adjusted, that only the AT-rich molecules of a DNA preparation will be denatured; this is the basis for selective marker inactivation.[164, 198, 206, 207] The T_m is also dependent on pH and ionic strength[164, 201] but not on associated proteins, divalent cations, or molecular weight.

Separation of the strands at denaturing temperatures is prevented in DNA's previously treated by reagents creating covalent bonds between the strands ("cross links"). Such cases, and denaturation by chemicals, will be mentioned in later sections.

b. Subcritical Inactivation. When the exposure of DNA solutions to temperatures above melting is prolonged beyond complete denaturation, a further much slower inactivation is observed, obviously brought about by another mechanism.[197] This type of inactivation already occurs at temperatures below T_m (i.e., in the absence of denaturation), where it is best studied. For this reason, it is referred to as subcritical inactivation.[198, 207, 208] It is believed to be due to both loss of purines[209] and hydrolysis of phosphodiester bonds.[210, 211] Its salient characteristics are the following[198]: It sets in only after a lag period, then proceeds exponentially to completion, leaving no residual activity. Different markers are unequally affected, and the order of their relative sensitivity is not the same as in denaturation. A study of its effects on linked markers leads to the conclusion that the basis of its selectivity is to be found in the unequal size of the markers.[198, 212] Two distinct mechanisms therefore appear to be responsible for the selective marker inactivation obtained by heat treatment: a size-dependent one, occurring even at temperatures below melting,

* The molecular weight is halved, at least with the usual DNA preparations made from bacteria.

and one dependent on G-C content, occurring only at denaturing temperatures, where it predominates overwhelmingly.

  c. *Renaturation*. One very important point concerning denaturation is its unexpected reversibility. Marmur and Lane[213] were able to show that the fate of a melted DNA depends on the rate of its subsequent cooling: a fast cooling ("quenching") preserves the denatured state, a slow one ("annealing") favors restoration. Maintenance for several hours at the renaturation temperature (some 25°C. below T_m) may be necessary,[180] even when the ionic strength is right and DNA concentration high enough. There are conflicting reports on whether renaturation truly follows the kinetics of a bimolecular reaction.[202, 214] Even under the best conditions, recovery is at most 50%, chain scissions being held responsible for the loss.[179, 202] Herriot confirmed that a new kind of particle was produced by the annealing procedure; his results, still difficult to interpret, suggest that renaturation may not be as simple a phenomenon as it appears to be.[214, 215] With partly denatured molecules, renaturation proceeds much more rapidly, and is independent of concentration and ionic strength.[205]

  Renaturation is a powerful tool; with its help many kinds of heterostranded (hybrid) molecules can be made at will: physical hybrids, with strands of unequal density or radioactivity,[178, 179] genetic hybrids, with differently marked strands,[213-215] and interspecific hybrids, whenever the genetic similarity of the two "parent" organisms allows sufficient pairing.[178, 179, 202] Examples will be given in later sections of the use to which such hybrids can be put in studying the mechanism of recombination.

  d. *The Residual Activity of Denatured DNA*. Exposure of DNA to temperatures above T_m leaves a few per cent of residual activity[31, 197, 198]; several workers have wondered what kind of molecule is responsible.

  According to Doty et al.,[178, 216] strand separation is complete in the quenched DNA solution, the presence of double strands, whatever their origin, is excluded, and the residual activity is an intrinsic property of single DNA chains, which must be able to penetrate, even if poorly. This opinion is shared by Guild[217] and by Ginoza and Zimm,[207] one argument being the concentration independence of the percentage of residual activity. However, the completeness of strand separation is contested by Geiduschek[205] and also by Roger and Hotchkiss[198]; if they are right, then it is to be expected that reactivation, now a process that occurs in a single molecular structure, should be independent of concentration.[205]

  In view of this disagreement, no conclusion will presently be drawn. That the single strands do not penetrate as well as double ones is a generally accepted fact, first established by Lerman and Tolmach.[197] No claim has ever been made that the poor transformation obtained with denatured DNA was due to an impaired integration.

2. Shear Degradation

As already mentioned, phage DNA, with a molecular weight of 1×10^8 or more, is degraded by the mere handling of its solutions. With the much shorter DNA particles present in the usual bacterial extracts, degradation requires that stronger shearing forces be applied, such as are developed by exposure to sonic waves,[87, 218, 219] or passage through an atomizer.[220] The effect consists in a clear-cut scission of the double helix, as is visible on electron micrographs.[155] As the unchanged UV-absorption and T_m demonstrate, these breaks occur with little or no denaturation. Shear degradation has a pronounced unlinking effect on loosely linked markers[221]; the inactivation produced by shearing is largely due to inability of the fragments to combine with bacterial receptor sites.[87, 88, 221, 222] These biological effects will be described in greater detail in the sections dealing with penetration and linkage.

3. Irradiation

The lesions produced in DNA by irradiations, whether ionizing or not, are many, and their identification has just begun. The main problem so far has been to elucidate their nature; it has not been possible, as was the case with heat treatment, to produce DNA with a single type of lesion and advance our understanding of transformation by using it. Interesting new types of lesion are produced, however.

a. Ultraviolet Light. The damage produced on transforming DNA by UV irradiation can be evaluated by chemical, physical, and biological methods. Chemical studies have revealed the unique sensitivity of pyrimidines (see Shugar[223] for a review) and the formation of a thymine covalent dimer (Berends,[224] Wacker.[225]) Some denaturation, restricted to internal regions of the molecule, has been shown to occur,[226-228] together with breaks in one nucleotide chain.[228] The most interesting lesion would seem to be the formation of interchain linkages,[226, 228] for which thymine dimers are held responsible; these cross links prevent complete chain separation under denaturation conditions and confer on denatured DNA some resistance to Lehman's enzyme.[227]

The activity of transforming DNA is destroyed by exposure to UV light (see below), but can be restored by subsequent illumination with visible light,[229] provided an enzyme responsible for this repair is present.[230] Since the cross links are believed to be the only UV-induced lesion repaired in the photoreactivation process,[225, 226, 231] it would seem that formation of these links is the main cause of UV-induced inactivation.

The differential inactivation by UV irradiation of the various measurable activities of a transforming DNA (i.e., ability to penetrate, to transform, and to inhibit transformation) will be treated in Section V, where transformation is analyzed step by step. Suffice it here to mention that UV inactivation of the transforming ability follows a two-component curve,[197, 232, 233] not due to population heterogeneity,[234] and that a selective UV inactivation of genetic markers has frequently been observed.[197, 206, 228, 235, 236] Unequal marker sizes are generally held responsible for this selective action,[228, 233] but the UV sensitivity of a given marker has been shown to depend also on the size of the molecule bearing it[228] and on the particular receptor strain on which the residual activity is being measured.[237]

b. Ionizing Radiations. The lesions produced in DNA by ionizing radiations (see review in ref. 221) are believed to consist of chain breakage, with denaturation extending on both sides of the break over several nucleotide pairs, so that another break occurring in the second chain within the denatured segment will rupture the duplex: a decrease in molecular weight is actually observed.[186] Indirect effects, due to ions and free radicals, undoubtedly add to the complexity of the damage.[76, 238] The inactivation curves of transforming DNA obtained with ionizing radiations are made of two exponentials, the sensitivity decreasing abruptly at a survival of a few per cent.[76, 221, 238-240] The radiosensitive molecular weight, or target size, which can be calculated from the rate of inactivation, depends in this case on the dose; this may be why its value was found to vary from 3×10^5 [239] to 6×10^6.[241] That the size of a marker must be much smaller than the target, itself a fraction of the average DNA particle, seems generally agreed upon.

Not all markers are equally sensitive to inactivation by ionizing radiations[221]; when equal sensitivity was observed with two markers,[197, 238a] they may have had the same size, since sensitivity is size dependent.[221, 238a]

4. CHEMICAL TREATMENT

Relatively mild and specific actions on DNA have recently been obtained with various chemicals.

a. Nitrous Acid. Nitrous acid, a well-known deaminating agent, has been applied to transforming DNA, and found to inactivate it under conditions where both viscosity[17] and molecular weight (Marmur, quoted in ref. 233) are unaffected. With adenine moieties changed into hypoxanthine, guanine into xanthine, and cytosine into uracil, a mutagenic action of nitrous acid could be suspected and has indeed been observed[235]; induction of mutation follows a one-hit kinetics. However, the action of nitrous acid is probably not as simple as it first appeared, since not all markers in pneumococcus DNA,[233] and possibly no markers at all in *Hemophilus* DNA,[242] can be made to mutate by nitrous acid treatment. Since even these apparently nonmutable markers are inactivated, attack on their bases must occur, and some mechanism other than deamination must come into play. It is tempting to speculate that the formation of interchain covalent bonds, shown by Geiduschek to occur during nitrous acid treatment,[243] is the operative mechanism, since cross-link formation is known to lead to inactivation. One important point supporting this hypothesis has already been established. Stuy showed that mutation has indeed taken place in the treated DNA, even when the mutated markers, for lack of integration, are scored as nonmutated.[242] Integration of the mutated markers would require that no cross links be formed in their vicinity. What the cross links actually are in this case, what the requirements are for their formation, and why these requirements are met with some markers and not with others, remain to be explained.

b. Alkylating Agents. Reputed as radiomimetic agents, mustard gases have been found to inactivate transforming DNA.[206, 244] Comparison of the relative sensitivities of different markers to nitrogen mustard and to UV discloses different modes of action for these agents, however.[197] From more systematic studies (reviewed by Lawley[245]) on the mode of action of alkylating reagents, the following three successive steps could be recognized: alkylation of the purine moieties, loss of the alkylated bases, and eventually break of the sugar-phosphate chain. With the mustards and other difunctional alkylating agents, guanine moieties become linked by alkyl chains, covalent bridges being established between strands whenever the two guanines are located on different strands.[245] The existence of cross links is revealed when mustard-treated DNA is exposed to denaturing conditions.[243]

c. Formamide. Formamide denatures DNA rapidly at room temperature. The resulting "single strands" (still endowed with residual activity) suffer no depurination or hydrolysis and reassociate spontaneously when formamide is removed by dialysis.[246] Urea is not as good a denaturing agent, requiring high concentrations (8 M) and high temperatures (65°C.[179]); at 5 M concentration and room temperature, it has been successfully used as a way of reducing molecular aggregation of native DNA.[76]

d. Other Chemicals. Formaldehyde, inactive on transforming DNA,[17] is of interest for its ability to react specifically with denatured DNA, and to prevent its renaturation.[247-250]

Acridines intercalate between adjacent nucleotide pair layers, the reaction being reversible.[251, 252]

5. ENZYMIC TREATMENT

In the studies made so far on the action of DNase on transforming DNA, pancreatic DNase I has generally been used. This enzyme is an endonuclease, attacking the strands at many points and yielding as final products di- and trinucleotides, with 5′-phosphomonoester end groups.[253] Inactivation of transforming DNA by this enzyme is exponential, suggesting that hydrolysis of one bond in one strand is enough to inactivate a marker.[31, 197, 221] If enzyme action is followed by viscosity measurements, however, an initial lag is observed.[17] This can be explained by the need for two breaks, occurring near each other on opposite strands, before the molecule is split in two.

Other DNA hydrolyzing enzymes are known (review in refs. 253 and 254), some of which are specific for native DNA (DNase II), others for denatured DNA (Lehman[255]), others attacking both kinds of nucleic acids (phosphodiesterases). Lehman's enzyme has been a very helpful tool in studying renaturation into hybrid molecules.[178]

6. Introduction of Isotopes or of Base Analogs into DNA

a. Radioactive Isotopes. H^3 and P^{32} are the two radioisotopes that have been used to label DNA. Tritiation is used mainly in connection with autoradiography for cytological localization of DNA.[129-132] Radiophosphorus has been used either for studying DNA penetration in bacteria directly,[29, 86, 142, 256-258] or for analyzing the consequences of its decay.[259, 260]

b. Heavy Isotopes. Used in connection with centrifugation in density gradients,[168] DNA labeling with heavy isotopes (particularly differential labeling of the twin strands) is a powerful tool for studying DNA behavior during duplication[182] or renaturation.[178, 179, 202] When such a labeling is obtained by growing bacteria in D_2O-N^{15} synthetic media, the buoyant density of DNA can be increased by some 0.040 g./cc., or more than enough for centrifugal separation, even of density hybrid molecules.[261]

c. Base Analogs. That pyrimidines halogenated in position 5 can be incorporated in DNA "instead of thymine" has been known for some time.[262-267] Only thymine analogs (not all of them however[268-270]) can so far be incorporated. Such halogenated DNA's are heavier than normal.[271] When 5-bromouracil-DNA (with as much as 60% of the thymine "replaced") was tried for its transforming properties, it was found to be fully active.[272, 273]

Words of warning have been given concerning these incorporations: The analog does not merely replace thymine, and all thymine moieties in DNA are not equally likely to be replaced[274]; in addition to being incorporated in DNA, the analog may interfere with cell wall synthesis.[275]

V. Analysis of the Transformation Process

If a genetic marker, initially present in a DNA particle in solution, is eventually to become a part of the bacterial genome, it must enter the competent cell (*penetration*), pair with its chromosomal counterpart in one of the nuclei (*synapsis*), and somehow react with the chromosome. The total process is usually demonstrated by determining two effects: (*1*) Some exogenous genetic material will now be replicated in pace with the chromosome at each cell division; (*2*) linkage appears between introduced and resident markers. The word *integration* has often been used to designate an insertion reaction leading to both effects. It is proposed that it be used exclusively when referring to the first effect, the second one being called, as usual, *recombination*. Justification for this restricted use of the term *integration* will be given when the reactions leading to both effects are considered.

Completion of transformation at the cellular level requires a sorting-out, by cellular division, of the transformed nuclei (*segregation*) and synthesis of new enzymes and products (phenotypic expression). These formal steps, first formulated by Hotchkiss,[276] will serve as a frame for the following account; but competence, a prerequisite for transformation, will be first treated.

A. Competence of the Recipient Bacteria

The outcome of a transformation experiment is rather unpredictable: some batches of a growth medium will permit transformation, others will not, although all were prepared in apparently the same way and support growth equally well. Even in a "good" medium, transformation may be very poor if DNA is added to the culture at the wrong time. The notion of competence emerged as the conclusion of a long struggle: competence (also called receptivity) is the transient physiological state, in which the bacteria must be at the time of exposure to DNA, if transformation is to follow (a somewhat more precise definition will be given in a later section). Mutation was excluded as the source of the observed unpredictability, since competence appears rapidly in a population—even a small one—and is lost after growth has stopped (McCarthy *et al.*[277]). Also, clones transformed for a first character do not, when transformed for a second one, develop higher levels of competence than the original population.[278]

1. The Building of Competence

Competence will appear only under narrow cultural conditions, which must be empirically determined. A change introduced in the eventually adopted procedure (e.g., in pH, temperature of incubation, ionic balance, agitation, preparation of the inoculum, etc.), may drastically reduce the competent fraction of the population, i.e., the frequency of transformation. In addition, the experience gained with one species is useless with another, as the following examples illustrate: (*1*) Competence in pneumococcus or

Hemophilus is obtained in rich media only: synthetic growth media have been developed,[279-282] but at best they lead to low transformation frequencies; this is not true of Catlin's medium, however.[283] With *B. subtilis*, addition of an excess of amino acids[106] or yeast extract[61, 75] to minimal medium inhibits transformation. (*2*) Growth in the presence of serum albumin[79, 284] is required for competence in pneumococcus, but albumin is inert in *Hemophilus*[285] and inhibitory in *B. subtilis*.[61] (*3*) Violent aeration of the culture either increases or decreases competence of a culture, depending on whether *B. subtilis* or pneumococcus is being used; but with *Hemophilus* the highest transformation frequencies are obtained with shaken cultures left unshaken for 90 minutes.[221, 278]

Generally accepted procedures for preparing competent cultures of pneumococcus, *Hemophilus*, and *B. subtilis* have been described by Ephrussi-Taylor,[39] Goodgal and Heriott,[278] and Anagnostopoulos and Spizizen,[94] respectively. Anti-R antibodies, once considered indispensable for transformation in pneumococcus, are not required when characters other than capsular are being studied.[38] They can be replaced with agar in low concentration,[277] aggregated growth being somehow required for capsule production.[66] Polyphosphates have been reported favorable for the competence of *B. subtilis*,[286] and Cu^{++} inhibitory.[94]

In spite of these apparent oddities, competence does have general characteristics: It is a property of the bacteria, not of the culture medium, and can be lost by mere washing,[277, 278] or by growth in fresh medium,[79, 277, 278, 287] but can be maintained for weeks in cells stored at $-40°C$. in 10–15% glycerol.[83]

2. COMPETENCE AS A FUNCTION OF TIME

The appearance of competence in a growing culture can be followed by adding DNA to the medium initially, and DNase at various times thereafter; its disappearance, by adding DNA at various times (Thomas[79]). During growth, an abrupt increase in the number of competent cells is generally observed; the subsequent decrease may or may not be sharp, depending on the medium. Frequently a narrow peak of competence may be observed, from which the mean duration of competence in individual bacteria has been estimated to be ca. 15 minutes.[79] The point on the growth curve at which competence increases again varies with the species: in the early (*Rhizobium*[288]) or in the late (*Hemophilus*[58, 81]; *B. subtilis*[29]) exponential phase, or at a time depending on the size of the inoculum (pneumococcus[7]). The later the appearance of competence, the greater the danger that expression cannot take place in an exhausted medium.[81]

When competence remains maximal for some time, this apparent stability is in fact due to a continuous population turnover (which implies that not all the cells were competent), the new competent cells appearing in waves lasting 10–20 minutes[287]; (note the good agreement with the figure obtained by Thomas, quoted earlier; the doubling time with which to compare, is ca. 25 minutes). Observance of these waves suggested to Hotchkiss that competence might be associated with a particular stage of the cell division cycle. He developed a procedure, based on temperature shifts, which was effective in inducing synchrony of division, and indeed observed the expected phasing of competence in synchronized cultures.[287] This beautiful demonstration is rather bewildering, however, since the cells have repeatedly gone through the same stage in earlier division cycles without then becoming competent. Another unexplainable observation is that the presence of proteins in the medium prolongs the duration of competence,[289-291] without having any effect on growth rate.

3. The Physiological Meaning of Competence

Competence develops in the absence of added DNA; once established, contact between cells and DNA results almost immediately in an irreversible initiation of transformation. The hypothesis of a DNA-induced permeation system has therefore never been seriously considered. Recently, however, the unexpected observation was made that genetically active DNA is released into the medium of an exponentially growing culture[67]; with this knowledge, the induction hypothesis might deserve reexamination. One would expect, if induction were at work, that appearance of competence should follow the release of the presumed inducer; what was observed, however, was that both release and competence were strikingly parallel.[67] While any conclusion is premature, an important lead may have been uncovered.

With some bacterial species, DNase activity is found in the culture medium[292]; absence of activity, allowing DNA accumulation, may be due to absence of enzyme activation or release of an inhibitory RNA[110, 293]; unidentified regulation processes may be suspected here.

In *B. subtilis* transformation, early observations seemed to suggest a correlation between some stage of the sporulation cycle and the appearance of competence.[29, 61, 294] The writer's experience is against the existence of any such correlation[75]: many asporogenous mutants are just as readily transformable as the spore-forming strain from which they were derived. In any case, since transformation occurs in many nonsporulating species, the kind of correlation suspected by Spizizen could not be of general significance.

The idea, originally proposed by Thomas,[79] and taken up by Spizizen,[29, 94, 106, 294] that wall alterations are necessary for DNA penetration, may seem to find some justification in the fact that free phage DNA in solution, while harmless to normal bacteria, can infect propoplasts.[295-299] Initially, this idea was based strictly on kinetic evidence, interpreted to mean that competence was a state of permeability to all macromolecules, including proteins.[79] No protoplasts could be seen in highly competent cultures, but competent cells were found to be more susceptible to osmotic shock than the total population.[289] The main difficulty with the Thomas-Spizizen hypothesis seems to be the selectivity of the penetration process associated with competence: good penetration is observed only with double-stranded DNA (see Section V,B), while all sorts of macromolecules can enter protoplasts (single-stranded DNA[295-297]; double-stranded DNA[298, 299]; viral RNA[300]; proteins[301]; and even nucleoproteins[297]); different penetration processes seem therefore to be involved in this case.

While competence, in cells stored in glycerol in the cold, is preserved for a few weeks at most, cell viability is preserved for many months. Fox and Hotchkiss found that when competence is lost, it can be quickly rebuilt upon reincubation. This rebuilding takes place in the absence of growth, provided all amino acids, glucose, albumin, and calcium are supplied; it is inhibited by chloramphenicol.[83] If noncompetent cells are frozen, however, no competence appears when the thawed culture is incubated. All the facts are compatible with the following interpretation: the DNA receptor sites, responsible for competence, are made of an unstable protein, which is slowly denatured during storage in the cold, but will be resynthesized in its active form when the frozen cells are thawed and incubated. Such an hypothesis makes it possible to account for the selectivity of permeation.

In conclusion, competence, in spite of much effort, is hardly better understood today than it was sixteen years ago, when it was termed "an alteration of the cell surface."[277] The transient nature of competence has apparently discouraged any attempt at checking this conclusion by immunological means.

The recently recognized possibility that viral infection in tissues may propagate from cell to cell in the form of free nucleic acids (Herriott[302]) should stimulate further study of the mechanisms by which bacteria and cells are made receptive to DNA penetration.

4. QUANTITATIVE ESTIMATION OF COMPETENCE

At saturating DNA concentrations, under the best conditions of competence, most markers are usually found to be transmitted with a frequency of a few per cent. This is the expected value, with some 50 DNA particles liberated per nucleus, on the assumptions that only one particle among the 50 carries any given marker, and that every reaction of a DNA particle with a competent cell eventually leads to a transformed cell. Still higher frequencies, however, have been recorded (up to 17% with synchronized cultures[287]). The fact that highly competent bacteria could be shown to react with more than one particle (at least 4[278]; up to 30 or more[83]) accounts for these higher frequencies.

If the above-mentioned assumptions are correct, it follows that practically all bacteria must be competent in a highly competent culture. This has actually been demonstrated by an indirect method utilizing inhibitory DNA,[303] and more directly, by measuring the penetration of radioactive transforming DNA.[256]

Lastly, the number of competent cells in any culture can be precisely calculated from the numbers of transformants obtained for two unlinked markers, transmitted both singly and together.[278]

5. BYPASSING OF COMPETENCE

As Kaiser and Hogness demonstrated, bacteria can be transformed by free DNA extracted from an abortive transducing phage. In *E. coli* the receptor cells need not be competent, or even transformable, provided a bacteriophage is present to help with DNA penetration.[73] The adopted definition of transformation applies to this phenomenon, even though competence plays no role here. Other ways of bypassing competence in transformation, such as the use of protoplasts (in the absence of phage) as receptor cells, had indeed been tried, but were generally found unsuccessful[304]; there is one unconfirmed report to the contrary.[305] Intriguing as they are, these observations throw no light on the nature of competence. No attempts to transform protoplasts made from known transformable strains have been reported, and it is not known whether material other than DNA penetrates into *E. coli* in the presence of a helper phage.

B. PENETRATION OF DNA INTO COMPETENT CELLS

A few minutes after transforming DNA has been in contact with competent bacteria, it becomes insensitive to inactivation by added DNase, and for this reason is said to have entered the cells, or to have been incorporated. A direct study of penetration requires that DNA be physically labeled; P[32] labeling has generally been used. Studies by Lerman and Tolmach,[86] Fox,[142] Fox and Hotchkiss,[83] and Goodgal and Herriott[256, 278] revealed the phenomenon to be a complex one.

1. THE TWO STEPS OF PENETRATION

Competent cells, exposed to P[32]-DNA and washed in the cold until no more radioactivity can be removed, release part of the radioactivity they had retained on mere rewarming, or, more rapidly, by DNase treatment;

more DNA is fixed, therefore, than has actually penetrated. This experiment demonstrates the existence of two kinds of fixation, reversible and irreversible. Reversible fixation can be shown to be an intermediate step, preliminary to the second.

When the amounts of DNA fixed, reversibly and irreversibly, are expressed per cell transformed for a single character, irreversible fixation alone is found to be constant. For each bacterium so transformed some 50 DNA particles are fixed, in a DNase-insensitive manner, by the bacterial population; this is also the number of DNA particles (of molecular weight 1×10^7), that are liberated per nucleus at cell lysis. Transformation of one bacterium for one character requires, therefore, that one genome equivalent of DNA be fixed irreversibly by the bacterial population.[83, 86, 142, 256, 278] This is true of both pneumococcus and *Hemophilus* transformation.

The radioactivity retained remains associated with the bacteria for many generations. Penetration is a property of high-molecular-weight DNA, no retention of radioactivity taking place with bacteria exposed to prehydrolyzed DNA or to RNA extracts.[86]

In the light of these facts, competence can be redefined as the ability of the cells to incorporate DNA, and transformation can be represented, like an enzyme-substrate reaction, by the following sequence:

$$S + D \rightleftharpoons SD \rightarrow \rightarrow T$$

Where S stands for receptor sites, D for DNA and T for transformants; the rate constants for all three reactions have been determined.[83]

2. THE REQUIREMENTS FOR PENETRATION

a. *Environmental Conditions.* The cells must have receptor sites for DNA to enter, but they need not grow. With pneumococcus, penetration occurs in saline, if supplemented with albumin, glucose, phosphate, and calcium (i.e., a medium not supporting growth).[83] With *Hemophilus*, albumin is dispensable; Versene and dinitrophenol are inhibitory,[306] but chloramphenicol is not.[307]

b. *Structure and Molecular Weight of DNA.* DNA damaged by various means has been tested for its ability to penetrate. The most striking results are obtained with heat treatments: while exposure to temperatures above melting decreases the capacity to penetrate and the transforming activity equally abruptly, exposure to subcritical temperatures inactivates the transforming ability only.[197] In other words, single-stranded DNA penetrates very poorly, but depurination with maintenance of the secondary structure is compatible with normal penetration. Similarly, DNA is still incorporated after inactivation by UV or by (bifunctional) nitrogen mustard,[197] two agents known to inactivate DNA mainly by creating cross links. Lastly, heat-denatured transforming DNA is reactivated (and therefore penetrates normally), when renatured with wild-type DNA.[213] The demonstration that the secondary structure is required for normal penetration is therefore well documented. Since other polynucleotidic double-helical structures are now known to exist, such as DNA-RNA hybrids[108, 308-310] and messenger RNA made *in vitro*,[311] the question arises whether they also would enter competent cells, and perhaps lead to purely phenotypic transformation. No data have been published yet on this interesting question.

The size of the DNA particle also plays a role, as was shown by mild DNase treatment[86] and by shear degradation; according to Litt *et al.*[87] and Rosenberg *et al.*,[222] a minimal molecular weight of 1×10^6 is required for penetration. Why the size must be so large is not understood. Doty's observation that transforming DNA inactivated by sonication recovers activity by annealing with undegraded DNA,[152] while surprising, emphasizes again the importance of the duplex structure in penetration.

3. The Species Specificity of Penetration

When little or no transformation is obtained with DNA's of heterospecific origin, the question of their ability to penetrate must be considered. *E. coli* DNA, although not transforming, was found to enter pneumococcus cells almost as well as the homospecific DNA, and penetration therefore seemed to be nonspecific.[86] Studied more systematically in *Hemophilus influenzae*, strain Rd, the problem was found to have no simple answer. DNA's from two strains of *H. parainfluenzae*, which do transform Rd, although at very low frequency, were found to penetrate normally,[258] but DNA from *B. megatherium*, strain KM, failed to penetrate,[139] in spite of the fact that the DNA's from KM and Rd have the same density and over-all composition. The reason for this difference in penetrating ability is unknown; differences in terminal nucleotide sequence, or even in tertiary structure, were considered, but physicochemical characterization of the DNA preparations employed was lacking.[139] The specificity of the reaction of the receptor sites with DNA seems to vary with the species of the recipient strain.

4. The Mechanism and Polarity of Penetration

When, at various times after fixation, transforming DNA is reextracted from DNase-treated pneumococci and tested for biological activity, it is found to pass through a transient inactive state. This eclipse phenomenon, first described by Fox,[312] (see Section V,D,2), has been further investigated by Lacks,[313] who exposed competent pneumococci to P^{32}-DNA, reextracted the washed cultures at various times of incubation, and analyzed the extracts on Lerman-Hershey columns. Immediately after entry, one-half of the radioactivity that had been fixed was present as highly polymerized single strands, very strongly adsorbed to the column, the other half being degraded to acid-soluble material, not retained by the column. When the incubation was prolonged, however, the radioactivity became associated with native DNA.

The initial conversion of DNA to the single-stranded state, discovered by Lacks, accounts beautifully for the eclipse period. Taken in conjunction with the known poor penetrating activity of extracellular single-stranded DNA, it suggests that strand separation is an essential part of the penetration process.[313] Lacks proposed a model, in which one end of the entering duplex meets a molecule of "DNase," which drags one strand into the cell, while splitting the other stepwise. The requirement of double-strandedness for penetration could thus be explained. Nucleases hydrolyzing native DNA in this way have not been described, but are worth looking for in wall or membrane preparations made from synchronized cultures of both competent and noncompetent cells.

The recovery of the introduced transforming activity must result from participation by the transforming strand in the reformation of a duplex structure. Fox found recovery to be insensitive to an excess of fluorodeoxyuridine, which allowed at most a 5% increase of DNA.[312] Duplex reformation by synthesis of a strand complementary to the one introduced therefore seems excluded, unless sufficient thymidylate is present in the intracellular pool. It seems more likely that pairing with chromosomal DNA is responsible for the observed recovery.

Lacks' study does not indicate whether the strand that enters undegraded is predetermined. It might be that the entering strand is "chosen" as having, for instance, a free OH group in the 3'-position at the end of the particle that reacts with the receptor site. (The reasons for doubting that DNA penetration is polarized, i.e., that one end only can react, are presented later in this section.) Which strand is degraded would then depend on which end of the duplex particle happens to hit a receptor site, but statistically both strands would be equally likely to penetrate. Several technical means are now available for marking the strands separately, which should make analysis of this question possible.

Density gradient centrifugation has been used by Ephrussi-Taylor to demonstrate the presence of single-stranded DNA during the eclipse period in pneumococcus.[314] No band of higher density was detected; several reasons might be invoked for this, but the lighter band that was observed remains to be explained. Perhaps the associated protein, assumed to be present in this band and responsible for its lower density, is indeed Lacks' enzyme, but the denaturation of protein in CsCl will make the demonstration difficult.

Lacks pointed out that the model he had described for DNA penetration in pneumococcus could not possibly apply to *Hemophilus*, since Voll and Goodgal's data[315] show there is no eclipse period with this organism. This conclusion may be questioned, however (see Section V,D,2,e).

Through his studies of the recombinations occurring between a λ phage and a λ DNA molecule entering *E. coli* with "the help" of the phage, Kaiser was led to suggest that this penetration was oriented, one end entering first.[124] Although this is conceivable in the case of an entire phage DNA molecule, one end of which only might have the proper sequence for penetration, the suggestion would seem to meet with difficulties if applied to bacterial DNA particles, which are believed to arise by breakage at variable points within predetermined regions. Rather well-mapped transforming DNA particles are now known, with which this problem of the polarity of penetration might be investigated.

How phage can help DNA penetration into noncompetent cells is not known; the mechanism involved differs from the one at work in usual transformation not only by the need for a helper, but also by the time and the DNA concentration required for penetration to take place.[73] It must be extremely inefficient, in view of the reported transformation frequency of 10^{-6}; with a molecularly homogeneous transforming DNA and no competence problem, a very high proportion of the cells should be transformed at saturating DNA concentrations. One would like to know the number of molecules fixed per transformed bacterium; whether single-stranded DNA can be "helped in"; whether there is an eclipse period; whether phage ghosts would help, etc. A gold mine has just been discovered; no doubt the rush will soon follow.

5. The Inhibition of Transformation by DNA

Hotchkiss[287] and Alexander *et al.*[58] have shown that transformation is inhibited by DNA not carrying the marker being selected. This early work demonstrated that inhibition is competitive and nonspecific, even calf thymus DNA being inhibitory. DNA from a given source can therefore be characterized by three biological activities: its ability to transform, its ability to penetrate, and its ability to inhibit transformation. It is important to know whether and how these activities are related. Two experimental approaches have been used; one is based on the fact that DNA from various bacterial species have unequal specific transforming activities, and consists in comparing their other two activities.[113] Similar comparisons are made in the other approach, employing preparations from one and the same DNA inactivated by various means.[197]

a. Quantitative Aspects. Even when present in large excess over the transforming DNA, an inhibitory DNA may fail to inhibit transformation. The fact is compatible with the competitive nature of inhibition, and simply means that bacterial receptor sites are not saturated. Consequently, the determination of the specific inhibitory activity of a DNA requires that saturating concentrations of the transforming DNA be used.[65, 303]

b. Structure and Size of the Inhibitory Molecule. The inhibitory activity is lost when DNA is denatured, but is retained by DNA inactivated at subcritical temperatures.[212, 316] Only the double-stranded form of DNA is therefore capable of inhibition, a conclusion further strengthened by the fact that the single-stranded DNA from the phage ϕX-174 is noninhibitory.[317]

When DNA is degraded by shear, its inhibitory activity decreases with molecular weight, the dependence on size being the same as for penetration.[222] When DNA is very carefully and progressively degraded by DNase, inhibitory activity is found first to increase, and then decrease,[318] as if the macromolecular polynucleotides first liberated were still active, leading to an increase in the concentration of inhibitory particles. Similarly, irradiation of DNA with low doses of UV increases its inhibitory activity[197]; the reasons for this are not understood.

c. The Specificity of Inhibition. Inhibition by DNA from a number of bacterial species has been measured on *Hemophilus* transformation[139]; a correlation was observed to exist between the relative inhibitory activity of a DNA and its ability to enter competent cells, some DNA's being completely devoid of both capacities.

Species specificity, although detected when *Hemophilus* is used as receptor, is not a general characteristic of inhibition. An illustration of this may be found in Pakula's study of the enzymic photoreactivation of UV-inactivated DNA.[319] *E. coli* DNA, not being eliminated from the reactivating enzyme preparation, masks the photoreactivation of the transforming DNA when pneumococcus or streptococcus transformation is used, but does not mask it in the case of the (*E. coli* DNA-insensitive) *Hemophilus* transformation. In appraising the data on inhibition, attention must therefore be paid to the organism being used. From the incomplete data available, the receptor sites of *Hemophilus* seem so far unique in being endowed with some species specificity in their reaction with DNA. With *B. subtilis*[106] and streptococci,[316] no weak inhibitors were found; DNA from *E. coli* is even said to be more potent an inhibitor of *B. subtilis* transformation than *B. subtilis* DNA itself.[106]

d. The Site of Inhibition. To summarize, a good correlation is observed between the penetrating and the inhibitory capacities of DNA, both having the same structural and size limitations, and requiring a duplex structure of molecular weight ca. 1×10^6. It is concluded that inhibition results from a competition for the access to the penetration mechanism.

Direct confirmation of this conclusion has been obtained by simultaneously measuring the penetration of, and transformation by, a radioactive DNA, in the presence of a nonradioactive inhibitory one. Penetration and transformation were inhibited to the same degree, as expected of a competition at the wall level.[258] This is not to say that internal competition at the chromosomal level does not occur, but only that its contribution is negligible. The result is not surprising, competition at this level being logically restricted to homologous particles not likely to be present in one and the same bacterium.[121]

C. Synapsis of the Interacting DNA's

If the capacity to penetrate is necessarily associated with the transforming activity of a DNA, the reverse need not be true. In fact, molecules capable of penetration only are known. These are either transforming molecules inactivated by such treatments as exposure to submelting temperature (see Section V,B,2,b), or undamaged molecules of heterospecific origin.[258] In order to explain why the latter fail to transform, it has been assumed that integration and recombination imply a previous specific pairing, or synapsis, of the reacting DNA's; pairing would at best be partial between homologous, but heterospecific, structures.[113] The hypothesis indeed accounts for most of the facts pertaining to heterospecific transformation.[121]

Just as a mutated gene reveals the existence of its normal alternative form, a case of imperfect pairing reveals the occurrence of the normal one. A more tangible demonstration was given by Doty et al.,[178, 179, 202] who showed that whenever an interspecific transformation occurs, the two DNA's involved do form hybrid molecules, when annealed together in solution. Pairing in any case seems such a logical necessity that it had been assumed to take place before any specific demonstration was given.[276]

It seems therefore that only one strand of the transforming DNA penetrates,[313] and that it then synapses. This pairing might conceivably occur in vivo, as it does in vitro, between two complementary strands. The hypothesis does not seem to be a tenable one, however. First, single-stranded DNA is not found in cell extracts, even prepared from synchronized cultures.[185, 190] Only short segments of DNA chains seem to be free of pairing at any one time during replication, the growing new chains each pairing with its template as soon as the latter has separated from its original partner. Second, structural considerations alone seem to exclude the hypothesis. Pairing must be of such a nature that it makes possible the formation of a recombinant strand, and this strand must both be normal (with 3′-5′-phosphodiester bonds only) and complete (with no segment missing). As shown in Fig. 4, such a strand can be formed only out of two strands of the same polarity, maintained in point-for-point juxtaposition by virtue of pairing. Pairing with a complementary strand (Fig. 4, model A) cannot do this, and is therefore excluded. A triple-stranded structure, similar to the one described by Zubay,[320] but resulting from the pairing of the introduced single strand with the chromosomal double strand (model B), would fulfil the requirements.

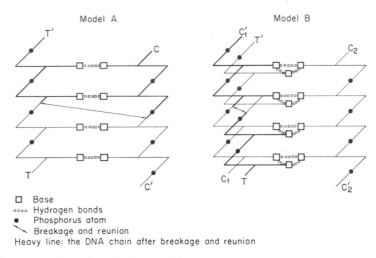

Model A   Model B

□   Base
∘∘∘∘   Hydrogen bonds
●   Phosphorus atom
＼   Breakage and reunion
Heavy line: the DNA chain after breakage and reunion

FIG. 4. The pairing of the transforming single strand (TT') with chromosomal DNA (CC'). Model A. Pairing with an antiparallel strand CC'; breakage and reunion lead to a lethal fragmentation of the genome. Model B. Pairing with a double-stranded structure $C_1C_1'-C_2C_2'$; in the resulting triple helical structure, breakage and reunion of the two parallel strands may occur without fragmentation of the genome.

A last word must be added concerning the imperfect pairing hypothesis invoked in interspecific transformations.[113] The facts that led to its formulation show that a "stamp of origin" is imprinted on the transforming DNA by the bacterial strain that last produced it[81]; it has been assumed, that the stamp was the species-specific sequence of nucleotides on both sides of the marker.[113] However, Arber and Dussoix,[321, 322] studying host-induced variation in *E. coli* phages, have described a situation which suggests an alternative interpretation for the results obtained in interspecific transformation. These authors found: (*1*) That the host-induced variation of phage is explained by a stamp of origin, attached to the viral DNA by its host and permitting recognition and degradation of the stamped DNA by another host; (*2*) that the same processes of stamping, recognition, and degradation exist also with *bacterial* DNA, as revealed by studies on mating *E. coli*. As remarked by Dussoix and Arber,[322] it is desirable to know more about the nature of the stamping recognition process, and also to see whether it plays a role in transformation. It is conceivable that a heterospecific DNA "molecule," stamped by attachment of an unidentified compound, may be destroyed most of the time in the cell before it had a chance to pair; this could be the mechanism responsible for the low frequencies observed in many interspecific transformations.

D. Integration and Genetic Recombination

The word *integration* will be used in the restricted sense defined in the introduction to Section V. The following description of the integration process is based on studies of pneumococcus transformation only; since there are reasons to suspect that the process may be different in *Hemophilus*,[313] generalization might lead to confusion.

We have described in Section I how all the early evidence led to the conclusion that in transformation resident markers are replaced by introduced ones. Ephrussi-Taylor[39, 40] has demonstrated in the case of capsule production that this exchange can occur *within* a gene (defined as a unit of function). Her demonstration is not as strong today as it appeared at the time, since the function turned out to be a complex one.[323, 324] However, the conclusion is still valid, as shown by the case of amylomaltase production.[212] The work of Ephrussi-Taylor provided an early demonstration that the functional gene contains many mutable sites, separable by recombination (see Pontecorvo[325] and Benzer[326] for references). Recombination may of course also occur *between* genes, even if they happen to be linked and located on one and the same DNA particle.

1. Genetic Linkage, Marker Size, and Map Building

When a mixture of two DNA's, each carrying one character only (A or B), is used in transformation experiments, doubly transformed AB clones are obtained together with the single (A or B) transformants.[38] With F_{AB}, F_A, and F_B designating the frequencies with which the three kinds of transformants are obtained, the following relation is observed: $F_{AB} \leqslant F_A \times F_B$. This is what is meant when A and B are said to be transmitted independently.

Independent transmission, as we have seen, is still the rule with two randomly chosen markers when introduced with one DNA extract made from an AB donor. There are exceptions, however, when F_{AB} is found to be much larger than the product $F_A \times F_B$. In such cases the markers, said to be linked genetically, have been shown to be carried by one and the same DNA particle, i.e., they are physically linked also.[30, 80] (Whether physical linkage may occur with genetically unlinked markers is not known, but theoretical ways of detecting such a situation, if it does exist, have been described.[327]) A particle therefore carries several genes, as expected in view of the fact that the entire genome (at least one thousand genes) is broken down to some fifty pieces. The relation $F_{AB} > F_A \times F_B$ is observed, even with unlinked markers, when DNA is used in excess and also when, the culture being poorly competent, the transformation frequencies are underestimated.[27] Linkage will therefore be indicated only when the above-mentioned relation holds true with a fully competent culture treated with low DNA concentrations.[31]

First described in pneumococcus by Hotchkiss and Marmur,[30] linkage has been found in other species also (*Hemophilus*,[31, 221, 328] *B. subtilis*[95-97, 106]). Linkage between two markers has been used to select indirectly transformants that could not be selected otherwise,[30, 31] and to determine whether a damaged marker can still be integrated.[211, 236, 242] The following method[97] should be helpful in obtaining an unspecified marker B linked to a specified marker A: an A^- strain is exposed to an A^+ DNA preparation that has been treated with nitrous acid; among the selected A^+ transformants, some have been jointly transformed for a B^- marker, induced by the treatment in the originally B^+ DNA.

It may be asked why two linked markers are not always integrated together.[31, 276] One answer might be that the DNA particle containing one of them does not always contain the other, the size of the particle being variable. However, linkage is relatively unaffected by the treatment to which DNA has been exposed, and consequently this seems an unlikely general explanation.[276] It must therefore be assumed that both markers are carried by nearly all the specific particles, but that the mechanism operating in transformation functions more easily for a shorter DNA segment; in other words, the probability of integration of a genetic segment is inversely related to its size.[329] This is shown by the good correlation existing between the sensitivity of a marker to heating at subcritical temperatures, or to UV irradiation, on the one hand, and the probability with which it will be integrated, on the other.[212, 233] Furthermore, with markers that can be dissociated by recombination into subunits, integration of the subunits is found to be more frequent than that of the entire marker.[330] There are apparently conflicting reports, however, of cases in which multiple transformations were obtained more frequently than single ones.[42, 221] One of these cases, linkage of the streptomycin and cathomycin resistance loci in *Hemophilus*, has been studied with the same mutants in two different laboratories, and opposite conclusions were reached (even when the different ways of presenting the data are taken into due account; compare references 31 and 221). Obviously, environmental conditions are important and were not the same in the two laboratories. This dependence of the integrated length upon physiological conditions[31, 84, 330] might interfere with the building of maps. The physiological control at work bears no relation with the degree of competence of the culture,[331] as could be anticipated, and its nature is entirely unknown.

Another difficulty in map building is the fact that genetic factors outside the marker may influence the frequency of its integration. An extreme case of this is probably seen in interspecific transformations, but similar phenomena exist within one species.[122]

In spite of these and other difficulties, reliable maps can be built, with some markers at least, particularly when two corrections are made: the first one introduces a reference marker and is aimed at eliminating experimental variables; the second one, aimed at eliminating differences among markers in their ability to be replaced, makes use of a reference transformation by wild-type DNA.[212] As was pointed out by Ephrussi-Taylor,[8] only those map distances which are not seriously affected by a reversal of the "cross" can be used without corrections; widely diverging distances should never be averaged[8] but can be corrected and used in map building.[327] Fair-to-good agreement between distances determined in reciprocal crosses is often obtained, particularly with small, nonoverlapping markers,[31, 95-97, 212] but wide discrepancies also are observed.[97] They are to be expected *a priori*[8] and on theoretical grounds,[327] since such factors as marker size and proximity of the marker to an end of the particle must intervene in some cases, together with the distance one is trying to determine.

Genetic analysis carried out by transduction in Demerec's laboratory has established that genes associated with similar phenotypes are often clustered and that a correspondence exists between the order of their loci on the linkage map and the sequence of the biochemical reaction steps under their control (see Chapter 2). The longest map so far obtained by transformation seems to support these important notions.[97]

In early attempts to determine the size of a genetic marker, ionizing radiations were used to inactivate DNA *in vitro*, and a radiosensitive molecular weight was calculated.[76, 238-240] The values obtained varied from 3×10^5 [239] to 1×10^6.[238a] When the transforming DNA was inactivated by sonication, a marker size of 1×10^6 was arrived at.[87] It was realized, however, that the measured size might not be the size of a marker at all, but rather the size required for the most size-dependent phenomenon, which might be penetration, pairing, or integration.[82, 87, 88, 222] More subtle devices had to be resorted to. From the rates of destruction of both the ability to penetrate and to transform, Lerman was able to calculate the size of the segment inactivated by a single lesion and this again was

1×10^{6}.[332] Fox went further and measured the size of the inserted fragment directly, by reextracting the DNA from cold bacteria that had just fixed a marked, heavily labeled P^{32}-DNA, and measuring the rate of decay of the radioactive marker.[260] The minimal estimate for the molecular weight of the integrated piece (still bigger than the marker itself) was 3×10^{5}.

2. MECHANISM OF INTEGRATION AND RECOMBINATION

Attempts to reconstruct the mechanism of integration and recombination utilize the information obtained by studying: (a) when these events take place (b) whether the introduced particle may function several times, and (c) the segregation of characters that occurs early in a transformed clone. These studies must therefore be reviewed before the mechanism is discussed.

a. The Time at Which Integration and Recombination Occur. This time is best determined in reextraction experiments (Fox and Hotchkiss [312, 333]), the principle of which will now be described. A DNA (I) is extracted from a donor strain carrying a resistance marker A; it is given, in a first experiment, to a recipient strain marked with a resistance marker B. After a short incubation period allowing for penetration, DNase is added, and at various times thereafter a sample of the culture is lysed and its DNA extracted. A series of preparations is thus obtained (DNA-II$_{t_0}$, DNA-II$_{t_1}$, etc.), the transforming activities of which are now assayed, for both characters A and B, in a second transformation experiment utilizing a doubly sensitive recipient strain. This powerful method made it possible to answer the following four questions.

1. Are the reextracted DNA's active in transformation for the introduced character? Early reextractions show that they are not, but this activity reappears very soon. In other words, DNA that has just penetrated is in an inactive state, but this state is transient and DNA soon "recovers."[312] By analogy with phage infection, this has been called an eclipse phenomenon. Ability to transform for character B served as a control and was present at all times. We already know that passage of DNA to the single-strand state is responsible for the eclipse period.[313] Whether DNA eclipses at penetration in *Hemophilus* will be discussed later (Section V,D,2,e).

2. When does integration take place? The onset of replication of marker A introduced into B cells was determined by following, as a function of time, the value of the ratio (A/B) of the input activity A to the "resident" activity B. The value was initially low (this is the eclipse again), but increased rapidly and at 5 minutes reached a value that remained constant thereafter. From that time on, therefore, an introduced marker A multiplies

at the pace of a chromosomal marker B, i.e., integration takes place almost immediately in all the transformed cells of a nonsynchronized population.[333]

3. When does recombination take place? The answer is obtained by choosing linked markers for A and B, and determining, in experiments similar to the one described, the time at which linkage appears between A and B. Recombination also was found to occur very early, being half maximal at 6 minutes after penetration.[312] In *Hemophilus*, the time required was even shorter.[315]

4. Are recovery and/or recombination dependent on DNA synthesis? The conclusion is that if they are, the amount of synthesis required is less than 5%.[312] Similar results were obtained with *Hemophilus*.[315]

The answers given to questions 2 and 3 above are disputed by Ephrussi-Taylor.[82, 334] This author observed that chloramphenicol, when present early enough after DNA penetration, will "kill" the yet unexpressed transformants preferentially; the drug behaves as if it were "curing" the transformants-to-be from their transforming DNA. A time comes, however, at which curability is lost, and this is interpreted as a sign of integration (in our terms, insertion). This, together with the spontaneous synchronization of her cultures, leads Ephrussi-Taylor to the following picture: insertion occurs (without duplication of the marker) only when the chromosome divides, but not necessarily at its first division. Duplication of the marker, however, will only occur at the next chromosomal duplication. The picture seems to be in agreement with results obtained later by the author with the direct method of Fox and Hotchkiss (results announced in ref. 190). It is hard to conceive how insertion could be at the same time obligatorily associated with chromosomal duplication and independent of DNA synthesis. It is also not clear why the same material, treated by essentially the same methods, should be synchronized in one laboratory and not in the other. Whatever the reason for this, the results obtained with synchronized cultures may be artifacts, due to the treatment applied[195]; this could be the origin of the present disagreement.

One last point needs a comment. Hotchkiss[65] and Ravin[335] observed a great variability in the number of transformants per culture, when series of parallel cultures, each started with less than one transformed cell, were examined. A variable delay in integration[335] need not be invoked, since the onset of multiplication in individual transformed cells may be irregular, as was shown by Hotchkiss.[65]

In conclusion, there seems to be no reason for doubting the correctness of Fox and Hotchkiss' results: With some markers, at least, both integration and recombination occur within a few minutes.

b. *Unique Occurrence of the Events Leading to Insertion.* The following point is generally agreed upon: The free transforming particle does not replicate as such in the cell prior to its insertion. If it did, or if it merely remained in the cell in an active form after inducing transformation, being transmitted intact to a daughter cell, recurrent transformations would occur. Ravin and Hotchkiss have shown that this does not happen. In intratype capsular transformation reactions, which lead to both autogenic and allogenic transformants,[39, 40] the two types are never found in one and the same clone (Ravin,[84] as completed in ref. 335).

A skillful statistical test made by Hotchkiss[65] shows that transformation results exclusively from an event determined by a brief contact of the cells with DNA. The model for the integration and recombination mechanism must be based on the fact that a transforming molecule functions only once.

   c. *The Information Obtained in Studying Segregation.* Transformants that have undergone many divisions on a selective medium while forming a colony, or nonselected transformants that have been reisolated, breed true; if, however, a culture that has just been treated with DNA is plated on a nonselective medium, no pure clones of transformants are obtained. The result in a diplococcal organism, in which moreover short chains of cells are frequently observed is not surprising.[276] But if, after a short exposure to DNA from a streptomycin resistant donor, a sensitive recipient culture is first allowed to undergo two divisions in liquid medium, then submitted to a streptomycin treatment killing all the sensitive cells and eventually plated on nutrient agar devoid of the antibiotic, 10 to 15 per cent of the colonies obtained are still mixed, each containing equal numbers of both types of cells. Sensitive cells may therefore be segregated from transformants already expressed (Hotchkiss[276]). The result may simply mean that some 10 per cent of the transformants, belated in their multiplication (see ref. 65), had not yet gone through their second segregation division at the time of the streptomycin treatment. It does not tell us much that was not already reported (except that streptomycin resistance is dominant in pneumococcus[276]), but it is not in contradiction with the already reported fact that in most cells, integration follows the incorporation of DNA almost immediately.

   d. *Copy Choice versus Breakage and Reunion.* Whenever a cell, penetrated by a piece of exogenous genetic material, acquires new inheritable traits, the question arises whether this material has been physically inserted into the resident genome (or into a copy being made of it), or whether the genetic message is transmitted without physical transfer

(Lederberg[336]). The first process, requiring as it does breakage and reunion of nucleotide chains, is often referred to as a crossing-over mechanism; it has been shown by Meselson and Weigle[337] and by Kellenberger et al.[338] to be responsible for recombination in a bacteriophage, where it may operate even in the absence of DNA replication.

The second process could operate only while the cell genome is being replicated, a segment of the replica being copied "by mistake" on the exogenous material. The two processes have different implications, which can serve to identify the one that is actually operating.

A requirement for DNA synthesis is equally compatible with both mechanisms; but insertion can take place in the absence of DNA synthesis only if breakage and reunion are at work. If the introduced particle is shown to transfer its information only once, breakage and reunion seem more likely; but they would certainly be excluded if the particle could function several times.

In transformation, as we have seen, insertion takes place in the absence of detectable DNA synthesis,[312, 315] and information is transferred only once.[65, 335] Physical insertion by breakage and reunion thus already appeared to be responsible for recombination, when a direct demonstration was provided by Fox.[260] A transforming DNA, heavily marked with radiophosphorus, was applied to nonradioactive cells in a nonradioactive medium, allowed to recombine, and reextracted at once. The effect on the transforming activity of the P^{32} decay was the same in the reextracted and the original DNA, showing that the marker itself had been inserted without duplication or fragmentation. While the absence of fragmentation is unexpected, and in apparent contradiction with Lacks' results,[313] the physical insertion is clearly demonstrated.

When crossing-over occurs in a cell undergoing meiosis or mitosis, the two reciprocal recombinant chromosomes are recovered in the progeny. However, when recombination occurs, as in transformation, between the complete genome of a cell and a segment of genetic material, the only products detected are cells in the genome of which a double crossing-over has introduced a genetic segment of exogenous origin. Even if the recombination process is symmetrical, recombination as we see it is nonreciprocal. It is convenient to speak of the first reaction as a switching-out, and of the second one as a switching-back to the cell genome.[330]

A molecular model (Fig. 4, model B) for these reactions has been proposed. It requires an enzyme that hydrolyzes homologous phosphodiester bonds on two parallel chains and re-forms them crisscross. Such an enzyme may have been detected in crude extracts of B. subtilis by

Lorkiewicz et al.[339] Among the still unanswered questions related to the insertion process are the following: (1) What is the meaning of Fox's finding[260] that the transforming particle is not fragmented during recombination, and how serious a threat is it to our present picture of the recombination process? (2) What is the meaning of Lacks' finding[313] that only one-fourth of the donor DNA incorporated is physically inserted? (3) What is the fate of the replaced segment, and of the discarded ends (if any) of the transforming strand? (4) What is the mode of action of the drugs which, like chloramphenicol[82] and mitomycin,[340] are said to cure cells of their transforming DNA? (5) Is insertion polarized? (6) Is the integration process the same in pneumococcus (where there is an eclipse period), in *Hemophilus* (where some data suggest there is none), and in *E. coli* (where the transformants keep segregating[73])? (7) Why is it that addition of genetic material is observed in pneumococcus in the case of intertype capsular transformation? Is there more than one integration process in this organism? Questions 6 and 7 will be discussed in the following section.

  e. The So-Called Special Cases. Apparently, several facts do not fit the process of integration and recombination as this has just been pictured. These facts will now be reviewed critically in an attempt to determine whether there is a real need for assuming more than one integration mechanism.

Intertype capsular transformations. Examples of capsular transformations responsible in part for the notion that transformation results from a replacement of a genetic segment by another have been given in Section I. They were examples of intratype reactions. The outcome of intertype transformations (studied mostly by MacLeod, Austrian, and their collaborators) proves to be more complicated. For lack of space, only the general findings will be reported.

  1. Direct transformation from one fully encapsulated type to another is possible,[341] e.g.,

$$S_{II}^{+} \times (S_{III}^{+}) \rightarrow S_{III}^{+} \tag{14}$$

but one still speaks of intratype transformation, when a rough mutant is used as receptor, e.g.,

$$S_{VIII}^{-} \times (S_{III}^{+}) \rightarrow S_{III}^{+} \tag{15}$$

  2. Capsule production is governed by several genes,[342, 343] e.g.,

$$S_{VIII}^{-} \text{ (mutant \#1)} \times (S_{VIII}^{-}) \text{ (mutant \#13)} \rightarrow S_{VIII}^{+} \tag{16}$$

  3. Simultaneous production of two serologically distinct capsular polysaccharides by one and the same cell does occur with some artificially produced strains:

$$S_{III\text{-}1}^{+} \times (S_{I}^{+}) \rightarrow S_{I}^{+} \text{ and } S_{I\text{-}III}^{+} \tag{17}$$

First observed in *Hemophilus*,[344] this binary capsulation may be produced also in pneumococcus[345]; such strains do not segregate at high frequency.

4. Several types of allogenic transformants may be obtained, along with autogenic ones, in the same experiment[323, 346, 347]:

$$S_{II}^- \times (S_{I\text{-}III}^+) \text{ [from reaction (17)]} \rightarrow S_{III\text{-}1}^+ , S_I^+ \text{ and a few } S_{I\text{-}III}^+ \text{ (but no } S_{III}^+). \quad (18)$$

5. As reaction 18 demonstrates, both the genome for the phenotype $S_{III\text{-}1}^+$ and the genome for the phenotype S_I^+ are simultaneously present in the $S_{I\text{-}III}^+$ transformants; reaction (17) therefore consisted of an addition of foreign genetic material.[323, 346, 347]

Many other important points could be cited concerning the biochemical aspects of polysaccharide biosynthesis,[323, 324] but here only the conclusions of the genetic studies need be given: (*1*) Polysaccharide synthesis involves several biochemical steps, each controlled by a gene, and the genes are closely linked. (*2*) A capsular genome, composed of several genes, behaves like one unit, carried by one DNA particle (see also ref. 335). (*3*) Capsular genomes of different types, which seem to have the same location in the total genome, do not recombine, and presumably do not synapse. (*4*) An entire capsular genome may either be exchanged for another one, or added without replacement.

How serious is the incompatibility of this situation with the model mechanism described in the previous section?

A capsular genome can be substituted for another one, although it is seemingly unable to pair with it. The conclusion that should obviously not be drawn is that pairing is a dispensable step in transformation. The only assumptions required to bring the facts in line with the model picture seem to be (Fig. 5, scheme B) that the capsular genome is a long mid-piece in the DNA particle carrying it, and that the end pieces which determine noncapsular material pair normally with their counterparts in the host. (Markers in these end pieces would be required to test the hypothesis; they might be obtained by the nitrous acid method[97]; see Section V,D,1.) If the hypothesis is correct, the absence of pairing would prevent the occurrence of recombination within the mid-piece, leaving insertion of the entire capsular genome as the only possible one (Fig. 5, scheme B_1').

The addition of exogenous bacterial genetic material, revealed by the existence of stable doubly capsulated strains, raises the same unsolved topological problems as the lysogenization phenomenon (See chapter 2).

The alternative seems to be either an insertion of the introduced segment into the continuity of the host genome (Campbell **347a**), or some kind of attachment to this genome, such that duplication of the attached segment is possible (Jacob and Wollman 347b). How then could integration occur if it is not due to insertion?

In order to answer this question, let us recapitulate the facts, while illustrating them with simple schemes (Fig. 5). Whenever the marker is small compared to the whole DNA particle (as it usually is), there is good pairing on both sides of it over a long distance (scheme A). The breakage and re-

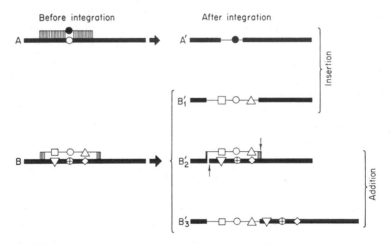

Fig. 5. Diagrammatic representation of integration. In the usual case, when the marker is short as compared with the DNA particle (scheme A), integration occurs with replacement of the resident marker; it results from the insertion of an introduced genetic segment into the genome of the cell and requires two "switching events," one at each end of the replaced segment (schemes A′ and B_1'). In the case of intertype capsular transformation (scheme B), integration may occur without replacement; such an addition reaction may result from either one (scheme B_2') or two (scheme B_3') "switching events."

union process can "switch out" in many places on one side of the marker, and switch back in, again in many places, on the other. The length of the exogenous material so introduced may vary, but the switching-back has so many opportunities to occur that it never fails, and insertion, i.e., replacement, is the rule (scheme A′). When there is a big piece with no pairing in the middle (scheme B), as is the case in intertype transformation, insertion (scheme B_1') is a rare outcome, since it requires two now unlikely switching events; the switching-back may be belated, or not occur at all, with addition as the result (scheme B_2'). This model implies a break at the arrows. Alternatively, addition might result from a duplication without break (scheme B_3'), reunion occurring between the two ends marked by an arrow on scheme B_2'. This last scheme has the disadvantage of assuming that chromosomal duplication can start anew at the break, i.e., at more than one point. Reasons for doubting that this is possible have been put forward by Maaløe.[196]

In conclusion, a choice cannot presently be made between the molecular models that have been discussed to account for the stable heterogenotes arising from transformation; it seems possible that, while insertion requires two switching events, one is enough to ensure integration and that the difference between insertion and addition is between a completed process and one that cannot go to completion.

Transformation in Hemophilus. The following has been observed in transformation of both pneumococcus and *Hemophilus:* Double-stranded DNA penetrates much more efficiently than denatured DNA; glucose, phosphate, and a divalent cation are required for penetration; the resident marker is generally replaced by the transforming one; smaller DNA sequences are inserted more often than longer ones, with possible exceptions; the measured degree of linkage between markers depends on physiological conditions; recombination occurs immediately and in the absence of detectable DNA synthesis; a marker of heterospecific origin is rarely accepted, when carried in by a heterospecific DNA particle, but is accepted with normal frequency, when reextracted from an interspecific transformant. Moreover, in both pneumococcus and *Hemophilus,* the frequencies and the time course of transformation are the same, and binary capsulation is observed. The presumption is great indeed that one and the same mechanism of transformation operates in both species.

Recently, Voll and Goodgal published data[315] interpreted by Lacks[313] to mean that the eclipse phenomenon described by Fox in pneumococcus[312] does not exist in *Hemophilus.* Lacks states the process of entry is different in this organism, assuming that DNA is still in the double-stranded state within the recipient cell; therefore the processes to follow also would have to be different. Some tables and figures in Voll and Goodgal's paper do lead to the conclusion drawn by Lacks (but not by the authors themselves). However, when the description of actual experiments is compared with the one given by Fox, the following points emerge. At the time of earliest examination (7 minutes at 36°C. after DNA was added), Voll and Goodgal found maximal recovery of the introduced marker. After 7 minutes at 37°C., the recovery observed by Fox in pneumococcus was already 30%. Proper study of the eclipse phenomenon in pneumococcus requires that temperature be lowered to 30°C. Voll and Goodgal worked at 36°C. only. To conclude, the absence of an eclipse period in *Hemophilus* is not clearly established by the present data.

The following experiment, made by Herriott with *Hemophilus*, may also be taken to indicate that DNA enters this organism as a double strand. A mixture of two DNA's, each carrying one of two resistance markers known to be linked, was annealed. Heterozygous renatured molecules were presumably formed with one marker on each strand. When a doubly sensitive strain was transformed with the annealed mixture, up to 50 times the random number of double transformants were obtained.[214, 215] It would seem, therefore, that two markers, initially present in complementary strands in an exogenous renatured DNA particle, end up in one and the same chromosomal strand. If this is confirmed, it will not be easy to explain. However, as Herriott pointed out, two questions must be answered before any such interpretation can be entertained. One has to do with the nature of the new structure formed by annealing, which might be more complex than anticipated. The other, which should be more easily solved, is whether the colonies scored as doubly transformed are pure and stable. As it stands today, the phenomenon described by Herriott cannot be clearly interpreted, and should not be taken to indicate that different recombination processes are operating in *Hemophilus* and in pneumococcus. To conclude, the mechanism of transformation still has not been shown to be different in the two species.

Phage-assisted transformation in E. coli. Nothing is known about the state of DNA after penetration in this case (see Section V,B,4); but as Kaiser and Hogness have demonstrated,[73] the integrated *Gal+* marker is still most of the time within the phage genome in the transformed cells. The instability of the transformed cells, which keep segregating *Gal−* cells, and the fact that upon UV induction of the transformants the released phages are still transducing the *Gal+* character[73] leave little doubt about this. Transformation in this case occurs by lysogenization, possibly by mere addition.

In conclusion, the mechanisms of penetration, integration, and recombination have not been shown to be the same in all transformable species, but a unitary picture is a cause worth fighting for. While this has been attempted, no claim is made that the picture presented is final.

E. PHENOTYPIC EXPRESSION

Enzymes are directly responsible for a cell phenotype, and phenotypic expression depends on the synthesis of specific proteins. Expression of a newly introduced genetic material occurs only under conditions permitting normal protein synthesis: it does not occur in saline, and is reversibly blocked by chloramphenicol[307] and 8-azaguanine.[348] Expression is therefore best followed by measuring the synthesis of an enzyme, rather than by measuring a character such as drug resistance, which may involve several unidentified steps. A comparison of the kinetics of enzyme synthesis after DNA penetration with the kinetics of integration can tell us whether integration is required for DNA to exert its physiological function. A clear answer to this question has been given by Lacks and Hotchkiss.[349]

A series of Mal⁻ mutants were isolated, unable to grow on maltose for lack of amylomaltase. The synthesis of this enzyme, followed after addition of wild-type DNA, was found to require only 6 minutes, and to reach a constant maximal rate at 10 minutes. The kinetics was the same in all mutants, although they were transformed to Mal^+ with unequal frequencies; but the final rate of enzyme synthesis was linearly related to the frequency of transformation. This rate was therefore proportional to the DNA that had been integrated, bearing no relation to the DNA that had merely been fixed. The constancy of the relative rate of enzyme synthesis after 10 minutes also shows the absence of transient expression in cells that were not genetically transformed. It could be concluded that DNA, after penetration, is in a physiologically inactive form until it is integrated.[349] This conclusion assumed further significance when DNA was shown to be reduced to the single-strand state by the penetration process.[313] Clearly then, DNA can be physiologically active only when it is integrated.

The opposite view also has been held,[334, 348] but it was based on indirect evidence; in addition, the trait being studied, resistance to streptomycin, is probably established by a more complex process than the mere synthesis of an enzyme.[349] How misleading the study of expression based on this trait can be is illustrated by the fact that, while 10 minutes are sufficient for an enzyme to be synthesized at maximal rate, a mean time of 60 minutes is required for streptomycin resistance to be fully expressed. Although based on the appearance of a drug resistance, the following observations seem to be generally valid: the slope of the per cent expression curve is independent of DNA concentration (Fox[353]); the individual transformants do not express synchronously[353, 353a]; the time required for expression may remain the same when the transforming DNA is of heterospecific origin[81]; but, even among physiologically similar mutants, it may depend on the particular marker being transferred.[42]

It may be asked whether the integration required for expression needs to be completed by insertion, or by an integration with the chromosome (as opposed to other genetic elements in the cell). Evidence from other fields makes it possible to answer this question. The Gal^+ gene is not inserted in the chromosome of the Gal^+ transformants of *E. coli*[73]; the genes for motility are not either, in the abortively transduced *Salmonella* cells described by Stocker *et al.*[350]; the Lac^+ gene is not integrated with the chromosome in the Lac^- strains of *E. coli*, carrying an F-Lac^+ episome (Jacob *et al.*[351]). Nevertheless, the characters in question are expressed. According, the primary requirement for DNA to be physiologically functional *in vivo* seems to be association with some genetic element (or a fragment thereof), presumably in the double-stranded form.

Since abortive transduction has been known for some time, abortive transformation has been looked for in several laboratories, but has never been observed. These unpublished failures could be understood only when penetration of free DNA was shown to be associated with a reduction to the single-strand state. The incompatibility of single-strandedness with the physiological function of DNA is further confirmed, as Lacks pointed out, by Wood and Berg's findings. Studying amino acid incorporation in *in vitro* systems, these authors observed an activation by T_2 DNA that disappeared upon denaturation of the latter.[352]

It is not yet known whether DNA-RNA complexes and messenger RNA are able to enter competent cells and produce transient, specific physiological changes; an indication that this might be so exists in Spizizen's work.[106] Balassa[114] has reported that the requirements for expression may sometimes be more complex than for growth.

In summary, expression of characters introduced by free DNA requires that integration first take place. It may be remarked that if the processes of DNA penetration and phenotypic expression are the same in animal and bacterial cells, the phenotypic transformation of human cells described by Kraus[132] (see Section III,E) means that genetic transformation has also been obtained in these cells. The fact that only a physiological demonstration could be given seems to be due to the lack of good selective markers and to the difficulty of growing clones.

VI. Transformation as a Tool in Genetic Analysis

In addition to being a subject of study per se, transformation has been used as a tool in genetic analysis; as such, it has its limitations, due to the fragmentation of the genome, introduced by the inevitable shear degradation of bacterial DNA. For this reason the building of complete chromosomal maps may be impossible by transformation alone. But in spite of the inherent difficulties (see Section V,D,1), it seems as reliable as transduction for mapping small genetic regions.[101] The case of the DNA particle carrying the genes controlling tryptophan synthesis in *B. subtilis*,[97] may be taken as an example.

Transformation has been used to analyze the mode of action of radiations on DNA, the most systematic approach being that of Stuy.[221, 236] However, its main value lies in the analysis of bacterial functions, where conjugational analysis is not available.

A. GENETIC ANALYSIS OF BACTERIAL PROPERTIES AND FUNCTIONS

Transformation studies made it possible to recognize that capsule production is a complex phenomenon, controlled by several genes, some of which are common to capsular genomes that determine different serological types.[323, 342, 343, 345] This recognition in turn led to the biochemical identification of the reactions controlled by these genes.[323, 324] The creation by transformation of strains producing a capsular substance endowed with a new serological specificity[354] also poses interesting biochemical problems that are still unsolved.

The genetic control of resistance to various antibacterial agents, as revealed in transformation experiments, should also help to elucidate the biochemical processes involved. Resistance to penicillin was studied first and found to be controlled by several genes, the effects of which were additive.[38] The approach served as a model in studying the genetic control of resistance to other drugs.

The control of resistance to streptomycin has been studied by many authors; several unlinked loci were detected, at which mutations increase the level of resistance[41, 43, 355, 356]; all mutations leading to high levels occur at the same locus.[43] An "enhancer" gene, increasing the resistance only of some mutants, has been detected by Bryan; unlinked to the resistance loci, it does not confer resistance by itself.[357] No streptomycin-dependent mutants have yet been isolated in pneumococcus; when DNA from one such mutant of a *Rhizobium* species was used in transformation experiments by Balassa and Gabor, a complex situation was revealed, four distinct types of transformants being obtained, of which two were resistant and two dependent.[358] Some mutants of *Streptococcus* were found by Pakula and Hulanika-Bankowska to be unequally resistant to streptomycin and dihydrostreptomycin.[359] It is regrettable that genetically known strains are not used more systematically in biochemical studies of resistance since, as Hsu and Herriott pointed out,[356] resistance is likely to be attained by different mechanisms in unlinked mutants.

Mutants resistant to erythromycin,[42] amethopterin,[360] or 8-azaguanine[361] also have various levels of drug resistance. These levels may be due either to single factors, or to a combination of factors, segregating in transformation. The factors conferring resistance to erythromycin, carried by one and the same DNA particle, may, in transformation, either substitute for one another (autogenic reactions) or become associated (allogenic reactions), in which case antagonistic effects as well as synergistic (more than additive) ones[42] may be observed.

Sporulation is another function which has been analyzed by transformation,[28, 294, 362] as well as by transduction.[102] Mutants with an impaired function may never form a mature spore (asporogenous mutants) or may, under conditions optimal for sporulation of the wild type, sporulate with a low frequency, characteristic for each mutant (oligosporogenous mutants[28]). Normal sporulation can be restored in both types by wild-type DNA, and DNA from other sporulation mutants is generally found to be just as effective in this respect; from this it has been concluded that sporulation genes are many, and generally unlinked.[28] The mutated forms of the sporulation genes can also be transmitted by transformation.[294] Genetically different mutants can be shown by morphological[363] and biochemical[364] studies to be blocked at various stages of the sporulation process. Study of sporulation is likely to reveal regulation mechanisms, which ought to be helpful in understanding cellular differentiation processes. Motility in *Bacillus* species is another property which is now being investigated with the help of transformation (Nasser and Koffler[365]). Those mutants which are blocked in the synthesis of flagellin, an easily purified protein of low molecular weight, should be good material with which to study coding problems, and the relation between structure and function in a structural protein; but other kinds of nonmotile mutants may also be expected, and here again an easy genetic classification of the mutants should greatly facilitate the physiological analysis.

A new approach to the problem of thermophily has been opened by McDonald and Matney, who have isolated thermophilic mutants (able to grow at 55°C.) from *B. subtilis* Marburg (which normally cannot grow above 52°C.). These workers have shown that the ability to grow at the higher temperature can be transferred by mutant DNA to the mesophilic wild type.[366] Marmur[367] has shown that DNA from a thermophile has a "normal" heat stability (i.e., one determined by base composition alone). It should now be possible, with some defined and easily purified proteins (e.g., exoenzymes, flagellin) to decide whether their physical properties depend on the origin (mesophilic or thermophilic) of the genes controlling their synthesis or on the type of cell that produced them.

The symbiotic fixation of molecular nitrogen, as occurs in the nodules that form on the roots of infected plants, is another important function in the analysis of which bacterial transformation, used jointly with plant genetics and biochemical studies on bacterial mutants, should prove helpful. This is shown by the work of R. Balassa,[368-370] as discussed by G. Balassa.[371] Host specificity, the basis for species definition within the genus *Rhizobium*, seems to be due to a single genetic factor, or at most a few linked ones, since a new specificity can be acquired by transformation (e.g., *R. japonicum*, or *R. lupini*, exposed to DNA from *R. meliloti*, will acquire the ability to form root nodules on alfalfa). It is not known whether these interspecific transformants have at the same time lost their initial specificity. A strain is said to be *ineffective* when it forms nodules with no nitrogen-fixing activity; effectiveness is another bacterial property which may be gained by transformation, independently of host specificity. It may be asked whether nodule formation on a given host requires, in addition to the right specificity, another bacterial property, infectivity, which would not be host specific; systematic transformation studies, carried out on a large number of mutant strains, should make it possible to answer this question.[371]

B. GENETIC ANALYSIS OF PROTEIN FINE STRUCTURE

The lesser complexity of viruses, their easy purification, and the infectivity of their free nucleic acid make them better suited than microorganisms for the study of gene-protein relationships. That the properties of a protein must be under the control of DNA was recognized early in transformation studies.[23, 372, 373] The proteins and their alterations were detected by their serological[23] or enzymic activities.[372-374]

The bacterial enzymes now known to be inactivated by mutation and reactivated by transformation include (in addition to lactic oxidase[373]) mannitol phosphate dehydrogenase,[49] uridine-diphosphoglucose dehydrogenase,[323] uridine-diphosphoglucuronic acid epimerase,[323] and amylomaltase.[212] However, in none of these cases has the nature of the structural change occurring in both the DNA and the protein been investigated.

Curiously, the only protein for which enzymic properties have been correlated with mapped changes in DNA structure is an enzyme that has not yet been purified. The reaction it catalyzes has *p*-aminobenzoate as its substrate, but its product, a precursor of the substances endowed with folic acid activity, has not been precisely identified. Its unique virtue lies in the fact that it retains its activity when altered by any one of several mutations, each altered form conferring on the mutant a characteristic level of resistance to sulfonamide or other analogs of the substrate.[330, 375, 376] The various genetic subunits in which mutation affects the properties of the enzyme were found to be linked, and their relative order could be determined.[330] Mutations in these subunits, when accumulated in the same strain, may have more than additive effects (potentiation). On the other hand, the sensitivity of the mutants to inhibition by various analogs of p-aminobenzoate, shows the various mutated enzymes to be unequally sensitive to inhibition by the analogs. The general conclusions are: (1) that, by using various analogs of the substrate, specific regions within the catalytic site of an enzyme can be characterized; and (2) that "parts of a gene have a point-for-point relationship to as many parts of a specific protein."[376] The formidable task of determining the chemical nature of the alterations, both in the DNA and in the corresponding protein, remains to be carried out.

The fact that transformation may be used so advantageously in so many physiological and structural studies suggests that it will not remain much longer in the hands of the happy few.

REFERENCES

[1] O. T. Avery, C. M. MacLeod, and M. McCarty, *J. Exptl. Med.* **79**, 137 (1944).
[2] A. W. Ravin, *Advances in Genet.* **10**, 61 (1961).
[3] M. McCarty, *Bacteriol. Revs.* **10**, 63 (1946).
[4] R. Austrian, *Bacteriol. Revs.* **16**, 31 (1952).
[5] R. D. Hotchkiss, *Harvey Lectures Ser.* **49**, 124 (1954).
[6] R. D. Hotchkiss, *in* "The Nucleic Acids" (E. Chargaff and J. N. Davidson, eds.), Vol. II, p. 435. Academic Press, New York, 1955.
[7] H. Ephrussi-Taylor, *Advances in Virus Research* **3**, 275 (1955).
[8] H. Ephrussi-Taylor, *in* "Growth in Living Systems" (M. X. Zarrow, ed.), p. 39. Basic Books, New York, 1961.
[9] S. Zamenhof, *in* "Phosphorus Metabolism" (W. D. McElroy and B. Glass, eds.), Vol. II, p. 301. Johns Hopkins Press, Baltimore, Maryland, 1952.
[10] S. Zamenhof, *Prog. in Biophys. Biophys. Chem.* **6**, 85 (1956).
[11] R. Thomas, *in* "Mécanismes d'autoreproduction" (A. J. Thomas, ed.), p. 253. Masson, Paris, 1957.
[12] F. Griffith, *J. Hyg.* **27**, 113 (1928).
[13] R. H. P. Sia and M. H. Dawson, *J. Exptl. Med.* **54**, 701 (1931).
[14] M. H. Dawson and R. H. P. Sia, *J. Exptl. Med.* **54**, 681 (1931).
[15] J. L. Alloway, *J. Exptl. Med.* **57**, 265 (1933).
[16] R. D. Hotchkiss, *Colloq. intern. centre natl. recherche sci. (Paris)* **8**, 57 (1949).
[17] S. Zamenhof, H. E. Alexander, and G. Leidy, *J. Exptl. Med.* **98**, 373 (1953).
[18] S. Zamenhof, *in* "The Chemical Basis of Heredity" (W. D. McElroy and B. Glass, eds.), p. 351. Johns Hopkins Press, Baltimore, Maryland, 1957.
[19] A. E. Mirsky, *Cold Spring Harbor Symposia Quant. Biol.* **12**, 15 (1947). (Discussion following Boivin's paper.)
[20] J. L. Alloway, *J. Exptl. Med.* **55**, 91 (1932).
[21] E. Chargaff, *in* "The Nucleic Acids" (E. Chargaff and J. N. Davidson, eds.), Vol. I, p. 307. Academic Press, New York, 1955.
[22] R. D. Hotchkiss, *in* "Phosphorus Metabolism" (W. D. McElroy and B. Glass, eds.), Vol. II, p. 426. Johns Hopkins Press, Baltimore, Maryland, 1952.
[23] R. Austrian and C. M. MacLeod, *J. Exptl. Med.* **89**, 451 (1949).
[24] S. Zamenhof, G. Leidy, H. E. Alexander, P. L. Fitzgerald, and E. Chargaff, *Arch. Biochem. Biophys.* **40**, 50 (1952).
[25] H. E. Taylor, *Compt. rend. acad. sci.* **228**, 1258 (1949).
[26] H. E. Alexander and G. Leidy, *Proc. Soc. Exptl. Biol. Med.* **78**, 625 (1951).

[27] A. W. Ravin. *J. Bacteriol.* **77**, 296 (1959).
[28] P. Schaeffer and H. Ionesco, *Compt. rend. acad. sci.* **251**, 3125 (1960).
[29] F. E. Young and J. Spizizen, *J. Bacteriol.* **81**, 823 (1961).
[30] R. D. Hotchkiss and J. Marmur, *Proc. Natl. Acad. Sci. U. S.* **40**, 55 (1954).
[31] S. H. Goodgal, *J. Gen. Physiol.* **45**, 205 (1961).
[32] C. M. MacLeod and M. R. Krauss, *J. Exptl. Med.* **86**, 439 (1947).
[33] A. Langvad-Nielsen, *Acta Pathol. Microbiol. Scand.* **21**, 362 (1944).
[34] H. F. Taylor, *J. Exptl. Med.* **89**, 399 (1949).
[35] R. Austrian, *J. Exptl. Med.* **98**, 35 (1953).
[36] R. Austrian, *J. Exptl. Med.* **98**, 21 (1953).
[37] R. Austrian and C. M. MacLeod, *J. Exptl. Med.* **86**, 439 (1949).
[38] R. D. Hotchkiss, *Cold Spring Harbor Symposia Quant. Biol.* **16**, 457 (1951).
[39] H. Ephrussi-Taylor, *Exptl. Cell Research* **2**, 589 (1951).
[40] H. Ephrussi-Taylor, *Cold Spring Harbor Symposia Quant. Biol.* **16**, 445 (1951).
[41] P. Schaeffer, *Ann. inst. Pasteur* **91**, 323 (1956).
[42] A. W. Ravin and V. N. Iyer, *J. Gen. Microbiol.* **26**, 277 (1961).
[43] M. B. Rotheim and A. W. Ravin, *Genetics* **46**, 1619 (1961).
[44] B. Thorell, *in* "The Nucleic Acids" (E. Chargaff and J. N. Davidson, eds.), Vol. II, p. 181. Academic Press, New York, 1955.
[45] R. G. E. Murray, *in* "The Bacteria" (I. C. Gunsalus and R. Y. Stanier, eds.), Vol. I, p. 64. Academic Press, New York, 1960.
[46] E. Kellenberger, *in* "Microbial Genetics." *Symposium Soc. Gen. Microbiol.* **10**, 39 (1960).
[47] E. M. Witkin, *Cold Spring Harbor Symposia Quant. Biol.* **16**, 357 (1951).
[48] R. Vendrely, *in* "The Nucleic Acids" (E. Chargaff and J. N. Davidson, eds.), Vol. II, p. 155. Academic Press, New York, 1955.
[49] J. Marmur and R. D. Hotchkiss, *J. Biol. Chem.* **214**, 383 (1955).
[50] S. Zamenhof, *Proc. Natl. Acad. Sci. U. S.* **46**, 101 (1960).
[51] R. M. Litman and H. Ephrussi-Taylor, *Compt. rend. acad. sci.* **249**, 838 (1959).
[52] A. Kornberg, *Science* **131**, 1503 (1960).
[53] J. Josse, A. D. Kaiser, and A. Kornberg, *J. Biol. Chem.* **236**, 864 (1961).
[54] A. D. Hershey and M. Chase, *J. Gen. Physiol.* **36**, 39 (1952).
[55] H. Fraenkel-Conrat, *Harvey Lectures Ser.* **53**, 56 (1959).
[56] A. Gierer, *in* "Microbial Genetics." *Symposium Soc. Gen. Microbiol.* **10**, 248 (1960).
[57] H. E. Alexander and G. Leidy, *J. Exptl. Med.* **97**, 17 (1953).
[58] H. E. Alexander, G. Leidy, and E. Hahn, *J. Exptl. Med.* **99**, 505 (1954).
[59] R. M. Bracco, M. R. Krauss, A. S. Roe, and C. M. MacLeod, *J. Exptl. Med.* **106**, 247 (1957).
[60] R. Pakula, Z. Fluder, E. Hulanicka, and W. Walczak, *Bull. acad. polon. sci.* **6**, 319 (1958).
[61] J. Spizizen, *Proc. Natl. Acad. Sci. U. S.* **44**, 1072 (1958).
[62] R. Balassa and M. Gabor, *Mikrobiologiya* **30**, 457 (1961).
[63] B. W. Catlin and L. S. Cunningham, *J. Gen. Microbiol.* **26**, 303 (1961).
[64] B. A. D. Stocker, M. R. Krauss, and C. M. MacLeod, *J. Pathol. Bacteriol.* **66**, 330 (1953).
[65] R. D. Hotchkiss, *in* "The Chemical Basis of Heredity" (W. D. McElroy and B. Glass, eds.), p. 321. Johns Hopkins Press, Baltimore, Maryland, 1957.
[66] A. W. Ravin, *Brookhaven Symposia in Biol.* **No. 8**, 33 (1955).
[67] E. Ottolenghi and R. D. Hotchkiss, *Science* **132**, 1257 (1960).
[68] R. D. Hotchkiss, *in* "Methods in Enzymology" (S. P. Colowick and N. O. Kaplan, eds.), Vol. III, p. 692. Academic Press, New York, 1957.

[69] L. F. Cavalieri, J. F. Deutsch, and B. H. Rosenberg, *Biophys. J.* **1**, 301 (1961).
[70] J. Marmur, *J. Mol. Biol.* **3**, 208 (1961).
[71] K. S. Kirby, *Biochem. J.* **66**, 495 (1957).
[72] J. Huppert and N. Rebeyrotte, *Biochim. et Biophys. Acta* **45**, 189 (1960).
[73] A. D. Kaiser and D. S. Hogness, *J. Mol. Biol.* **2**, 392 (1960).
[74] P. Schaeffer, unpublished observations.
[75] P. Schaeffer and H. Ionesco, *Compt. rend. acad. sci.* **249**, 481 (1959).
[76] H. Ephrussi-Taylor, *in* "The Chemical Basis of Heredity" (W. D. McElroy and B. Glass, eds.), p. 299. Johns Hopkins Press, Baltimore, Maryland, 1957.
[77] K. Burton, *Biochem. J.* **62**, 315 (1956).
[78] R. D. Hotchkiss, *in* "Methods in Enzymology" (S. P. Colowick and N. O. Kaplan, eds.), Vol. III, p. 708. Academic Press, New York, 1957.
[79] R. Thomas, *Biochim. et Biophys. Acta* **18**, 467 (1955).
[80] R. D. Hotchkiss, *J. Cellular Comp. Physiol.* **45**, Supp. 2, 1 (1955).
[81] P. Schaeffer, *Ann. inst. Pasteur* **91**, 192 (1956).
[82] H. Ephrussi-Taylor, *Intern. Congr. Microbiol. 7th Stockholm*, p. 51 (1958).
[83] M. S. Fox and R. D. Hotchkiss, *Nature* **179**, 1322 (1957).
[84] A. W. Ravin, *Exptl. Cell Research* **7**, 58 (1954).
[85] R. Thomas, *in* "Actualités Biochimiques" (M. Florkin and J. Roche, eds.), No. 21. Masson, Paris, 1962.
[86] L. Lerman and L. J. Tolmach, *Biochim. et Biophys. Acta* **26**, 68 (1957).
[87] M. Litt, J. Marmur, H. Ephrussi-Taylor, and P. Doty, *Proc. Natl. Acad. Sci. U.S.* **44**, 144 (1958).
[88] L. F. Cavalieri and B. H. Rosenberg, *Proc. Natl. Acad. Sci. U.S.* **44**, 853 (1958).
[89] H. E. Alexander and G. Leidy, *Proc. Soc. Exptl. Biol. Med.* **73**, 485 (1950).
[90] H. E. Alexander and W. Redman, *J. Exptl. Med.* **97**, 797 (1953).
[91] M. Jarai, *Acta Microbiol. Acad. Sci. Hung.* **8**, 81 (1961).
[92] A. Wacker and L. Laschet, *Arzneimittel-Forsch.* **10**, 488 (1960).
[93] D. Perry and H. D. Slade, *J. Bacteriol.* **83**, 443 (1962).
[94] C. Anagnostopoulos and J. Spizizen, *J. Bacteriol.* **81**, 741 (1961).
[95] E. W. Nester and J. Lederberg, *Proc. Natl. Acad. Sci. U.S.* **47**, 52 (1961).
[96] E. Ephrati-Elizur, P. R. Srinivasan, and S. Zamenhof, *Proc. Natl. Acad. Sci. U.S.* **47**, 56 (1961).
[97] C. Anagnostopoulos and I. P. Crawford, *Proc. Natl. Acad. Sci. U.S.* **47**, 378 (1961).
[98] P. C. Fitz-James, *J. Biophys. Biochem. Cytol.* **8**, 507 (1960).
[99] W. R. Romig and A. M. Brodetsky, *J. Bacteriol.* **82**, 135 (1961).
[100] C. B. Thorne, *J. Bacteriol.* **83**, 106 (1962).
[101] E. Ephrati-Elizur and M. S. Fox, *Nature* **192**, 433 (1961).
[102] I. Takahashi, *Biochem. Biophys. Research Communs.* **5**, 171 (1961).
[103] G. Ivanovics and K. Csiszar, *Naturwissenschaften* **13**, 309 (1962).
[104] H. C. Shen, M. M. Hung, S. C. T'sai, H. C. Ch'en, and W. Y. Chang, *Chem. Abstr.* **55**, 17747a (1961).
[105] C. A. Shamoian, A. Canzanelli, and J. Melrose, *Biochim. et Biophys. Acta* **47**, 208 (1961).
[106] J. Spizizen, *Federation Proc.* **18**, 957 (1959).
[107] S. Brenner, F. Jacob, and M. Meselson, *Nature* **190**, 576 (1961).
[108] M. Hayashi and S. Spiegelman, *Proc. Natl. Acad. Sci. U. S.* **47**, 1564 (1961).
[109] R. Austrian, *Bull. Johns Hopkins Hosp.* **91**, 189 (1952).
[110] B. W. Catlin, *Science* **124**, 441 (1956).
[111] B. W. Catlin, *J. Bacteriol.* **79**, 579 (1960).
[112] G. Leidy, E. Hahn, and H. E. Alexander, *J. Exptl. Med.* **104**, 305, (1956).

[113] P. Schaeffer, *Symposia Soc. Exptl. Biol.* **No. 12,** 60 (1958).
[114] R. Balassa, *Acta Microbiol. Acad. Sci. Hung.* **2,** 51 (1954); *ibid.* **4,** 77 (1957).
[115] R. Balassa, *Naturwissenschaften* **42,** 422 (1955).
[116] R. Pakula, E. Hulanicka, and W. Walczak, *Bull. acad. polon. sci.* **6,** 325 (1958).
[117] B. W. Catlin, *Science* **131,** 608 (1960).
[118] J. Marmur, E. Seaman, and J. Levine, *J. Bacteriol.* **85,** 461 (1963).
[119] P. Schaeffer, *Ann. inst. Pasteur* **94,** 167 (1958).
[120] A. W. Ravin, *Bacteriol. Revs.* **24,** 201 (1960).
[121] P. Schaeffer, Ph. D. Thesis, University of Paris, 1961.
[122] D. M. Green, *Exptl. Cell Research* **18,** 466 (1959).
[123] K. Szende, T. Sik, F. Ordögh, and B. Györffy, *Biochim. et Biophys. Acta* **47,** 215 (1961).
[124] A. D. Kaiser, *J. Mol. Biol.* **4,** 275 (1962).
[125] G. P. Berry and H. M. Dedrick, *J. Bacteriol.* **31,** 50 (1936); *ibid.* **32,** 356 (1936).
[126] R. E. Gardner and R. R. Hyde, *J. Infectious Diseases* **71,** 47 (1942).
[127] M. H. D. Smith, *Ann. N. Y. Acad. Sci.* **54,** 1141 (1952).
[128] L. Kilham, *Proc. Soc. Exptl. Biol. Med.* **95,** 59 (1957).
[128a] W. K. Joklik, P. Abel and I. H. Holmes, *Nature* **186,** 992 (1960).
[129] S. M. Gartler, *Nature* **184,** 1505 (1959).
[130] K. G. Bensch and D. W. King, *Science* **133,** 381 (1961).
[131] E. Bohrenfreund and A. Bendich, *J. Biophys. Biochem. Cytol.* **9,** 81 (1961).
[132] L. M. Kraus, *Nature* **192,** 1055 (1961).
[133] F. M. Sinsheimer and D. J. Hutchison, *Biochim. et Biophys. Acta* **36,** 246 (1959).
[134] M. H. F. Wilkins, A. R. Stokes, and H. R. Wilson, *Nature* **171,** 738 (1953); *ibid.* **172,** 759 (1953).
[135] R. E. Franklin and R. G. Gosling, *Nature* **171,** 740 (1953).
[136] J. D. Watson and F. H. C. Crick, *Nature* **171,** 737, 964 (1953).
[137] J. D. Watson and F. H. C. Crick, *Cold Spring Harbor Symposia Quant. Biol.* **18,** 123 (1953).
[138] L. D. Hamilton, R. K. Barclay, M. H. F. Wilkins, G. L. Brown, H. R. Wilson, D. A. Marvin, H. Ephrussi-Taylor, and N. S. Simmons, *J. Biophys. Biochem. Cytol.* **5,** 397 (1959).
[139] P. Schaeffer, R. S. Edgar, and R. Rolfe, *Compt. rend. soc. biol.* **154,** 1978 (1960).
[140] M. E. Reichmann, S. A. Rice, C. A. Thomas, and P. Doty, *J. Am. Chem. Soc.* **76,** 3047 (1954).
[141] S. H. Goodgal and R. M. Herriott, *J. Gen. Physiol.* **44,** 1229 (1961).
[142] M. S. Fox, *Biochim. et Biophys. Acta* **26,** 83 (1957).
[143] R. M. Herriott and S. H. Goodgal, personal communication.
[144] E. Freese, *Cold Spring Harbor Symposia Quant. Biol.* **23,** 13 (1958).
[145] A. D. Hershey and E. Burgi, *J. Mol. Biol.* **2,** 143 (1960).
[146] P. F. Davison, *Proc. Natl. Acad. Sci. U.S.* **45,** 1560 (1959).
[147] P. F. Davison, *Nature* **185,** 918 (1960).
[148] C. Levinthal and P. F. Davison, *J. Mol. Biol.* **3,** 674 (1961).
[149] I. Rubinstein, C. A. Thomas, and A. D. Hershey, *Proc. Natl. Acad. Sci. U.S.* **47,** 1113 (1961).
[150] P. F. Davison, D. Freifelder, R. Hede, and C. Levinthal, *Proc. Natl. Acad. Sci. U.S.* **47,** 1123 (1961).
[151] J. Cairns, *J. Mol. Biol.* **3,** 756 (1961).
[152] P. Doty, *Harvey Lectures Ser.* **55,** 103 (1959–1960).
[153] J. Eigner, C. Schildkraut, and P. Doty, *Biochim. et Biophys. Acta* **55,** 13 (1962).
[154] C. Levinthal and C. A. Thomas, *Biochim. et Biophys. Acta* **23,** 453 (1957).
[155] C. E. Hall and P. Doty, *J. Am. Chem. Soc.* **80,** 1269 (1958).

[156] J. Cairns, *J. Mol. Biol.* **4,** 407 (1962).
[157] A. Kleinschmidt, D. Lang, and R. K. Zahn, *Z. Naturforsch.* **16b,** 730 (1961).
[158] F. Jacob and E. L. Wollman, *Symposia Soc. Exptl. Biol.* **No. 12,** 75 (1958).
[159] K. Y. Lee, R. Wahl, and E. Barbu, *Ann. inst. Pasteur* **91,** 212 (1956).
[160] A. N. Belozersky and A. S. Spirin, *in* "The Nucleic Acids" (E. Chargaff and J. N. Davidson, eds.), Vol. 3, p. 147. Academic Press, New York, 1960.
[161] N. Sueoka, *J. Mol. Biol.* **3,** 31 (1961).
[162] R. Rolfe and M. Meselson, *Proc. Natl. Acad. Sci. U.S.* **45,** 1039 (1959).
[163] N. Sueoka, J. Marmur, and P. Doty, *Nature* **183,** 1429 (1959).
[164] P. Doty, J. Marmur, and N. Sueoka, *Brookhaven Symposia in Biol.* **No. 12,** 1 (1959).
[165] J. Marmur and P. Doty, *Nature* **183,** 1427 (1959).
[166] J. Marmur and P. Doty, *J. Mol. Biol.* **5,** 109 (1962).
[167] C. L. Schildkraut, J. Marmur, and P. Doty, *J. Mol. Biol.* **4,** 430 (1962).
[168] M. Meselson, F. W. Stahl, and J. Vinograd, *Proc. Natl. Acad. Sci. U.S.* **43,** 581 (1957).
[169] R. Rolfe and H. Ephrussi-Taylor, *Proc. Natl. Acad. Sci. U.S.* **47,** 1450 (1961).
[170] A. W. Ravin and H. Ephrussi-Taylor, *1st Ann. Meeting, Am. Soc. Cellular Biol.* (1961).
[171] H. Ephrussi-Taylor, *Proc. Intern. Congr. Biochem., 3rd Brussels,* (1955).
[172] L. S. Lerman, *Cold Spring Harbor Symposia Quant. Biol.* **21,** 46 (1956).
[173] A. Bendich, H. B. Pahl, and S. M. Beiser, *Cold Spring Harbor Symposia Quant. Biol.* **21,** 31 (1956).
[174] S. M. Beiser, H. B. Pahl, H. S. Rosenkranz, and A. Bendich, *Biochim. et Biophys. Acta* **34,** 497 (1959).
[175] J. D. Mandell and A. D. Hershey, *Anal. Biochem.* **1,** 66 (1960).
[176] N. Sueoka and T. Y. Cheng, *J. Mol. Biol.* **4,** 161 (1962).
[177] F. Lanni, *Bacteriol. Proc. (Soc. Am. Bacteriologists)* p. 45 (1959).
[178] J. Marmur, C. L. Schildkraut, and P. Doty, *in* "The Molecular Basis of Neoplasia," p. 9. 15th Ann. Symposium on Fundamental Cancer Research, Houston, Texas, Univ. Texas Press, Austin, Texas, 1961.
[179] C. L. Schildkraut, J. Marmur, and P. Doty, *J. Mol. Biol.* **3,** 595 (1961).
[180] J. Marmur and P. Doty, *J. Mol. Biol.* **3,** 585 (1961).
[181] M. Delbrück and G. S. Stent, *in* "The Chemical Basis of Heredity" (W. D. McElroy and B. Glass, eds.), p. 699. Johns Hopkins Press, Baltimore, Maryland, 1957.
[182] M. Meselson and F. W. Stahl, *Proc. Natl. Acad. Sci. U.S.* **44,** 671 (1958).
[183] C. Levinthal and C. A. Thomas, *in* "The Chemical Basis of Heredity" (W. D. McElroy and B. Glass, eds.), p. 737. Johns Hopkins Press, Baltimore, Maryland, 1957.
[184] R. Rolfe, *J. Mol. Biol.* **4,** 22 (1962).
[185] L. F. Cavalieri and B. H. Rosenberg, *Biophys. J.* **1,** 317, 323, 337 (1961).
[186] L. F. Cavalieri, R. Finston, and B. H. Rosenberg, *Nature* **189,** 833 (1961).
[187] C. E. Hall and L. F. Cavalieri, *J. Biophys. Biochem. Cytol.* **10,** 347 (1960).
[188] M. H. F. Wilkins, *J. chim. phys.* **58,** 891 (1961).
[189] V. Luzzati, D. Luzzati, and F. Masson, *J. Mol. Biol.* **5,** 375 (1962).
[190] H. Ephrussi-Taylor, *J. chim. phys.* **58,** 1090 (1961).
[191] I. R. Lehman, *Ann. N. Y. Acad. Sci.* **81,** 745 (1959).
[192] F. J. Bollum, *J. Biol. Chem.* **234,** 2733 (1959).
[193] E. McFall and G. S. Stent, *Biochim. et Biophys. Acta* **34,** 580 (1959).
[194] F. E. Abbo and A. B. Pardee, *Biochim. et Biophys. Acta* **39,** 478 (1960).
[195] M. Schaechter, M. W. Bentzon, and O. Maaløe, *Nature* **183,** 1207 (1959).
[196] O. Maaløe, *Cold Spring Harbor Symposia Quant. Biol.* **26,** 45 (1961).

[197] L. S. Lerman and L. J. Tolmach, *Biochim. et Biophys. Acta* **33**, 371 (1959).
[198] M. Roger and R. D. Hotchkiss, *Proc. Natl. Acad. Sci. U.S.* **47**, 653 (1961).
[199] S. A. Rice and P. Doty, *J. Am. Chem. Soc.* **79**, 3937 (1957).
[200] R. Thomas, *Experientia* **7**, 261 (1951).
[201] R. Thomas, *Biochim. et Biophys. Acta* **14**, 231 (1954).
[202] P. Doty, J. Marmur, J. Eigner, and C. Schildkraut, *Proc. Natl. Acad. Sci. U.S.* **46**, 461 (1960).
[203] V. Luzzati, *J. chim. phys.* **58**, 899 (1961).
[204] M. Beer and C. A. Thomas, Jr., *J. Mol. Biol.* **3**, 699 (1961).
[205] E. P. Geiduschek, *J. Mol. Biol.* **4**, 467 (1962).
[206] S. Zamenhof, G. Leidy, S. Greer, and E. Hahn, *J. Bacteriol.* **74**, 194 (1957).
[207] W. Ginoza and B. H. Zimm, *Proc. Natl. Acad. Sci. U.S.* **47**, 639 (1961).
[208] W. Ginoza and W. R. Guild, *Proc. Natl. Acad. Sci. U.S.* **47**, 633 (1961).
[209] S. Greer and S. Zamenhof, *J. Mol. Biol.* **4**, 123 (1962).
[210] J. Eigner, H. Boedtker, and G. Michaels, *Biochim. et Biophys. Acta* **51**, 165 (1961).
[211] C. A. Sluis and J. H. Stuy, *Biochem. Biophys. Research Communs.* **7**, 213 (1962).
[212] S. Lacks and R. D. Hotchkiss, *Biochim. et Biophys. Acta* **39**, 508 (1960).
[213] J. Marmur and D. Lane, *Proc. Natl. Acad. Sci. U.S.* **46**, 453 (1960).
[214] R. M. Herriott, *Proc. Natl. Acad. Sci. U.S.* **47**, 146 (1961).
[215] R. M. Herriott, *J. chim. phys.* **58**, 1103 (1961).
[216] R. Rownd, J. Lanyi, and P. Doty, *Biochim. et Biophys. Acta* **53**, 225 (1961).
[217] W. R. Guild, *Proc. Natl. Acad. Sci. U.S.* **47**, 1560 (1961).
[218] S. G. Laland, W. A. Lee, W. G. Overend, and A. R. Peacoke, *Biochim. et Biophys. Acta* **14**, 356 (1954).
[219] P. Doty, B. B. McGill, and S. A. Rice, *Proc. Natl. Acad. Sci. U.S.* **44**, 432 (1958).
[220] L. F. Cavalieri, *J. Am. Chem. Soc.* **79**, 5319 (1957).
[221] J. H. Stuy, Ph. D. Thesis, University of Utrecht, Netherlands, 1961.
[222] B. H. Rosenberg, F. M. Sirotnak, and L. F. Cavalieri, *Proc. Natl. Acad. Sci. U.S.* **45**, 144 (1959).
[223] D. Shugar, in "The Nucleic Acids" (E. Chargaff and J. N. Davidson, eds.), Vol. 3, p. 39. Academic Press, New York, 1960.
[224] W. Berends, *J. chim. phys.* **58**, 1034 (1961).
[225] A. Wacker, *J. chim. phys.* **58**, 1041 (1961).
[226] J. Marmur and L. Grossman, *Proc. Natl. Acad. Sci. U.S.* **47**, 778 (1961).
[227] L. Grossman, D. Stollar, and K. Herrington, *J. chim. phys.* **58**, 1078 (1961).
[228] J. Marmur, W. F. Anderson, L. Matthews, K. Berns, E. Gajewska, D. Lane, and P. Doty, *J. Cellular Comp. Physiol. Suppl.* 1, **58**, 33 (1961).
[229] C. S. Rupert, S. H. Goodgal, and R. M. Herriott, *J. Gen. Physiol.* **41**, 451 (1958).
[230] C. S. Rupert, *J. Gen. Physiol.* **43**, 573 (1960); **45**, 703, 725 (1962).
[231] D. L. Wulff and C. S. Rupert, *Biochem. Biophys. Research Communs.* **7**, 237 (1962).
[232] N. Rebeyrotte and R. Latarjet, *Strahlentherapie* **111**, 85 (1960).
[233] R. M. Litman, *J. chim. phys.* **58**, 997 (1961).
[234] C. S. Rupert and S. H. Goodgal, *Nature* **185**, 556 (1960).
[235] R. M. Litman and H. Ephrussi-Taylor, *Compt. rend. acad. sci.* **249**, 838 (1959).
[236] J. H. Stuy, *Photochem. Photobiol.* **1**, 41 (1962).
[237] R. Pakula, E. Hulanicka, and W. Walczak, *Bull. acad. polon. sci.* **7**, 217 (1959).
[238] H. Ephrussi-Taylor and R. Latarjet, *Biochim. et Biophys. Acta* **16**, 183 (1955).
[238a] J. Marmur and D. J. Fluke, *Arch. Biochem. Biophys.* **57**, 506 (1955).
[239] W. R. Guild and F. M. Defilippes, *Biochim. et Biophys. Acta* **26**, 241 (1957).
[240] R. Latarjet, H. Ephrussi-Taylor, and N. Rebeyrotte, *Radiation Research Suppl.* **1**, 417 (1959).

150 PIERRE SCHAEFFER

241 D. J. Fluke, R. Drew, and E. C. Pollard, *Proc. Natl. Acad. Sci. U.S.* **38**, 180 (1952).
242 J. H. Stuy, *Biochem. Biophys. Research Communs.* **6**, 328 (1962).
243 E. P. Geiduschek, *Proc. Natl. Acad. Sci. U.S.* **47**, 951 (1961).
244 R. M. Herriott, *J. Gen. Physiol.* **32**, 221 (1948).
245 P. D. Lawley, *J. chim. phys.* **58**, 1011 (1961).
246 J. Marmur and P. O. P. Ts'o, *Biochim. et Biophys. Acta* **51**, 32 (1961).
247 H. Fraenkel-Conrat, *Biochim. et Biophys. Acta* **15**, 307 (1954).
248 L. Grossman, S. S. Levine, and W. S. Allison, *J. Mol. Biol.* **3**, 47 (1961).
249 D. Stollar and L. Grossman, *J. Mol. Biol.* **4**, 31 (1962).
250 K. I. Berns and C. A. Thomas, *J. Mol. Biol.* **3**, 289 (1961).
251 L. S. Lerman, *J. Mol. Biol.* **3**, 18 (1961).
252 V. Luzzati, F. Masson, and L. S. Lerman, *J. Mol. Biol.* **3**, 634 (1961).
253 L. A. Heppel and J. C. Rabinowitz, *Ann. Rev. Biochem.* **27**, 613 (1958).
254 M. Laskowski, *Ann. N. Y. Acad. Sci.* **81**, 776 (1959).
255 I. R. Lehman, *J. Biol. Chem.* **235**, 1479 (1960).
256 S. H. Goodgal and R. M. Herriott, *in* "The Chemical Basis of Heredity" (W. D. McElroy and B. Glass, eds.), p. 336. Johns Hopkins Press, Baltimore, Maryland, 1957.
257 P. Schaeffer, *Compt. rend. acad. sci.* **245**, 230 (1957).
258 P. Schaeffer, *Compt. rend. acad. sci.* **245**, 375 (1957).
259 G. S. Stent and C. R. Fuerst, *Advances in Biol. Med. Phys.* **7**, 1 (1960).
260 M. S. Fox, *Proc. Natl. Acad. Sci. U.S.* **48**, 1043 (1962).
261 J. Marmur and C. L. Schildkraut, *Nature* **189**, 636 (1961).
262 F. Weygand, A. Wacker, and H. Dellweg, *Z. Naturforsch.* **7b**, 19 (1952).
263 D. B. Dunn, J. D. Smith, S. Zamenhof, and G. Griboff, *Nature* **174**, 305 (1954).
264 D. B. Dunn and J. D. Smith, *Biochem. J.* **67**, 494 (1957).
265 S. Zamenhof, B. Reiner, R. De Giovanni, and K. Rich, *J. Biol. Chem.* **219**, 165 (1956).
266 S. Zamenhof, K. Rich, and R. De Giovanni, *J. Biol. Chem.* **232**, 651 (1958).
267 S. Zamenhof, *Ann. N. Y. Acad. Sci.* **81**, 784 (1959).
268 A. Wacker, S. Kirschfeld, D. Hartmann, and D. Weinblum, *J. Mol. Biol.* **2**, 69 (1960).
269 A. Wacker, S. Kirschfeld, and D. Weinblum, *J. Mol. Biol.* **2**, 72 (1960).
270 A. Wacker, S. Kirschfeld, and L. Träger, *J. Mol. Biol.* **2**, 241 (1960).
271 W. Szybalski, Z. Opara-Kubinska, and E. Ephrati-Elizur, *Federation Proc.* **19**, 306 (1960).
272 E. Ephrati-Elizur and S. Zamenhof, *Nature* **184**, 472 (1959).
273 W. Szybalski, Z. Opara-Kubinska, Z. Lorkiewicz, E. Ephrati-Elizur, and S. Zamenhof, *Nature* **188**, 743 (1960).
274 H. S. Shapiro and E. Chargaff, *Nature* **188**, 62 (1960).
275 A. Tomasz and E. Borek, *Proc. Natl. Acad. Sci.* **46**, 324 (1960).
276 R. D. Hotchkiss, *in* "Enzymes: Units of Biological Structure and Function" (O. H. Gaebler, ed.), p. 119. Academic Press, New York, 1956.
277 M. McCarty, H. E. Taylor, and O. T. Avery, *Cold Spring Harbor Symposia Quant. Biol.* **11**, 177 (1946).
278 S. H. Goodgal and R. M. Herriott, *J. Gen. Physiol.* **44**, 1201 (1961).
279 M. H. Adams and A. S. Roe, *J. Bacteriol.* **49**, 401 (1945).
280 H. P. Rappaport and W. R. Guild, *J. Bacteriol.* **78**, 203 (1959).
281 M. B. Talmadge and R. M. Herriott, *Biochem. Biophys. Research Communs.* **2**, 203 (1960).
282 L. O. Butler, *J. Gen. Microbiol.* **27**, 51 (1962).

[283] B. W. Catlin and G. G. Schloer, *J. Bacteriol.* **83**, 470 (1962).

[284] R. D. Hotchkiss and H. Ephrussi-Taylor, *Federation Proc.* **10**, 200 (1951).

[285] H. E. Alexander and G. Leidy, *J. Exptl. Med.* **93**, 345 (1951).

[286] M. Kohiyama and H. Saito, *Biochim. et Biophys. Acta* **41**, 180 (1960).

[287] R. D. Hotchkiss, *Proc. Natl. Acad. Sci. U.S.* **40**, 49 (1954).

[288] R. Balassa, *Acta Microbiol. Acad. Sci. Hung.* **4**, 85 (1957).

[289] R. Thomas, *Biochem. J.* **66**, 38 P (1957).

[290] R. Thomas, *Biochim. et Biophys. Acta* **40**, 50 (1960).

[291] I. Masamune, M. Abe, and D. Mizuno, *Japan. J. Med. Sci. & Biol.* **13**, 23 (1960).

[292] M. McCarthy, *J. Exptl. Med.* **88**, 181 (1948).

[293] B. W. Catlin and L. S. Cunningham, *J. Gen. Microbiol.* **19**, 522 (1958).

[294] J. Spizizen, *in* "Spores II" (H. O. Halvorson, ed.), p. 142. Burgess, Minneapolis, Minnesota, 1961.

[295] R. Wahl, J. Huppert, and L. Emerique-Blum, *Compt. rend. acad. sci.* **250**, 4227 (1960).

[296] P. H. Hofschneider, *Z. Naturforsch.* **15b**, 441 (1960).

[297] G. D. Guthrie and R. L. Sinsheimer, *J. Mol. Biol.* **2**, 297 (1960).

[298] F. Meyer, R. S. Mackal, M. Tao, and E. A. Evans, Jr., *J. Biol. Chem.* **236**, 1141 (1961).

[299] R. L. Sinsheimer, B. Starman, C. Wagler, and S. Guthrie, *J. Mol. Biol.* **4**, 142 (1962).

[300] J. Fouace and J. Huppert, *Compt. rend. acad. sci.* **254**, 4387 (1962).

[301] J. Huppert, R. Wahl, and L. Emerique-Blum, *Biochim. et Biophys. Acta* **55**, 182 (1962).

[302] R. M. Herriott, *Science* **134**, 256 (1961).

[303] P. Schaeffer, *Compt. rend. acad. sci.* **245**, 451 (1957).

[304] J. Lederberg and J. St. Clair, *J. Bacteriol.* **75**, 143 (1958).

[305] E. Chargaff, H. M. Schulman, and H. S. Shapiro, *Nature* **180**, 851 (1957).

[306] F. Gros and P. Schaeffer, unpublished results.

[307] S. Goodgal, *Intern. Congr. Genet. 10th Montreal*, **2**, 100 (1958).

[308] B. D. Hall and S. Spiegelman, *Proc. Natl. Acad. Sci. U.S.* **47**, 137 (1961).

[309] S. Spiegelman and B. D. Hall, *Proc. Natl. Acad. Sci. U.S.* **47**, 1135 (1961).

[310] E. P. Geiduschek, T. Nakamoto, and S. B. Weiss, *Proc. Natl. Acad. Sci. U.S.* **47**, 1405 (1961).

[311] E. P. Geiduschek, J. W. Moohr, and S. B. Weiss, *Proc. Natl. Acad. Sci. U.S.* **48**, 1078 (1962).

[312] M. S. Fox, *Nature* **187**, 1006 (1960).

[313] S. Lacks, *J. Mol. Biol.* **5**, 119 (1962).

[314] H. Ephrussi-Taylor, *Compt. rend. soc. biol.* **154**, 1951 (1960).

[315] M. J. Voll and S. H. Goodgal, *Proc. Natl. Acad. Sci. U.S.* **47**, 505 (1961).

[316] R. Pakula, E. Hulanicka, and W. Walczak, *Bull. acad. polon. sci.* **8**, 49 (1960).

[317] R. L. Sinsheimer, personal communication, 1959.

[318] F. Gros and R. D. Hotchkiss, quoted in reference 65, unpublished.

[319] R. Pakula, E. Hulanicka-Bankowska, and W. Walczak, *Bull. acad. polon. sci.* **8**, 269 (1960).

[320] G. Zubay, *Proc. Natl. Acad. Sci. U.S.* **48**, 456 (1962).

[321] W. Arber and D. Dussoix, *J. Mol. Biol.* **5**, 18 (1962).

[322] D. Dussoix and W. Arber, *J. Mol. Biol.* **5**, 37 (1962).

[323] R. Austrian, H. P. Bernheimer, E. E. B. Smith, and G. T. Mills, *J. Exptl. Med.* **110**, 585 (1959).

[324] G. T. Mills and E. E. B. Smith, *Brit. Med. Bull.* **18**, 27 (1962).

[325] G. Pontecorvo, *Symposia Soc. Exptl. Biol.* **No. 6,** 218 (1952).

[326] S. Benzer, *in* "The Chemical Basis of Heredity" (W. D. McElroy and B. Glass, eds.), p. 70. Johns Hopkins Press, Baltimore, Maryland, 1957.

[327] G. Balassa and G. Prévot, *J. Theoret. Biol.* **3,** 315 (1962).

[328] S. H. Goodgal and R. M. Herriott, *Genetics* **42,** 372 (1957).

[329] R. D. Hotchkiss, *Symposia Soc. Exptl. Biol.* **No. 12,** 49 (1958).

[330] R. D. Hotchkiss and A. H. Evans, *Cold Spring Harbor Symposia Quant. Biol.* **23,** 85 (1958).

[331] V. N. İyer and A. W. Ravin, *Bacteriol. Proc.* (*Soc. Am. Bacteriologists*) p. 44 (1962).

[332] L. S. Lerman, *Intern. Congr. Genet. 10th Montreal,* **2,** 164 (1958).

[333] M. S. Fox and R. D. Hotchkiss, *Nature* **187,** 1002 (1960).

[334] H. Ephrussi-Taylor, *in* "Microbial Genetics." *Symposium Soc. Gen. Microbiol.* **10,** 132 (1960).

[335] A. W. Ravin, *Genetics* **45,** 1387 (1960).

[336] J. Lederberg, *J. Cellular Comp. Physiol.* **45,** Suppl. 2, 75 (1955).

[337] M. Meselson and J. J. Weigle, *Proc. Natl. Acad. Sci. U.S.* **47,** 857 (1961).

[338] G. Kellenberger, M. L. Zichichi, and J. J. Weigle, *Proc. Natl. Acad. Sci. U.S.* **47,** 869 (1961).

[339] Quoted in W. Szybalski, *J. chim. phys.* **58,** 1098 (1961).

[340] G. Balassa, *Ann. inst. Pasteur* **102,** 547 (1962).

[341] R. Austrian, *Bull. Johns Hopkins Hosp.* **90,** 170 (1952).

[342] C. M. MacLeod and M. R. Krauss, *J. Exptl. Med.* **103,** 623 (1956).

[343] S. Jackson, C. M. MacLeod, and M. R. Krauss, *J. Exptl. Med.* **109,** 429 (1959).

[344] G. Leidy, E. Hahn, and H. E. Alexander, *J. Exptl. Med.* **97,** 467 (1953).

[345] R. Austrian and H. P. Bernheimer, *J. Exptl. Med.* **110,** 571 (1959).

[346] R. Austrian and H. P. Bernheimer, *in* "The Chemical Basis of Heredity" (W. D. McElroy and B. Glass, eds.), p. 346. Johns Hopkins Press, Baltimore, Maryland, 1957.

[347] R. Austrian, H. P. Bernheimer, E. E. B. Smith, and G. T. Mills, *Cold Spring Harbor Symposia Quant. Biol.* **23,** 99 (1958).

[347a] A. M. Campbell, *Adv. Genet.* **11,** 101 (1962).

[347b] F. Jacob and E. L. Wollman, *in* "Recent Progress in Microbiology" (G. Tuneval, ed.), p. 15. Almqvist and Wiksell, Stockholm, 1959.

[348] M. Abe, *Japan. J. Med. Sci. & Biol.* **12,** 441 (1959).

[349] S. Lacks and R. D. Hotchkiss, *Biochim. et Biophys. Acta* **45,** 155 (1960).

[350] B. A. D. Stocker, N. D. Zinder, and J. Lederberg, *J. Gen. Microbiol.* **9,** 410 (1953).

[351] F. Jacob, P. Schaeffer, and E. L. Wollman, *in* "Microbial Genetics." *Symposium Soc. Gen. Microbiol.* **10,** 67 (1960).

[352] W. B. Wood and P. Berg, *Proc. Natl. Acad. Sci. U. S.* **48,** 94 (1962).

[353] M. S. Fox, *J. Gen. Physiol.* **42,** 737 (1959).

[353a] M. Abe and D. Mizuno, *Biochim. et Biophys. Acta* **32,** 464 (1959).

[354] S. M. Beiser and R. D. Hotchkiss, *Federation Proc.* **13,** 486 (1954).

[355] K. Hashimoto, *Japan. J. Microbiol.* **1,** 1 (1957).

[356] I. C. Hsu and R. M. Herriott, *J. Gen. Physiol.* **45,** 197 (1961).

[357] B. E. Bryan, *J. Bacteriol.* **82,** 461 (1961).

[358] R. Balassa and M. Gabor, *Mikrobiologiya* **30,** 457 (1961).

[359] R. Pakula and E. Hulanicka-Bankowska, *Bull. acad. polon. sci.* **9,** 79 (1961).

[360] F. M. Sirotnak, R. B. Lunt, and D. J. Hutchison, *J. Bacteriol.* **80,** 648 (1960).

[361] F. M. Sirotnak, R. B. Lunt, and D. J. Hutchison, *Nature* **187,** 800 (1960).

[362] P. Schaeffer, H. Ionesco, and F. Jacob, *Compt. rend. acad. sci.* **249,** 577 (1959).

[363] A. Ryter, H. Ionesco, and P. Schaeffer, *Compt. rend. acad. sci.* **252,** 3675 (1961).

[364] J. Szulmajster and P. Schaeffer, *Biochem. Biophys. Research Communs.* **6,** 217 (1961).

[165] D. S. Nasser and H. Koffler, *Bacteriol. Proc. (Soc. Am. Bacteriologists)* **62,** 43 (1962).

[366] W. C. McDonald and T. S. Matney, *Bacteriol. Proc. (Soc. Am. Bacteriologists)* **62,** 43 (1962).

[367] J. Marmur, *Biochim. et Biophys. Acta* **38,** 342 (1960).

[368] R. Balassa, *M.T.A. Agrártud. Osztálykõzl.* **2,** 307 (1953), as quoted in G. Balassa, *Bacteriol. Revs.* **27,** 228 (1963).

[369] R. Balassa, *Naturwissenschaften* **43,** 133 (1956).

[370] R. Balassa, *Acta Microbiol. Acad. Sci. Hung.* **4,** 77 (1957).

[371] G. Balassa, *Bacteriol. Revs.,* **27,** 228 (1963).

[372] R. Austrian and M. S. Colowick, *Bull. Johns Hopkins Hosp.* **92,** 375 (1953).

[373] H. Ephrussi-Taylor, *Exptl. Cell Research* **6,** 94 (1954).

[374] S. Udaka, J. Koukol, and R. Vennesland, *J. Bacteriol.* **78,** 714 (1959).

[375] R. D. Hotchkiss and A. H. Evans, *in* "Drug Resistance in Microorganisms" (G. E. W. Wolstenholme and C. M. O'Connor, eds.), p. 183. Churchill, London. 1957.

[376] R. D. Hotchkiss and A. H. Evans, *Federation Proc.* **19,** 912 (1960).

CHAPTER 4

Bacterial Episomes

PATRICE DRISKELL-ZAMENHOF[*, †]

I. Introduction: The Episome Concept

In bacteria, the existence of varied mechanisms of genetic transfer and in particular the special properties of the process of sexual conjugation have made possible the recognition of a new class of genetic elements. These elements, differing both from normal chromosomal structures and from plasmids (cytoplasmic elements able to reproduce in an autonomous fashion[1]), may control quite different bacterial characters, but manifest similar properties and behave similarly in bacterial crosses. The consideration of such similarities led Jacob and Wollman[2] to form a new concept and to propose the term *episomic elements* or *episomes* to designate genetic elements of an accessory nature, structures which appear to be additions to a cell's genome and which, within this host cell, may be established in two distinct, possibly mutually exclusive states: the autonomous, independently replicating, cytoplasmic state and the integrated or chromosomally attached state.

In the past two or three years, episomic elements have been the subject of much discussion. The reader is referred in particular to the works of

* Unpublished work of the author was supported by Grant No. E 2317 from the National Institutes of Health to the University of California, Berkeley.

† This manuscript was prepared during support by Grant No. 01760 from the National Institutes of Health to Columbia University, New York.

Jacob *et al.*,[3] of Jacob and Wollman,[4] of Campbell,[5] of Smith and Stocker,[6] of Sneath,[7] and of Watanabe.[8] The role of some episomic elements in bacterial conjugation is discussed by Clark and Adelberg,[9] and is further described by Gross in Chapter 1 of the present volume. It is the intention of the author of the present chapter to confine herself to presentation and illustration of the episome concept, to discussion of the properties of those genetic elements considered to be episomic in nature, and to discussion of their possible role in nuclear-cytoplasmic interrelationships. It is to be hoped that consideration of the most current pertinent literature available lends value to a review which might otherwise be considered repetitious.

II. General Properties of Bacterial Episomes

Five types of genetic units which exhibit certain common properties considered to be characteristic of episomic elements have been studied in bacteria: temperate bacteriophages or, more specifically, the genetic material thereof; sex factors or fertility factors; genetic determinants for the production of antibacterial agents called colicins; genetic elements involved in the infectious heredity of multiple drug resistance in the Enterobacteriaceae, and a transmission element controlling the infectious transfer of the lactose determinant in *Salmonella typhosa*. Jacob and Wollman[4] have discussed the properties these genetic elements share which permit their designation as episomic. Such characteristics will be summarized here.

The properties controlled by episomes are, under normal conditions, nonessential as the genetic elements may be either present in, or absent from, bacterial cells. Lysogeny, fertility in bacterial crosses, the production of certain antibiotics, and drug resistance may all be dispensed with in nature without detriment to the continued functional existence of a bacterial cell.

The spontaneous acquisition of an episomal element is not observed. Genetic transfer by conjugation, transduction, or perhaps transformation from a bacterial cell harboring episomic elements to a cell from which they are absent is required, except in the case of infective temperate bacteriophages.

Episomes may be present in a host bacterium either in the autonomous or in the integrated state. In general, the integrated state appears to proscribe the autonomous, although alternation of episomes between the two states does occur.

The autonomous state of an episomic element is characterized by its transfer independently of the bacterial chromosome during conjugation, by its capacity for spontaneous elimination[3] or elimination following treatment of its host cell with salts of heavy metals,[10] acridine dyes,[11] or other agents, and by a host cell phenotype peculiar to the episome concerned.

The integrated state of an episome is characterized by the linkage relationships with chromosomal markers it exhibits in bacterial crosses, and by its relative insensitivity to dyes and metal salts.

Episomic elements in the integrated state do not appear to form part of the structural continuum of the bacterial chromosome, but are attached to it and may participate in genetic recombination with an adjacent chromosomal region.

Thus far, all genetic elements considered to be episomic have been shown to possess the ability to mediate the transfer of bacterial genes from one cell to another.

III. The Bacterial Episomes

The clearest and best-defined examples of episomic elements, the episomic prototypes, are the temperate bacteriophages, coliphage lambda (λ) in particular. The properties exhibited by these genetic elements which led to the formulation of the episome concept will be discussed in some detail. Other nonviral episomic elements will be similarly discussed within limits of current knowledge.

A. TEMPERATE BACTERIOPHAGES

Detailed discussion of temperate bacteriophages and of the lysogenic state of their bacterial hosts may be found in the reviews of Lwoff,[12] of Bertani,[13] of Jacob and Wollman,[14] and of Whitfield.[15] Campbell[5] has devoted considerable discussion to temperate phages as episomes. In the present discussion, the characteristics of temperate phages, bacteriophage λ in particular, as episomes rather than as viral elements will be stressed.

The genetic material of a temperate phage can establish a stable association with that of its host cell, and is thus an element of extrinsic nature added to a host cell's genome. A given bacterial strain may be lysogenic or not; hence the temperate phage is dispensable. Two alternative series of events may occur in a suitable host cell upon the introduction of a temperate phage genome: the latter may enter the autonomous (vegetative) state or the integrated (prophage) state.

1. THE AUTONOMOUS STATE

The autonomous state of this episomic element is characterized by its unrestricted replication which occurs more rapidly than that of the genome of its host. Full functional expression of the episome during the autonomous state results in death and lysis of the host with concomitant release of infectious phage particles. Studies by Jacob et al.[16] and by Jacob[17] on defective phage genomes, in which a mutation prevents the completion of one of the stages involved in the production of mature, infectious phage, have revealed the control exerted by the phage genome over events occurring during the vegetative cycle of phage development. New cellular syntheses permitting vegetative multiplication of the phage are apparently induced, e.g., the early protein synthesis reported by Thomas[18] to be necessary for vegetative multiplication of temperate coliphage λ, and the phage genome seems to establish its own enzymic replication pattern. Synthesis of the protein components of the mature phage and the production of organized infectious particles are also subject to control by the genetic material of the phage. In the autonomous state, therefore, the temperate phage may be visualized as being insensitive to cellular mechanisms of control and as determining new types of functions in the host.

In the vegetative phase, the phage genome can be eliminated from members of a bacterial population by treatment with heat[19] or with chloramphenicol.[20]

As the consideration of viral functions manifested in the vegetative state is beyond the scope of the present work, the reader is referred to the reviews of Kellenberger[21] and of Séchaud[22] for discussions of vegetative phage multiplication and maturation and of the intracellular development of bacteriophage λ, respectively.

2. THE INTEGRATED STATE

In the integrated or prophage state, the phage genome is intimately associated with the genome of its host and behaves as a bacterial constituent, replicating in coordination with the division of the host bacterium. In most cases, only one prophage is associated with the single chromosome of each bacterial nucleus.[23-25] The viral potentialities of the phage genome are not expressed and the synthesis of phage components and infective particles does not occur. The information necessary for the production of mature phage is retained, however, and progeny of such lysogenic cells are capable of liberating infectious particles without additional infection.
[12, 13, 26, 27]

a. Sites of Prophage Attachment. The early experiments of Lederberg and Lederberg,[28] Wollman,[29] and Appleyard,[30] employing bacterial crosses of lysogenic and nonlysogenic strains of *Escherichia coli* K12, suggested that the property of lysogeny for bacteriophage λ was under the control of a chromosomal determinant which was the prophage itself. Subsequent to clarification of the processes of genetic transfer during conjugation of *E. coli* K12, a complete analysis of the genetic determination of the lysogenic state which confirmed the early results was reported by Jacob and Wollman.[27] Crosses between lysogenic parents each carrying a different mutant λ prophage showed segregation patterns of the prophage characters among recombinants indicating that the prophage sites were allelic and linked to determinants controlling the fermentation of galactose. The λ prophage itself was shown to be the determinant of λ lysogeny and to occupy a specific position on the bacterial chromosome: linked to the gal_b cistron which controls phosphogalactotransferase.[31-33]

Similar genetic analysis has been extended to a series of different prophages of *E. coli*, and each was found to occupy a unique position on the bacterial chromosome, with an interesting exception: no specific point of attachment to the bacterial chromosome could be assigned to the prophage of phage 363, the only one studied known to be able to carry out transduction of known genetic markers.[34]

Genetic determinations of the sites of attachment of other prophages have been reported by Frédéricq,[35] Bertani,[13] Bertani and Six,[36] and Wollman and Jacob.[31]

b. Mode of Prophage Attachment. The precise structural arrangement of a prophage with respect to its specific chromosomal site remains undefined. Bertani[13] has described in some detail a number of possible structural relationships between the prophage and the bacterial chromosome, but of the models proposed, only one appears to be favored by the greater part of the recent experimental evidence: The prophage does not replace an allelic segment of the nonlysogenic host genome by some manner of crossing-over. The prophage is an addition to the host chromosome, fixed in some manner at a specific site thereof. The entire length of the prophage is not inserted into the structural continuity of the chromosome; it appears that the prophage and the chromosome actually are structurally independent. The prophage seems to be adherent to or synapsed with its chromosomal receptor site in a stable manner.

That the prophage is not substituted for an allelic chromosomal segment is illustrated by the fact that bacteria rendered nonlysogenic by exposure to ultraviolet light[31] or by the decay of radiophosphorus atoms incorporated into their DNA molecules[27] may be relysogenized with the same phage (or a mutant thereof) with normal efficiency. Loss of the prophage would represent a deletion, assuming the allelic substitution hypothesis to be correct, and relysogenization would not be possible. Since this is obviously not the case, one must conclude that the prophage is an added rather than a replacing structure.

The complete insertion of the prophage into the chromosomal continuum would have two predictable results if the phage genome were located between two closely linked host markers: In bacterial crosses, bacteria carrying mutants of the prophage should exhibit recombination patterns of the two markers correlated with recombinational events occurring between the prophage markers, and the apparent linkage between the two bacterial markers should be decreased as a result of the intercalation of the prophage material. Experimental data are not in agreement with the hypothesis of complete insertion.

Jacob and Wollman[27] crossed lysogenic strains of *E. coli* K12 which carried different multiple mutants of phage λ in order to determine whether correlation existed between recombination of prophage markers and recombination of bacterial markers on either side of the phage genome. Recombination between the prophage markers was observed to be considerably more frequent than recombination between the outside bacterial markers, and although an orientation of the prophage with respect to the bacterial chromosome was indicated, independence of prophage λ with regard to the chromosome was suggested. Calef and Licciardello,[37] employing similar techniques, found that the distribution of prophage markers among bacteria recombinant for the bacterial markers located on either side of the prophage indicated a linear arrangement of the prophage markers with respect to the bacterial markers. However, the order of prophage markers is different from that determined in genetic experiments with vegetative λ mutants. This anomalous behavior of the prophage does not suggest complete insertion. For an alternate point of view, see Campbell.[5]

Jacob and Wollman,[34] employing transduction experiments using phage 363 as a vector, have located the site of phage 18 between two closely linked methionine markers in a chromosomal region where linkage relationships with other markers have been well defined. In bacterial crosses, no difference was found in the recombination frequencies between the two methionine markers whether both parents were nonlysogenic or lysogenic for phage 18. Insertion of phage 18 in its entirety in the continuity of the bacterial chromosome is thus unlikely. Bacterial crosses also yielded results indicating that prophage 18 behaves as a genetic element of a definite length which overlaps one of the methionone markers without altering its function. It is difficult to conceive of such an overlap being compatible with total insertion of the prophage into the bacterial linkage group.

Convincing direct evidence is lacking either for or against partial insertion of the phage genome into the physical structure of the bacterial chromosome. However, two lines of indirect evidence strongly suggest the structural independence of prophage and bacterial chromosome.

1. As stated, nonlysogenic cells can be recovered among the survivors of bacterial populations undergoing the decay of incorporated radiophosphorus.[27] These nonlysogenic bacteria retain no trace of the lysogenic state, and no genetic marker from the prophage can be recovered or even detected by superinfection with mutant phages. The prophage is lost as a whole, but the structural integrity of the now nonlysogenic bacterial chromosome is apparently retained.

2. Further suggestive evidence for the structural independence of pro-

phage and bacterial chromosome may be found in studies of the λ-mediated transduction of bacterial genes controlling galactose (*gal*) utilization.[38, 39] This phenomenon of restricted *gal* transduction is discussed in Chapter 2 of the present volume. Suffice it to say here that a λ prophage can on occasion recombine with the adjacent region of the host cell's chromosome with the resultant replacement of a segment of prophage genome with the closely linked *gal* markers controlling the utilization of galactose. The recombinant prophage, λdg, is hence defective, but can lysogenize *gal⁻* recipients with the production of defectively lysogenic, phenotypically *gal⁺* clones. Such transductants are heterogenotes carrying the *gal⁻* allele in the bacterial chromosome and the *gal⁺* allele as part of the prophage. These heterogenotes constantly give rise to nonlysogenic, *gal⁻* haploid segregants as the λdg prophage is lost as a whole. One can conclude that in these strains the λdg prophage is not an integral part of the chromosome, but is attached to it.

If adherence or attachment of the prophage to the bacterial chromosome represents the most likely structural relationship, the problem of total or partial association must be considered. In the case of prophage 18, Jacob and Wollman[34] have suggested that the phage genome is synapsed over the totality, or the major part, of its length with its host chromosome. Different methods of genetic analysis positioned this prophage at different, although very closely linked, sites. It was proposed that the two locations found corresponded to the extremities of its attachment to the bacterial chromosome.

In contrast, a limited segment of the λ chromosome appears to be involved in the attachment of the prophage to the bacterial chromosome. Kaiser,[40] employing crosses between mutants of λ in which the capacity to lysogenize is lost, has demonstrated that lysogenization (attachment of the prophage to the bacterial chromosome) is controlled by a short segment of the phage linkage group, the *C* region. This small region is located at about the middle of the linkage group, which is thus divided into arms, each bearing genetic loci having other bacteriophage functions pertaining to the production of mature phage particles. Levine[41] has found a similar situation to pertain to the case of the temperate phage P22 of *Salmonella*. Kaiser and Jacob[42] have shown that the *C* region also controls the specificity of prophage location on the bacterial chromosome. Prophage 434 is attached to a different chromosomal region than is λ. Recombinants of a 434 × λ cross having a 434 *C* region surrounded by a predominantly λ genome have been isolated, and have been found to lysogenize at the site specific for phage 434, not that specific for λ.

The nature of the stable attachment of prophages to their chromosomal receptor sites is as yet undefined. Jacob and Wollman[43] have pointed out that although a λdg prophage retains the *C* region of the phage genome, which corresponds to a specific site of the bacterial chromosome, and also carries a bacterial segment homologous with a portion of the bacterial genome, the linkage of λdg to the chromosome is much less stable than that of a normal prophage. It was suggested that a prophage and the corresponding region of the host chromosome are not homologous, but in some way complementary structures. However, more recent evidence indicates that there is homology between phage λ itself and the bacterial chromosome.[43a] A certain extent of molecular hybridization[43b] can occur, i.e., some complementarity is exhibited, between the DNA (deoxyribonucleic acid) of λ and the messenger RNA[43c] of *E. coli*. As messenger RNA (ribonucleic acid) is believed to consist of sequences of bases complementary to base sequences in its template DNA, homology between at least some λ DNA base sequences and *E. coli* DNA base sequences is indicated.

Available evidence thus favors the picture of prophages as added structures, located on the bacterial chromosome but not incorporated into it. Admittedly, the number of lysogenic systems studied has been small, and extension of findings in these systems to others may be unjustifiable. The mode of attachment of phage genome to bacterial chromosome may differ among prophages. It may vary between the extremes of complete insertion and homologous or complementary pairing. Although prophage λ appears to be superficially, although stably, attached to the chromosome, other prophages of *E. coli* may be associated in quite another manner. Jacob and Wollman[27] observed that the amount of prophage material that could be inactivated by the decay of P^{32} independently of the bacterial chromosome was small in the case of certain prophages, and that no nonlysogenic cells appeared among the survivors of P^{32}-labeled cells lysogenic for these phages. Such prophages may actually be inserted into the continuity of the host genome. However, in the absence of evidence to the contrary, this reviewer will continue to regard the integrated state of the episomic element λ as one of some degree of structural independence.

Campbell,[5] while not strongly favoring insertion hypotheses, gives extensive consideration to them, and has proposed new mechanisms which, although based on hypothesis, are nevertheless ingenious.

c. Immunity and Repression. The so-called immunity of lysogenic bacteria is one of the criteria of the lysogenic state. Viral functions, those involved in the production of mature, infectious phage particles, are prevented, whether the genetic material controlling these functions be present in the prophage or be introduced into the lysogenic cell by superinfection with homologous, or mutant, bacteriophages. The prophage genes controlling functions which are characterized as viral are repressed, an obvious requirement for the maintenance of the lysogenic state. The expression of early function necessary for the initiation of vegetative phage multiplication is prevented, and phage-specific protein components are not synthesized during the growth of lysogenic bacteria. Superinfection immunity, the inability of a lysogenic cell to support the lytic growth of homologous or mutant phages, does not involve the inability of the superinfecting phages to adsorb to the lysogenic cell nor the inability of these phages to inject their genetic material, but rather involves the prevention of phage multiplication. The superinfecting phage genome neither replicates nor is degraded, but is slowly diluted out of the infected cell and its progeny during bacterial growth.[44, 45] The mechanisms involved in superinfection immunity and in repression of the viral functions of prophage genes may very well be identical.

A considerable amount of evidence has been presented indicating that immunity is expressed cytoplasmically through the mediation of a specific immunity substance, a repressor. Studies of transient zygotes formed during bacterial crosses between λ-lysogenic and nonlysogenic cells have provided some of this evidence. When lysogenic donors and nonlysogenic recipient cells are used, transfer of the chromosomally attached prophage into the recipient causes the prophage to enter the vegetative state, and the zygote is lysed. This phenomenon, termed *zygotic* induction, [46, 47] does not occur if the zygote if formed by mating either a nonlysogenic or a lysogenic donor with a lysogenic recipient. The vegetative state is not induced and the zygotes not only remain viable, but also exhibit immunity against superinfection with phage λ. As the type of conjugation employed involves the transfer of chromosomal elements but of little or no cytoplasmic material,[48] one may conclude that immunity is expressed by a cytoplasmic factor in the lysogenic cell, and that zygotic induction is in effect a release of the viral prophage genes from repression.[17]

Corroborative evidence was obtained by the preparation by a means to be discussed subsequently of heterogenotic partial diploid cells with the genetic constitutions $gal^-(\lambda)^+/gal^+(\lambda)^-$ and $gal^-(\lambda)^-/gal^+(\lambda)^+$.[3] Both types of cells exhibit immunity patterns identical to those of normal haploid cells lysogenic for λ, and can give rise to $(\lambda)^-$ nonimmune segregants. This segregation of sensitive cells from immune ones indicates that the property of immunity is dominant over nonimmunity and is expressed in the cell cytoplasm.

Studies of noninducible (ind^-) mutants of phage λ by Jacob and Campbell[49] give convincing support to the proposition that the immunity of lysogenic bacteria is conferred by the formation of a specific cytoplasmic repressor substance, the synthesis of which is controlled genetically by the prophage. Normal λ prophages (ind^+) are induced to enter the vegetative phase by exposure of their lysogenic host cells to ultraviolet light.[12] However, ind^- λ prophages are not induced by ultraviolet light although they are still subject to zygotic induction. Bacterial cells doubly lysogenic for λ ind^+ and λ ind^- prophages or λ ind^+/λ ind^- diploid cells cannot be induced by ultraviolet treatment, indicating the dominance of the ind^- character over the ind^+ character. If cells lysogenic for λ ind^+ are induced with ultraviolet light and immediately superinfected with λ ind^- phage, vegetative reproduction of the normal λ prophage is prevented. The repression of vegetative replication was seen to be specific. Only prophages exhibiting the λ immunity pattern are prevented from entering the vegetative phase after ultraviolet induction by superinfection of their host cells with the λ ind^- mutant phage. These observations were interpreted as indicating that λ ind^- mutant phages control the production of a product that reverses or overcomes the effects of induction, that they bring about the formation of a cytoplasmic repressor in larger quantity or of greater stability than do normal λ prophages.

The genetic determination of immunity and repression in the bacteriophage λ-$E.$ $coli$ system has been well defined. However, a thorough discussion of the subject is beyond the scope of the present review, and a summary of salient points must suffice.

As stated previously, the C region of the λ linkage group has been found not only to control the capacity of the phage to lysogenize, but also to determine the specific site of prophage attachment. Kaiser[40] has shown that three functional units of the C region (C_I, C_{II}, and C_{III}) must cooperate in the establishment of lysogeny. The C_{II} and C_{III} units function early in the process and are necessary for lysogenization, while the C_I unit functions late, and its continued activity is necessary for maintenance of the lysogenic state. Kaiser and Jacob[42] have demonstrated that the C region also determines both immunity and the sensitivity to immunity, i.e., both the capacity of a prophage to generate specific immunity upon its host bacterium and the sensitive response of a newly introduced phage genome to the immunity of the lysogenic cell are controlled by the C region of the phage linkage group. More specifically, the determinants of immunity are localized in the C_I region.

The so-called "clear mutants" of phage λ arise through mutational events in the C_I region. These C_I mutants are unable to lysogenize or to grow in lysogenic cells, as they still respond to the immunity conferred upon a host by wild-type λ. Plaques of these mutants on a sensitive indicator strain of $E.$ $coli$ are clear, in contrast to the turbid plaques elicited by wild-type λ. Kaiser[40] has shown that C_I mutants may lysogenize in mixed infection with C_I^+ phages, producing $C_I C_I^+$ doubly lysogenic clones. C_I^+ but never C_I single lysogens may be recovered among segregants, suggesting that the C_I^+ character is dominant over the C_I character. The

C_I locus thus may control the synthesis of an active repressor, and C_I mutants may be characterized by the inability to do so.[43]

Virulent inducer mutants of λ are unable to establish lysogeny, but do overcome immunity and can grow on bacteria lysogenic for normal λ. This virulent character (V) has been shown to be a result of multiple genetic changes, one of which is positioned in the C_I region.[42, 50] The V character is dominant to the V^+ character and may represent an inability to respond to immunity, a loss of sensitivity to a repressor.[43]

The previously mentioned noninducible (ind^-) mutation of λ has been located at a particular site of the C_I locus. The capacity of an ind^- mutant to inhibit the induction of vegetative phage development in bacteria lysogenic for λind^+ does not depend on the genetic constitution of the phage genome carrying the mutation except in the case of $C_I ind^-$ double mutants: these mutants can no longer inhibit induction. The ind^- mutation thus appears to affect the function which is eliminated by the C_I mutations, the synthesis of functional repressor.[49]

The above findings, confirmed by recent work of Sussman and Jacob,[51] strongly suggest that the specific repression of viral functions in lysogenic bacteria is determined by a regulator gene, C_I, of the prophage itself

Although detailed analysis such as the foregoing has not yet been carried out, similar situations of immunity and repression appear to pertain in the case of other temperate phage-bacterium systems, namely, those of the Salmonella phage P22,[52] and of coliphages P1[53] and P2.[13]

The nature and mode of action of the cytoplasmic repressor assuring specific immunity in lysogenic systems are still in doubt. There is available some indirect evidence that the repressor comprises RNA, at least in part.

The synthesis of repressor can apparently take place in the presence of inhibitors of protein synthesis. Lysogenization of sensitive cells following infection by temperate phage is actually favored by addition of chloramphenicol to the system.[13, 54] Zygotic induction of λ prophage is prevented in the presence of chloramphenicol, although the transfer of chromosome from lysogenic donor to sensitive recipient is inhibited to little or no extent.[49] Levine and Cox[55] have reported that E. coli cells carrying λ and S. typhimurium cells lysogenic for the prophage of phage PLT22 are protected against induction of vegetative phage development by treatment with chloramphenicol before treatment with inducing agents. These results, together with those of Jacob and Campbell,[49] indicate an accumulation of repressor, in the apparent absence of protein synthesis, which prevents prophage induction. Levine and Cox found that pretreatment with chloramphenicol plus 5-fluorodeoxyuridine also provided repression of prophage induction. However, pretreatment with chloramphenicol plus 6-azauracil failed to elicit the accumulation of repressing material. It was concluded that the repressor is RNA-like.

Corroborative evidence for the RNA nature of the repressor has been reported by Fisher.[56] Bacterial crosses were employed during which some transfer of cytoplasmic material from donor to recipient cells apparently occurs, and it was found that if donors lysogenic for λ are mated with non-lysogenic recipients, the latter are passively immunized against super-infection with λ phage as well as against zygotic induction from λ prophage injected as a chromosomal element.[57] Lysogenic donor cells were grown in the presence of inhibitors of protein, DNA, and RNA synthesis. Inhibitors of both protein and DNA synthesis had no apparent effect on the ability of the donor cells to immunize. However, growth in the presence of inhibitors of RNA synthesis brought about a significant decrease in the ability of donor cells to immunize recipients. It was considered likely that the repressor is RNA.

In contrast, Jacob et al.[58] have recently suggested that the repressor consists of a protein or polypeptide, or at least contains a protein or poly-peptide component. Indirect evidence was presented indicating that the expression of the C_I regulator gene of the bacteriophage linkage group involves the formation of a polypeptide as the gene product.

The effects of certain suppressor mutations, those believed to act at the level of polypeptide formation,[59, 60] on various mutations of the C_I locus were studied. It is known[61] that some mutations affecting structural genes of λ prevent its multiplication in a strain of E. coli (112) which can neither ferment galactose, synthesize cysteine, nor synthesize histidine. However, multiplication is not prevented in mutants of 112 (112-Su) which carry a suppressor gene which restores both the ability to ferment galactose and to synthesize cysteine.[62] Of 300 independently isolated C_I mutants of the noninducible mutant λind^- which form clear plaques on 112 as a result of failure to produce an active repressor and hence to lysogenize,[49] 11 were observed to produce turbid plaques on 112-Su, i.e., were able to lysogenize. It thus appeared that certain types of bacterial suppressors affecting struc-tural genes of λ can restore the C_I^+ phenotype of some C_I alleles, which were designated C_{ISu_a}.

That the system of repression is actually involved was shown by induc-tion of 112 $(\lambda)^+$ and 112-Su $(\lambda)^+$ by ultraviolet light with subsequent superinfection of both strains with the ind^- C_{ISu_a} mutant. Vegetative development of λ^+ bacteriophage was inhibited only in 112-Su $(\lambda)^+$; the C_I mutation was overcome.

These results were taken to imply that the expression of the C_I regulator gene, as in the case of genes of structure, involves the translation of informa-tion into a polypeptide as the product of expression. In view of the functions believed to be performed by the repressor, the suggestion was made that it is a product of low molecular weight, hence is not likely to be an enzyme synthesizing the repressor but rather the repressor itself or a constituent thereof.

The view was expressed that such findings are not incompatible with the observation that repression can be established in the presence of inhibitors of protein synthesis, if a very small number of repressor molecules are sufficient to provide complete repression. Under conditions of inhibition of the synthesis of protein, RNA messengers[63, 64] of the C_I gene may accumulate in such a fashion that a small number of repressor molecules can be formed almost immediately upon relief of inhibition, resulting in full and immediate repression. That repressor molecules are indeed present in small numbers in lysogenic cells is suggested by the apparent breakdown of immunity in lysogens when exposed to large multiplicities of superinfecting homologous phage.[58, 65] Infecting phage genomes appear to tie up repressor molecules, which may be present in numbers on the order of 30 per cell.

The observations reported by Jacob et al.[58] are not incompatible with the findings that inhibitors of RNA synthesis interfere with the production of repressor, if a type of RNA is a constituent of the repressor or if the synthesis of messenger RNA is prevented by the inhibitors employed.

Although a considerable body of suggestive evidence has been presented, direct evidence has yet to be provided that the repressor involved in systems of phage-specific immunity is RNA, protein, or a complex of the two materials.

d. Recombination with the Bacterial Chromosome. Of all the temperate phages studied, only lamboid phages of *E. coli* K12 have been shown to participate in genetic recombination with an adjacent chromosomal region while in the attached, or prophage, state. The discovery by Morse[66] of specific or restricted transduction mediated by phage λ provided the background for the subsequent genetic and physical studies clarifying the nature of such a genetic interaction between prophage and bacterial chromosome.

Morse et al.[38, 39] have shown that when vegetative phage production is induced by ultraviolet light in *E. coli* K12 *gal*$^+$ (λ)$^+$ cells, a small proportion of the phage liberated (10^{-4} to 10^{-6}) are capable of transferring genes for galactose fermentation from the original host bacteria into *gal*$^-$ recipients which are subsequently lysogenized. The *gal*$^+$ transductants are heterogenotes, partial diploids carrying two sets of galactose markers: i.e., their own and those introduced by the transducing phages. Lysates from λ-lysogenic cells containing this low proportion of transducing phage are designated LFT (low frequency transducing). Morse[67] has recently shown that roughly the same proportion of *gal*-transducing phages occur in spontaneous lysates. Ultraviolet induction thus appears to augment the production of phage in general, not transducing phage in particular.

The multiplicities of infection usually employed for transduction with LFT lysates provide for infection of the transductants with normal, non-transducing λ. The heterogenotes are thus doubly lysogenic. Upon induction, such heterogenotes release transducing phage and normal phage in approximately equal numbers. These lysates are designated HFT (high frequency transducing).

The *gal* genes, which are closely linked to the specific attachment site of prophage λ, are the only markers known to be transduced by λ. In addition, transducing particles occur only in λ lysates prepared by induction of λ-lysogenic cells, not in lysates prepared by lytic, external infection of sensitive cells with λ. It thus seems likely that the interaction of λ in the prophage state with the *gal* region of the bacterial chromosome is responsible for the production of transducing elements in which a stable association between phage and bacterial genetic material exists.

The nature of the transducing elements in an HFT lysate has been the subject of extensive investigation. Transducing λ phages are defective. They can lysogenize and confer specific immunity upon their host cells, but are unable to multiply vegetatively and produce infectious particles unless in the presence of normal, "helper" phage. Such *gal*-transducing λ phages are designated λdg (λ-defective-galactose).[68, 69]

In λdg, it appears that a segment of the phage chromosome has been replaced by the segment of bacterial chromosome carrying the *gal* markers. Genetic studies of Arber[70] have shown that λdg lacks a large piece of phage genome in the middle of the mapped linkage group of the phage. This segment amounts to approximately one-fourth of the total length of the linkage map.

Weiglé *et al.*[71] have reported that independently arising populations of λdg each have a characteristic density, and supposedly a characteristic DNA content per particle, some being more dense and some being less dense than normal λ. Campbell[72, 73] has shown that independently arising lines of λdg differ in their content of λ genetic markers, i.e., differ in the length of the deleted chromosomal segment. The missing regions all contain a common segment, however. In general, the densities of different lines of λdg were found to increase with increasing length of the terminal segment still present in the λdg genome.

More recently, attention has been given to the nature of *gal*-transducing λ elements present in LFT lysates. Weiglé[74] found that the transducing particles in LFT lysates include a variety of classes with altered densities, and that they transmit their particular densities to the λdg phages of HFT lysates derived from them, the λdg densities remaining constant. A large proportion of the LFT transducing phages were found to be defective, and it was suggested that they are identical to the λdg elements of HFT lysates.

In contrast, Fraser[75] has reported that density changes can occur during the course of formation of an HFT transducing λdg from an LFT element in a transduced clone. These changes in density are ascribed to recombinational events occurring between LFT elements and the normal λ phage necessary as "helpers" in LFT transductional events. Genetic studies indicate that HFT particles, i.e., λdg particles, differ from at least some LFT elements in that the former carry a genetic marker not present in the latter, derived presumably from a normal helper phage. It thus appears that not all LFT transducing phages are of the λdg type.

The mechanism of the original recombinational event between prophage and bacterial chromosome remains undefined. Weiglé et al.[71] suggested that a process analogous to double crossing-over is involved. This seems unlikely in view of the variety of densities exhibited by transducing particles in LFT lysates. The recombinational event thus appears to be nonreciprocal rather than one of simple recombination between homologous areas of the phage chromosome and the bacterial chromosome. Genetic studies of Campbell[76] led to the conclusion that the recombination between λ prophage and the bacterial chromosome may involve unequal crossing-over or translocation, or that the homologies between the λ chromosome and the bacterial chromosome are so extremely poor as to prevent normal pairing.

More recently, a different scheme was proposed by Campbell[5] to account for the formation of λdg and also to account for the anomalies of the genetic map of λ in the prophage state reported by Calef and Licciardello.[37] A reversible circularization of genetic material was suggested to account for the various properties of the genetic map of vegetative λ, prophage λ, and transducing λ. The assumption was made that λ prophage is inserted into the chromosome and that breaks at the original insertion sites restore normal λ upon induction. Rare and unique breaks at different points would then account for the production of transducing λ. This scheme is further developed by Campbell in Chapter 2 of the present volume.

Whatever be the nature of the recombinational event occurring during the production of transducing λ, it should be pointed out that although a segment of the bacterial chromosome can be incorporated into the genome of λ, the converse incorporation has never been encountered.

3. ALTERNATION OF NUCLEAR AND CYTOPLASMIC STATES

The capacity of temperate bacteriophages to undergo transition from the autonomous state to the integrated state, the capacity to lysogenize, is genetically controlled by the phage itself. However, the varied responses of sensitive bacterial cells elicited by infection with temperate phage are governed by nongenetic factors, i.e., the variability of bacterial responses is of a phenotypic nature. Upon infection of a sensitive population by temperate phage, several different series of events may occur.[19] In a fraction of the population, the productive or lytic response is elicited, resulting in cell lysis and the production of new phage particles. In another fraction, the lysogenic or reductive response may occur, resulting in the production of lysogenic clones from the infected cells. Another very small fraction may respond in a refractory manner, surviving without becoming lysogenic. A lethal response, cell death without the release of phage, may occur rarely.

The relative frequencies of occurrence of the major response patterns are determined by the physiological state of the cells and by the conditions under which infection is carried out. The frequency of lysogenization can be increased by lowering the temperature from 37° to 20°C.,[77] by employing high multiplicities of infection,[78] and by exposing phage-bacterium complexes to inhibitors of protein synthesis or to proflavin immediately after infection.[54, 79] The particular stage of a cell in the division cycle also appears to influence the determination of the lysogenic response. Lark and Maaløe[80] showed that the frequency of lysogenization is doubled when a cell is infected during the phase of nuclear doubling.

The currently held view[19, 52, 53] is that lysogenization represents nongenetic and genetic interactions between phage and infected cells. The former involves the physiological decision made by the cell, whether to give the lytic or lysogenic response upon infection; the latter involves the processes attendant to attachment of the phage genome to the chromosome of its host, the "reduction" of the newly introduced phage genome to the prophage state.[12]

The decision not to lyse is made very early, during the first few minutes after infection and before the first cell division following infection. This is shown by the fact that variables which may shift the response toward the reductive or lytic are efficient only during the first 6 or 8 minutes following infection,[81] and by observations that the progeny of a single infected cell may include both lysogenic and nonlysogenic individuals, but rarely if ever include individuals exhibiting lytic as well as nonlytic responses.[19, 52] The decision not to lyse probably precedes reduction of the phage genome to prophage. Zinder[52] and Luria et al.[53] have shown that reduction very often does not occur until several generations after the initial infection.

However, the infecting phage does appear to initiate replication and multiply vegetatively to some extent before lysogenization occurs. This has been suggested by the observed effects of the decay of incorporated P^{32} on the development of temperate phage,[82] by the frequency of occurrence of recombinant prophages recovered from cells infected with phages of different genetic constitution, [13, 41, 53] and by the discovery of multiple lysogeny resulting from single infection.[83] In fact, some vegetative replication appears to be a prerequisite for lysogenization. Jacob et al.[16] and Arber[70] have shown that certain defective forms of phage λ which are unable to multiply vegetatively are essentially unable to establish lysogeny unless in mixed infection with normal, "helper" phage. The normal phage permits the defective one to multiply so that its subsequent reduction occurs. Lysogenic, immune recipients will not support this cooperative lysogenization.[69, 84]

Six,[85] employing the E. coli C-phage P2 system in which more than one phage can be carried at different sites, found that the frequency of the actual reductive event is low in an immune cell, being approximately 0.05 per superinfecting phage. The number of cells in which the infecting phage is reduced to prophage was seen to be proportional to the multiplicity of infection employed. If such a low probability of reduction pertains in other bacteriophage systems, the requirement for multiplication preceding lysogenization becomes somewhat more understandable.

Transition from the attached or integrated state to the autonomous state may occur spontaneously in a small fraction of a population of growing, lysogenic cells. The rate of spontaneous production of infective phage is constant for any given lysogenic strain, but varies between 10^{-2} and 10^{-5} depending on the particular prophage carried.[14] The mechanisms involved in this spontaneous transition to the vegetative state are as yet undefined.

Lwoff et al.[86] first noted that the treatment of certain lysogenic strains with ultraviolet (UV) light brought about lysis of the entire population and release of infective phage particles. This induction of the transition from the integrated to the autonomous state has subsequently been shown to be elicited by a variety of physical and chemical agents, as well as by manipulations of metabolic balance. In addition to ultraviolet light, X-rays[87] and γ-rays[88] are effective. Induction of vegetative phage development mediated by the decay of incorporated P^{32} has been reported.[89] Nitrogen mustards,[90, 91] organic peroxides, epoxides and ethyleneimines,[92] hydrogen peroxide,[92, 93] azaserine,[94] UV-irradiated leucovorin,[95] sodium thiolactate, glutathione, and sulfathiazole[91] have all been shown to act as inducers. The antitumor antibiotic, mitomycin C,[96] and the folic acid analog, aminopterin,[97] are efficient inducers. Transient thymine deprivation of thymine-requiring lysogenic cells also brings about massive induction of vegetative phage development.[98, 98a,b] The mechanism by which phage development is initiated after treatment of lysogenic bacteria with an inducing agent is obscure. Estimation of the size of the induction target by means of X-rays,[88] and analysis of induced and spontaneous phage production by doubly lysogenic cells[99] suggest that the primary effect is on the bacterial component of the lysogenic complex and that prophage development is a secondary effect. The nature of the various inducing agents found effective leads one to assume that host cell nucleic acids are involved. The observations of Melechen and Skaar[98] and of Ben-Gurion[97] indicate that, indeed, a disturbance of DNA synthesis is needed for induction, the former investigators noting that protein synthesis must accompany the inhibition of DNA synthesis. It would appear, therefore, that induction involves the upset of a delicate metabolic balance, which is somehow responsible for a change in the stable relationship between repressor molecules and prophage genes. The cross induction phenomenon, intercellular transfer of the inductive action of UV irradiation among lysogenic populations of *E. coli* K12, is unique to UV; hence the mode of action of this agent may be different from that of other inducing agents.[99a]

Induction may also be elicited by the transfer of a prophage into a sensitive, nonimmune cytoplasm either by transduction[100, 101] or by bacterial conjugation.[47] Such transfer induction is considered to occur as a result of the release of specific repression.

It must be noted that a genetic factor of sorts is involved in the transition from the attached to the vegetative state. Not all lysogenic systems can be induced to form vegetative phage. Inducible and noninducible strains have been isolated in the same bacterial species.[99, 102] The inducible character of a prophage appears to depend upon its specific site of attachment to the host chromosome. Noninducible prophages do give rise to vegetative phage spontaneously, although at a rate considerably lower than do inducible prophages.[14]

4. Phage-Controlled Host Cell Modifications

One of the most interesting properties of the episomic elements under discussion is their capacity to modify various characteristics of their hosts. In most cases, the only detectable differences between lysogenic and nonlysogenic derivatives of the same bacterial strain are the ability to liberate infectious phage particles and the exhibition of phage-specific immunity. In other systems, however, differences apparently unrelated to the lysogenic state have been observed.

One such difference is illustrated by the phenomenon of *interference*. The presence of a particular prophage may interfere with the capacity of lysogenic bacteria to support the vegetative replication of some entirely unrelated phages, which multiply normally on the corresponding nonlysogenic derivatives. Many examples of such interference phenomena have been described in various bacterial species[103, 104] (see review by Bertani[13]). Perhaps the most interesting example of this was reported by Benzer,[104a] who noted that *E. coli* (λ)$^+$ populations will not support the multiplication of certain mutants of phages T2, T4, and T6 (*rII* mutants), but will allow complete development of any other mutants of these virulent phages. The interference of prophage with *rII* phages is controlled by the *C* region of the former, and appears to be related to the attachment site specificity. Related lamboid phages having different sites of attachment do not exhibit interference with *rII* mutants.[27, 42]

Other differences between lysogenic and nonlysogenic cells of a given strain are attributable to the process of phage conversion, the modification of one or more host properties attendant to lysogenization or even infection by a particular temperate phage. The production of toxin by *Corynebacterium diphtheriae* is perhaps the most striking example of such a phenomenon. Freeman[105] observed that a great number of toxinogenic strains of this organism are lysogenic and liberate phage which can infect other strains which do not produce toxin or harbor prophages; the survivors of such an infection are "converted," they are toxinogenic and resistant to the phage. Subsequently, it has been established that toxinogeny can be passed from one strain to another by lysogenization, that toxinogeny is lost when the prophage is lost, and that toxinogeny and lysogeny are acquired simultaneously.[106, 107] The capacity to confer toxinogeny upon recipients is apparently restricted to a few temperate phages of *C. diptheriae*,[108-110] and it has been suggested[110] that this capacity segregates in crosses between related temperate phages.

Phage conversion also occurs in the genus *Bacillus*. The presence of a particular prophage in *B. megaterium* has been reported to modify colonial morphology. Loss of the prophage is correlated with restoration of normal morphology.[111]

In the genus *Salmonella*, the capacity to form new somatic antigens is conferred by the presence of certain prophages. Loss of the antigenic determinants is always found to be associated with loss of the prophage.[112, 113] The reader is referred to the papers of Robbins and Uchida[114, 115] for a summary of phage conversions in *Salmonella* species and for a discussion, in chemical terms, of the structural changes in somatic antigens brought about by some converting phages. Phage conversion involving an alteration of somatic antigens has also been reported in *Pseudomonas aeruginosa*.[115a]

The attached state of a converting phage is not necessarily prerequisite to its modification of host properties. In some cases, the converting function is expressed in the autonomous state. Barksdale[116] has found that the production of toxin in lysogenic cells of *C. diphtheriae* can be correlated with lytic development and production of free phage, and has recently suggested[116a] that bacteriophage synthesis, either following infection of sensitive cells or following induction of lysogens, is a prerequisite for toxinogenesis. In addition, Uetake *et al.*[117] have observed that certain *Salmonella* phages can cause the formation of new somatic antigens by their hosts within as little as 5 minutes after infection, even by hosts destined to lyse.

The phenomenon of phage conversion differs from that of transduction, although the two processes share some characteristics. In the former, every infecting particle is potentially able to confer a certain property on its host, whereas transducing phage usually occur at low frequencies in transducing lysates. In addition, and perhaps of most importance, conversion does not involve the transfer of known bacterial genes, as none of the properties conferred on a host by a converting phage have ever been observed to arise as a result of the mutation of bacterial genes. A detailed discussion of phage conversion in various bacterial species may be found in the review by Barksdale.[116]

Another host-cell modification dependent upon the presence of a particular prophage is the apparent diminution in virulence of strains of *Bacillus anthracis* lysogenic for certain mutants of phage W.[118] The modified pathogenicity of such strains is ascribed to a competition between the processes involved in prophage induction and those involved in the formation of capsular material necessary for maximum virulence, both series of events being induced by the high CO_2 tension in the mammalian body. The modification of the host is thus detrimental, making it much less likely to survive in a normal environment.

Other host-cell modifications, which may actually be instances of phage conversion, induced by temperate phages have been reported. In staphylococci, alterations in phage typing patterns, in susceptibility to penicillin, and the capacity to produce toxin are effected by lysogenization with appropriate phages.[118a] In *Bacillus cereus*, lysogeny and toxinogeny also appear to be interdependent.[118b]

5. Physical and Chemical Nature

All temperate phages in the free state thus far examined have been found to consist of DNA with a protein coat. The prophage presumably consists of phage DNA only. Free λ phage has a density of 1.508 g. per cubic centimeter,[71] a particle weight of 2.2×10^{-16} g.,[21] and a DNA content of 1.1×10^{-16} g. as measured by chemical means.[22] This latter value is in excellent agreement with the value of 2.3×10^5 DNA-phosphorus atoms determined by Stent and Fuerst.[119] The λ prophage genome contains the same amount of DNA as does the genome of the free phage, as demonstrated by their like sensitivities to the decay of incorporated radiophosphorus[120] and to ultraviolet irradiation.[101]

Phage P1 has a buoyant density of 1.482 g. per cubic centimeter.[121] It seems likely that phage P1 contains the same amount of DNA as does phage λ, as the UV sensitivities of the two are very much the same.[101]

Phage P22 has a buoyant density of 1.45 g. per cubic centimeter.[122] The DNA of P22 has been studied, and is found to have the properties expected for double-stranded molecules of molecular weight 40×10^6.[123] Hartman and Kozinski[124] observed that the rate of P^{32}-decay inactivation of P22 is approximately one-third of that of phage T4 labeled with the same specific radioactivity. As phage T4 contains 5×10^5 DNA-phosphorus atoms,[125] one may conclude that phage P22 contains about 1.7×10^5 DNA-phosphorus atoms.

B. FERTILITY FACTORS

Conjugation in *Escherichia coli* involves the transfer of genetic material from donors (males) to recipients (females), and is mediated by the establishment of specific male-female unions of mating cells and the subsequent formation of a cellular bridge between the conjugal partners through which the genetic material is transferred. The sexual differentiation of *E. coli* strains into males and females is determined genetically and physiologically, and is controlled by a fertility factor, or sex factor, F, present in male cells but absent from female cells (F^-).[127-130] Although female variants can arise in male populations, the converse situation has never been observed.

Bacterial conjugation and the role of F in the process have been the subject of recent reviews by Hayes *et al.*,[126] by Clark and Adelberg,[9] and by Gross (Chapter 1 of the present volume), and will not be discussed in detail here. The episomic nature of the fertility factor of *E. coli* K12 has been well established and, as it alone has been subjected to detailed analysis, will be the subject of the greater part of the present discussion.

1. THE AUTONOMOUS STATE

Male cells harboring F in the autonomous state are designated F^+. In contrast to the temperate bacteriophages, multiplication of F in the autonomous state is of no pathological consequence to host cells. With the exception of the rare production of F^- variants due to the irreversible loss of the sex factor, the F-bacterium association is a stable one.

That F is carried in an autonomous state by F^+ cells is shown by the fact that the introduction of a few such cells into a culture of female cells brings about a spread of the F^+ character throughout the entire population. The kinetics of this process of conversion indicate that the sex factor can multiply more rapidly than the genome of its host and exists in a number of copies greater than one in each initial F^+ male cell.[131, 131a] In genetic studies with F^+ donor cells,[130, 132, 133] F does not exhibit linkage to any chromosomal gene, and is thus regarded as an extrachromosomal element.

In the autonomous state, the sex factor can be efficiently eliminated from populations of F^+ cells by treatment with cobalt or nickel ions[10] or with acridine dyes.[11] Such cells rendered F^- are said to be disinfected or **cured**.

When F$^+$ donors and F$^-$ recipients are mixed in a bacterial cross, the rapid and efficient formation of mating couples may be observed microscopically.[128] As stated, F particles are then transferred efficiently from donors into female partners, thus converting them into males of the same type. Jacob and Wollman[135] and Sneath and Lederberg[136] have shown that a minimum time of 4 minutes is required for the transmission of F to begin under optimum conditions. In addition to F, F$^+$ donors can also transfer nongenetic, presumably cytoplasmic, materials to their conjugal partners. The transfer of ultraviolet-irradiation products which induce prophage λ,[134] and the transfer of the repressor of λ phage development[56, 57] have been reported.

The rapidity and efficiency with which autonomous F is transferred to recipient cells suggest that this genetic element is not randomly distributed in the cytoplasm of its host. It may be located at, or even in, the cell envelope, or else the processes involved in the establishment of specific cell contacts may induce some manner of mobilization and directed transmission of randomly distributed particles.

From such F$^+$ × F$^-$ crosses, recombinants which have received genetic determinants known to be located on the F$^+$ male chromosome can be isolated. The frequency of occurrence of recombinants is extremely low with respect to the observable frequency of conjugation. In some cases, only one recombinant clone may be selected for as many as one hundred thousand male cells involved in a cross. In F$^+$ cultures, then, only a very small proportion of cells are capable of transferring chromosomal material to recipients. Factors responsible for the low fertility of F$^+$ populations will be discussed subsequently.

2. THE INTEGRATED STATE

Cells harboring the sex factor in the attached or integrated state are designated Hfr (high frequency of recombination). Such males are isolated from F$^+$ populations and, when mated with females, rapidly form conjugal pairs and transfer chromosomal material at high frequency to recipients, recombinants for chromosomal genes thus issuing at high frequency from bacterial crosses. Autonomous F is not transmitted to recipients in such crosses and is thus not carried by Hfr males as an independently transferable element.[132, 137] The observation[11] that treatment with acridine dyes does not induce loss of the Hfr male character supports the conclusion that the Hfr male state is not controlled by autonomous F.

It has been established that all the cells of a given Hfr strain transfer their chromosomes in a specifically oriented manner, the leading locus, point of origin (O), being the same for all donor cells and being followed in order by a linear array of markers in a precise time sequence.[139-142] The determinant of maleness of the Hfr type, attached F, is transferred in linkage with bacterial genes located at the tail end of the chromosome, and is the last determinant to be transferred to zygotes.[141, 142] Inheritance of maleness of the Hfr type is thus a very infrequent event among recombinants, and requires for fullest expression the introduction by the donor of the point of origin as well as of attached F.[133]

a. Site of Chromosomal Attachment. In contrast to the specificity of attachment sites exhibited by numerous prophages, the sex factor may become attached at any one of a number of chromosomal locations; there is apparently little or no preference for a site of attachment. That this is the case was noted by Jacob and Wollman during studies of the nature of fertility of F+ cultures which led to their brilliant formulation of the currently held concepts of the structural organization of genetic information in *E. coli.*

It was proposed that the fertility of F+ cultures is attributable to the emergence of rare, spontaneous Hfr mutants in populations of F+ cells. The application of the fluctuation test of Luria and Delbrück[143] to F+ populations showed that the fertility of independent cultures of an F+ strain varied widely, whereas the fertility of different samples of the same culture was more or less equivalent, results strongly in support of the above view. For a discussion of other factors which may contribute to the fertility of F+ cultures, see Clark and Adelberg.[9] A large number of Hfr strains were isolated from clones of Hfr cells on a plate spread with F+ cells after location of the clones by replica plating[144] onto a selective medium spread with a culture of suitable recipients.[145] Upon mating with suitable recipients, a number of these new Hfr strains were observed to differ in the sequence of genetic markers transferred at high frequency. Although only one sequence was transferred by members of a given strain, chromosomal segments transferred by different strains were seen to be the reverse of one another, to overlap one another, or to show linkage of markers which in other strains appeared to be located near the two chromosomal extremities. Despite these unforeseen results, the relative positions of various bacterial markers with respect to one another were the same for all strains. It was concluded that the chromosome of F+ male cells is a closed, circular structure and that different Hfr strains are produced by breakage of the continuous structure at different points to form a linear structure transferable to recipients in the observed, oriented manners.[141]

The F+ to Hfr transition was thus considered to be the consequence of the stable attachment or integration of the sex factor at one of many possible, randomly chosen sites on the bacterial chromosome, predisposing the circular structure to open at the point of interaction into a linear structure bounded at one extremity by attached F, and at the other by O, the leading locus during conjugation.

The mode of attachment of F to the chromosome in Hfr cells is unknown. However, as will be discussed subsequently, complete insertion of the sex factor into the linear continuity of the bacterial chromosome may not be the case.

b. Recombination with the Bacterial Chromosome. Striking similarities between the sex factor and temperate phage genomes are further exemplified by the finding that the attached sex factor can occasionally incorporate an adjacent segment of the bacterial chromosome and return to the autonomous state, the new structure behaving thereafter as a single unit of replication. This process is quite analogous to the transduction of *gal* genes by phage λ.

That such an interaction between attached F and the bacterial chromosome may occur was first suggested by Adelberg and Burns,[146, 147] who isolated from a particular Hfr strain a variant harboring a new type of sex factor. Upon conjugation, this variant transfers its sex factor as an autonomous unit independently of the chromosomal markers which, however, are also transferred efficiently with the same order of injection as that of the original Hfr strain from which the variant was isolated. Recipient cells which receive this sex factor become males of the variant type, able to transfer the chromosome as well as the sex factor at high frequency and with the characteristic orientation of marker transfer. The attachment of the sex factor to the bacterial chromosome in the variant strains is an unstable one, kinetic studies of zygote formation indicating a rapid alternation between the attached and the cytoplasmic states.

Adelberg and Burns devised a numbering system for strains of the sex factor, the wild-type sex factor of *E. coli* K12 being designated F_1, and the new variant sex factor F_2. Unlike F_1, F_2 has a high affinity for the bacterial chromosome and has a preferential site of attachment, always attaching at a specific site between the loci *pro* (controlling proline synthesis) and *lac* (controlling lactose fermentation). F_2 thus appears to retain the "memory" of the chromosomal site at which the sex factor was attached in the original Hfr strain, a site closely linked to *lac*. Attachment of F_2 to the chromosome apparently does not affect the maintenance and free transmissibility of the autonomous population. It was proposed that F_2 arose by genetic exchange between attached F_1 and the bacterial chromosome followed by a return of the sex factor to the autonomous state. The incorporation of chromosomal material into F would then explain the high affinity exhibited by F_2 for the original site of attachment, and would, in strains harboring F_2, ensure specific homologous pairing with the bacterial chromosome and the consequent fixation of F_2 to its specific chromosomal site.

Studies of Driskell-Zamenhof and Adelberg[148] have shown that F_2 contains essential material in excess of that F_1 comprises. The sensitivity of the former to the decay of incorporated radiophosphorus at a given specific radioactivity is about twice that of the latter, in support of the contention that F_2 carries an incorporated segment of the bacterial chromosome.

Driskell[149] has demonstrated that F_2 is not merely a "mutant" form of F_1, and that the variant properties of the former are attributable solely to the presence in it of an incorporated chromosomal element conferring homology with the chromosome of the host cell. Introduction of F_2 into a strain carrying a deletion of the *lac* region resulted in the production of males indistinguishable from the classic K12 type, exhibiting low fertility and random order of injection of markers. In the absence of a host chromosomal segment homologous to that carried by F_2, this sex factor behaves precisely as does F_1, having a low and nonspecific affinity for the bacterial chromosome.

Acridine treatment of the strain in which F_2 first arose resulted in the production of F⁻ cells which were found to carry a locus which exhibits a high affinity for any sex factor subsequently introduced. The males thus produced are always of the F_2 type. This locus is located at the site of F attachment in the Hfr from which F_2 arose, and has been designated *sfa-2* (sex factor affinity).[147] It is believed to represent the incorporation of sex factor material into the bacterial chromosome, and to have been formed by genetic exchange between the attached sex factor and the chromosome during the formation of the variant F_2. The presence of this inserted material thus confers on the chromosome homology with autonomous sex factors, and determines the specific site of their attachment with the resultant production of donors with a particular point of origin. These views are supported by the finding that the *sfa-2* locus is cotransducible with the *lac* locus to an extent of about 30%, and that the transductants all become donors of the F_2 type upon infection with F_1.[149]

It appears therefore, in view of the increased size of F_2 over F_1, that the formation of F_2 involved an unequal genetic exchange between the attached sex factor and the bacterial chromosome, unequal crossing-over. However, the region of chromosomal homology carried by F_2 and the *sfa-2* locus of the original F_2 male strain may be replicas of regions retained in their normal positions in the original genetic elements.

Richter[150-152] has reported findings that may be interpreted in terms of the formation of an *sfa* locus. An unstable Hfr was produced during a UV-elicited mutation from *mal*⁺ (maltose) to *mal*⁻. Upon infection with F_1, rare F⁻ recombinants which had inherited terminal markers from the unstable Hfr became Hfr cells of a type identical to that of the original. It would appear that the rare F⁻ recombinants had inherited a part of integrated sex factor (the "Hfr₃ locus") which would segregate in subsequent crosses. The proposed recombinational event between F and the bacterial chromosome to produce the Hfr₃ locus, which event presumably occurred during the mal^+ to mal^- mutation, was not observed to be accompanied by a complementary alteration in the sex factor.

With the above background, a comment on the possible mode of attachment of F to the chromosome of Hfr cells may be interposed. Driskell-Zamenhof and Adelberg[148] employed P^{32}-labeled males as donors of F_1 or F_2, and unlabeled females carrying $sfa-2$ as recipients. After transfer of labeled F, the conversion mixture was stored at $-196°C$. and assayed daily for the proportion of "new males" present in the initially female component of the mixture. As expected, the proportion of new males decreased as P^{32} decay proceeded, the rate of P^{32}-decay inactivation of transferred F_2 being about twice that of transferred F_1. If, in the original Hfr strain in which F_2 arose, the determinant of maleness represented a total, linear insertion of F into the continuity of the chromosome, then the detachment and return to the autonomous state of the unit composed of F plus an additional chromosomal segment should yield a structure consisting of F with a piece of chromosomal material attached to one of its extremities. In the system employed, the homology with the bacterial chromosome conferred on F_2 by the presence of such chromosomal material is essentially unnecessary for expression of maleness by newly infected recipients, as they carry $sfa-2$, and become relatively high frequency donors even upon infection with F_1. Therefore, if the above structure pictured for F_2 is correct, one would expect that the rates of P^{32}-decay inactivation of F_2 and F_1 would be the same, as P^{32} disintegrations occurring in the chromosomal portion of F_2 would presumably have little or no effect on F function itself. As this is obviously not the case, one must conclude that the chromosomal segment contained in F_2 is intercalated into the F material, so that lethal P^{32} disintegrations causing scissions of DNA double helices[89] and occurring within the chromosomal component would result in disruption of the entire F_2 complex. The production of such a structure from a totally inserted sex factor is difficult to envisage. The most economical hypothesis is that, in the Hfr parent of the original F_2 strain at least, the sex factor is not inserted in its entirety into the structural continuity of the bacterial chromosome, but rather is attached (or partially inserted) in such a manner that a free "arm" is available for whatever events of unequal crossing-over or of errors in copying may take place (however, see Chapter 1 for Gross' hypothesis for the mode of attachment of F to the chromosome).

Following the initial discoveries of Adelberg and Burns, screenings of different Hfr cultures by various investigators[153, 154] resulted in the isolation of several variant strains harboring specific sex factors with characteristic sites of chromosomal attachment. Each variant sex factor, designated F′ (F prime) could be characterized by autonomous reproduction in its host cells, by its ability to be transferred serially from host to host, by its susceptibility to elimination by acridine dyes, and by the fact that each F′ factor could evoke at reasonably high frequency a characteristic pattern of transfer of chromosomal loci in the linkage sequence peculiar to the original Hfr from which it was derived. As the isolation from such an F′ population of a stable Hfr strain carrying integrated F has been reported,[154a] the F′ elements may also be regarded as episomes.

The isolation of such F′ strains led to the prediction that variant sex factors carrying a known genetic marker(s) and capable of serial transfer could be obtained from Hfr strains in which the particular marker was closely linked to attached F. Such F-bacterial marker complexes have indeed been obtained, the first of which was described by Jacob and Adelberg.[154] Selection for the premature entrance into recombinants of genes located at the terminal end of various Hfr linkage groups resulted in the isolation of strains harboring either an F-associated lactose marker (F-*lac*) or an F-associated proline marker (F-*pro*). These F′ strains are unstable, and segregate out cells exhibiting the recessive female phenotype at a rate of approximately 10^{-3} divisions. The F′ strains are thus heterogenotic, and carry two parental alleles of the marker in question. The F′ elements can be transferred to recipients efficiently and independently of chromosomal markers, which are also transferred with the orientation of the ancestral Hfr. Recipients of these F′ units subsequently behave as do the variant donors. The properties of these heterogenotes were said to suggest some manner of rapid alternation between the autonomous and the integrated states of F′.

By incubating Hfr strains and F⁻ strains together so that the latter could be infected by F⁺ revertants, Hirota and Sneath[155] were able to isolate newly infected F′ strains in which various markers had become associated with F. These F′ strains were likewise observed to be heterogenotes, as they gave rise to segregants carrying the recessive alleles of the recipient cells, and were easily cured of their F′ units by acridine dyes, resulting in the loss of F as well as of its associated chromosomal determinant. The strains can transfer their variant sex factors to F⁻ recipients, and, in general, exhibit the ability to transfer chromosomal characters as do their Hfr parents, although with reduced frequency.

Many of the F′ strains studied have been observed to segregate a variety of types differing from the original with respect to both sexual type and allelic state. Haploid segregants, homogenotes, and heterogenotes of almost every possible type can be obtained. Recombination between the bacterial chromosome and the chromosomal segment (merogenote[9]) carried in F' thus occurs. Recombination also occurs between two different merogenotes. Two forms of the variant sex factor F_8, each carrying different *gal* genes, were observed to recombine to give wild-type gal^+ heterogenotes. F_{13} elements carrying different *lac* genes were seen to behave similarly.[155]

The mode of formation of such F' elements is difficult to assess. Recombination between F and the host chromosome, as proposed for F_2, may be responsible, as may translocation of a chromosomal segment into or onto the sex factor. In the case of F_{13}, simple fragmentation of the terminal end of the ancestral Hfr may have occurred. Hirota and Sneath[155] have observed that a polarized order of marker entry occurs upon transfer of this particular F' to recipients. The determinant of maleness, F, enters last and, analogously to chromosomal transfer, the process can be interrupted so that haploid, F^- recombinants are obtained. F_{13} thus behaves as does the bacterial chromosome, a fact which strongly suggests, as pointed out by Campbell,[5] that the relationship of F to its merogenote in the F' unit is the same as that of F to the bacterial chromosome in an Hfr. Nevertheless, it is quite possible that mechanisms involved in the production of F' particles may vary from event to event.

In this connection one should point out that the transfer of F_{13} to an F^- cell is often accompanied by the detachment of F from the F_{13} unit, so that progeny of the infected cell become carriers of wild-type F_1. This process, of striking analogy to zygotic induction of prophage, suggests that F in F_{13} and, by extension, F in the parent Hfr may be loosely attached or synapsed to the chromosome, as is believed by many to be the case with prophage.

Given the proper type of Hfr, therefore, essentially any genetic marker of a bacterial cell can become associated with the sex factor and thereby generate a single unit of replication and transmission which can be transferred serially with high efficiency. In this form, the sex factor exhibits a specific affinity for the chromosome of its host, and can confer the capacity for efficient, oriented chromosome transfer. F-merogenote transfer, quite similar to phage-mediated transduction, is called "F-duction" or "sexduction."[156] The merogenote carried by F apparently retains its normal capacities, even during intergeneric transfer. The β-galactosidase formed by F-*lac* elements retains its identity whether the host cells be *Escherichia coli*, *Pasteurella pestis*, or *Serratia marcescens*.[156a]

The process of sexduction provides a means in addition to classical transductional analyses whereby functional analysis and cistron identification can be performed in bacteria. Discussion of the latter may be found in the reviews of Clowes[157] and of Lederberg.[32] The use of sexduction in the clarification of the functional expression of *lac* genes in *E. coli* and of the genetic control of regulatory mechanisms in the synthesis of the proteins involved is brilliantly expounded by Jacob and Monod.[64] Somewhat more recently, Garen and Echols[158-160] have applied sexduction to an analysis of the genetic control of the synthesis of alkaline phosphatase by *E. coli*.

As mentioned previously, sexduction was employed to obtain corroborative evidence that the specific immunity of lysogenic cells is expressed cytoplasmically. Cells chromosomally *gal*⁻ and nonlysogenic but carrying the sexducing unit F-*gal*⁺-λ exhibit precisely the same immunity pattern as normal, haploid, lysogenic cells.

The functions expressed by merogenotes in the episomic state have permitted an estimate to be made of the number of sexducing particles, and hence of sex factors in general, present in host cells. Jacob et al.[161] observed that the amount of β-galactosidase produced by *lac*⁻/F-*lac*⁺ heterogenotes is two to three times as much as that produced by haploid *lac*⁺ cells. Garen and Echols[160] observed that the alkaline phosphatase activity of cells harboring an F′ element carrying the corresponding determinant was twofold higher than that of haploid, phosphatase-positive cells. It would appear, therefore, that there exist approximately two copies of the sex factor per chromosome (or nucleus) in host cells.

The existence of sexducing elements has facilitated the detection of defective mutants of the sex factor incapable of transferring their associated merogenotes and of mediating chromosomal transfer. The presence of the defective sex factor is shown by the heterogenotic state of host cells and by their ability to give rise to haploid F⁻ cells. Work is now in progress on a range of sex factor mutants which are apparently defective for one or another function of F. Attempts are being made to identify the sex factor function and to obtain recombinants from defective F particles (F. Jacob, personal communication).

In this regard, the study of sex factors defective in a function(s) other than the capacity to mobilize genetic material has also involved the use of an F′ element. Cuzin[162] has reported the isolation from UV-irradiated cells harboring F-*lac* of strains carrying a defective sex factor designated F_{D5}-*lac*. Such defective strains behave as donors of both the episome and the chromosome, but with a frequency of only about 10^{-4} of that exhibited by F-*lac* strains. The defective strains will act as recipients in bacterial crosses in a more fertile manner than will F-*lac* strains, although the fertility does not approach that of F⁻ strains. Cells harboring F_{D5}-*lac* appear to be resistant to "male-specific" bacteriophages attacking only donor cells.[163] It appears that F_{D5}-*lac* is defective in its capacity to evoke the synthesis of phage receptor sites and surface structures involved in the establishment of mating pairs, not to infer either the identity or the nonidentity of these structures.

The results of Cuzin provide some clarification of the observations reported by Hirota and Iijima.[164] The latter investigators isolated strains regarded as intermediate between F^+ and F^- from F^+ cultures resistant to cobalt and nickel ions and from F^+ cultures subjected to short treatment with acridine dyes. These F_i strains were fertile with both F^+ and F^- strains, but more so with the former. The occasional appearance of F^+ cells in F_i cultures was noted. The presence of a diminished number of sex factors in F_i strains was proposed to account for their behavior, but it now seems likely that F_i strains actually carry defective sex factors, and that the appearance of F^+ cells in such strains represents a spontaneous reversion at the mutant site involved.

The properties of sexducing particles have made possible the transfer of various markers from one strain of *E. coli* to another. Maas and Maas[164a] infected a mutant of *E. coli* B with F-*lac*, thereby converting it to a genetic donor and making possible the transfer to strain K12 of a marker never observed to arise in the latter.

Thus, the ability of the attached sex factor to undergo recombination with the bacterial chromosome, while of considerable interest in itself, provides means whereby genetic analyses in *E. coli* may be performed which would otherwise be impossible.

c. Immunity and Repression. It has been stated that the attached or integrated state of the sex factor is incompatible with the autonomous state, that Hfr cells do not harbor autonomous, freely transmissible F.[3] This is based on observations that F is chromosomally attached in Hfr cells and is transferred very rarely and in linkage with terminal markers during conjugation, even though Hfr cells arise in F^+ populations and have ample chance to be reinfected.

As pointed out by Fisher,[57] in contrast to F^+ donors, Hfr donors transfer essentially no cytoplasmic material during mating and may harbor autonomous F, although it is not detectable by transfer. However, clonal analysis of genetically similar Hfr, F^+, and F^- cells infected with the F-*lac* element of Jacob and Adelberg has permitted Scaife and Gross[165] to demonstrate that multiplication of F-*lac* is completely inhibited in Hfr cells. It is therefore likely that autonomous F_1 is excluded from cells carrying attached F, a phenomenon of striking similarity to the system of specific immunity in the case of prophage.

Results in apparent contradiction to the above have been reported by Cuzin.[166] A stable clone of Hfr cells harboring F-*lac* of Jacob and Adelberg was isolated from crosses between a suitable F′ strain and a phenocopied[129, 130] Hfr. That the F-*lac* unit multiplied in the autonomous state was shown by the capacity of the Hfr (F-*lac*) strain to segregate *lac*⁻ cells and to transfer F-*lac* serially. The Hfr character of the strain was conserved, as it was able to transfer two distinct oriented sequences of markers upon conjugation, one characteristic of the F-*lac* intermediate donor and one characteristic of the original Hfr donor. Cuzin pointed out that these results are not incompatible with the existence of a system of repression and immunity in the fertility system of *E. coli*, if one assumes that in the cross a form of F-*lac* was selected which is analogous to the virulent mutants of phage λ and hence is not sensitive to repression by the homologous, integrated episome.

Clark[166a] has reported that two sex factors may coexist indefinitely in the same cell if both are stably attached to the host chromosome. Such a strain, a "double male," carrying two stably attached sex factors, transfers genetic material to recipients in the form of two independent, nonhomologous linkage groups. Any given cell appears to transfer one or the other linkage group, not both.

The possibility therefore exists that sex factors control a system of immunity and repression similar to that controlled by prophage. The detachment of F from F_{13} upon transfer into F⁻ recipients has already been compared to the phenomenon of zygotic induction. That a "release of repression" may occur when F is introduced into a "nonimmune" F⁻ cell is suggested by the observable rapid spread of F throughout the members of an F⁻ population exposed to a few F⁺ donors. This statement is based on the observations discussed below.

As stated previously, there exists a rather small number of copies of F per cell. Some manner of control mechanism must exist in F⁺ cells regulating the number of autonomous F particles present, as their nonpathological associations with hosts may be perpetuated indefinitely and the low F/nucleus ratio maintained. The existence of controlling mechanisms which regulate the multiplication of autonomous sex factors in F⁺ cells has recently been demonstrated.[155, 162] Autonomous F_1 elements in some way inhibit proper multiplication of "superinfecting" F′ units. The rate at which multiplication of the latter occurs, rather than the capacity to multiply, seems to be affected; segregational patterns indicate that the F′ elements cannot multiply rapidly enough to be distributed to all members of a clone.

In general, during any one transfer event, only one F particle is transferred to a recipient, as judged by the exponential nature of P³²-decay inactivation curves of transferred sex factors.[148] On rare occasions, however, a second sex factor may be introduced.[166b] As donors have only a very limited number of F particles to transfer, as only one sex factor is transferred to any one recipient, and as an undetermined number of generations of growth must occur before maleness is expressed phenotypically by such newly infected cells,[149] one might conclude that the introduction of an F particle into the F$^-$ cytoplasm results in a release of regulation so that F now multiplies at an accelerated rate and can spread infectiously. Direct evidence has been obtained that, in liquid medium, newly infecting F particles multiply faster than their recipient hosts.[166b]

Although it appears that autonomous sex factors somehow regulate their own multiplication and that the attachment of F to the chromosome in the F$^+$ to Hfr transition results in physiological changes preventing the cytoplasmic maintenance of the sex factor, the possibility exists that the host cell exerts some control over the replication of F. Certain F^r (F-refractory) strains described by Lederberg and Lederberg[167] apparently cannot be infected with F$_1$. They show no fertility with F$^-$ cells in crosses, nor are they able to transmit any type of fertility factor. It is tempting to suggest that such F^r cells are truly F$^-$ and have undergone a mutation which conditions the overproduction of a repressor substance.

As mentioned previously, some sexducing particles may be defective. Although normal autonomous F prevents the stable establishment of F-*lac* in the same cells, de Haan and Stouthamer[166b] have isolated strains harboring both F-*gal* and F-*lac* elements. Defectiveness with respect to a system of regulation is indicated. In addition, F′ strains exhibit a reasonably efficient transfer of chromosomal markers to recipients, but the frequency of transfer is still considerably lower than that shown by their ancestral Hfr cells. It is possible that the specific pairing of F′ particles with the chromosome permits interactions to occur which are sufficient to induce the formation of a linear, transferable chromosomal structure, but which do not involve actual attachment of F′ to the chromosome, except in rare cases.[154a] That F′ strains do not obligatorily possess an attached sex factor is shown by their conversion to females upon treatment with acridines. Phosphorus-starved F$_2$ males have been converted to females by causing them to transfer F to recipients. This process was designated "sex-curing."[149] Defectiveness of F′ elements with respect to the ability to form stable chromosomal attachments may exist.

3. ALTERNATION OF STATES

During conjugation, the introduction of autonomous F into an F$^-$ cell is not followed by a "decision" of the recipient whether or not to permit integration of the element. Autonomous F remains so in the recipient and its progeny, and the transition to the integrated state occurs only rarely, at a rate of approximately 10^{-4} per cell per division.[3]

Unlike phage λ, F$_1$ can become attached to the bacterial chromosome at any one of a great variety of points. Although such attachment makes possible the conversion of the F^+ circular chromosome to the rectilinear Hfr chromosome, the transition from autonomous to integrated states does not necessarily cause breakage and opening up of the linkage group. Taylor and Adelberg[168] have shown that Hfr cells in the stationary phase of growth, which are phenocopied and behave as if they were incapable of donating genetic material, exhibit genetic linkage over the point of attachment of F when employed as recipients in crosses. However, Frédéricq[169] has reported that Hfr strains in the exponential phase of growth can occasionally act as recipients in genetic crosses and, as such, exhibit recombination patterns indicating no linkage at all over the site of F attachment. It would appear, therefore, that discontinuity in the Hfr chromosome occurs only in cells capable of chromosome transfer, and that the F^+ to Hfr transition merely predetermines a donor capacity which is not fully expressed until triggered by some process.

Although a physiological decision of a cell apparently does not determine the transition of F from the autonomous to the integrated state, the use of UV-treated F^+ populations for screening for the presence of Hfr cells[170] suggests that UV may increase the frequency of transition, either by its effect on F and/or the bacterial chromosome or by altering the physiolgical state of the F^+ cell.

The transition of F from the integrated to the autonomous state occurs spontaneously at a frequency varying from Hfr to Hfr, i.e., Hfr strains differ in their reversion rate to the F^+ condition. No methods to induce mass reversion to the F^+ state have been reported.

In contrast to the apparent detachment of F from F_{13} upon introduction into the F^- cytoplasm, no phenomenon resembling zygotic induction is observed when attached F is transferred to an F^- by conjugation with a normal Hfr[133] or by cotransduction with a linked genetic marker.[171] F remains in the integrated state. When F alone is transduced into an F^- from either F^+ or Hfr, it remains in the autonomous state.[172]

4. Host Cell Modifications

Quite analogous to the case of the temperate bacteriophages, the presence of the sex factor in the autonomous, the integrated, or the F' state confers new properties on its hosts. Not only are cells converted to actual or potential donors of genetic material, but are also modified with respect to their capacity to support phage multiplication, their surface properties, and their motility.

Zinder[173] has reported the isolation of the bacteriophage SP6 which grows on F^- but not on Hfr, F^+, or F' Salmonella (F factor from E. coli K12). The phage adsorbs to all mating types, but progeny ensue only from females. It was concluded that SP6 is excluded by the presence of the F factor, much as r mutants of phage T4 are excluded by phage λ.

Cells harboring F show a greater tendency to autoagglutinate, agglutinate at a higher pH, and take an acid stain more easily than do F⁻ cells.[174, 175] The presence of certain surface antigens is determined by F, these structures being absent from the corresponding F⁻ strains.[176-178] Introduction of F into a cell brings about a change in its electrokinetic mobility, a decrease in its electronegativity.[179] Donor cells have surface structures which are periodate-labile and are responsible for the formation of mating pairs during conjugation; sublethal periodate treatment of females has no effect on their capacity to form mating couples.[136] The sex factor determines the presence of receptor sites for the adsorption of RNA-containing "male-specific" bacteriophages which cannot adsorb to F⁻ cells,[163, 180-182] and also determines the loss or alteration of receptor sites for DNA-containing "female-specific" phages.[182]

One is tempted to suppose that the surface differences between males and females are attributable to a single structural change induced by F. That this may be the case is suggested by the finding that periodate treatment of males decreases the rate of adsorption of male-specific phage, indicating that surface components involved in forming mating pairs may serve as receptor sites for phage attachment.[185] In addition, the correlation between the acquisition of resistance to male-specific phages and reduction of fertility in crosses is suggestive.[162, 183]

An as yet obscure host cell modification associated with the presence of F is a decreased motility. Skaar et al.[184] observed that screening F⁺ cultures to select for the highest motility and development of flagellar antigens led to recovery of F⁻ cells. It was shown that this is a result of a selective advantage of F⁻ variants rather than an induction of them by the techniques employed, which were analogous to those used for the attenuation of κ (kappa) particles in Paramecium.[185]

5. PHYSICAL AND CHEMICAL NATURE

Sex factors of E. coli K12 have been shown to contain DNA as the major, if not the only, constituent essential for function.

Initial experiments of Driskell and Adelberg[186] and of Lavallé and Jacob[187] demonstrated that F' agents are phosphorus-containing elements. Sex factors transferred from P³²-labeled donors to unlabeled recipients were observed to lose their capacity to function as determinants of maleness as P³² decay proceeded. The DNA nature of the sex factor has deen inferred from the generation of a single replicative unit by F and an associated chromosomal element, as in sexducing particles. The first direct demonstration that this is apparently the case was provided by studies of the effects of the antibiotic mitomycin C (MC) on the incorporation of P^{32} into the F_1 and F_2 particles of strain K12.[148, 186] Under suitably controlled conditions, MC evokes an inhibition of net DNA synthesis while having no detectable effect on RNA or protein synthesis.[188, 189] A level of MC not affecting RNA or protein synthesis but inducing about 60% inhibition of net DNA synthesis was found to inhibit incorporation of P^{32} into F_2 particles and nuclei of F_2 donor cells 68 and 64%, respectively, as determined by relative rates of P^{32}-decay inactivation of the genetic elements labeled in the presence and absence of MC. The correlation between the extent of MC-induced inhibition of P^{32} incorporation into F_2 and nuclei not only indicates a common composition for the genetic units, but also supports the conclusion that RNA, in amounts detectable by methods employed, is not an essential constituent of F. The DNA nature of F_1 was similarly determined.

Marmur et al.[189a] have reported that episomal transfer involves a transfer of DNA from donor to recipient. Serratia marcescens was infected with an F-lac element and DNA was prepared from the recipients. Cesium chloride density-gradient centrifugation showed that S. marcescens DNA had a density of 1.718 g./cm.³, corresponding to a guanine + cytosine (GC) content of 58%. The DNA prepared from F-lac-infected recipients showed two satellite bands, however. One with a density of 1.709 g./cm.³, corresponding to the GC content of 50% characteristic of E. coli and one with a density of 1.703 g./cm.³, corresponding to a GC content of 44%. The latter species of molecules comprised about one-tenth of the total satellite DNA which, in turn, amounted to about 1% of the total cellular DNA. The transfer of F-lac thus appears to involve the transfer of two types of DNA.

Somewhat more recently, Herman and Forro[190] reported that H^3-thymine-labeled F_1 donors transfer radioactive material to F^- recipients, as detected by autoradiographic analysis of colonies formed by recipient cells. Silver[190a] has observed that the transfer of the F_{13} element is accompanied by transfer of C^{14}-thymidine. Recipient cells were lysed with phage, and the liberated radioactive material determined. It seems reasonable to conclude that sex factors of E. coli K12 comprise DNA. RNA, if present, contributes little to the determination of sexual polarity in K12 strains.

From the rates of P^{32}-decay inactivation of sex factors labeled with a known specific radioactivity, Driskell-Zamenhof and Adelberg[148] calculated that F_1 contains between 8.5×10^4 and 2.5×10^5 DNA-phosphorus atoms, and is comparable to about 2% of the bacterial chromosome. Similarities between F_1 and λ therefore extend to the sizes of the genetic elements, λ containing 2.3×10^5 phosphorus atoms.[119] F_2 was calculated to contain between 1.9×10^5 and 5.4×10^5 DNA-phosphorus atoms, and is comparable to approximately 4 or 5 % of the chromosome. Lavallé and Jacob[187] have estimated the F "function" of the sexducing elements F-*lac* and F-*gal* to comprise about 4×10^5 phosphorus atoms. Such a value cannot be considered to be a true representation of F "function" of F_1, as the structural relationships between chromosomal loci and "F" in sexducing particles are unknown, as are the possible effects upon F of lethal disintegrations in adjacent or intercalated material responsible for functions other than those of F.

Herman and Forro[190] observed that F_1 transfer from H^3-thymine-labeled males involved the transfer of about 1 % of the total label of an F^+ male chromosome. As it is believed that only one F particle at a time is transferred to a recipient, these results are in reasonably good agreement with the above.

Silver[190a] has observed that C^{14}-thymidine transfer comparable to 3.2 % of the total cellular label accompanies transfer of F_{13} into recipients. This large element, which carries bacterial genes for purine-dependence, methylene blue-sensitivity, resistance to phage T6, phosphatase production, and lactose utilization, may then contain almost 10^6 phosphorus atoms and be comparable in size to almost 10 % of a bacterial chromosome.

6. OTHER BACTERIAL SYSTEMS

Sexual differentiation of one form or another has been observed in various wild strains of *E. coli*.[191, 192] Fertility factors appear to be involved in all cases, but have not been studied in detail. The commonly held view is that F factors of many donor strains differ in several respects from that of strain K12.

Sexual differentiation and genetic transfer have also been described in *Pseudomonas aeruginosa*.[193, 194] Fertility appears to be controlled by a transmissible agent somewhat similar to the sex factor of *E. coli*, except that it cannot be eliminated with acridine dyes.[195, 196]

C. COLICINOGENIC FACTORS

Colicins are bacteriocidal substances of peptide, protein, or lipocarbohydrate-protein nature[197, 198] which are produced by various members of the Enterobacteriaceae and are active on other members of the family, including *E. coli*. About 20 groups of colicins are distinguishable, and are designated alphabetically, e.g. E1, E2, I, K. The synthesis of colicin is of lethal consequence to the productive cells; death may or may not be accompanied by lysis. Upon exposure of susceptible cells to colicins, death but not lysis ensues. Each colicin has a particular host range which depends on the presence of specific receptor sites on the bacterial cell surface.[199, 200] Resistant mutants arise spontaneously and appear to have lost the specific receptor sites for colicin adsorption.[201] Detailed description of colicins and their modes of action may be found in the reviews of Frédéricq[202-204] and of Jacob and Wollman.[205] More recent information is treated by Ivànovics.[206]

The potential capacity of a bacterial cell to produce colicin is a stable hereditary property. Such cells are called colicinogenic. Colicinogeny, like lysogeny, is a dispensable property and, upon rare occasions of loss, can be regained only by means other than mutation. The genetic determinants that confer the capacity to produce colicins are called *colicinogenic factors*. The designations *col E1*, *col I*, etc. are used for the factors controlling the production of colicins E1, I, etc. *Col* factors share certain properties with temperate bacteriophages, or rather the genetic material thereof, and with sex factors; the episomic nature of the genetic determinants of colicinogeny is discussed below.

1. THE AUTONOMOUS STATE

Frédéricq[207] first observed that colicinogeny can be transferred from *col+* to *col−* strains in mixed culture. In *E. coli* the transfer of the determinant for synthesis of colicin E1 appeared to be a consequence of conjugation, as it occurred only between *col E1* F+ cells and *col−* F− cells.[208] When F+ *col E1* cells are mixed with F− *col−* cells, the transfer of colicinogeny begins in about 5 minutes,[139] and more than 50% of the recipients acquire *col E1* in 1 hour.[209] In such bacterial crosses, nearly all (rare) recovered genetic recombinants prove to be *col E1*, but no linkage of the colicinogenic determinant to any chromosomal marker is observed; *col E1* is transferred independently of the chromosome. The reciprocal cross, F+ *col−* × F− *col+*, does not result in the transfer of the *col−* property to recipients. Such considerations prompted Frédéricq[207, 210, 211] to propose that the genetic determinant for E1 production is a cytoplasmic element capable of autonomous multiplication.

Although the transfer of *col E1* requires the presence of the sex factor in the donor, F− cells of *E. coli* can transfer the *col I* element efficiently.[212] *Col I* thus appears to permit conjugation, and makes possible its own transmission as well as that of any other *col* factor harbored by its host. The analogy of *col I* to F is striking.

Certain strains of *Salmonella*, *Shigella*, and *Escherichia* can transfer colicinogeny to noncolicinogenic *Salmonella*.[207, 213, 214] The transmission of colicinogeny among *S. typhimurium* strains has been studied in detail by Stocker and associates.[6, 215, 216] *Col I* or *col B* derivatives of strain LT-2 can transmit their colicinogenic property to *col−* strains in mixed culture. Prolonged incubation appears to be necessary to attain a reasonable frequency of transfer, but this was found to be a result of the fact that stock cultures of *col+* cells which have carried the genetic determinant for more than thirty generations contain a very small proportion of cells, about 10^{-3}, which can actually transmit *col I* at any one time, although all cells still carry the determinant. In contrast, cells in which *col I* is newly introduced can transfer the property quite efficiently, about 50 % of the donors transmitting *col* to recipients in an hour. This high transmissibility persists up to seven generations after infection. In mixed *col I-col⁻* stock cultures, it appears that a small fraction of cells initiates transfer to a very small number of recipients, and that these newly infected cells start an "epidemic" spread of *col* throughout the recipient population so that the proportion of *col⁺* cells increases rapidly even though the total cell count may remain essentially constant. The *col I* or *col B* agents must therefore multiply autonomously and at a rate faster than that of the bacterial genome during such matings.

Col E1 and *col E2* LT-2 cells transfer little or no colicinogeny to recipients. When newly infected with *col I*, however, *col E1*, *col E2*, and *col E1, E2* cells can transfer all the determinants with high efficiency, and can initiate an epidemic of the doubly or triply colicinogenic character among recipients. Although *col I* is necessary for pair formation and conjugation, the other *col* factors also appear to exist in an autonomous state, at least during and immediately after transfer.

As will be noted subsequently, the *col I* agent can mediate chromosomal transfer, albeit at low frequency. Although transfer of colicinogeny is accompanied by transfer of genetic markers in these experiments, no linkage of *col* to any marker has been reported, an additional confirmation of the assumption that *col I* may exist as an autonomous agent.

Furness and Rowley[191] have reported the elimination of colicinogenic factors by treatment of host cells with cobalt salts. Acridine dyes do not eliminate *col* factors but do inhibit their transfer, which may indicate a low efficiency of curing (H. Ozeki, unpublished; cited in ref. 5).

2. THE INTEGRATED STATE

That the *col E1* factor may exist in the integrated state has been indicated by Alfoldi *et al.*[209, 217] Various Hfr strains colicinogenic for E1 and differing in their order of injection of markers were observed to transfer the *col* character to a given recipient at different frequencies. The time at which the zygotes began to receive *col* also differed from cross to cross. In reciprocal matings, *col⁻* Hfr's × *col⁺* recipients, the *col⁻* property was never received in zygotes or their progeny, however. This was found to be a consequence of lethal zygosis, the killing of many zygotes as a result of conjugation and, presumably, as a result of the introduction of the *col⁻* determinant. The extent of lethal zygosis in such reciprocal crosses was observed to depend on the particular Hfr strain used as donor. For any given Hfr strain, a strict correlation was seen to exist between the degree of lethal zygosis in crosses employing *col⁻* donors and the frequency of transfer of *col E1* in reciprocal crosses employing *col⁺* Hfr's. It appears that the *col⁻* property corresponding to the inability of the cell to produce E1 is chromosomally located. It is believed to be near the region of the chromosome controlling threonine synthesis. Alfoldi *et al.* propose that in the Hfr strains studied the *col E1* factor is itself located at this locus.

However, in a recent report of similar experiments, Clowes[217a] states that no correlation was found among the level of *col E1* transfer, the order of injection of markers of the Hfr strains used, and the extent of lethal zygosis. A plasmid[1] nature of the determinant was suggested.

An analysis of the state of *col* factors *E2*, *I*, and *V* in strains of *E. coli* K12 has been carried out by de Zwaig and co-workers,[217b] employing strains and methods similar to those of Alfoldi *et al.*[209, 217] No evidence for a chromosomal attachment of these determinants was obtained, and it was proposed that these *col* factors occupy an exclusively extrachromosomal state in F⁺ and Hfr bacteria. No lethal zygosis was detected, nor was the *col⁻* allele of any of the determinants.

Frédéricq,[217c] reporting preliminary experiments, states that strains have been isolated in which a sex factor linked to a *col* factor is in the Hfr state. These strains do not transfer either element at high frequency, and linkage of both agents to the terminal chromosomal marker has been demonstrated.

As stated previously, in *Salmonella*, *col I* is freely transmissible only by cells newly infected with the determinant. In populations of cells which have carried *col I* for about thirty generations, only a small proportion can transfer colicinogeny. In the great majority of cells of such populations, *col I* is not readily transferable although the agent is still present. In these cells, *col I* is presumed[6, 215, 216] to be in the integrated state, to have become associated with the bacterial chromosome in some manner.

The capacity of some of the *col* factors to mediate chromosomal transfer suggests that a *col*-chromosome association may exist at times.

There obviously exists a difference of opinion among investigators studying determinants of colicinogeny as to their capacity to assume the integrated state. The reader should be cognizant of this and should appraise past and future publications critically.

3. ALTERNATION OF STATES

Little can be said about the transition of *col* factors from the autonomous to the integrated state. This change appears to occur at relatively high frequency in *S. typhimurium* harboring *col I*, as freely transmissible, autonomous *col* all but disappears within about thirty generations after introduction, although the capacity of the cells to produce colicin I remains. In *E. coli*, however, the autonomous to integrated transition of *col I* appears to occur at low frequency if at all. *Col I* is readily transmissible by *col+ E. coli* cells whether it is newly introduced or has been carried for many generations. High transmissibility in this system is a stable property.[212]

Transition of *col I* from the integrated to the autonomous state may occur spontaneously at a rate of about 10^{-4}, hence the presence of this proportion of cells which can transfer *col* efficiently in old cultures of *col+ S. typhimurium* cells.

Transition of *col E1* from the integrated to the autonomous state may occur during crosses between *col+* Hfr cells and F⁻ cells of *E. coli*. Examination of the progeny of individual zygotes isolated by micromanipulation showed that whenever a zygote has received the *col+* property, all its progeny are colicinogenic. *Col E1* must therefore multiply autonomously and at a rate faster than the bacterial chromosome in such zygotes and their clonal descendants.[4] It is not clear whether this transition occurs in the donor as an initial consequence of conjugation or in the recipient upon introduction of the chromosomally attached *col* factor, a process analogous to transfer or zygotic induction of prophage. The transition from the integrated to the autonomous state apparently does not result in the synthesis of colicin, as no lethal effects are observed on either donor or recipient cells.

4. PHYSICAL AND CHEMICAL NATURE

Silver and Ozeki[218] have demonstrated and measured the transfer of DNA accompanying the transmission of *col I*, *col E1*, and *col E2*. Colicinogenic *S. typhimurium* donors labeled with C^{14}-thymidine were employed, and the amount of radioactive material liberated upon phage-induced lysis of unlabeled recipients was measured and related to the number and type of *col* factor transferred, as determined genetically. Labeled donors which transferred *col I*, or *col I* and *col E1*, or *col I* and *col E1* and *col E2* were observed to transfer increasing amounts of thymidine (DNA), the correlation between the number of types of determinants transferred and the amount of DNA transferred being quite close. It was proposed that the colicinogenic factors contain DNA and that only one copy of each factor is transferred. One should recall that the same can be said for the sex factor of *E. coli*.[148]

Colicinogenic donors labeled with C^{14}-leucine (for protein) and C^{14}-uracil (for RNA) were not observed to transfer measurable amounts of material. However, Silver and Ozeki state that the resolution of the experiments was such that the presence of RNA and/or protein in the colicinogenic factors cannot be excluded.

From the amount of labeled material transferred, the degree of labeling of the donors and the known amount of DNA per cell of *S. typhimurium*, the sizes of the colicinogenic factors were estimated. *Col I*, *col E1*, and *col E2* are said to contain 6×10^4, 7×10^4, and 3×10^4 nucleotide pairs, respectively, and are thus comparable in size to the wild-type sex factor of *E. coli*.

These values are much larger than the one proposed by Lavallé and Jacob[187] for the phosphorus atom content of *col E1*. A comparison of the rate of P^{32}-decay inactivation of this determinant with the published[219] rate of inactivation of phage λ containing P^{32} at the same specific radioactivity led these investigators to propose that *col E1* contained no more than 10^4 P atoms, i.e., 5×10^3 nucleotide pairs. As pointed out be Silver and Ozeki, the P^{32} experiments provide an estimate of the size of the particular determinant controlling the synthesis of colicin E1, but the *col* factor itself may contain several other genes concerned with the colicinogenic state, its maintenance, transfer, and phenotypic expression.

5. OTHER EPISOMIC CHARACTERISTICS

Determinants of colicinogeny exhibit properties in addition to those mentioned previously which are believed to support their classification as episomic elements. These properties do not all conform precisely to the classical definition of episomic characteristics but are nonetheless highly reminiscent of the characteristics of temperate phages and/or sex factors.

Col factors confer on their hosts the potential capacity to produce new proteins or protein-like substances, the colicins. *Col I*, at least, appears to determine new cell surface properties which permit conjugation. Cells recently infected with *col I* are observed to form clumps of two to at least twenty cells. *Col⁻* cells will adhere to such clumps and to individual *col I* cells. The formation of such pairs is rapid, about 30 % formed in 2 minutes, but is followed by a delay in the transfer of *col* factors. Clumping is not observed in *col⁻* cultures or among cells which have carried *col I* for many generations.[6, 215] It was proposed that old cultures of *col I* cells from which *col* is not freely transmissible carry the determinant in the integrated state, but, unlike the sex factor, *col I* cannot direct the synthesis of pairing sites while attached to the host chromosome. As pointed out by Clark and Adelberg,[9] however, failure of stock cultures of *col I* cells to transfer colicinogen may reflect an inability to form effective mating pairs not because of the attached state of *col*, but rather because of the accumulation of a *col*-determined cytoplasmic repressor which prevents synthesis of the surface substances.

Other host cell modifications associated with the establishment of colicinogeny have been discussed by Hamon.[219a] Colicinogenic strains of *S. typhi* and *S. paratyphi* B sometimes exhibit important changes in their lysotyping schemes when compared to the parental, non-*col⁺* strain; sensitivities to specific typing phages are reduced. The nature of this modification is not understood. In addition, the introduction of certain colicinogenic determinants into lysogenic strains of *E. coli* appears to inhibit the induction of the prophage by UV. Development of the prophage into mature, infectious phage is markedly depressed, while colicin is elaborated in considerable quantities. A competition between the induction of phage maturation and the induction of colicin production seems to exist.

Colicinogenic strains are immune to the colicins they produce, and the immunity is specific.[204, 220] One interesting exception was reported by Ryan et al.[221] A strain of *E. coli* that does not ordinarily produce colicin will liberate, after treatment with ultraviolet light, colicin which kills the producing strain. Immunity is not conferred by a loss of receptor sites such as occurs in the formation of resistant mutants, but is in some way dependent upon the presence of a *col* factor. The relation between the capacity to produce a certain colicin and immunity to its lethal action is obscure. Colicins are not reproduced in the cells they kill and supposedly contain no genetic material. Immunity may involve a *col*-directed repression of host cell processes that are required for the killing process to proceed, or a *col*-controlled synthesis of enzymes or inhibitors that destroy or inactivate the corresponding colicin when it is applied externally. This synthesis would be repressed in cells actively producing colicin. *Col+* cells are immune to the level of colicin they produce, but are in some cases killed by high concentrations.[220, 222] Similar "multiplicity effects" are observed in the case of temperate bacteriophages. When the number of superinfecting phage becomes large enough, immunity appears to break down.[58, 223]

Quite analogous to the induction of vegetative phage development in lysogenic bacteria is the induction by various means of the synthesis of colicin by colicinogenic bacteria. The relationship between the state of *col* factors and the synthesis of the corresponding colicin is unknown. Inducing agents may not bring about an alternation of state as they do in the case of prophage, but may disrupt a system of repression regulating the expression of genes of the *col* factor controlling colicin synthesis. Ultraviolet light is the agent first noted to induce colicin production.[224] The original observation was subsequently confirmed,[225-227] and the action of the inducing agent shown to increase the number of colicinogenic cells producing colicin rather than the amount of colicin being liberated by any particular fraction of the population.[228] Hydrogen peroxide, organic peroxides, and nitrogen mustard have been shown to be efficient inducers of colicin production,[225] as have mitomycin C[229] and thymine deprivation.[98a] The production of colicin can therefore be induced by the same agents that induce the production of vegetative phage. In both systems, the response elicited by an inducing agent is strongly dependent upon the physiological state of the bacterial cells both before and after treatment. Inducibility of lysogenic cells and colicinogenic cells depends on genetic factors. Some bacterial strains can be induced, some cannot. However, in contrast to the existence of inducible and noninducible prophages, inducibility of colicinogenic bacteria seems not to be dependent on the type of *col* factor carried and must therefore involve genetic factors of the host cells.[205]

The phenomenon of lethal zygosis, the death of F^- col^+ zygotes following the introduction of the *col*⁻ determinant from an Hfr, is not at all understood. It is in a sense comparable to, but the reciprocal of, zygotic induction. The introduction into a colicinogenic recipient of the chromosomal region at which *col* may at times become attached might permit an interaction between the colicinogenic factor and its corresponding chromosomal site which either activates genes for the production of colicin (of lethal consequence to the producing cell) or prevents the synthesis of a repressor of colicin synthesis, or, on the other hand, causes immunity to break down so that the zygote becomes sensitive to the colicin already liberated by the recipient culture. No experimental data are available to support any of the above hypotheses. Ben-Gurion[230] has proposed that the "lethal zygote" formed in some *col*-resistant Hfr *col*⁻ $\times$ F^- *col*⁺ crosses is one which has received the presumed *col*⁻ allele from the donor but not the colicin-resistant determinant, and is therefore sensitive to, and killed by, the colicin that other cells produce, as the *col*⁺ recipients are not resistant to their colicin, but immune.

Thus, determinants of colicinogeny exhibit considerable similarity to prophages and sex factors. End products of the full phenotypic expression of the first two determinants, colicins and infective phage particles, respectively, are actually quite different, although superficially they appear to be similar. Colicins are perhaps most accurately compared to the proteins of the bacteriophage coat or tail which are involved with phage attachment to specific receptor sites on the bacterial cell surface. In some cases, colicins may share specific receptor sites with certain bacteriophages. Mutants isolated for resistance to particular colicins are observed to be resistant to certain phages, and vice versa.[231-233] However, the phages and colicins which have such common receptor sites are not related serologically.[4]

D. Resistance Transfer Factor (RTF)

A fourth genetic determinant, the properties of which suggest its classification among the episomes, is that controlling the transfer of drug resistance among genera of the Enterobacteriaceae. The term multiple drug resistance indicates a resistance to streptomycin (*Sm*), chloramphenicol (*Cm*), tetracycline (*Tc*) and sulfonamide (*Su*). The term R factors is employed to designate the multiple drug resistance and various combinations of drug resistances, e.g., (*Su, Sm, Cm*), (*Su, Sm, Tc*), (*Cm, Tc*), (*Su, Sm*), which can be easily transferred from cell to cell by conjugation. The multiple resistance factor and the various combinations are transferred as units;

segregation is rarely observed. The problem of transmissible drug resistance initially drew attention from the medical standpoint, as it was found that R factors can be transferred among almost all genera of Enterobacteriaceae, and to other genera also, among which *Vibrio comma* is perhaps the most notable. The fact that such transfer has been demonstrated to occur in the mammalian intestinal tract as well as *in vitro* is of obvious importance in these days of the chemotherapeutic approach to the treatment of enteric diseases. More recently, however, the infective heredity of drug resistance has been subject to extensive genetic analysis. Although numerous investigators have viewed the problem from the genetic standpoint, Watanabe and associates[234-238] have provided most of the evidence indicating that R factors are "carried" and transferred by a determinant termed RTF (resistance transfer factor) to which episomic properties can be ascribed. By virtue of the episomality of RTF, R factors themselves, said to be composed of RTF plus attached or incorporated determinants of drug resistance, evidence an episomic nature. The detailed review by Watanabe[8] of studies on transmissible drug resistance is of particular value to the linguistically limited reader, as it covers in considerable detail studies published thus far only in Japanese.

1. THE AUTONOMOUS STATE

As stated, the R factors controlling multiple drug resistance and various combinations of resistance can be readily transferred among genera of Enterobacteriaceae by mixed cultivation *in vitro*. The frequencies of transfer differ from donor to donor and from recipient to recipient. Frequencies ranging from 10^{-2} to 10^{-7} per donor cell are observed. Transferred resistance factors are rapidly phenotypically expressed; most of the factors involved in multiple drug resistance do not require cell division and segregation for expression. Although chromosomal *Sm* resistance is believed to be recessive to its sensitive allele,[239] the *Sm*-resistance factor of multiple drug resistance is expressed phenotypically in some of the recipients before the first cell division.[8]

The transfer of R factors can be interrupted by treatment with a blendor or phage T6, thus demonstrating that transfer involves cell-to-cell contact or conjugation. Conjugation and R factor transfer begin within a very short time after donor and recipient cells are mixed.[8]

The sex factor of *E. coli* K12 is not required for the transfer of R factors, as they can be transferred among strains of K12 regardless of their sex. In the case of transfer of R factors from Hfr cells to recipients, the resistance factors appear to be transferred independently of the host chromosome, when selection for the transfer of resistance is performed.

If a small number of cells carrying R factors are introduced into a large population of drug-sensitive cells, the R factors appear to spread rapidly throughout the recipient population, indicating that the R factors are multiplying more rapidly than are host chromosomes. Stocker et al.[240] have described the production of HFC (high-frequency colicinogeny-transferring) cultures in which they demonstrated the high infectivity of S. typhimurium cells newly infected by the col I factor. Similar procedures have been employed with R factors, and populations were obtained which transferred R factors with extremely high frequencies, up to 8 per original donor cell in the HFRT (high-frequency-resistance-transfer system) culture. In the newly infected cells, therefore, R factors must multiply autonomously at a very rapid rate.[8]

These findings together with the observation that R factors can be transferred independently of host chromosomal determinants indicate that the resistance factors can exist in the autonomous state and can replicate independently. This assumption is supported by the observations [236, 241] that R factors can be eliminated by treatment of host cells with acridine dyes. No segregated elimination is observed.

From the results of transduction studies to be noted subsequently, Watanabe and Fukasawa[237] suggested that the resistance factors are linked in the order $Su—Sm—Cm—Tc$, and that the causative role in conjugation and transfer of R factors and their autonomous replication is played by a determinant termed *resistance transfer factor* (RTF), which is assumed to "carry" the resistance factors and to be located distally to Tc.

2. The Integrated State

a. Site of Chromosomal Attachment. Watanabe and Fukasawa (cited in ref. 8, p. 101) have performed kinetic analyses of the transfer of R factors and chromosomal markers by Hfr strains of E. coli K12. When the transfer of chromosomal determinants was selected for, it was noted that recombinants possessing R factors were only those which had received the segment of donor chromosome between the loci controlling thiamine independence and mannitol utilization. It was assumed that R factors may be integrated or attached at a particular site between the *thi* and *mtl* loci, and are transferred during conjugation as chromosomal markers. All recombinants for the region between *thi* and *mtl* did not carry R factors, however. Watanabe and Takano (cited in ref. 8, p. 101) showed that some of these recombinants were produced by Hfr cells that had lost their R factors, but that others were produced by Hfr cells that apparently carried R factors attached at another site. Hfr strains with stably attached R factors were isolated, and although the site(s) of attachment has not been precisely determined, it was stated that its probable location is near the site of sex factor attachment in one clone derived from a particular Hfr strain used. Although this site is not stated by Watanabe,[8] an examination of original papers by the author of the present work leads her to conclude that the site in question lies between the *lac* and *gal* determinants, more closely linked to the latter. Thus, there appears to be no strict limitation to a single site of R factor attachment. The integrated state of R factors is of a variable degree of stability; in some clones, considerable instability is characteristic, while in others, the R factors are integrated stably.

R factors determining various combinations of drug resistances were also often found to be attached between *thi* and *mtl*, indicating that a determinant common to all, i.e., RTF, is responsible for integration.

b. Recombination with the Bacterial Chromosome. That RTF and R factors can recombine with the chromosome of their host while in the integrated state is suggested indirectly. It is assumed that the resistance factors themselves originated from bacterial chromosomal determinants. As epidemiological studies of drug-resistant enteric pathogens show that strains resistant to all four of the drugs under consideration appeared from the start, Watanabe and Fukasawa[237] proposed that the multiple drug resistance factors were picked up by RTF in a single step from the chromosome of some unknown host. Successive acquisition of resistance factors during the development of multiple drug resistance is not indicated. This proposal necessitates the possibility that RTF became attached to the host chromosome one or more times, and in this state incorporated the host determinants by some manner of recombinational process. R factors were compared to F′ elements, and their transfer by conjugation to sexduction.

Studies on the spontaneous segregation of multiple resistance factors by Watanabe and Fukasawa[237] and Watanabe and Lyang[242] and the reports of Akiba *et al.*,[243] Nakaya *et al.*[244] and Mitsuhashi *et al.*[245] on the isolation from nature of bacterial strains carrying R factors with a variety of combinations of resistance determinants led Watanabe to propose that the mechanism of spontaneous segregation of resistance factors involves genetic exchange between the factors carried by RTF and the host chromosome. The R factors carrying various combinations of markers were accounted for by assuming multiple or repeated crossovers between multiple drug resistance factors and the host genome. It was assumed that genetic exchange between R factors and chromosome occurs when the former are in the integrated state. Direct evidence for genetic exchange, i.e., the isolation of drug-resistant clones with no RTF, was not obtained by Watanabe and Lyang.[242] However, Ginoza and Painter[246] have recently reported the incorporation of chromosomal genes into an R factor as well as the apparent incorporation of R factor markers into the host chromosome. Circular models of the transmissible resistance factors have also been presented to account for the mechanism of spontaneous segregation.[242]

Recombination of one type of segregant R factor with another has been observed. Details are discussed by Watanabe.[8]

3. ALTERNATION OF STATES

As stated, the spontaneous transition from the integrated to the autonomous state may occur with variable frequencies in different clones harboring integrated R factors. There are two experimental observations which suggest that this transition may be stimulated or induced by artificial means. Although acridine derivatives are observed to eliminate transmissible drug resistance from treated strains,[236] they do so with low frequencies. It was proposed that this low frequency of elimination might be due to the prevalence of integrated R factors, which, in analogy to the attached sex factors of Hfr strains, are insensitive to the action of acridines. However, if drug-resistant cells are irradiated with UV light before acridine treatment, the elimination of R factors becomes quite efficient. This was proposed to represent an "induction" of integrated R factors by UV comparable to the UV induction of prophage.[236] In addition, studies by Watanabe and Fukasawa[236] and Watanabe and Takano (cited in ref. 8, p. 106) on the effects of UV irradiation or treatment with mitomycin C on the transfer of R factors by Hfr strains with stably integrated determinants showed that the frequencies of transfer per surviving donor cell increased significantly, as did the absolute transfer frequencies. The phenomena were again compared to prophage induction.

4. HOST CELL MODIFICATIONS

That R factors may elicit modifications of the cell surface of their hosts is indicated by the fact that cell-to-cell contact is necessary for transfer and that it occurs among *E. coli* K12 strains regardless of the presence of the sex factor in the donors. Iijima[247] found that *col E1*, which requires for transfer the mediation of a fertility factor, can be transferred by F$^-$ *col* E_1^+ cells carrying R factors, indicating the formation of mating pairs and conjugation bridges.

Iijima[247] has also shown that treatment of F$^-$ cells carrying R factors with sodium periodate transiently deprives them of the ability to transfer the determinants to recipients. This result suggests that R factors permit F$^-$ cells to conjugate and transfer R factors to other F$^-$ recipients by eliciting the production of a mating substance of polysaccharide nature termed *R substance*. This substance is apparently not the same as the mating substance of male strains of *E. coli* K12, as F$^-$ cells containing R factors are not sensitive to male-specific phage known to attack K12 strains harboring the sex factor, F.[248]

5. PHYSICAL AND CHEMICAL NATURE

Watanabe,[8] citing unpublished work, states that studies of the effects of decay of incorporated P^{32} on R factors in *E. coli* K12 indicate that RTF itself consists of DNA in amounts comparable to the DNA contents of phage λ and F-*lac*, F-*gal*. (This reviewer assumes that a content of about 3×10^5 DNA phosphorus atoms is implied by Watanabe.) Data and additional information are not available at this time.

A recent brief report by Falkow *et al.*[249] is of considerable interest with respect to the possible origin of R factors as well as to the physicochemical nature thereof. *Proteus mirabilis* was infected with F-*lac* or with an R factor for multiple drug resistance. DNA was prepared from the recipient *P. mirabilis* and from *Proteus* carrying F-*lac* or the R factor and was subjected to cesium chloride density-gradient centrifugation. The *Proteus* DNA was found to have a guanine + cytosine (GC) content of 38% and a density of 1.698 g./cm.³. DNA of the *Proteus* harboring F-*lac* showed a satellite band at a density of 1.710 g./cm.³ (50% GC) which represented about 3% of the total DNA. The DNA of *Proteus* harboring R factors showed two satellite bands, however: one at a density of 1.710 g./cm.³ and a second at a density of 1.718 g./cm.³ (58% GC). The two satellites represented about 7% of the total DNA.

The R factor thus appears to contain two types of DNA, one (50% GC) characteristic of bacterial genera such as *Escherichia*, *Shigella*, and *Salmonella*, and the other (58% GC) typical of *Serratia*.[43b] This may indicate a heterogeneous origin of the drug resistance determinants or reflect a difference in composition between RTF itself and its incorporated or attached material.

If one assumes a nucleus of *P. mirabilis* to contain about 10^7 DNA phosphorus atoms and the number of R factors per nucleus to be about 2, the above findings indicate that the R factor contains about 3.5×10^5 DNA phosphorus atoms.

Bacteriophage P1 has been observed to transduce the entire multiple-resistance factor.[237] As stated previously, phage P1 contains approximately 2×10^5 DNA phosphorus atoms. This value would appear to set an upper limit for the size of the R factor.

6. OTHER EPISOMIC CHARACTERISTICS

A phenomenon suggestive of immunity in lysogenic cells or of the apparent regulation of numbers of sex factors by F^+ cells has been observed by Mitsuhashi and by Watanabe and Fukasawa (cited in ref. 8, p. 97). Additional R factors can be introduced into recipients already harboring heterologous R factors, e.g., segregant factors. However the frequencies of transfer are only about 1% of those observed when drug-sensitive recipients are employed. It was concluded that RTF controls the suppression of R-factor acceptance, as such was observed with a variety of combinations of resistance factors.

Fisher[250, 251] has shown that the energy afforded by oxidative phosphorylation is required by *E. coli* K12 donors during sex factor-mediated chromosome transfer. Egawa *et al.* (cited in ref. 8, p. 91) have reported that a similar energy supply is required for the transfer of multiple drug resistance.

As will be noted subsequently, Sugino and Hirota[248] have reported that R factors can mediate chromosome transfer in *E. coli* K12. An additional similarity of R factors to F is seen by their affinity for an *sfa* (sex factor affinity) locus. Richter[152] has isolated F$^-$ strains carrying a locus termed *Hfr$_3$* which exhibits a very high affinity for the sex factor. Introduction of F into such strains results in the production of Hfr$_3$ males of high fertility with a given order of injection markers. Introduction of R factors into F$^-$ (Hfr$_3$) cells is followed by the formation of fertile Hfr$_3$ male cells which exhibit an order of injection of markers identical to that promoted by F factors.[248]

E. THE F$_0$ TRANSMISSION FACTOR

Baron *et al.*[252] isolated from natural sources a strain of *Salmonella typhosa*, ST2, which could transmit the capacity to utilize lactose as a sole carbon source to members of various genera of Enterobacteriaceae. Further studies of strain ST2 by Falkow and Baron[253] yielded evidence which suggests that ST2 carries a transmission element, termed F$_0$, which has incorporated the *lac* region and which exhibits episomic proportion. F$_0$ *lac* appears to behave as a unit of replication and transfer. That the *lac* determinants carried and transferred by F$_0$ are essentially the same as those of *E. coli* K12 has been demonstrated by transduction studies and tests for complementation of K12 chromosomal *lac* genes. F$_0$ was not identified, as its presence can thus far by detected only be means of the *lac* character it carries. It is apparently not of a colicinogenic or bacteriophage nature.

1. THE AUTONOMOUS STATE

Strain ST2 transfers F$_0$-*lac* at a frequency of about 10^{-2} to 10^{-3} per donor cell to various recipients during a 90-minute mating period. Transfer begins about 5 minutes after the onset of mating and can be interrupted by mechanical agitation, indicating that cell-to-cell contact is necessary. Cells receiving F$_0$-*lac* are in turn effective donors of the element, but are unchanged in their capacity to act as donors or recipients of chromosomal determinants. F$_0$-*lac* is lost from host cells at a rate of about 5 per 10^6 divisions, indicating that such hosts are heterogenotes for the *lac* region.

E. coli K12 Hfr strains which harbor F_0-*lac* transfer it to zygotes within 5 minutes after contact is established. The transfer is apparently unlinked with chromosomal markers, F_0-*lac* entering recipients separately from the host chromosome.

The above observations suggest that F_0-*lac* may exist as an autonomous, cytoplasmic element. Examination of the levels of β-galactosidase production by cells carrying F_0-*lac* indicates that there may be 2 or 3 F_0-*lac* determinants per host chromosome.

2. The Integrated State

The possibility exists that the transmission element F_0 was attached to the chromosome of its host when the *lac* determinant was incorporated. That F_0-*lac* may at times assume the integrated state is suggested by its apparent recombination with the host chromosomal *lac* marker. Transmissible F_0-*lac*⁻ elements have been detected which probably arose by recombination of F_0-*lac*⁺ with the host *lac*⁻ allele. Haploid *lac*⁺ nondonor cells have been isolated which have presumably incorporated the *lac*⁺ marker and possibly the F_0 element into the host genome.

F_0-*lac* may on occasion become integrated after transduction into recipients. Among *Shigella* recipients in which stable transduction to *lac*⁺ apparently did not involve lysogenization, 30 % were able to transfer *lac*⁺ (F_0-*lac*⁺) serially, indicating close linkage of the determinants. In the remaining 70 % in which *lac*⁺ was stably integrated, it is likely that at least some cells carried an integrated or incorporated F_0-*lac*⁺ (see Falkow and Baron[253]).

Ultraviolet irradiation of ST2 cells carrying F_0-*lac* brings about a considerable increase in the frequency of its transfer per viable cell over the unirradiated control. The possibility that F_0-*lac* undergoes alternation between a chromosomal and a cytoplasmic site and is "induced" by UV cannot be ignored. This may in part account for the failure of acridine orange to eliminate the element from strain ST2.

3. Other Episomic Characteristics

F_0 exhibits some degree of mutual repression with the sex factor of *E. coli* K12. F⁻ strains harboring F_0-*lac* still behave as recipients for chromosomal markers, but exhibit resistance to infection with the sex factor. F_0-*lac* can be introduced into F⁺ and Hfr cells, but with low efficiency. Hfr and F⁺ strains carrying F_0-*lac* transfer this element at a reduced frequency. F_0-*lac* is very unstable in some Hfr (F_0-*lac*) strains, being lost at a rate of 1 in 10^3 divisions.

It is assumed that F_0-*lac* controls the formation of a mating substance which enables its hosts to pair in order to effect transfer. An immunological relationship has been demonstrated between cells carrying F_0-*lac* and cells carrying autonomous or integrated sex factors. Bacteriophage specific for donor strains of *E. coli* K12 do not attack F^- (F_0-*lac*) cells, however, and K12 male strains do not become resistant to this phage after infection with F_0-*lac*.[253]

F. ELEMENTS OF SUGGESTIVE EPISOMIC NATURE

1. THE FIMBRIATION, OR PILIATION, FACTOR

Fimbriae (pili) are filamentous, hair-like appendages unrelated to motility radiating from the cell surfaces of many Gram-negative organisms.[254] A genetic determinant controlling their synthesis can be transferred by sexual recombination among strains of *E. coli* K12, from K12 to *Salmonella typhosa*, and from K12 to *E. coli* B/r. The determinant has been mapped between the chromosomal loci controlling threonine independence and thiamine independence, lying close to the former.[255-257]

Brinton *et al.*[256] observed that a recipient can be made stably fimbriated by introduction of the chromosomal determinant during conjugation or unstably fimbriated by transduction of the marker. The instability of fimbriated transductants and the frequencies of cotransduction of fimbriation with other markers led these investigators to believe their observations inconsistent with the view that the property is controlled by a stable determinant of exclusively chromosomal location and to propose that the fimbriation factor can exist in a given strain in different states, depending on the method employed to introduce it. As these surface structures are not essential to the cell and as they and their controlling element may be irreversibly lost, the question of the episomic nature of the fibriation factor has been raised.

The genetic control of fimbriation has recently been shown to be complex and may be polygenic,[257, 258] and its consideration is beyond the scope of the present review. Further investigation is required before the episomic nature of the element(s) controlling fimbriation can be proposed.

2. THE MUTABILITY-TRANSFER FACTOR

A transmissible element enhancing the mutation rate to streptomycin (*Sm*) resistance in strains of *E. coli* has been discovered by Gundersen, Jyssum, and Lie.[259] The element appears not to affect the mutation rates of other genetic loci. The element, termed *Mu*, is irreversibly lost with a frequency approaching 10^{-2}, and this loss is enhanced by treatment of host cells with UV irradiation and acridine derivatives. *Mu* may be transferred to recipients by mixed culture. The presence of the sex factor in the donors enhances the frequency of transfer which, however, will occur in its absence. Attempts to locate the *Mu* character on the *E. coli* chromosome were unsuccessful; in crosses between *E. coli* K12 Hfr's and Mu^+ recipients, the character did not segregate among recombinants as if it were chromosomally located.

All observations appear to indicate that *Mu* is an extrachromosomal, infective element.

3. THE SPOROGENIC FACTOR

Jacob *et al.*[3] and Jacob and Wollman[4] have suggested that sporulation in bacilli may be controlled by a genetic determinant(s) of episomic nature. A discussion of the factors and events involved in sporulation upon which this suggestion was based is of an extent prohibitive to consideration in the present review. The reader is referred to the literature.

IV. Episomic Mediation of Genetic Transfer

Perhaps the most important property of episomic elements is their ability to effect the transfer of genetic information from or by their hosts.

Some temperate bacteriophages can transfer one or more genetic determinants from their host cells to recipients by the process of transduction. Restricted transduction has been mentioned previously with respect to bacteriophage λ and its capacity to transfer a specific segment of host genome, the *gal* marker, to recipients. General transduction is carried out by various other temperate phages and may be viewed as a nonselective incorporation of any host determinant by infecting phage genomes and its subsequent transfer to recipients via mature infectious phage. In Chapter 2 of this volume, Campbell gives detailed consideration to restricted and general transduction processes and discusses their use in genetic mapping, cistron identification, and chemical genetics.

The temperate bacteriophage τ (*tau*) is a female-specific phage which will form plaques on F⁻ strains, but not on Hfr or F⁺ strains of *E. coli* K12. Male cells are infected, but no lysogenization or lysis occurs. It is tempting to propose that the presence of F represses the viral or prophage functions of τ. F⁻ cells in which τ is reduced to the prophage state have been reported to act as donors of chromosomal material (Hakura and Hirota, cited in refs. 8, p. 105, and 248, p. 907).

As noted previously, the sex factor of *E. coli* K12 can mediate the transfer of one or more host markers by sexduction or by the transfer of segments of host chromosome during conjugation. The various aspects of F-promoted merogenote and chromosome transfer have been thoroughly discussed by Clark and Adelberg[9] and by Gross (Chapter 1).

The colicinogenic determinant *I*, when newly introduced into *Salmonella typhimurium*, can effect a very low frequency transfer of fairly large chromosomal segments by recipient hosts. The presence of *col E1* in the newly infected cells elevates the recombination frequency they exhibit. It was suggested that *col E1* facilitates the opening of a presumed circular chromosome so that its transfer by *col I* can occur more efficiently.[212] *Col I* also promotes chromosome transfer by *E. coli* F⁻ strains. In this case, recent colicinogenization is not required, and the very low frequencies of recombination are not elevated in the presence of *col E1*.[212]

Sugino and Hirota[248, 260] have reported that the introduction of certain R factors into F⁻ strains of *E. coli* K12 enables the latter to transfer chromosomal material. The transfer is polarized from R⁺F⁻ cells to R⁻F⁻ recipients, and fairly large chromosomal segments are transferred at frequencies of about 10^{-8} per donor cell. The linkage relationships observed in R-promoted genetic transfer are essentially those known from F-promoted conjugations. Elimination of these R factors with acridines results in a complete loss of fertility. The distribution of unselected markers among recombinants and the recombination frequency appear to vary with the particular R factor employed. This may indicate that an integrated state of the R factor is involved, the site of association being different for each R factor.

The F_0 transmission element has not been observed to confer upon recipient hosts the capacity to transfer chromosomal segments. However, proper conditions and bacterial participants may be found in which chromosome transfer may be detected. Thus far, genetic transfer mediated by F_0 is confined to its conjugal transfer of the *lac* determinant.

In addition to controlling the intercellular transfer of bacterial chromosomal determinants, episomic elements can potentiate or effect the transfer of other episomes. The presence of the sex factor in *E. coli* K12 cells enhances their capacity to transfer the *Mu* factor.[259] Cells carrying *col E1* and others can transfer them efficiently only if F or certain *col* factors, e.g., *col I*, are present also.[6, 208] It would appear that the capacity of F and *col I* to bring about the formation of stable, conjugal pairs by their hosts is responsible for their potentiation of transfer of other episomes.

The ability of the sex factor to effect the transfer of segments of bacterial chromosome by conjugation or by sexduction provides for the intercellular transfer of any suitably positioned episomes in the integrated state. The sexduction of λ prophage has been reported, and has been instrumental in providing corroborative evidence for the cytoplasmic expression of the immunity of lysogenic bacteria[3] and in facilitating studies of cellular regulation, which will be noted subsequently.[261]

Transfer of each of the episomic types can be mediated by transduction, itself effected by an episome (or maturation form thereof). Transduction of prophages,[100, 101] of the sex factor,[171, 172] of various *col* factors,[262, 263] and of the F_0-*lac* element[253] have been carried out successfully. R factors have been transduced in *E. coli* with phage P1 and in *Salmonella typhimurium* LT2 with phage P22.[237, 244] With phage P1, all four resistance factors were introduced simultaneously in the majority of transductants, the resistance factors segregating only rarely. All transductants could subsequently transfer the acquired resistances by conjugation. With phage P22, however, consistent segregation was observed, and the majority of transductants were unable to transfer drug resistance by conjugation. Watanabe and Fukasawa[237] were thus led to propose that each individual resistance factor is not an episome, but that they all are attached to, and transferred by an episomic element termed RTF. The process of transfer of drug resistance is thus comparable to sexduction. The patterns of segregation of the resistance factors in transduction suggested the linear arrangement of the factors with respect to RTF which was mentioned previously.

Transductional analysis of R factors conferring fertility on *E. coli* F⁻ hosts[248] has shown that the determinant of fertility is identical with or at least very closely linked to the determinant of infectious transmissibility, RTF. The fertility determinant can be separated from the determinants for drug resistance, but is closely linked to them.

Kaiser and Hogness[264] have found that λdg DNA will transform *gal⁻ E. coli* to *gal⁺*. Analysis of the transformed cells shows that phage genes are also present; hence the active DNA carries phage genes as well as galactose genes and is probably the entire λdg chromosome. Phage λ or its genome is required to effect this genetic transformation of *E. coli* with the DNA isolated from λdg. Transformation occurs only if the recipient cells exposed to λdg DNA are simultaneously infected with wild-type λ. The role of λ phage itself in the process is not certain. It appears to act as a type of "helper" phage, supplying functions absent in the λdg DNA. These may involve the adsorption and penetration of the DNA or the various processes attendant to the reduction to prophage of injected λ-defective phage chromosomes.

V. Episome-Episome Interactions

A. ELIMINATION OF PROPHAGES BY F

Cohen[265] has observed that the introduction of the episome F-*lac* into *E. coli* B has as a consequence the elimination or exclusion of certain prophages. If cells lysogenic for the defective prophage X or for phage P2 or a derivative are infected with F-*lac*, the prophages appear to be lost, judging from the loss of immunity and the incapacity to liberate infective phage particles.

A suppression of the expression of prophage genes is not involved, as *lac⁻* segregants of *E. coli* B which have lost F-*lac* also do not appear to carry the prophage originally present.

This phenomenon does not occur when F-*lac* is introduced into cells of *E. coli* K12 or into hybrids of K12 and B lysogenic for one of the above phages. The prophages remain in the sexduced cells.

Elimination of prophage does not occur if *E. coli* B cells are infected with wild-type F_1 or with F-*gal*. There thus appears to exist some type of competition between episomes which depends on the genotype of the receptor and on the nature of the episome introduced.

One should consider the possibility that the attachment sites of the prophages in question are located very near the *lac* region of the *E. coli* B chromosome and that pairing of F-*lac* with its homologous region effects prophage elimination in some way.

B. Elimination of Colicinogenic Factors by RTF

Kato *et al.*[266] have reported that R factors can eliminate colicinogenic determinants from host cells. When R factors of a variety of constitutions were transferred to the doubly colicinogenic strain *E. coli* K235 K^+X^+, *col* K or *col* X was observed to be lost by a proportion of the progeny. The corresponding colicin was not produced nor was immunity to its action exhibited. The elimination of unrelated bacterial markers was not observed. An element common to all the R factors, i.e., RTF, appeared to be responsible.

Epistasis of RTF and *col* factors, i.e., a simple inhibition of the production of colicin and the expression of immunity, cannot account for the phenomenon. Removal of R factors from the apparently *col⁻* cells with acriflavin does not restore the original phenotype. Cells are still incapable of producing colicin and are sensitive to its action. Acriflavin was shown to be ineffective in removing the *col* factors themselves.

It was observed that when R factors were introduced, not all recipients lose colicinogeny at once; mixed clones are formed containing cells which produce a small amount of colicin as well as noncolicinogenic cells which are partially susceptible to the parental colicin. It would appear the RTF interferes with the autonomous replication of these *col* factors which are thus diluted out during subsequent host generations.

C. Interaction between RTF and F

Watanabe and co-workers have observed interactions between the determinant RTF and the sex factor which include an apparent epistasis of RTF to F, a suppression or masking of the genetic expression of the latter, when both elements are harbored by a single cell.

The frequency of transfer of R factors of various types to recipients is halved if the recipient cells carry F either in the autonomous or in the integrated state. Likewise, the presence of R factors in recipient cells lowers the frequency with which wild-type F, F′ elements and chromosomal material can be introduced.[238] The possibility that an incompatibility of cell surface structures is involved cannot be eliminated. As noted previously, cells harboring R factors or F have periodate-sensitive "mating substances" which are not identical.

Hfr, F_1, and F′ strains infected with multiple resistance factors or various segregant types are essentially unable to transfer host chromosomal segments, F_1, or F′ particles, respectively, to *E. coli* F⁻ recipients.[238, 244] Some chromosome transfer by Hfr cells does occur, but at frequencies reduced about 100-fold from normal. The sex factors in such cells are not irreversibly inactivated or eliminated, as cells from which R factors are lost spontaneously regain their original ability to transfer genetic material. The presence of F in donor strains does not appear to interfere with their capacity to transfer R factors.[238]

The introduction of R factors into Hfr, F_1, and F′ cells confers upon them resistance to male-specific phages. Resistance has been shown to involve the inability of the phage to adsorb to such cells.[267] The synthesis of the specific receptor sites for the phage appears to be prevented. This alteration of the cell surface may account in part for the inability of male strains of *E. coli* K12 carrying R factors to transfer genetic material in a normal manner. The efficiency of formation of conjugal pairs may be reduced. However, as R factors can be transferred with normal efficiency from such male strains, their inability to transfer autonomous F particles may involve other variables.

The fact that the above interactions between R factors and F occur when multiple resistance factors or various segregant types are employed supports the contention that these R factors contain a common determinant, RTF, responsible for the phenomena observed.

With respect to the synthesis of specific cell-surface constituents, RTF appears to be epistatic to F. It has been proposed[238, 267] that the presence of RTF in a cell harboring F prevents the synthesis of specific surface constituents controlled by the latter, surface structures peculiar to RTF being synthesized instead. The possibility that RTF only modifies the surface structures synthesized by F is suggested by a comparable situation involving bacteriophage conversion.[115]

VI. Episomic Elements, Cellular Regulatory Mechanisms, and the Evolutionary Scheme

Normal systems of regulation in a cell may be altered upon introduction of an episomic element. New controls may be superimposed or various processes withdrawn from their normal regulation by bacterial genes. This is particularly obvious in the case of cells carrying a prophage. The system of repression assuring specific immunity in lysogenic cells may be viewed as a superimposed system of regulation. Bacterial genes may be withdrawn from their usual regulatory systems by incorporation into the genetic material of a sex factor or a prophage. That this is the case has been demonstrated for the *E. coli*-λdg system by Buttin,[268, 269] by Yarmolinsky,[270, 271] and by Starlinger.[272] The insertion of the *gal* region into the λ genome does not appear to modify the internal system of regulation of the *gal* genes. However, during vegetative development of λdg, the formation of enzymes of the galactose pathway appears to be under the control of the phage genome. Introduction of λdg particles derived from inducible *gal+* cells into *gal−* cells is followed by constitutive synthesis of the pertinent enzymes. If the same λdg particles are introduced into a cell lysogenic for λ (and hence immune), the galactose enzymes are not synthesized until inducer is added. If the immune cells are treated with UV after introduction of λdg, the immunity mechanism breaks down, and constitutive synthesis occurs. The bacterial genes are said to be *derepressed*. Similarly, when heterogenotic cells carrying such λdg particles as prophage are irradiated, the induction of the prophage is accompanied by constitutive enzyme synthesis. Of particular interest is the fact that this is also observed after irradiation of haploid *gal+* cells carrying wild-type λ as prophage.

Similar experiments have been done by Revel and co-workers[273, 275] employing the defective transducing phage P1 dl, a derivative of P1 that carries the *lac* region of *E. coli*.[267] Analogous results were obtained: constitutive synthesis of β-galactosidase was observed during vegetative multiplication of P1 dl elements derived from inducible cells.

It thus appears that while the viral functions of a prophage are repressed, the expression of associated bacterial genes is under normal cellular and bacterial control by bacterial regulatory genes. However, when viral genes are released from repression so that they can express themselves in vegetative phage multiplication, a derepression of the associated bacterial functions occurs and they are withdrawn from the systems of control of the host cell. The fact that λ prophage, upon induction with UV, can effect this derepression at an adjacent chromosomal site not incorporated into the phage genome suggests that elements of episomic nature may be potentially capable of bringing about marked changes in the cellular regulatory mechanisms of their hosts, particularly in response to changes in environmental or intracellular conditions.

Recently, Jacob and Brenner[154a] have presented an hypothesis concerning the regulation of DNA synthesis in bacteria. "L'hypothèse du replicon" is ingenious in design and is favored by the results of several unrelated studies, as will be noted subsequently. The new concepts will be considered here as they pertain to the ability of episomic elements to regulate perhaps the most important sequence of events in the life of a cell: the replication of its genome. Any transmissible element which is able to assume control of the DNA synthesis of its host cell is of obvious interest to those concerned with the genesis of neoplastic growth.

The chromosome(s) of a bacterium or a phage and an episomic element are said to constitute units of independent replication or *replicons*, the reproduction of which is governed by the presence and activity of certain specific determinants which they themselves carry. A replicon is characterized by at least two specific determinants: a structural gene governing the synthesis of a specific cytoplasmic element, an active element of replication termed an *initiator*; an operator gene[161] of replication, a *replicator*, a specific element upon which the corresponding initiator acts and which permits the replication of the deoxyribonucleotide sequence attached to it. The two elements are specific. The initiator of a given replicon acts only on the replicator of this replicon, not on an heterologous unit. A given replicator is responsive only to the action of its homologous activator. Once this specific interaction has occurred, all the DNA associated with the replicator is copied.

When a phage introduces its genome into a bacterial cell, its initiator interacts with its replicator, and vegetative phage multiplication ensues independently of the bacterial chromosome. When reduction to prophage occurs, however, the specific system of immunity is said to prevent the synthesis of initiator by the phage, and the replication of its genome is thus controlled by the replicon to which it is attached, the bacterial chromosome.

The same may be said for F. In F+ cells it may be pictured as replicating in an autonomous manner under its own regulatory system. In Hfr cells, the sex factor attached to the chromosome is normally replicated coordinately with the chromosome under the control of the bacterial replicator, the system specific for F being suppressed. Upon conjugation, however, it is proposed that the system of F replication is activated so that the F initiator acts on the F replicator and induces the formation of a chromosomal replica, synthesis beginning at the point of attachment of F and progressing down the length of the chromosome, one of the copies then being transferred to the conjugal partner. The possibility exists that any episome capable of mediating chromosome transfer may act in a similar manner. Thus, under certain conditions, an episomic element may assume control of the replication of the DNA of its host cell.

The above hypothesis finds support in the observation of Bouck and Adelberg[277] that DNA synthesis in Hfr cells is required for the initiation of chromosome transfer. That it is a replica of the Hfr chromosome synthesized under the control of the F system of replication that is transferred during mating is suggested by the following[154a]: Acridine dyes affect the autonomous replication of F, but not its replication in Hfr Strains, where it is presumably under the control of the chromosomal replicator. The F system of replication appears therefore to be more sensitive than the bacterial system. It is observed that acridine derivatives inhibit genetic transfer by Hfr cells. In addition, temperature-sensitive mutants of F have been obtained which replicate normally at 30°C. but cannot replicate properly at 37°C. and are hence diluted out from their hosts. In Hfr strains in which this F mutant is attached to the chromosome, no thermosensitivity is observed, as the host replicon is not affected at 37°C. However, during conjugation, such Hfr cells transfer their chromosomes much more efficiently at 30° than at 37°C.

Chromosome replication in *Bacillus subtilis* has been shown to be sequential and to exhibit polarity.[278] The relative frequencies of various markers in transforming DNA isolated at various stages of growth have permitted the construction of a genetic map indicating that replication starts at a fixed point and proceeds linearly.

Maaløe[279] has proposed a model for the replication of the *E. coli* chromosome involving a regular, oriented synthesis of DNA. Cairns,[280] on the basis of autoradiographic studies, has suggested a polarity of *E. coli* chromosome replication. That this may actually be the case is indicated by the studies of Nagata[281, 282] on the pattern of duplication of λ prophage in synchronized cultures of Hfr cells. The kinetics of prophage duplication over one DNA replication cycle were observed to be strain specific and to be directly correlated with the *E. coli* linkage map. It was concluded that chromosome duplication is polarized and in Hfr cells starts from the terminus at which F is attached and proceeds forward.

Phenomena following the introduction of an episome into its host are sometimes suggestive of cellular differentiation. Stable, host cell modifications induced by episomes have been noted previously, bacteriophage conversion phenomena being particularly suggestive. Changes in host cell phenotype may be associated with a change in state of any episomic element carried. In the case of the sex factor, transition from the integrated state to the autonomous state renders its host cell susceptible to environmental conditions effecting an elimination of the element, thereby changing the nature of the cell and its clonal descendants. On the other hand, transition of F from the autonomous to the integrated state effectively removes the capacity of its host to infect neighboring recipients with the element and thereby halts the spread of its associated characteristics throughout a population.

The temptation to apply episomic models to the processes of regulation and differentiation in other biological systems is strong, but as pointed out by Jacob and Wollman,[4] our understanding of the genetic and physiological behavior of the germ cells and somatic cells of higher organisms must be improved before this can be done effectively.

It is quite possible that episomic elements played an important role in the evolutionary differentiation of at least some bacterial groups. As discussed by Ravin,[283] the evolution of a bacterial population into forms better adapted to survive and thrive in new ecological situations involves the selection of cells with new and "improved" genotypes. These arise through the action of mutation and, presumably, recombination. The mediation of genetic transfer by episomes, by means of conjugal chromosome transfer, sexduction, or transduction, would serve to distribute various mutant characters throughout a population. The role of episomes in evolutionary processes would thus be to enhance the speed at which genetic variety is acquired in a bacterial population and to provide for a greater number of possible genetic types.

The existence of episome-mediated gene transfer facilitates an examination of evolutionary relationships among bacteria. Organisms which are very closely related may be assumed to have a certain degree of genetic homology. As a measure of homology, genetic compatibility, i.e., the extent to which genetic recombination can occur, can be used. For a discussion of conjugal interactions among Enterobacteriaceae, see Gross (Chapter 1) and Mäkelä et al.[283a] Another measure of genetic homology, or more correctly nucleic acid homology, is molecular hybridization, the in vitro formation of hybrid DNA molecules between strands of DNA isolated from different bacterial species. A considerable body of evidence indicates a very close relationship between genetic compatibility, molecular hybrid formation, and taxonomic status (see Marmur et al.[43b] for a review). Studies combining the two indices of genetic homology, as reported by Falkow et al.[284] for E. coli K12 and Salmonella, constitute the basis of future work on the molecular basis of evolutionary phenomena.

With respect to the evolutionary differentiation of the episomes themselves, little can be said. The origin and development of viral elements is unknown. A possible mode of origin of the nonviral episomes has been suggested by Luria et al.[276] If a segment of bacterial chromosome is incorporated into the genome of a prophage, such as in the formation of the λdg and P1 dl elements, the resulting unit may be so defective with respect to the production of viral components that it appears to be devoid of viral properties except those involving autonomous replication. Thus, RTF and F_0 may represent defective phage genomes which are associated with the bacterial determinants for drug resistance and lactose utilization, respectively. Over ten years ago, Hayes[132] expressed the idea that F might be some sort of defective prophage. Frédéricq[217c] has compared colicinogenic determinants to the genomes of defective virulent phage. It is stated that in some cases virulent phages may kill bacteria in the absence of reproduction and cell lysis, as do colicins. A protein located at the tip of the phage tail is held responsible, and the lethal protein of phage T6 is said to be closely related to colicin K. The suggestion was made that *col* factors may represent the genomes of defective phage which have lost the capacity to bring about the formation of infectious phage particles and to elicit lysis, yet retain the determinant for the synthesis of lethal protein. One should recall that no serological relationships have been detected among the colicins and phages examined.[4] However, it was also pointed out that *col* factors could be of entirely independent origin and represent a stage in the evolution of virulent bacteriophage. As stated previously, phage τ is said to confer fertility on F⁻ strains of *E. coli* in which it is reduced to prophage. As other episomic elements may also confer fertility, one is tempted to accept the possibility of a viral origin of nonviral episomes.

In conclusion, we find in the bacterial world forms exhibiting specialized physiological and genetic features, of considerable interest in themselves, that render them particularly valuable for the investigation of basic problems of development and heredity. In many phases of science, progress can be made by generalization. As our knowledge of the cell increases and improves, a careful extension of the episome concept to cellular regulation and differentiation in higher organisms may provide clarification of heretofore obscure phenomena.

ACKNOWLEDGMENTS

The author is indebted to Drs. T. Watanabe, S. Silver, W. Maas, and R. Clowes for making their manuscripts available to her prior to publication.

REFERENCES

1 J. Lederberg, *Physiol. Revs.* **32,** 403 (1952).
2 F. Jacob and E. L. Wollman, *Compt. rend. acad. sci.* **247,** 154 (1958).
3 F. Jacob, P. Shaeffer, and E. L. Wollman, *in* "Microbial Genetics." *Symposium Soc. Gen. Microbiol.* **10,** 67 (1960).
4 F. Jacob and E. L. Wollman, "Sexuality and the Genetics of Bacteria," Chapter 16, p. 311. Academic Press, New York, 1961.
5 A. Campbell, *Advances in Genet.* **11,** 101 (1962).
6 S. M. Smith and B. A. D. Stocker, *Brit. Med. Bull.* **18,** 46 (1962).
7 P. H. A. Sneath, *Brit. Med. Bull.* **18,** 41 (1962).
8 T. Watanabe, *Bacteriol. Revs.* **27,** 87 (1963).
9 A. J. Clark and E. A. Adelberg, *Ann. Rev. Microbiol.* **16,** 289 (1962).
10 Y. Hirota, *Nature* **178,** 92 (1956).
11 Y. Hirota, *Proc. Natl. Acad. Sci. U. S.* **46,** 57 (1960).
12 A. Lwoff, *Bacteriol. Revs.* **17,** 269 (1953).
13 G. Bertani, *Advances in Virus Research* **5,** 151 (1958).
14 F. Jacob and E. L. Wollman, *in* "The Viruses" (F. M. Burnet and W. M. Stanley, eds.), Vol. 2, p. 319. Academic Press, New York, 1959.
15 J. W. Whitfield, *Brit. Med. Bull.* **18,** 56 (1962).

[16] F. Jacob, C. R. Fuerst, and E. L. Wollman, *Ann. inst. Pasteur* **93,** 724 (1957).

[17] F. Jacob, *Harvey Lectures Ser.* **54,** 1 (1960).

[18] R. Thomas, *Virology* **9,** 275 (1959).

[19] M. Lieb, *J. Bacteriol.* **65,** 642 (1953).

[20] R. Ting, *Virology* **12,** 68 (1960).

[21] E. Kellenberger, *Advances in Virus Research* **8,** 1 (1961).

[22] J. Séchaud, *Arch. sci. (Geneva)* **13,** 427 (1960).

[23] G. Bertani, *Cold Spring Harbor Symposia Quant. Biol.* **18,** 65 (1953).

[24] F. Jacob, "Les bactéries lysogènes et la notion de provirus." Masson, Paris, 1954.

[25] J. F. Whitfield and R. K. Appleyard, *J. Gen. Microbiol.* **17,** 453 (1957).

[26] F. Jacob, "Monographies de l'Institut Pasteur." Masson, Paris, 1954.

[27] F. Jacob and E. L. Wollman, *in* "The Chemical Basis of Heredity" (W. McElroy and B. Glass, eds.), p. 468. Johns Hopkins Press, Baltimore, Maryland, 1957.

[28] E. M. Lederberg and J. Lederberg, *Genetics* **38,** 51 (1953).

[29] E. L. Wollman, *Ann. inst. Pasteur* **84,** 281 (1953).

[30] R. K. Appleyard, *Genetics* **39,** 440 (1954).

[31] E. L. Wollman and F. Jacob, "La sexualité des bactéries." Masson, Paris, 1959.

[32] E. M. Lederberg, *in* "Microbial Genetics." *Symposium Soc. Gen. Microbiol.* **10,** 115 (1960).

[33] K. Kurahashi, *Science* **125,** 114 (1957).

[34] F. Jacob and E. L. Wollman, *in* "Recent Progress in Microbiology." *Intern. Congr. Microbiol. Stockholm* **7,** 15 (1959).

[35] P. Frédéricq, *Compt. rend. soc. biol.* **147,** 2046 (1953).

[36] G. Bertani and E. Six, *Virology* **6,** 357 (1958).

[37] E. Calef and G. Licciardello, *Virology* **12,** 81 (1960).

[38] M. L. Morse, E. M. Lederberg, and J. Lederberg, *Genetics* **41,** 142 (1956).

[39] M. L. Morse, E. M. Lederberg, and J. Lederberg, *Genetics* **41,** 758 (1956).

[40] A. D. Kaiser, *Virology* **3,** 42 (1957).

[41] M. Levine, *Virology* **3,** 22 (1957).

[42] A. D. Kaiser and F. Jacob, *Virology* **4,** 509 (1957).

[43] F. Jacob and E. L. Wollman, "Sexuality and the Genetics of Bacteria," Chapter 15, p. 285. Academic Press, New York, 1961.

[43a] G. Attardi, S. Naono, F. Gros, S. Brenner, and F. Jacob, *Compt. rend. acad. sci.* **255,** 2303 (1962).

[43b] J. Marmur, C. L. Schildkraut, and P. Doty, *in* "The Molecular Basis of Neoplasia," p. 9. University of Texas Press, Austin, 1962.

[43c] S. Brenner, F. Jacob, and M. Meselson, *Nature* **190,** 576 (1961).

[44] F. Jacob and E. L. Wollman, *Cold Spring Harbor Symposia Quant. Biol.* **18,** 101 (1953).

[45] G. Bertani, *J. Bacteriol.* **67,** 696 (1954).

[46] F. Jacob and E. L. Wollman, *Compt. rend. acad. sci.* **239,** 455 (1954).

[47] F. Jacob and E. L. Wollman, *Ann. inst. Pasteur* **91,** 486 (1956).

[48] A. B. Pardee, F. Jacob, and J. Monod, *J. Mol. Biol.* **1,** 165 (1959).

[49] F. Jacob and A. Campbell, *Compt. rend. acad. sci.* **248,** 3219 (1959).

[50] F. Jacob and E. L. Wollman, *Ann. inst. Pasteur* **87,** 653 (1954).

[51] R. Sussman and F. Jacob, *Compt. rend. acad. sci.* **254,** 1517 (1962).

[52] N. D. Zinder, *Virology* **5,** 291 (1958).

[53] S. E. Luria, D. K. Fraser, J. N. Adams, and J. W. Burrous, *Cold Spring Harbor Symposia Quant. Biol.* **23,** 71 (1958).

[54] E. Bertani, *Virology* **4,** 53 (1957).

[55] M. Levine and E. Cox, *Bacteriol. Proc.* p. 163 (1961).

[56] K. W. Fisher, *Brit. Med. Bull.* **18**, 19 (1962).

[57] K. W. Fisher, *J. Gen. Microbiol.* **28**, 711 (1962).

[58] F. Jacob, R. Sussman, and J. Monod, *Compt. rend. acad. sci.* **254**, 4214 (1962).

[59] S. Benzer and S. P. Champe, *Proc. Natl. Acad. Sci. U. S.* **47**, 1025 (1961).

[60] C. Yanofsky, D. R. Helinski, and B. M. Maling, *Cold Spring Harbor Symposia Quant. Biol.* **26**, 11 (1961).

[61] E. L. Wollman, *Ann. inst. Pasteur* **84**, 281 (1953).

[62] A. Campbell, *Virology* **14**, 22 (1961).

[63] S. Brenner, F. Jacob, and M. Messelson, *Nature* **190**, 576 (1961).

[64] F. Jacob and J. Monod, *J. Mol. Biol.* **3**, 318 (1961).

[65] L. E. Bertani, *Virology* **13**, 378 (1961).

[66] M. L. Morse, *Genetics* **39**, 984 (1954).

[67] M. L. Morse, *Genetics* **47**, 255 (1962).

[68] W. Arber, G. Kellenberger, and J. Weiglé, *Schweiz. Z. allgem. Pathol. u. Bakteriol.* **20**, 659 (1957).

[69] A. Campbell, *Virology* **4**, 366 (1957).

[70] W. Arber, *Arch. sci. (Geneva)* **11**, 259 (1958).

[71] J. Weiglé, M. Messelson, and K. Paigen, *J. Mol. Biol.* **1**, 379 (1959).

[72] A. Campbell, *Virology* **9**, 293 (1959).

[73] A. Campbell, *Virology* **14**, 22 (1961).

[74] J. Weiglé, *J. Mol. Biol.* **3**, 393 (1961).

[75] D. K. Fraser, *Virology* **17**, 397 (1962).

[76] A. Campbell, *Virology* **11**, 339 (1960).

[77] G. Bertani and S. J. Nice, *J. Bacteriol.* **67**, 202 (1954).

[78] J. Boyd, *J. Pathol. Bacteriol.* **63**, 445 (1951).

[79] J. R. Christensen, *Virology* **4**, 184 (1957).

[80] K. G. Lark and O. Maaløe, *Biochim. et Biophys. Acta* **15**, 345 (1954).

[81] A. Lwoff, A. S. Kaplan, and E. Ritz, *Ann. inst. Pasteur* **86**, 127 (1954).

[82] G. S. Stent and C. R. Fuerst, *Virology* **2**, 737 (1956).

[83] G. Bertani, *Virology* **18**, 131 (1962).

[84] A. Campbell and E. Balbinder, *Genetics* **44**, 309 (1959).

[85] E. Six, *Virology* **14**, 220 (1961).

[86] A. Lwoff, L. Siminovitch, and N. Kjeldgaard, *Ann. inst. Pasteur* **79**, 815 (1950).

[87] R. Latarjet, *Ann. inst. Pasteur* **81**, 389 (1951).

[88] H. Marcovich, *Ann. inst. Pasteur* **90**, 303 (1956).

[89] G. S. Stent and C. R. Fuerst, *Advances in Biol. and Med. Phys.* **7**, 1 (1960).

[90] F. Jacob, *Compt. rend. acad. sci.* **234**, 2238 (1952).

[91] H. Williams-Smith, *J. Gen. Microbiol.* **8**, 116 (1953).

[92] A. Lwoff and F. Jacob, *Compt. rend. acad. sci.* **234**, 2308 (1952).

[93] A. Lwoff and L. Siminovich, *Ann. inst. Pasteur* **82**, 676 (1952).

[94] J. S. Gots, T. J. Bird, and S. Mudd, *Biochim. et Biophys. Acta* **17**, 449 (1955).

[95] E. Borek and J. Rockenbach, *Federation Proc.* **14**, 184 (1955).

[96] N. Otsuji, M. Sekiguchi, T. Iijima, and Y. Takagi, *Nature* **184**, 1079 (1959).

[97] R. Ben-Gurion, *Biochem. Biophys. Research Communs.* **8**, 456 (1962).

[98] N. E. Melechen and P. Skaar, *Virology* **16**, 21 (1962).

[98a] N. Sicard and R. Devoret, *Compt. rend. acad. sci.* **255**, 1417 (1962).

[98b] D. Korn and A. Weissbach, *Biochim. et Biophys. Acta* **61**, 775 (1962).

[99] F. Jacob, *Ann. inst. Pasteur* **83**, 295 (1952).

[99a] A. M. Ryan, Doctoral Dissertation, Columbia University, New York, 1963.

[100] F. Jacob, *Virology* **1**, 207 (1955).

[101] W. Arber, *Virology* **11**, 273 (1960).

[102] H. Ionesco, *Compt. rend. acad. sci.* **233**, 1702 (1951).

[103] E. S. Anderson and A. Felix, *J. Gen. Microbiol.* **13**, 519 (1953).

[104] G. Bertani, *Ann. inst. Pasteur* **84**, 273 (1953).

[104a] S. Benzer, *Proc. Natl. Acad. Sci. U.S.* **41**, 344 (1955).

[105] V. J. Freeman, *J. Bacteriol.* **61**, 675 (1951).

[106] N. B. Groman, *J. Bacteriol.* **66**, 184 (1953).

[107] N. B. Groman, *J. Bacteriol.* **69**, 9 (1955).

[108] W. L. Barksdale and A. M. Pappenheimer, Jr., *J. Bacteriol.* **67**, 220 (1954).

[109] L. Barksdale, *Compt. rend. acad. sci.* **240**, 1831 (1955).

[110] N. B. Groman and M. Eaton, *J. Bacteriol.* **70**, 637 (1955).

[111] H. Ionesco, *Compt. rend. acad. sci.* **237**, 1794 (1953).

[112] S. Iseki and T. Sakai, *Proc. Japan Acad.* **29**, 127 (1953).

[113] S. Iseki and K. Kashiwagi, *Proc. Japan Acad.* **31**, 558 (1955).

[114] P. W. Robbins and T. Uchida, *Biochemistry* **1**, 323 (1962).

[115] P. W. Robbins and T. Uchida, *Federation Proc.* **21**, 702 (1962).

[115a] B. Holloway and G. Cooper, *J. Bacteriol.* **84**, 1321 (1962).

[116] L. Barksdale, *Bacteriol. Revs.* **23**, 202 (1959).

[116a] L. Barksdale, L. Garmise, and R. Rivera, *J. Bacteriol.* **81**, 527 (1961).

[117] H. Uetake, S. E. Luria, and J. W. Burrous, *Virology* **5**, 68 (1958).

[118] G. Ivánovics, *J. Gen. Microbiol.* **28**, 87 (1962).

[118a] J. E. Blair and M. Carr, *J. Bacteriol.* **82**, 984 (1961).

[118b] R. A. Altenbern, *Biochem. Biophys. Research Communs.* **9**, 109 (1962).

[119] G. S. Stent and C. R. Fuerst, *J. Gen. Physiol.* **38**, 441 (1955).

[120] G. S. Stent, C. R. Fuerst, and F. Jacob, *Compt. rend. acad. sci.* **244**, 1840 (1957).

[121] R. C. Ting, *Virology* **16**, 115 (1962).

[122] D. E. Sheppard, *Virology* **17**, 212 (1962).

[123] C. A. Thomas and T. Pinkerton, cited in P. E. Hartman and A. W. Kozinski, *Virology* **17**, 233 (1962).

[124] P. E. Hartman and A. W. Kozinski, *Virology* **17**, 233 (1962).

[125] A. D. Hershey, M. D. Kamen, J. W. Kennedy, and H. Gest, *J. Gen. Physiol.* **34**, 305 (1951).

[126] W. Hayes, F. Jacob, and E. L. Wollman, *in* "Methodology in Basic Genetics" (W. J. Burdette, ed.), p. 129. Holden-Day, San Francisco, California, 1963.

[127] W. Hayes, *Nature* **169**, 118 (1952).

[128] T. F. Anderson, E. L. Wollman, and F. Jacob, *Ann. inst. Pasteur* **93**, 450 (1957).

[129] L. L. Cavalli, J. Lederberg, and E. M. Lederberg, *J. Gen. Microbiol.* **8**, 89 (1953).

[130] W. Hayes, *J. Gen. Microbiol.* **8**, 72 (1953).

[131] J. Lederberg, L. L. Cavalli, and E. M. Lederberg, *Genetics* **37**, 720 (1952).

[131a] J. Lederberg, *Intern. Congr. Microbiol. Abstr.* **7**, 59 (1958).

[132] W. Hayes, *Cold Spring Harbor Symposia Quant. Biol.* **18**, 75 (1953).

[133] E. L. Wollman and F. Jacob, *Compt. rend. acad. sci.* **247**, 536 (1958).

[134] E. Borek and A. Ryan, *Biochim. et Biophys. Acta* **41**, 67 (1960).

[135] F. Jacob and E. L. Wollman, *Compt. rend. acad. sci.* **240**, 2566 (1955).

[136] P. H. A. Sneath and J. Lederberg, *Proc. Natl. Acad. Sci. U. S.* **47**, 86 (1961).

[137] L. L. Cavalli, *Boll. Ist. sieroterap. milan.* **29**, 281 (1950).

[138] E. L. Wollman and F. Jacob, *Compt. rend. acad. sci.* **240**, 2449 (1955).

[139] E. L. Wollman, F. Jacob, and W. Hayes, *Cold Spring Harbor Symposia Quant. Biol.* **21**, 141 (1956).

[140] E. L. Wollman and F. Jacob, *Ann. inst. Pasteur* **95**, 641 (1958).

[141] F. Jacob and E. L. Wollman, *Compt. rend. acad. sci.* **245**, 1840 (1957).

[142] F. Jacob and E. L. Wollman *in* "The Biological Replication of Macromolecules." *Symposia Soc. Exptl. Biol.* **No. 12,** 75 (1958).

[143] S. E. Luria and M. Delbrück, *Genetics* **28,** 491 (1943).

[144] J. Lederberg and E. M. Lederberg, *J. Bacteriol.* **63,** 399 (1952).

[145] F. Jacob and E. L. Wollman, *Compt. rend. acad. sci.* **242,** 303 (1956).

[146] E. A. Adelberg and S. N. Burns, *Rec. Genet. Soc. Am.* **28,** 57 (1959).

[147] E. A. Adelberg and S. N. Burns, *J. Bacteriol.* **79,** 321 (1960).

[148] P. J. Driskell-Zamenhof and E. A. Adelberg, *J. Mol. Biol.* **6,** 483 (1963).

[149] P. J. Driskell, Doctoral Dissertation, University of California, Berkeley, 1962.

[150] A. Richter, *Genetics* **42,** 391 (1957).

[151] A. Richter, *Proc. 10th Intern. Congr. Genet.,* Montreal **2,** 232 (1958).

[152] A. Richter, *Genet. Research Cambr.* **2,** 333 (1961).

[153] Y. Hirota, *Rec. Genet. Soc. Am.* **28,** 75 (1959).

[154] F. Jacob and E. A. Adelberg, *Compt. rend. acad. sci.* **249,** 189 (1959).

[154a] F. Jacob and S. Brenner, *Compt. rend. acad. sci.* **256,** 298 (1963).

[155] Y. Hirota and P. H. A. Sneath, *Japan. J. Genetics* **36,** 307 (1961).

[156] F. Jacob and E. L. Wollman, *Compt. rend soc. biol.* **154,** 1960 (1960).

[156a] H. Condamine and G. Stanier, cited in G. Martin and F. Jacob, *Compt. rend. acad. sci.* **254,** 3589 (1962).

[157] R. C. Clowes, *in* "Microbial Genetics." *Symposium Soc. Gen. Microbiol.* **10,** 92 (1960).

[158] H. Echols, A. Garen, S. Garen, and A. Torriani, *J. Mol. Biol.* **3,** 425 (1961).

[159] A. Garen and H. Echols, *J. Bacteriol.* **83,** 297 (1962).

[160] A. Garen and H. Echols, *Proc. Natl. Acad. Sci. U. S.* **48,** 1398 (1962).

[161] F. Jacob, D. Perrin, C. Sanchez, and J. Monod, *Compt. rend. acad. sci.* **250,** 1727 (1960).

[162] F. Cuzin, *Compt. rend. acad. sci.* **255,** 1149 (1962).

[163] T. Loeb, *Science* **131,** 932 (1960).

[164] Y. Hirota and T. Iijima, *Nature* **180,** 655 (1957).

[164a] R. Maas and W. K. Maas, *Proc. Natl. Acad. Sci. U. S.* **48,** 1887 (1962).

[165] J. Scaife and J. D. Gross, *Biochem. Biophys. Research Communs.* **7,** 403 (1962).

[166] F. Cuzin, *Compt. rend. acad. sci.* **254,** 1211 (1962).

[166a] A. J. Clark, *Genetics* **48,** 105 (1963).

[166b] P. G. de Haan and A. H. Stouthamer, *Genet. Research Cambr.* **4,** 30 (1963).

[167] J. Lederberg and E. M. Lederberg, *in* "Cellular Mechanisms in Differentiation and Growth" (D. Rudnick, ed.), p. 101. Princeton Univ. Press, Princeton, New Jersey, 1956.

[168] A. L. Taylor and E. A. Adelberg, *Biochem. Biophys. Research Communs.* **5,** 400 (1961).

[169] P. Frédéricq, *Compt. rend. soc. biol.* **154,** 2146 (1960).

[170] A. L. Taylor and E. A. Adelberg, *Genetics* **45,** 1233 (1960).

[171] S. K. DeWitt and E. A. Adelberg, *J. Bacteriol.* **83,** 673 (1962).

[172] W. Arber, *Virology* **11,** 273 (1960).

[173] N. D. Zinder, *Science* **133,** 2069 (1961).

[174] G. A. Maccacaro, *Nature* **176,** 125 (1955).

[175] G. A. Maccacaro and R. Comolli, *J. Gen. Microbiol.* **15,** 121 (1956).

[176] G. A. Maccacaro and C. Colombo, *Nature* **178,** 421 (1956).

[177] L. LeMinor and S. LeMinor, cited in *Cold Spring Harbor Symposia Quant. Biol.* **21,** 150 (1956).

[178] I. Ørskov and F. Ørskov, *Acta Pathol. Microbiol. Scand.* **48,** 37 (1960).

[179] M. Turri and G. A. Maccacaro, *Giorn. microbiol.* **8,** 1 (1960).

[180] T. Loeb and N. D. Zinder, *Proc. Natl. Acad. Sci. U. S.* **47**, 282 (1961).

[181] J. E. Davis, J. H. Strauss, Jr., and R. L. Sinsheimer, *Science* **134**, 1427 (1961).

[182] R. Dettori, G. A. Maccacaro, and G. L. Piccinin, *Giorn. microbiol.* **9**, 141 (1961).

[183] A. J. Clark, unpublished. Cited in ref. 9, p. 306.

[184] P. D. Skaar, A. Richter, and J. Lederberg, *Proc. Natl. Acad. Sci. U. S.* **43**, 329 (1957).

[185] J. R. Preer, *Genetics* **33**, 349 (1948).

[186] P. J. Driskell and E. A. Adelberg, *Bacteriol. Proc.* p. 186 (1961).

[187] R. Lavallé and F. Jacob, *Compt. rend. acad. sci.* **252**, 1678 (1961).

[188] S. Shiba, A. Terawaki, T. Taguchi, and J. Kawamata, *Biken's J.* **1**, 179 (1958).

[189] S. Shiba, A. Terawaki, T. Taguchi, and J. Kawamata, *Nature* **183**, 1056 (1959).

[189a] J. Marmur, R. Rownd, S. Falkow, L. S. Baron, C. Schildkraut, and P. Doty, *Proc. Natl. Acad. Sci. U. S.* **47**, 972 (1961).

[190] R. K. Herman and F. Forro, Jr., *Abstr. Biophys. Soc.* FB-11 (1962).

[190a] S. Silver, *J. Mol. Biol.* **6**, 349 (1963).

[191] G. Furness and D. Rowley, *J. Gen. Microbiol.* **17**, 550 (1957).

[192] H. L. Bernstein, *Symposium Soc. Exptl. Biol.* **No. 12**, 93 (1958).

[193] B. W. Holloway, *J. Gen. Microbiol.* **13**, 572 (1955).

[194] B. W. Holloway, *J. Gen. Microbiol.* **15**, 221 (1956).

[195] B. W. Holloway and P. Jennings, *Nature* **181**, 855 (1958).

[196] B. W. Holloway and B. Fargie, *J. Bacteriol.* **80**, 362 (1960).

[197] C. Cocito and J. Vandermeulen-Cocito, *Giorn. microbiol.* **6**, 146 (1958).

[198] W. F. Goebel, G. T. Barry, and T. Shedlovsky, *J. Exptl. Med.* **103**, 577 (1956).

[199] P. Bordet, *Compt. rend. soc. biol.* **142**, 257 (1948).

[200] P. Bordet and J. Beumer, *Compt. rend. soc. biol.* **142**, 259 (1948).

[201] P. Frédéricq, *Rev. belge pathol. et méd. exptl.* **19**, Suppl. 4 (1948).

[202] P. Frédéricq, *Ann. Rev. Microbiol.* **11**, 7 (1957).

[203] P. Frédéricq, *Protoplasma* **48**, 583 (1957).

[204] P. Frédéricq, *Symposium Soc. Exptl. Biol.* **No. 12**, 104 (1958).

[205] F. Jacob and E. L. Wollman, *in* "Bacteriophages" (M. H. Adams, ed.), Chapter 20, p. 381. Wiley (Interscience), New York, 1959.

[206] G. Ivànovics, *Bacteriol. Revs.* **26**, 108 (1962).

[207] P. Frédéricq, *Compt. rend. soc. biol.* **148**, 399 (1954).

[208] P. Frédéricq, *Compt. rend. soc. biol.* **148**, 746 (1954).

[209] L. Alfoldi, F. Jacob, and E. L. Wollman, *Compt. rend. acad. sci.* **244**, 2974 (1957).

[210] P. Frédéricq and M. Betz-Bareau, *Compt. rend. soc. biol.* **147**, 1100, 1113, 1653, 2043 (1953).

[211] P. Frédéricq, *Ann. soc. roy. sci. méd. et nat. Bruxelles* **8**, 15 (1955).

[212] H. Ozeki, S. Howarth, and R. C. Clowes, *Nature* **190**, 986 (1961).

[213] Y. Hamon, *Compt. rend. acad. sci.* **242**, 2064 (1956).

[214] H. Ozeki, Doctoral Dissertation, University of London, 1960.

[215] B. A. D. Stocker, *in* "Microbial Genetics." *Symposium Soc. Gen. Microbiol.* **10**, 1 (1960).

[216] H. Ozeki, B. A. D. Stocker, and S. M. Smith, *J. Gen. Microbiol.* **28**, 671 (1962).

[217] L. Alfoldi, F. Jacob, E. L. Wollman, and R. Mazé, *Compt. rend. acad. sci.* **246**, 3531 (1958).

[217a] R. C. Clowes, *Genet. Research Cambr.* **4**, 163 (1963).

[217b] R. N. deZwaig, D. N. Anton, and J. Puig, *J. Gen. Microbiol.* **29**, 473 (1962).

[217] P. Frédéricq, *J. Theoret. Biol.* **4**, 159 (1963).

[218] S. Silver and H. Ozeki, *Nature* **195**, 873 (1962).

[219] G. S. Stent, C. R. Fuerst, and F. Jacob, *Compt. rend. acad. sci.* **244**, 1840 (1957).

[219a] Y. Hamon, *Ann. inst. Pasteur* **192**, 363 (1957).
[220] P. Frédéricq, *Compt. rend. soc. biol.* **150**, 1514 (1956).
[221] F. J. Ryan, P. Fried, and F. Mukai, *Biochim. et Biophys. Acta* **18**, 131 (1955).
[222] Y. Hamon, *Ann. inst. Pasteur* **92**, 363 (1957).
[223] L. Bertani, *Virology* **3**, 378 (1961).
[224] J. Jacob, L. Siminovitch, and E. L. Wollman, *Compt. rend. acad. sci.* **233**, 1500 (1951).
[225] F. Jacob, L. Siminovitch, and E. L. Wollman, *Ann. inst. Pasteur* **83**, 295 (1952).
[226] P. Frédéricq, *Compt. rend. soc. biol.* **148**, 1276 (1954).
[227] Y. Hamon and Z. V. Lewe, *Ann. inst. Pasteur* **89**, 336 (1955).
[228] H. Ozeki, B. A. D. Stocker, and H. deMargerie, *Nature* **184**, 337 (1959).
[229] T. Iijima, *Biken's J.* **5**, 1 (1962).
[230] R. Ben-Gurion, *J. Gen. Microbiol.* **30**, 173 (1963).
[231] P. Frédéricq, *Schweiz. Z. allgem. Pathol. u. Bakteriol.* **9**, 385 (1946).
[232] P. Bordet, *Rev. immunol.* **11**, 323 (1947).
[233] P. Frédéricq, *Ann. inst. Pasteur* **84**, 294 (1953).
[234] T. Watanabe and T. Fukasawa, *Biochem. Biophys. Research Communs.* **3**, 660 (1960).
[235] T. Watanabe and T. Fukasawa, *J. Bacteriol.* **81**, 669 (1961).
[236] T. Watanabe and T. Fukasawa, *J. Bacteriol.* **81**, 679 (1961).
[237] T. Watanabe and T. Fukasawa, *J. Bacteriol.* **82**, 202 (1961).
[238] T. Watanabe and T. Fukasawa, *J. Bacteriol.* **83**, 727 (1962).
[239] J. Lederberg, *J. Bacteriol.* **61**, 549 (1951).
[240] B. A. D. Stocker, S. M. Smith and H. Ozeki, *J. Gen. Microbiol.* **30**, 201 (1963).
[241] S. Mitsuhashi, K. Harada, and M. Kameda, *Nature* **189**, 947 (1961).
[242] T. Watanabe and K. W. Lyang, *J. Bacteriol.* **84**, 422 (1962).
[243] T. Akiba, K. Koyama, Y. Ishiki, S. Kimura, and T. Fukushima, *Japan. J. Microbiol.* **4**, 219 (1960).
[244] R. Nakaya, A. Nakamura, and Y. Murata, *Biochem. Biophys. Research Communs.* **3**, 654 (1960).
[245] S. Mitsuhashi, H. Hashimoto, K. Harada, R. Egawa, and T. Matsuyama, *Gunma J. Med. Sci.* **10**, 59 (1961).
[246] H. S. Ginoza and R. B. Painter, *Bacteriol. Proc.* p. 29 (1963).
[247] T. Iijima, *Japan. J. Genetics* **37**, 187 (1962).
[248] Y. Sugino and Y. Hirota, *J. Bacteriol.* **84**, 902 (1962).
[249] S. Falkow, J. Wohlhieter, R. Citarella, and L. S. Baron, *Bacteriol. Proc.* p. 31 (1963).
[250] K. W. Fisher, *J. Gen. Microbiol.* **16**, 120 (1957).
[251] K. W. Fisher, *J. Gen. Microbiol.* **16**, 136 (1957).
[252] L. S. Baron, W. F. Carey, and W. M. Spilman, *Proc. Natl. Acad. Sci. U. S.* **45**, 976 (1959).
[253] S. Falkow and L. S. Baron, *J. Bacteriol.* **84**, 581 (1962).
[254] C. C. Brinton, *Nature* **183**, 782 (1959).
[255] C. C. Brinton and L. S. Baron, *Biochim. et Biophys. Acta* **42**, 298 (1960).
[256] C. C. Brinton, P. Gemski, S. Falkow, and L. S. Baron, *Biochem. Biophys. Research Communs.* **5**, 293 (1961).
[257] G. A. Maccacaro and W. Hayes, *Genet. Research Cambr.* **2**, 394 (1961).
[258] G. A. Maccacaro and W. Hayes, *Genet. Research Cambr.* **2**, 406 (1961).
[259] W. B. Gundersen, K. Jyssum, and S. Lie, *J. Bacteriol.* **83**, 616 (1962).
[260] Y. Sugino and Y. Hirota, *Japan. J. Genetics* **36**, 395 (1961).
[261] G. Buttin, F. Jacob, and J. Monod, *Compt. rend. acad. sci.* **250**, 2471 (1960).

[262] H. Ozeki and B. Stocker, *Heredity* **12**, 525 (1958).
[263] P. Frédéricq, *Compt. rend. soc. biol.* **153**, 357 (1959).
[264] A. D. Kaiser and D. S. Hogness, *J. Mol. Biol.* **2**, 392 (1960).
[265] D. Cohen, *Compt. rend. acad. sci.* **254**, 3587 (1962).
[266] Y. Kato, M. Hanaoka, and T. Amano, *Biken's J.* **5**, 77 (1962).
[267] T. Watanabe, T. Fukasawa, and T. Takano, *Virology* **17**, 218 (1962).
[268] G. Buttin, F. Jacob, and J. Monod, *Compt. rend. acad. sci.* **250**, 2471 (1960).
[269] G. Buttin, *Cold Spring Harbor Symposia Quant. Biol.* **26**, 213 (1961).
[270] M. B. Yarmolinsky and H. Wiesmeyer, *Proc. Natl. Acad. Sci. U. S.* **46**, 1626 (1960).
[271] M. B. Yarmolinsky, E. Jordan, and H. Wiesmeyer, *Cold Spring Harbor Symposia Quant. Biol.* **26**, 217 (1961).
[272] P. Starlinger, *J. Mol. Biol.* **6**, 128 (1963).
[273] H. R. Revel, S. E. Luria, and B. Rotman, *Proc. Natl. Acad. Sci. U. S.* **47**, 1956 (1961).
[274] H. R. Revel and S. E. Luria, *Proc. Natl. Acad. Sci. U. S.* **47**, 1968 (1961).
[275] H. R. Revel, S. E. Luria, and N. L. Young, *Proc. Natl. Acad. Sci. U. S.* **47**, 1947 (1961).
[276] S. E. Luria, J. N. Adams, and R. C. Ting, *Virology* **12**, 348 (1960).
[277] N. Bouck and E. A. Adelberg, *Biochem. Biophys. Research Communs.* **11**, 24 (1963).
[278] H. Yoshikawa and N. Sueoka, *Proc. Natl. Acad. Sci. U. S.* **49**, 559 (1963).
[279] O. Maaløe, *Cold Spring Harbor Symposia Quant. Biol.* **26**, 45 (1961).
[280] J. Cairns, *J. Mol. Biol.* **6**, 208 (1963).
[281] T. Nagata, *Biochem. Biophys. Research Communs.* **8**, 348 (1962).
[282] T. Nagata, *Proc. Natl. Acad. Sci. U. S.* **49**, 551 (1963).
[283] A. W. Ravin, *Bacteriol. Revs.* **24**, 201 (1960).
[283a] P. H. Mäkelä, J. Lederberg, and E. M. Lederberg, *Genetics* **47**, 1427 (1962).
[284] S. Falkow, R. Rownd, and L. S. Baron, *J. Bacteriol.* **84**, 1303 (1962).

Chapter 5

Genetic Recombination in *Streptomyces*

G. Sermonti and D. A. Hopwood

I. Introduction

The streptomycetes have the most complex colonial organization to be found among the bacteria. Their colonies have a superficial resemblance to mold colonies, but are on a much smaller scale. They have even been considered to be intermediate between bacteria and fungi,[1] but their cellular dimensions, their cytology, and, as we shall see, their genetics, place them without doubt among the bacteria.

The streptomycetes may be regarded as one of the most advanced groups of bacteria, and for this reason many people were stimulated to investigate their genetic system during the time when the process of conjugation in *Escherichia coli* was beginning to reveal some of its peculiar features (see Chapter 1). At the same time, the discovery of the parasexual cycle in imperfect fungi[2] had made accessible to genetic analysis and breeding a large group of industrial microorganisms. The streptomycetes, which produce all widespread antibiotics except the penicillins, appeared to be the next group to which to extend genetic investigations.

A search for gene recombination in the streptomycetes was begun in many laboratories in about 1954, and the following year the first successful result was published by Sermonti and Spada-Sermonti.[3] This report was soon followed by others,[4-10] and genetic recombination was obtained in many species of the genus *Streptomyces*; there were very few negative reports.

Attempts to obtain practical results in the industrial field are still in progress, and most of them are unpublished, while investigation of the genetic system of *Streptomyces* has been virtually confined to the strain A3(2) of *Streptomyces coelicolor*, studies on other strains having been abandoned or limited to particular problems. In this chapter we shall describe the present state of knowledge of the genetic system of the streptomycetes, with particular reference to *S. coelicolor* A3(2). This topic has been the subject of a recent monograph,[11] and the reader is referred to it for more detailed information. The genetics of this strain must serve as a model for the genus, and the studies with other streptomycetes, which are reviewed in a later section of the chapter, may be compared with it. A few preliminary observations on the industrial applications of streptomyces genetics are described near the end of the chapter.

II. Gene Recombination in *Streptomyces coelicolor* A3(2)

A. The Organism

1. Cultural Characteristics

Streptomyces coelicolor (*S. violaceoruber*, according to Kutzner and Waksman[12]) grows vigorously on a variety of agar media, both complex and synthetic. The minimal growth requirements are satisfied by glucose, nitrate, or other simple source of nitrogen, and small quantities of inorganic ions. This makes the isolation and characterization of biochemical mutants a simple operation. This species is distinguished by producing a pigment which is blue and diffusible at alkaline pH, and red and bound to the hyphae at acid pH.

2. Morphology

The characteristic feature of the streptomycetes, which distinguishes them from the other actinomycetes, is the production of regular chains of aerial spores. Colonies that arise on agar media from an inoculum of isolated spores reach a diameter of 2–3 mm. after about 4 days incubation at 28–30°C. Several hundred well-isolated colonies may be grown on a Petri dish. The young colonies are slightly shiny, and very coherent since they consist of an interconnected and intertwined system of hyphae. When they are 3–4 days old, the colonies assume a dry powdery appearance because of the production of aerial hyphae, followed by sporulation. The colonies then consist of a lower layer of mycelium and an upper layer of spores and sporulating hyphae.

The spores of *Streptomyces coelicolor* are roughly spherical, about 1–1.5 μ in diameter, and are surrounded by a wall about 30 mμ thick; this wall is frequently overlain by remnants of the wall of the parent hypha in which the spores are produced in chains.[13] Each spore usually contains a single chromatinic body,[14] and a single corresponding nuclear region is visible in electron micrographs of thin sections of spores.[15] No visible membrane separates the nuclear region from the cytoplasm. Studies of genetic segregation, which are described below, indicate that each spore usually contains a single haploid genome, and the results of mutational and radiokinetic studies are in agreement with this.

. The spores germinate by producing one or more fine germ tubes whose walls are continuous with that of the parent spore. The germ tubes elongate and branch repeatedly to produce a system of interconnected hyphae, the substrate or vegetative mycelium. The colony increases in size by the radial growth of the hyphae at the margin of the colony, and other hyphae penetrate into the agar. The diameter of the hyphae of the substrate mycelium varies from about 0.3 to 1.0 μ. Cytological evidence of hyphal anastomosis in the substrate mycelium of the streptomycetes is inconclusive owing to the small size of the hyphae. There have been several reports of hyphal fusion; probably the most convincing pictures are those of Gregory,[16] who studied *Streptomyces scabies*. The cytoplasm of the hyphae is divided into compartments by septa; each compartment contains several nuclear regions, which vary from small spherical structures to complex lobed bodies.

Certain branches of the substrate hyphae grow upward and give rise to a system of hyphae of rather larger diameter.[17] The hyphae of this aerial mycelium are eventually transformed into chains of spores by septation of the hyphae.[13] The process of spore formation is preceded by a series of characteristic changes in the configuration of the nuclear material in the aerial hyphae.[14] In the young hyphae, the nuclear material is in the form of long rods which fill a large part of the space between adjacent septa. These nuclear rods subdivide, in a manner whose details are still unclear, to produce progressively shorter rods and eventually spherical chromatinic bodies, one of which is included in each spore.

Many features of the cytology of *Streptomyces coelicolor* are identical with those of typical eubacteria. The nuclear bodies stain with basic dyes in the same way as those of eubacteria and like them remain stainable at all stages of their division, and divide without the formation of recognizable spindles. Electron micrographs of thin sections of *S. coelicolor* are strikingly similar to those of most eubacteria; the nuclear bodies are recognizable as regions of lower average density than the cytoplasm, containing fine fibrils,[15] and there is no nuclear membrane. The cytoplasm is extremely electron dense owing to its high content of ribonucleoprotein particles and it differs from that of eubacteria only in containing a larger membranous component.[18, 19] The walls of the hyphae resemble those of Gram-positive eubacteria in their thickness and appearance in thin sections,[13] and also in their chemical composition,[20] being composed of amino sugars and a small number of characteristic amino acids, including diaminopimelic acid.

B. Formal Genetics

1. Techniques

The techniques for the harvesting and plating of spores, for the isolation of biochemical and resistance mutants for use as genetic markers, and for the characterization of segregants are essentially those used in fungal genetics.[2] Special methods for making crosses, and for the detection and analysis of heterogenotes will be mentioned briefly in the appropriate sections of this chapter, while full details will be found in the monograph by Hopwood and Sermonti.[11]

2. Selective Analysis of Mixed Cultures

The first attempt to analyze the genetic system of *Streptomyces coelicolor* A3(2) was made by Hopwood[21] using a selective analysis of the recombinants obtained from mixed cultures of genetically marked strains. When two strains differing by a number of nutritional and resistance markers are inoculated together on a slope of complete medium, they grow to give a mixed culture, which becomes covered with spores after 3 to 4 days. If these spores are collected in water and sown on an appropriate selective medium which does not allow the growth of the parental strains, a small proportion of them (about 10^{-3} to 10^{-5}) give rise to colonies; these turn out to be new, stable strains carrying the parental markers in new combinations.[3, 4, 21, 22]

In a four-point cross, it is possible to select nine different genotypes of recombinants, the other seven genotypes, including the two parental ones, not being recoverable on a medium on which neither parent can grow. The various recombinant genotypes appear in repeated crosses with reproducible relative frequencies; certain pairs of markers show a regular tendency to segregate in the parental combinations, while others tend to segregate independently (Table I). By studying crosses in which the same markers were in different coupling arrangements, it was possible to establish linkage between certain loci and two linkage groups were identified.[21] The distances between the loci in the same linkage group showed reasonable additivity. Thus a preliminary linkage map was constructed which allowed the subsequent investigation of the genetic system of *S. coelicolor*.

With the discovery of heterogenotes (see next section), a more reliable method for the location of new markers in *S. coelicolor* became available which does not require the selection of rare recombinants within a huge

TABLE I
SELECTIVE ANALYSIS OF A CROSS IN *S. coelicolor* A3(2)*,†

		Cross‡: $\frac{met\text{-}2 \quad +}{+ \quad his\text{-}1}$ Regions: 1		$\frac{str\text{-}1 \quad phe\text{-}1}{+ \quad +}$ Regions: 2	

Crossover in regions	Selectable recombinant genotypes‡	Selective media (minimal medium +)				Average number of recombinants for each crossover pattern
		Methionine	phenylalanine, histidine, streptomycin	Phenylalanine	Methionine, histidine, streptomycin	
—	m + + +	64				53
	+ h s p		42			
1	+ + s p		5	7		4
	+ + + +	1		4		
2	m │ o │	26			27	20
	+ h s +		12		13	
1,2	+ + s +	1	0	1	1	1
	+ + + p			0		
	h m s +				1	
Total recombinants per medium		92	59	12	42	

Recombination in region 1 = 4 + 1/53 + 4 + 20 + 1 = 7%
Recombination in region 2 = 20 + 1/53 + 4 + 20 + 1 = 28%

* Unpublished data of Hopwood.

† Recombinants recovered on four selective media.

‡ *met-2* (*m*), *his-1* (*h*), *phe-1* (*p*) = requirement for methionine, histidine, or phenylalanine, respectively; *str-1* (*s*) = resistance to streptomycin. Equal volumes of spore suspension from the mixed culture were plated on the four media, and all recombinants were classified for the unselected markers. The frequencies of genotypes produced by the same crossover pattern are assumed to be equal, and they have been averaged.

population of parental spores. However, the analysis of recombinants obtained directly from mixed cultures of marked strains is still an efficient method for detecting very close linkages, like those between mutations of identical phenotype. Strains and media for such an analysis are chosen in such a way that on one medium recombinants between two unlinked or loosely linked loci may be selected, and on another recombinants between the two markers being studied.[21] If, for the same number of spores plated, the colony counts on the second medium are much lower than on the first, a close linkage is indicated. Selective analysis is also useful for establishing the order of two closely linked mutational sites with respect to outside markers (Table II).

3. ANALYSIS OF HETEROZYGOUS CLONES (HETEROCLONES)

a. Detection of Heteroclones. Among the colonies that grow on a selective medium when spores from a mixed culture are sown on it, there are a few

TABLE II

DETERMINATION OF THE ORDER OF TWO CLOSELY LINKED LOCI IN LINKAGE GROUP I OF *S. coelicolor* A3(2) WITH RESPECT TO OUTSIDE MARKERS*

Arrangement of markers†:	Cross a			Cross b		
	met-2　*his-1*　+　+			*met-2*　+　*his-9*　+		
	+　　+　　*his-9*　*arg-1*			+　　*his-1*　+　　*arg-1*		
Regions:	1	2	3	1	2	3
Crossover in regions	Genotypes of recombinants‡		Observed numbers	Genotypes of recombinants‡		Observed numbers
2	+ + + +		29	m + + a		26
1,2	m + + +		8	+ + + a		10
2,3	+ + + a		7	m + + +		10
1,2,3	m + + a		0	+ + + +		4

* Data from Hopwood and Sermonti.[11]

† *met-2* (*m*) = requirement for methionine; *his-1*, *his-9* = requirement for histidine; *arg-1* (*a*) = requirement for arginine.

‡ Recombinants were selected on minimal medium plus arginine and methionine (selecting for crossing over in region 2, which is less than 1 unit long).

that turn out to contain a mixture of different genotypes. These mixed colonies are particularly common when selection is for two closely linked nutritional markers. They are usually smaller than the true recombinants, and their characteristic property is that they are not transferred by replica plating on to a medium of the same composition as that on which they were first selected[23] (Fig. 1). The great majority of their spores have one or the other of the two nutritional requirements against which selection was made, indicating that the colonies must have been able to grow on the original selective medium by virtue of being heterozygous for the two loci in question.

The nature of the mixed colonies becomes clear when we consider the genotypes of their spores with respect to the whole set of markers employed

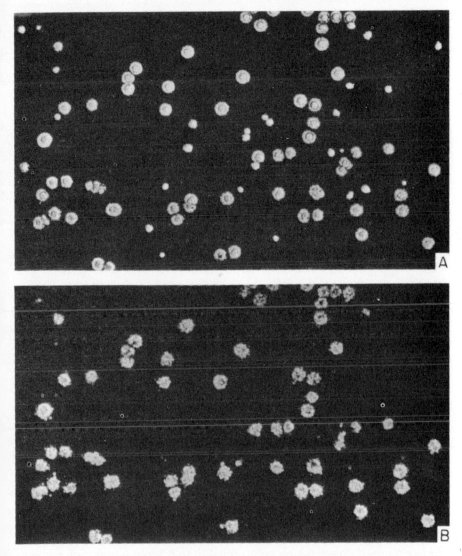

FIG. 1. Detection of heteroclones. A. Colonies arising on a medium selective for closely linked markers in repulsion. B. A replica plate on the same medium. Note that the large colonies (haploid recombinants) give rise to growth on the replica plate, while the small colonies (heteroclones) do not.

in the cross. These genotypes are determined by harvesting spores from a mixed colony in a drop of water and sowing them on complete medium; a sample of the resulting colonies is then classified for the markers introduced into the cross. The markers appear in all possible combinations, with frequencies which are explicable in terms of the linkage relations of the loci (Table III). There is no excess of parental genotypes, so that the two parental genomes must be associated in a state formally equivalent to diploidy. The nucleus at the origin of such colonies will be referred to as a heterogenote,[24] and the colonies as heteroclones.[23]

The number of different genotypes of segregants recoverable from a

TABLE III

SEGREGANTS RECOVERED FROM A HETEROCLONE OF *S. coelicolor* A3(2)*·†

Linkage groups:		I		II	
Arrangement of markers‡:		+ his-1 + met-2 + arg-1		gua-1 + + + str-1 phe-1	
Regions:		1 2		3 4	

			Combinations of markers of group I‡									Crossover in regions
			+h+	m+a	m++	+ha	mh+	++a	+++	mha	Total	
		+ s p	64	18	10	4	1	1	1	0	99	—
		g + +	19	9	3	1	2	0	0	0	34	
		+ s +	21	5	1	5	0	0	0	0	32	4
Combinations		g + p	3	3	1	1	0	0	0	0	8	
of markers of		+ + +	15	2	1	0	0	0	0	0	18	3
group II‡		g s p	0	0	1	0	0	0	0	0	1	
		+ + p	0	0	0	0	0	0	0	0	0	3,4
		g s +	0	0	0	0	0	0	0	0	0	
		Total	122	37	17	11	3	1	1	0	192	
Crossover in regions			—		2		1		1, 2			

* Unpublished data of Hopwood.

† Each figure is the frequency of a segregant genotype: markers of group I are given at the head of the column, and those of group II at the left of the row. The table shows the independent segregation of the markers in the two linkage groups: χ^2 of independence (calculated from figures in the first 4 columns and the first 5 rows: 12 d.f.) = 14.64; $P = 0.27$.

‡ *met-2* (*m*), *his-1* (*h*), *arg-1* (*a*), *gua-1* (*g*), *phe-1* (*p*) = requirement for methionine, histidine, arginine guanine, or phenylalanine, respectively; *str-1* (*s*) = resistance to streptomycin.

heteroclone appears to be limited only by the size of the sample of segregants examined. We must therefore postulate a large number of segregational events (meioses) occurring within the colony; this means that the original heterogenote must have undergone many equational divisions (mitoses) before segregating. Segregation is virtually complete by the time the spores are formed. Thus, in a genetic analysis we can assume that all the colonies obtained by sowing spores from a heteroclone on to complete medium are the products of segregation, and the main disadvantage of a selective analysis is overcome.

Various irregularities are found in the pattern of segregation of every heteroclone, usually showing themselves as the absence or deficiency of one or more alleles. These disturbances reduce the amount of information available for genetic analysis but, on the other hand, they throw some light on the nature of the heterogenotes themselves. Since the irregularities vary from colony to colony, each heteroclone has to be considered separately.

In the selection of the heteroclones, we have to choose between two alternatives. We can select under conditions which necessitate the presence of the maximum number of markers, and also hinder as far as possible the formation of sectors capable of growth on the selective medium; these conditions occur on minimal medium with few or no growth factor supplements, and are those required for formal genetic analysis and for the study of smaller disturbances in the segregations. Alternatively, if we wish to study the range of possible types of heteroclone, we need to select for a pair of closely linked nutritional markers in repulsion, on a medium supplemented with all the other growth requirements of the parents. Under these conditions, few loci usually show segregation, the test of independence between linkage groups (see later) can rarely be applied, and the reliability of the segregation data is difficult to verify; furthermore, the formation of sectors cannot be completely prevented. However, a larger number and a much greater variety of heteroclones are recoverable, the majority of them lacking many markers, and often all the markers on one member of the pair of chromosomes not bearing the selected loci are absent.

In the following paragraphs we shall describe the formal genetic analysis of heteroclones selected on minimal medium supplemented with few or no growth factors. Although the presence of growth factors may result in the emergence of easily recognized sectors, the segregation of the markers in the heteroclone seems otherwise to be unaffected by the supplements present in the selective medium.

b. Independent Segregation of Two Linkage Groups. In most of the heteroclones, the markers in the two linkage groups segregate independently; that is, no preferential association of various combinations of markers in the first linkage group with those in the second is observed. In nearly all heteroclones failing to show independent segregation of markers in the two linkage groups, this is due to an excess of only one, or rarely of two, genotypes, which could have emerged as sectors during the development of the colony. A test of independence between the two linkage groups (see Table III) is therefore used routinely to judge the reliability of the segregation and so to eliminate colonies in which haploid subclones have emerged.

A special kind of mixed colony which is recognized by the test of independence is one in which the two parental genotypes make up the bulk of the segregants, usually together with one or more rare recombinant classes.

These colonies have been interpreted as heterokaryons, in which the two parental genomes must be isolated from one another in such a way that opportunities for recombination rarely occur.

Once independence has been demonstrated, the two linkage groups can be considered separately for the purposes of elaborating the data. Both linkage groups have shown the same type of behavior with regard to the disturbance of the segregations, and there is no obvious correlation between the disturbances in the two groups. The two linkage groups will therefore be considered formally as two different chromosomes in the two following sections, in which we discuss models to account for the observed segregations.

c. Models for the Treatment of Segregation Data. Complementary genotypes hardly ever segregate from the heterogenotes in equal numbers, even if the markers of a single linkage group are considered. The great majority of the segregation patterns can be interpreted, and the data elaborated, on the basis of two general models, which apply to single linkage groups.

1. In some segregations, all the deviations from equality of the frequencies of complementary genotypes can be attributed to a single disturbance, which influences directly only the locus whose allele ratio deviates most from 1:1. This locus is always one of the terminal loci in the linkage group. The allele ratios at the other loci are progressively less unbalanced, and at all of them the less frequent allele is contributed by the same parent. To describe this situation, a model has been adopted in which the chromosome carrying the less frequent alleles is truncated at a point distal to the most unbalanced locus:

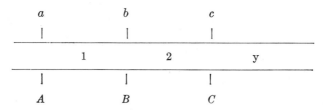

The deletion of the chromosome segment distal to the point of truncation functions as a haplolethal, and the reduction in the frequency of c is due to the necessity for a crossover between the locus of c and the breakage point (that is, in region y) in order to form a complete chromosome carrying the allele c. On this model, the frequencies of all the segregant classes carrying c must be reduced in the same proportion relative to the complementary classes carrying C (Table IV). This proportion, which corresponds to the allele ratio c/C, gives an estimate of the distance y.

From the point of view of the formal genetic analysis, the most important consequence of a single disturbance, whatever its cause, is that it does not invalidate the estimation of recombination frequencies between pairs of loci simply by expressing the numbers of segregants with recombinant genotypes as a percentage of the total segregants, since the frequencies of

TABLE IV

SEGREGATION IN A HETEROCLONE OF *S. coelicolor* A3(2) OF MARKERS IN LINKAGE GROUP II SHOWING A SINGLE DISTURBANCE*

Arrangement of markers†‡:	str-1	ade-3	+	
	+	+	ura-1	
Regions:	1	2	y	
Allele ratios:	$\frac{43}{88}$	$\frac{33}{98}$	$\frac{28}{103}$	

Crossover in regions	Genotypes of segregants‡			Observed numbers
—	+	+	ura	77
1	str	+	ura	16
2	str	ade	ura	8
1,2	+	ade	ura	2
y	str	ade	+	19
1,y	+	ade	+	4
2,y	+	+	+	5
1,2,y	str	+	+	0
				131

Recombination in region 1 = 22/131 = 17%
Recombination in region 2 = 15/131 = 11%
Recombination in region y = 28/131 = 21%

$$\chi^2 \text{ (3 d.f.)§} = 0.785; P = 0.85$$

* Data from Hopwood *et al.*[25]
† A terminal deletion distal to $ura-1^+$ (indicated by dotted line) has been postulated to account for the disturbance in the segregation (see p. 232).
‡ str-1 = resistance to streptomycin; ade-3, ura-1 = requirement for adenine or uracil.
§ Testing departure from equality of ratios between the frequencies of complementary classes.

the parental and recombinant classes are altered proportionately. Recombination percentages between many pairs of loci have been determined from data of heteroclones showing a single disturbance in their segregation for one linkage group, and the results are consistent.[11] They also agree

with those obtained by selective analysis, when available, except that
the distances calculated from the results of selective analysis are systematically larger. The order of groups of loci can be determined by examining the segregation of trios of loci, and identifying the double crossover
classes by their low frequencies.

2. A single disturbance in one linkage group is not sufficient to explain
the anomalies in the segregation in many of the heteroclones. Two lethal
points in a single linkage group have often to be postulated, and almost
invariably they turn out to be at opposite ends of the two homologous
chromosomes, that is, in the *trans* configuration. The most obvious evidence of such double disturbances is the deviation from 1:1 of the allele
ratios at both the terminal loci, but in opposite directions (see the first
example in Table V). This may not be evident if one of the lethal points
is relatively distant from the group of loci under consideration (see the
second example in Table V), but the presence of two disturbances is revealed when the frequencies of the various segregant classes are examined.

When two disturbances in *trans* are implicated, the ratios between the
frequencies of complementary classes are not constant, and a significant
deviation allows the distinction of segregations of this kind from those
with a single disturbance (Table V). A consequence of this situation is
that the recombination frequencies are overestimated.[11]

The model for the elaboration of the data is as follows:

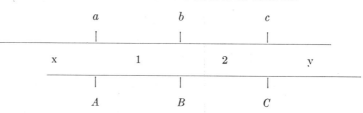

Two haplolethal deletions are postulated, external to the two terminal
loci, and in the *trans* configuration. Clearly only odd numbers of crossovers
(single or triple) can give rise to viable segregants in which both ends of the
chromosome are complete.

If we consider three loci, four of the eight classes correspond to single
crossovers (*ABC, aBC, abC, abc*) and the other four to triples (*Abc, ABc,
AbC, aBc*). Obviously the first four classes are relatively common, and the
last four very much rarer (Table V). The observed numbers of segregants
of the four classes that correspond to single crossovers provide estimates
of the relative frequencies of crossing over in the four regions (x, 1, 2, and
y). If the length of one region is already known (from data of segregations
with a single disturbance), the others can be calculated from it. In this
way a new locus can be mapped from segregation data showing two dis-

turbances in the same linkage group, so long as at least two known loci are segregating in the same linkage group as the unknown marker.

d. *Anomalous Segregations.* The great majority of the data collected so far can be interpreted in terms of the two models proposed. However, in

TABLE V

SEGREGATION IN HETEROCLONES OF *S. coelicolor* A3(2) WITH DOUBLE DISTURBANCES*

Linkage group†:	I				II			
Arrangements of markers‡§:	+ + arg-1 acr-3 his-1 +				+ + ade-3 his-3 str-1 +			
Regions:	x	1	2	y	x	1	2	y
Allele ratios:	$\frac{74}{24}$	$\frac{51}{47}$	$\frac{26}{72}$		$\frac{142}{24}$	$\frac{127}{39}$	$\frac{84}{82}$	

Crossover in regions	Genotypes of segregants‡			Observed numbers	Genotypes of segregants‡			Observed numbers
x	acr	his	+	20	his	str	+	20
1	+	his	+	27	+	str	+	18
2	+	+	+	22	+	+	+	43
y	+	+	arg	25	+	+	ade	80
x,1,2	acr	+	+	3	his	+	+	1
x,1,y	acr	+	arg	1	his	+	ade	3
x,2,y	acr	his	arg	0	his	str	ade	0
1,2,y	+	his	arg	0	+	str	ade	1
				98				166

χ^2 (3 d.f.)‖ = 42.94; $P \ll 0.01$ χ^2 (3 d.f.)‖ = 110.02; $P \ll 0.01$

* Unpublished data of Hopwood and of Spada-Sermonti.

† Data for the two linkage groups come from different heteroclones.

‡ *acr, str* = resistance to acriflavin or streptomycin; *his, arg, ade* = requirement for histidine, arginine or adenine.

§ Two terminal deletions in *trans* (indicated by dotted lines) have been postulated to account for disturbances in the segregations (see p. 234)

‖ See footnote § to Table IV.

exceptional cases it is necessary to postulate a rearrangement of the markers with respect to their coupling in the parent strains in order to adapt them to one of the models.

Two kinds of rearrangement have been found. The first is homozygosity of one or more terminal markers. In segregations of this kind, one allele at a locus is missing altogether, but its absence is not reflected in a disturbance in segregations at linked loci of the kind that would be expected if a lethal point coincided with the missing allele, or a deletion included it. The simplest explanation is that the missing marker has been replaced by its allele, which is now in the homozygous condition. The second kind of rearrangement, of which only a few examples have been found so far, is a change in the coupling arrangement of the markers in a linkage group with respect to the parental configuration, but all the loci remain heterozygous.

Some other anomalous segregations can be accounted for by trivial effects, such as sectors in the heteroclones, but certain rarer anomalies so far remain unexplained.

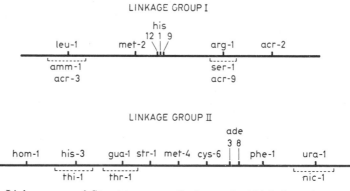

Fig. 2. Linkage map of *Streptomyces coelicolor* strain A3(2). Locations of markers not already published are based on unpublished data of Hopwood, with the exception of *acr*, which were located by Sermonti and Spada-Sermonti.

4. The Linkage Map

Figure 2 shows the genetic map of *Streptomyces coelicolor* strain A3(2). All the markers so far studied are located in two linkage groups. All attempts to detect linkage between the terminal markers of different linkage groups have failed. We cannot assert that the two linkage groups correspond to two independent chromosomes, although this is at the moment a simpler hypothesis than a nonrandom distribution of marked loci or of crossovers along a single chromosome. The length of each linkage group, as estimated by the analysis of the segregants from heterogenotes, is of the order of 50 recombination units. Thus the total known map barely exceeds 100 units in length; it is somewhat longer if we use data from selective analysis.

In eubacteria, several examples have been found in which loci controlling different steps in the same biosynthetic pathway are located next to one another on the linkage map[26]; the equivalent loci in fungi, although not always randomly distributed, do not usually occur in close proximity. The most fully studied example of a cluster of related loci in a bacterium is the series of histidine loci of *Salmonella*, all of which occupy a short uninterrupted segment of the chromosome.[27] In *Streptomyces coelicolor*, the loci *his-1*, *his-9*, and *his-12*, which control different reactions in histidine synthesis, are located in a short region in linkage group I, while a fourth locus, *his-3*, lies in linkage group II. The few data that are available therefore suggest that *S. coelicolor* resembles eubacteria in the close linkage of some groups of related loci, although this tendency may not be so pronounced.

C. THE GENETIC SYSTEM

1. LINES OF EVIDENCE

The data collected and analyzed by the methods that have just been described allow us to build up a preliminary picture of the genetic system in which recombination occurs. Separation of the cells during nuclear transfer, and study of the delay in phenotypic expression of the recombinant genotypes, which have been so useful in building up a picture of the genetic system of *Escherichia coli* K12,[28] have so far not been possible in *S. coelicolor* owing to its filamentous growth habit. However, a glimpse of the events leading to the emergence of spores containing recombinant genomes is provided by the fortunate discovery of exceptional heterogenotes, in which the segregation process is not yet complete. Most of our information is derived from the interpretation of the final results of the process of segregation in the heterogenotic colonies (heteroclones).

2. CONJUGATION

Direct proof that the transfer of genes from one hypha to another in the mixed culture occurs by a process of cell conjugation has not been obtained. Claims of hyphal anastomosis in other streptomycetes have been made by several authors,[16, 29, 30] but they must be regarded as indecisive. Moreover, even if hyphal anastomosis is proven, there is no evidence that it is the process responsible for gene transfer. If gene transfer occurred through a narrow bridge, as in *E. coli* K12,[31] this would not be seen in the light microscope.

The occurrence of conjugation processes is strongly suggested by the facts that heterokaryotic hyphae can be isolated from mixed cultures of nutritionally marked strains of many streptomycetes (Section III, A), and that in *S. coelicolor* A3(2) the existence of heterogenotes containing two nearly complete parental genomes can be demonstrated. The transfer of large pieces of genetic material from strain to strain was in fact indicated

even by the first data on gene recombination in this organism.[4] It is difficult to imagine the transfer of complete or nearly complete genomes from
one hypha to another by a mechanism that does not involve some kind of
conjugation.

Mixtures of spores do not give rise to recombinants if they are not
allowed to germinate, while recombinants can be isolated from mixed
cultures before the aerial mycelium has begun to form, so that it is very
probable that conjugation occurs among the hyphae of the substrate
mycelium.

In certain streptomycetes, such as *S. griseus*,[32] the only result of conjugation seems to be the formation of heterokaryotic hyphae, while in *S.
coelicolor* A3(2) we find almost exclusively zygotes. Rare heterokaryons
seem to be formed in *S. coelicolor* A3(2), especially in the least fertile combinations of strains, but proof that they are true heterokaryons and not
syntrophic growths of mycelium has not been obtained for this strain.
The formation of heterokaryons is particularly significant since it implies
the passage of whole nuclei from cell to cell, which is hardly ever found in
the eubacteria. However, we cannot yet say whether heterokaryosis is
related to zygote formation, or whether the two are distinct phenomena.

3. Sexuality

Two groups of strains of *Streptomyces coelicolor* A3(2) have been
recognized. Strains of the first group give no or very few recombinants when
crossed among themselves, while those of the second group are fertile when
crossed with each other or with strains of the first group (Fig. 3). Some
crosses are fertile when the selection is for certain markers, but sterile when
other markers are selected. The situation is comparable with that in
Escherichia coli K12. The two groups of strains would correspond to F$^-$
and F$^+$ or Hfr strains of *E. coli*, respectively.[33] We shall call the strains of
S. coelicolor R$^-$ and R$^+$ (R = recombination) until such time as the basis
of the difference is better understood.

From a cross between an R$^+$ and an R$^-$ strain, a sample of each of the
parental genotypes was isolated. All 12 of those having the genotype of the
R$^+$ parent were fertile when crossed with the R$^-$ parent, while about half
of those carrying the markers of the R$^-$ parent were fertile with an R$^-$
tester strain. The fertility was, however, relatively low. This indicates that
the transfer of a factor conferring fertility occurred with a very high
efficiency, while the frequency of transfer of chromosomal markers, as
judged by the recovery of recombinant spores, was of the order of 10^{-4}.
Nearly all the recombinants turned out to be R$^+$. The same behavior was
found in another cross involving different strains. These observations indicate the presence of a contagious factor, not integrated in the genome,
which promotes fertility in *S. coelicolor* A3(2).

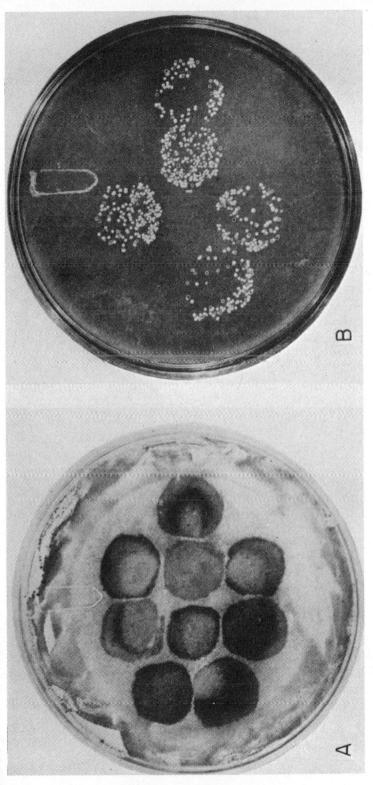

Fig. 3. Spot testing for fertility. A. Three day-old mixed cultures on complete medium; spots of strains to be tested (*arg-1 ura-1*) were replica plated on a background of a sterile tester strain (*his-1*). E. Replica plate of the mixed cultures on minimal medium plus arginine (selective for recombinants between *his-1* and *ura-1*). Five of the tested strains are fertile, while four are sterile.

In crosses between R^+ and R^- strains, the R^+ parent appears to contribute fewer markers to the progeny than the R^- strain.[33a]

4. NATURE OF THE HETEROGENOTIC NUCLEI

Following conjugation, heterogenotic nuclei are formed. Such nuclei reveal themselves in the cells that give rise to the heteroclones, and their constitution is analyzed by studying the segregants in the heteroclones. However, these nuclei probably do not represent the primary zygote nuclei, but are derived from them by subsequent multiplication.

The nuclei that give rise to the heteroclones are often very incomplete, many markers from one or other or from both parents being absent. Usually the markers of one member of one of the pairs of chromosomes are absent when they are not necessary for growth on the selective medium (Table VI). Even when heteroclones are selected on minimal medium, where the wild-type alleles of all the nutritional markers are indispensable, the segregation of the markers shows irregularities which reveal chromosomal deficiencies in the regions outside the marked loci. These irregularities in segregation could also be explained by postulating lethal genes at the points that have been represented formally as the ends of truncated chromosomes, but such a hypothesis is improbable in view of the extreme variability of the types of disturbances from heteroclone to heteroclone.

The nuclei that give rise to the heteroclones can therefore be considered as heterogenotes with more or less extensive chromosomal deficiencies. What we cannot yet say is whether these deficiencies are already present in the primary zygotes. Although this is likely, postzygotic elimination of chromosome segments must also be postulated to explain the fact that there are often deficiencies in the contributions of both parents to the genetic make-up of the heteroclones.

The association of the two genomes (or parts of them) in the heterogenotic nuclei is comparable with that in the diploid nucleus of a higher organism, since the two genomes divide synchronously for a number of nuclear generations before eventually interacting to give rise to recombinants. However, the association between the two genomes is probably different from that in higher organisms because of the absence of a nuclear membrane in *Streptomyces*.

5. MULTIPLICATION OF THE HETEROGENOTIC NUCLEI

The large number of different recombinant genotypes recoverable from each heteroclone that originates from a heterogenotic nucleus indicates that the original nucleus must have undergone a number of divisions before segregating. Since the frequencies of the rarest genotypes are less than 10^{-4},[23] at least many thousands of segregants must arise independently within the colonies, and therefore at least several thousand hetero-

TABLE VI

SEGREGATION IN HIGHER ORDER HETEROCLONES ISOLATED ON A MEDIUM SELECTIVE FOR WILD-TYPE ALLELES AT TWO CLOSELY LINKED LOCI (*Met-2* AND *His-1*)*·†

Linkage group:		I		II	
Arrangement of markers:		$\dfrac{met\text{-}2 \; + \; arg\text{-}1}{+ \; his\text{-}1 \; +}$		$\dfrac{str\text{-}1 \; ade\text{-}3 \; +}{+ \; + \; phe\text{-}1}$	

Allele ratios

Linkage group	Markers‡	Allele ratios in heteroclone			
		1	2	3	4
I	met/+	35/15	14/36	22/77	7/40
	+/his	36/14	17/33	62/37	12/35
	arg/+	31/19	29/21	79/20	0/47
II	str/+	50/0	50/0	99/0	0/47
	ade/+	50/0	50/0	99/0	47/0
	+/phe	50/0	50/0	99/0	47/0

Segregation in linkage group I

Genotypes‡			Observed numbers in heteroclone			
			1	2	3	4
met	+	arg	22	10	17	0
+	his	+	6	16	12	35
met	+	+	12	4	3	7
+	his	arg	7	17	33	0
+	+	arg§	2	2	29	0
met	his	+	1	0	2	0
+	+	+§	0	1	3	5
met	his	arg	0	0	0	0
			—	—	—	—
			50	50	99	47

* Unpublished data of Hopwood and Spada-Sermonti.

† The primary heteroclone showed segregation at all 6 loci.

‡ *met, his, arg, ade, phe* = requirement for methionine, histidine, arginine, adenine, phenylalanine, respectively; *str* = resistance to streptomycin.

§ Genotypes that could grow on the selective medium and emerge as sectors.

genotic nuclei must have been formed from the original nucleus and undergone segregation. In fact, if a heteroclone colony is broken up into small fragments and the resulting suspension of spores and small pieces of hypha is plated on a suitable selective medium, more than a thousand new heterogenotic colonies can be obtained.

Examination of some of these colonies shows that a large proportion of the secondary heterogenotic nuclei resemble the primary one, but some of them differ, indicating the occurrence of chromosomal changes during the multiplication of the heterogenotic nuclei. The following changes have been found: loss of a chromosome (indistinguishable from homozygosity of all the markers of one linkage group), accentuation of terminal deletions, establishment of homozygosity of one or more terminal markers, and rare changes in the coupling arrangements of pairs of alleles. At the moment it is difficult to calculate the frequencies of such processes, since the mere identification of each situation requires a complex analysis.

6. FORMATION OF RECOMBINANTS

Stable haploid recombinants can be obtained directly by plating spores from the mixed culture, or by plating spores from the heteroclones. The segregation patterns obtained are substantially similar, except for the obvious difference that the recombinant spores in the mixed culture are accompanied by a great majority of spores of the parental genotypes. A simplifying hypothesis is that the recombinants in the mixed culture arise from heteroclones growing in the culture; thus all recombinants may be produced from a transient heterozygous stage. The occurrence of other processes of recombination in the mixed culture cannot, however, be excluded.

The spores produced by a heteroclone are almost exclusively haploid, and the markers of the two linkage groups segregate completely independently. It is difficult to say whether reduction of the two linkage groups is always contemporaneous and whether crossing over is synchronized with reduction. Sometimes crossing over appears to occur independently of reduction (mitotic crossing over), to give rise to heterogenotes with new arrangements of markers, but we cannot rule out the possibility that such rearrangements, which have so far been observed rarely, arise by a reassociation of haploid products (recycling of meiosis[34]).

We may summarize our tentative picture of the process of recombination in *S. coelicolor* A3(2) as follows: Heterozygous nuclei are produced following transfer of probably incomplete nuclei from hypha to hypha of the substrate mycelium by a process of conjugation; the heterozygous nuclei multiply, and during their multiplication chromosomal losses and chromosomal terminal deletions occur, and possibly some mitotic crossing over; finally haploid recombinants arise by crossing over and reduction.

III. Genetic Phenomena in Other Streptomycetes

A. BALANCED HETEROKARYOSIS

Heterokaryosis in *Streptomyces* was first found by Bradley and Lederberg[32] in three different species. It was recognized by the production of colonies capable of growth on minimal medium by mixtures of two auxo-trophic strains. Prototrophy could not be perpetuated through the spores, which had exclusively parental genotypes, while colonies of both parental genotypes arose from fragments of mycelium of the heterokaryotic colonies isolated by means of a micromanipulator. Similar results were obtained by Braendle and Szybalski[5, 6] with various other species of *Streptomyces*, and by Saito[8] with *S. griseoflavus*.

Braendle *et al.*[35] found that strains of the two parental phenotypes recovered from a heterokaryon gave rise to new heterokaryons with a much higher frequency than the original strains. The ability to give high yields of heterokaryons was preserved for several subcultures, but eventually disappeared.

Heterokaryosis in *S. scabies* has been used to study the apparent cytoplasmic inheritance of tyrosinase production; this is discussed on page 246 while the occurrence of heterokaryosis in *S. coelicolor* A3(2) has been mentioned on page 231.

The term "heterokaryons" has been applied by Bradley[36] to almost stable prototrophic strains of *S. coelicolor* producing rare parental segregants (see later, p 244) Whatever the nature of these strains, they are not heterokaryons in the sense in which the term has been applied to molds[37] and adopted to describe formally comparable phenomena in streptomycetes.

B. GENE RECOMBINATION

1. GENETIC SYSTEMS RESEMBLING THAT OF *S. coelicolor* A3(2)

Genetic recombination has been reported in several strains belonging to various species of the genus *Streptomyces*, and only a few attempts to detect it have been unsuccessful. Only in a few strains have investigations been carried far enough to allow comparison with the results obtained with *S. coelicolor* A3(2). All the authors who have used multiply marked strains and plated spores from mixed cultures on suitably supplemented selective media have found a great variety of recombinant phenotypes among these spores, and the great majority of the recombinants have proved to be stable on repeated subculture. Such results have been obtained with *S. coelicolor* strain I.S.S.,[3, 22, 38] in *S. fradiae*,[6] and in *S. griseoflavus*,[39] and have generally been taken as demonstrating the haploid nature of the recombinants, and of the parental strains.

In *S. griseoflavus*, however, certain observations contradicted the conclusion of haploidy[39]; these were the cytological observation of bipartite spore nuclei, the finding of a two-hit survival curve after treatment with X-rays (in contrast to the one-hit curve of *S. coelicolor* A3(2)[11] and *S. coelicolor* I.S.S.[39]), and the observation that many reversions of biochemical mutations gave rise to mixed colonies. However, this heterogeneity of the partial revertants was not perpetuated, nor were heterozygous spores produced by heterokaryotic mycelia, so that the presumed diploidy of the spores could not have resulted from the fusion of unlike nuclei, but presumably by duplication of a single haploid nucleus.

Another general observation is the regular occurrence of mixed colonies among the recombinants recovered on selective media; this suggests that transient heterogenotes occur in other strains besides *S. coelicolor* A3(2). Such mixed colonies have been found in each of the three species mentioned above. Although the numbers of different genotypes recovered from a single colony were not large (up to four in *S. coelicolor* I.S.S. and three in *S. griseoflavus*) the segregation is very probably of the same kind as that observed in *S. coelicolor* A3(2), the ability to give rise to mixed colonies not being perpetuated through the spores.

Thus as far as we can say, studies of recombination in various species of *Streptomyces* by methods which allow the recovery of different kinds of auxotrophic segregants seem to be in substantial agreement.

2. STUDIES LIMITED TO PROTOTROPH SELECTION

In certain strains of *Streptomyces*, recombination has been studied by the selection of exclusively prototrophic colonies on minimal media. This limitation appears to have been due in one case (Bradley) to the particular object of studying heterokaryosis, and in the other (Alikhanian) to the necessity of not introducing too many nutritional markers into strains that were to be used to study the genetics of antibiotic production.

On the basis of studies with strains of *Streptomyces coelicolor* different from A3(2), Bradley[36] questioned the occurrence of true recombination in this species, and attributed to heterokaryosis the production of prototrophs from mixed cultures of auxotrophic strains. This interpretation was based on the recovery of very rare (less than 10^{-3}) parental segregants amongst the spores produced by the prototrophic colonies. In later papers, the recovery of new recombinant phenotypes was reported, and as an alternative hypothesis to heterokaryosis, heterozygosity was put forward, as well as "a complex series of genetic interactions."[40] Even the occurrence of "haplophase gene recombination" was considered a possibility, but not as the major process. As an argument against true recombination was brought the observation that two unselected markers always showed the presumed dominant phenotype in crosses in which they were in different coupling arrangements with nutritional markers.[40] However, the expression of these unselected characters was extremely irregular.

The situation reported by Alikhanian and his collaborators in *Streptomyces aureofaciens*[10] and *S. rimosus*,[7] two tetracycline-producing species, resembles in some ways that reported by Bradley in his strains of *S. coelicolor*, probably because both studies suffered from the same technical limitations. Among the prototrophic recombinants selected from mixed cultures of two single auxotrophs, some were stable, but others gave rise to a small percentage (rarely exceeding 1%) of one or other or of both parental phenotypes.

The significance of these occasional segregations, of a kind quite different from those observed in other species of *Streptomyces*, is difficult to determine, in view of the limited number of markers employed. However, it is doubtful if we can exclude the possibility that some of the supposed segregants arose because of incomplete purification of prototrophic clones selected in the presence of a heavy background of parental spores.

Prototrophic recombinants were obtained by Alikhanian et al.[41] by plating on minimal medium auxotrophs treated with phage grown on complementary auxotrophic strains and this was interpreted as evidence for actinophage-mediated transduction. Since no proof of the cell-free nature of the phage lysates from the donor strain was given, it cannot be ruled out that the prototrophs originated by an interaction between cells. Some of the prototrophs gave rise to a mixture of different phenotypes, and were interpreted as incomplete "diploids." The "donor" phenotype segregated with such a high frequency that the transfer of a complete or almost complete genome seems the simplest explanation, and this could hardly have been mediated by a phage.

Prototrophs were obtained by Jarai[41a] by adding DNA prepared from prototrophic or auxotrophic strains of *Streptomyces aureofaciens* to spores of auxotrophic strains plated on minimal medium. In the absence of controls carried out in the presence of DNase and of proofs of the cell-free state of the DNA preparations, the occurrence of transformation cannot be regarded as conclusively demonstrated. Moreover, the very high frequency of double transformants in Jarai's experiments would imply the transfer of a very large segment of the donor genome.

3. INTERSPECIFIC RECOMBINATION IN STREPTOMYCES

Braendle and Szybalski[6] reported several unsuccessful attempts to obtain interspecific recombination in *Streptomyces* by growing various combinations of auxotrophic mutants belonging to different species in mixed culture. Recently, Alačević[42] reported positive results for similar experiments with mutants of *S. coelicolor*, *S. rimosus*, and *S. aureofaciens*. These results need confirmation, particularly since her report makes no mention of controls of the stability of the mutants involved. The occurrence of recombination in certain interspecific combinations could be important in the study of the taxonomic relationships of strains within the genus *Streptomyces*.

C. Cytoplasmic Inheritance—Episomic Elements

There is little information on cytoplasmic inheritance in bacteria because of the lack of suitable systems for revealing it, although episomes in the nonintegrated state[43] may be regarded as a special kind of cytoplasmic determinant. On the other hand, heterokaryosis in fungi has allowed the identification of numerous cytoplasmic variants,[44] all connected with dispensable functions. Heterokaryons in *Streptomyces* may turn out to be a valuable tool for the study of cytoplasmic inheritance, allowing the mixing of cytoplasms without the transfer of information between nuclei.

Gregory and Shyu[45] reported the apparent cytoplasmic inheritance of the ability to produce tyrosinase in *Streptomyces scabies*. Tyrosinase-negative mutants were recognized by their failure to produce a dark pigment on media containing tyrosine; they arose from the wild-type strain with a high spontaneous frequency (0.2%) and were never observed to revert. Heterokaryons between positive and negative strains were always tyrosinase-positive. All the segregants from the heterokaryons, over 99% of which had the parental combinations of nutritional markers, were always tyrosinase-positive, irrespective of the coupling of the tyrosinase character with the nutritional markers in the strains used to synthesize the heterokaryons. The conclusion of cytoplasmic inheritance of the ability to produce tyrosinase was based on this observation, and support for the hypothesis was found in the discovery that growth of the organism in a medium containing acriflavin increased the proportion of tyrosinase-negative mutants arising from the wild-type strain to about 50%.[46]

In view of its high frequency of transfer from R^+ to R^- strains in mixed cultures (p. 238), the fertility factor in *S. coelicolor* A3(2) probably represents a second example of a cytoplasmic determinant in *Streptomyces*.

Since the actinophages in the vegetative state are presumably located in the cytoplasm, they may be mentioned in this section. They were first described by Wiebols and Weiringa,[47] and have been found to attack the mycelium only in certain stages of its development; the aerial hyphae and spores are not lysed.[48] The first clear evidence of true lysogeny in *Streptomyces* was obtained by Welsch,[49] who found that some strains still harbored the phage after six successive subcultures in the presence of phage antiserum. All attempts to induce the prophage with mutagenic agents were unsuccessful.

IV. *Streptomyces* Genetics and Antibiotic Production

Nearly all antibiotics of widespread use are produced by species of the genus *Streptomyces*, synthesis of the antibiotic being obtained in pure cultures grown for periods of a few days in large fermentation vessels. Breeding for antibiotic production has the same objectives as breeding for increased production in a food crop, except that the product of the microorganism is a single molecular species; productivity has to be improved, degeneration of the organism has to be avoided, and susceptibility to attack by parasites (actinophages) has to be eliminated. Here we shall not deal with increases in antibiotic yield obtained by the selection of spontaneous or induced variants, because such studies, even though important from an industrial point of view, have made no contribution to understanding the genetics of the streptomycetes nor have exploited the potentialities of their genetic system.

The isolation of mutant strains which differ qualitatively from the parent strain in the antibiotic they produce is more interesting because the effects of the mutations can be better interpreted in biochemical terms. One such study is that of McCormick *et al.*[50] who obtained a mutant of *S. aureofaciens* that produced a tetracycline differing from the wild-type antibiotic by lacking the methyl group in the 6-position. Such genetic control of methylation, like that of the presence or absence of other chemical groups, is well known in other organisms. In the streptomycetes, as in the penicillia,[51] production of an altered antibiotic may be therapeutically important because changes in the spectrum of activity or in the toxicity of an antibiotic can result from small modifications in its structure.

Analysis by recombination of the genetic control of antibiotic production is still in a very preliminary stage, and the only papers published are those of Alikhanian's group on tetracycline-producing strains, whose genetic system is unfortunately little known (see p. 244).

In *S. aureofaciens*,[10] arginine-requiring mutants (which made up 99% of the auxotrophic mutants that were obtained) produced little or no antibiotic, while a mutant requiring isoleucine and valine produced traces of antibiotic. Prototrophs obtained from combinations of various of the *arg*− mutants with the (*isl* + *val*)− mutant usually produced much more antibiotic than the auxotrophic parents, but less than the original prototrophic ancestors. From certain combinations, however, the prototrophic recombinants reached a level of production somewhat higher than that of the ancestral strains. Five prototrophs obtained from mixtures of pairs of *arg*− mutants were inactive. Comparable results were obtained in *S. rimosus*[7] as far as the quantity of antibiotic produced by auxotrophic mutants and prototrophic recombinants was concerned.

In *S. rimosus*, two groups of mutants were obtained which produced no antibiotic; mutants of one group (*white*) produced a substance which was also isolated from cultures of the wild type, which was converted by mutants of the second group (*black*) into oxytetracycline.[52] From a cross of a *white* mutant resistant to streptomycin and a *black* mutant sensitive to streptomycin, a *black* streptomycin-resistant "recombinant" was obtained, which produced the wild-type titer of oxytetracycline.[53] This suggested that the two mutations blocking antibiotic synthesis were at different loci; however, it also indicates that production of the black color was not due to the same mutations blocking antibiotic production in mutants of the *black* phenotype. The recovery of the presumed double mutant was also claimed; this was a *white* streptomycin-sensitive "recombinant" which did not produce oxytetracycline when grown in combination with either mutants of the *black* or the *white* phenotype.

Mindlin *et al.*[54] obtained prototrophs from a mixed culture of two auxotrophs originating from different starting strains of *S. rimosus*; these prototrophs had various combinations of the characters of the parents (resistance to streptomycin and X-rays, response to increased corn steep in the medium, antibiotic activity). One of the prototrophs produced more antibiotic than the two ancestral strains, and less foam during fermentation.

In all the studies by Alikhanian's group, variability among the recombinants was limited by selection against two nutritional markers. Study of the genetic system of *S. coelicolor* has shown that under appropriate experimental conditions (segregation from heterogenotes) the number of recombinant types is potentially unlimited. Exploitation of such a system in antibiotic-producing strains could allow analysis of the biosynthetic steps in antibiotic formation, as well as yielding a vast supply of variability for use in practical breeding.

The occurrence of interspecific recombination (see p. 245) might eventually allow the isolation of strains producing antibiotics with some of the properties of two related metabolites found in different species.

V. Genetic Systems of Streptomycetes and Eubacteria

The genetic system of *Streptomyces*, as revealed by the studies of *S. coelicolor* A3(2), shows some remarkable similarities with recombination mediated by conjugation in *Escherichia coli* K12. Thus, in their genetics as well as in their morphology, the streptomycetes seem to resemble the eubacteria.

Perhaps the most obvious resemblance is the occurrence of incomplete heterogenotes. Even though we cannot say whether the incompleteness is primary in *S. coelicolor* (and some postzygotic changes certainly take place), its mere occurrence indicates a bacterial genetic system, since no eukaryotic microorganism (fungus or alga), nor any higher organism, has similarly incomplete diploid nuclei. Loss of chromosomes leading to aneuploidy results in partial diploidy in higher organisms and diploid molds, but the incompleteness is of a different kind.

A second similarity between *S. coelicolor* A3(2) and *E. coli* K12 is the transient nature of the heterogenotes. In an Hfr × F⁻ cross in *E. coli*, partial diploidy persists for only a few cell generations, and in fact multiplication of the fragment of donor chromosome has been denied.[55] Exceptionally, however,[56] the heterogenotes of *E. coli* K12 persisted for a comparable number of cell generations to those of *S. coelicolor* A3(2). Among these relatively stable heterogenotes, Lederberg *et al.*[57] found some rearrangements of the kind found in *S. coelicolor* A3(2), namely, homozygosity and postzygotic eliminations, the latter revealed by incompleteness of the genomes contributed by both parental strains.

A third feature common to *Streptomyces* and eubacteria is the tendency for loci controlling different steps in the same biosynthetic pathway to be closely linked in clusters. In *S. coelicolor* A3(2), there is possibly a slightly greater degree of dispersion of the loci, some being situated far from the main cluster.

A final striking parallel between *S. coelicolor* A3(2) and *E. coli* K12 is in their fertility systems. A factor (R) which controls the ability to undergo recombination has been postulated in *S. coelicolor* A3(2), and it appears to be transferred with high frequency from R^+ to R^- strains in mixed cultures. Thus, this factor resembles the F' factor of *E. coli* K12, but nothing is yet known of its relationship to the chromosome. In its property of conferring only a reduced fertility upon transfer it resembles the fertility factor of *Pseudomonas aeruginosa*.[58]

There are certain points of divergence between the genetic systems of *S. coelicolor* A3(2) and *E. coli* K12. The most obvious is the presence of two linkage groups in *S. coelicolor*. The existence of two chromosomes can never be definitely established on the basis of recombination frequencies because new markers uniting the two existing linkage groups may later be found; this happened in *E. coli* K12 and in bacteriophage T4. However, the location of the loci in two groups appears to be on a firmer basis in *S. coelicolor*, on the one hand because of their invariably independent segregation, and on the other because the terminal "deletions" of one pair of chromosomes show no apparent preferential association with those of the other pair. The presence of two linkage groups is particularly interesting in view of the fact that the transfer of markers in *E. coli* crosses appears to depend on the continuity of the chromosome on which they are borne; when this continuity is interrupted, the transfer ceases.

A phenomenon observed in the streptomycetes and not in the eubacteria is heterokaryosis, which is probably made possible by the mycelial habit of the streptomycete colony. Heterokaryosis implies the transfer of a complete nucleus from one cell to another, which is found in eubacteria only as a limiting case.[59] It remains to be seen whether heterokaryosis is a prerequisite for or an alternative to recombination. Incidentally, heterokaryons may provide a means of recognizing extranuclear inheritance in *Streptomyces*.[45]

Other apparent differences between the genetic systems of eubacteria and streptomycetes may be due to technical advantages or limitations determined by the different growth habits of the two groups of organisms. In the streptomycetes, it is difficult to study the processes of nuclear transfer and the formation of the primary zygotes, which take place in a mass of intertwined hyphae; on the other hand, it is possible to collect a great deal of information on the mechanisms of multiplication and segregation of the heterogenotic nuclei. A complete analysis of segregant progeny, without recourse to selective techniques, which had not been possible before in the bacteria, can be achieved in the heteroclones of *Streptomyces coelicolor*.

REFERENCES

[1] S. A. Waksman, "The Actinomycetes." Chronica Botanica, Waltham, Massachusetts, 1950.
[2] G. Pontecorvo, *Advances in Genet.*, **5,** 142 (1953).
[3] G. Sermonti and I. Spada-Sermonti, *Nature* **176,** 121 (1955).
[4] D. A. Hopwood, *J. Gen. Microbiol.* **16,** ii (1957).
[5] D. H. Braendle and W. Szybalski, *Proc. Natl. Acad. Sci. U. S.* **43,** 947 (1957).
[6] D. H. Braendle and W. Szybalski, *Ann. N. Y. Acad. Sci.* **81,** 824 (1959).
[7] S. I. Alikhanian and S. Z. Mindlin, *Nature* **180,** 1208 (1957).
[8] H. Saito, *Can. J. Microbiol.* **4,** 571 (1958).
[9] K. F. Gregory, *Ann. N. Y. Acad. Sci.* **81,** 851 (1959).
[10] S. I. Alikhanian and L. N. Borisova, *J. Gen. Microbiol.* **26,** 19 (1961).
[11] D. A. Hopwood and G. Sermonti, *Advances in Genet.* **11,** 273 (1962).
[12] H. J. Kutzner and S. A. Waksman, *J. Bacteriol.* **78,** 528 (1959).
[13] A. M. Glauert and D. A. Hopwood, *J. Biophys. Biochem. Cytol.* **10,** 505 (1961).
[14] D. A. Hopwood and A. M. Glauert, *J. Biophys. Biochem. Cytol.* **8,** 257 (1960).
[15] D. A. Hopwood and A. M. Glauert, *J. Biophys. Biochem. Cytol.* **8,** 267 (1960).
[16] K. F. Gregory, *Can. J. Microbiol.* **2,** 649 (1956).
[17] D. A. Hopwood, *J. Gen. Microbiol.* **22,** 295 (1960).
[18] A. M. Glauert and D. A. Hopwood, *J. Biophys. Biochem. Cytol.* **6,** 515 (1959).
[19] A. M. Glauert and D. A. Hopwood, *J. Biophys. Biochem. Cytol.* **7,** 479 (1960).
[20] C. S. Cummins and H. Harris, *J. Gen. Microbiol.* **18,** 173 (1958).
[21] D. A. Hopwood, *Ann. N. Y. Acad. Sci.* **81,** 887 (1959).
[22] G. Sermonti and I. Spada-Sermonti, *J. Gen. Microbiol.* **15,** 609 (1956).
[23] G. Sermonti, A. Mancinelli, and I. Spada-Sermonti, *Genetics* **45,** 669 (1960).
[24] M. L. Morse, E. M. Lederberg, and J. Lederberg, *Genetics* **41,** 758 (1951).
[25] D. A. Hopwood, G. Sermonti, and I. Spada-Sermonti, *J. Gen. Microbiol.* **30,** 249 (1963).
[26] M. Demerec and P. E. Hartman, *Ann. Rev. Microbiol.* **13,** 377 (1959).
[27] P. E. Hartman, J. C. Loper, and D. Šerman, *J. Gen. Microbiol.* **22,** 323 (1960).
[28] F. Jacob and E. L. Wollman, "Sexuality and the Genetics of Bacteria." Academic Press, New York, 1961.
[29] F. Carvajal, *Mycologia* **39,** 426 (1947).

[30] S. G. Bradley, D. L. Anderson, and L. A. Jones, *Ann. N. Y. Acad. Sci.* **81**, 811 (1959).
[31] T. F. Anderson, E. L. Wollman, and F. Jacob, *Ann. inst. Pasteur* **93**, 450 (1957).
[32] S. G. Bradley and J. Lederberg, *J. Bacteriol.* **72**, 219 (1956).
[33] E. L. Wollman, F. Jacob, and W. Hayes, *Cold Spring Harbor Symposia Quant. Biol.* **21**, 141 (1956).
[33a] G. Sermonti and S Casciano, *J. Gen. Microbiol.* **33**, 293 (1963).
[34] J. Lederberg, *Proc. Natl. Acad. Sci. U. S.* **43**, 1060 (1957).
[35] D. H. Braendle, B. Gardiner, and W. Szybalski, *J. Gen. Microbiol.* **20**, 442 (1959).
[36] S. G. Bradley, *J. Bacteriol.* **73**, 581 (1957).
[37] G. Pontecorvo, *Cold Spring Harbor Symposia Quant. Biol.* **11**, 193 (1946).
[38] G. Sermonti and I. Spada-Sermonti, *Ann. N. Y. Acad. Sci.* **81**, 854 (1959).
[39] H. Saito and Y. Ikeda, *Ann. N. Y. Acad. Sci.* **81**, 862 (1959).
[40] S. G. Bradley, *Genetics* **45**, 613 (1960).
[41] S. I. Alikhanian, T. S. Iljina, and N. D. Lomovskaya, *Nature* **188**, 245 (1960).
[41a] Jarai, *Acta Microbiol. Acad. Sci. Hung.* **8**, 81 (1961).
[42] M. Alačević, *Nature* **197**, 1323 (1963).
[43] F. Jacob and E. L. Wollman, *Compt. rend. acad. sci.* **247**, 154 (1958).
[44] J. A. Roper, *Cold Spring Harbor Symposia Quant. Biol.* **23**, 141 (1958).
[45] K. F. Gregory and W. Shyu, *Nature* **191**, 465 (1961).
[46] K. F. Gregory and W. Shyu, *Microbial Genetics Bull.* No. **18**, 11 (1962).
[47] G. L. W. Wiebols and K. T. Wieringa, "Bacteriophagie, een algemeen voorkommend verschijnsel." Veenman, Wageningen, Netherlands, 1936.
[48] H. B. Woodruff, T. D. Nunheimer, and S. B. Lee, *J. Bacteriol.* **54**, 535 (1947).
[49] M. Welsch, *Ann. N. Y. Acad. Sci.* **81**, 974 (1959).
[50] J. R. D. McCormick, N. O. Sjolender, U. Hirsch, E. Jensen, and A. P. Doerschuk, *J. Am. Chem. Soc.* **79**, 4561 (1957).
[51] E. P. Abraham and G. G. F. Newton, *Endeavour* **20**, 92 (1961).
[52] S. I. Alikhanian, N. V. Orlova, S. Z. Mindlin, and Z. M. Zaitzeva, *Nature* **189**, 939 (1961).
[53] S. Z. Mindlin, T. A. Kubishkina, and S. I. Alikhanian, *Antibiotics (USSR) (English Transl.)* **6**, 623 (1961).
[54] S. Z. Mindlin, S. I. Alikhanian, and A. V. Vladimirov, *Sci. Repts. Ist. Super. Sanità* **1**, 469 (1961).
[55] T. F. Anderson, *Cold Spring Harbor Symposia Quant. Biol.* **23**, 47 (1958).
[56] J. Lederberg, *Proc. Natl. Acad. Sci. U. S.* **35**, 178 (1949).
[57] J. Lederberg, E. M. Lederberg, N. D. Zinder, and E. R. Lively, *Cold Spring Harbor Symposia Quant. Biol.* **16**, 413 (1951).
[58] B. W. Holloway and B. Fargie, *J. Bacteriol.* **80**, 362 (1960).
[59] A. L. Taylor and E. A. Adelberg, *Genetics* **45**, 1233 (1960).

CHAPTER 6

Genetic Fine Structure in Bacteria

ROYSTON C. CLOWES

I. Introduction

In cells of higher organisms, chromosomes are clearly visible as thread-like structures appearing within the nucleus at cell division; they can be seen to be equivalently distributed to the daughter cells. It is ironical that in bacteria where the hereditary material can be extracted, purified, and manipulated in a variety of physical and chemical ways, chromosomes have only very recently been clearly demonstrated, and appear to be much less complicated structural entities.[1]* It seems very likely, however, that this reflects secondary physical arrangements, rather than more fundamental differences. The use of the term "bacterial chromosome" is to this extent justified and in fact, the genetic and molecular details of the hereditary material of bacteria form the basis of many of the modern concepts of genetic structure.

Many novel systems of genetic transfer which have been described in

---

* See Hayes.[1] However, very recently, two independent approaches have produced the most compelling evidence so far published. The beautiful electron micrographs of Kleinschmidt *et al.*[1] show a continuous fiber with a cross-section dimension less than 50 A. The autoradiographs of Cairns[1] show a continuous double-stranded structure of length 700–900 μ. From both these very diverse techniques it is rational to assume that the bacterial chromosome consists of a double chain with a cross section of <5 mμ and a length over 10^5 times as great (700–900 μ), and is compatible with a continuous simple double helix of deoxynucleotides.

detail in previous chapters exist in bacteria. All these systems to a greater or lesser extent transfer fragments of genetic material from one cell into another, and are thus admirably suited to the study of small chromosomal regions. Moreover, since bacteria are haploid organisms,[2] their genetic analysis is much simplified, and is uncomplicated by problems of dominance and other perturbations inherent in diploids. In addition, all bacterial systems so far investigated (with the exception of the *Actinomyces*; see Chapter 5) appear to possess only one genetic structure or chromosome in each nucleus.[3-5] Bacterial genetic systems thus present the ultimate in simplicity of genetic organization; this characteristic, combined with the facility with which one may accumulate and handle enormous populations, makes them an ideal tool for genetic studies.

II. Correlation of the Gene with the Ultimate Genetic Units of Recombination, Function, and Mutation

A. THE CLASSICAL GENE

1. FORMAL GENETIC ANALYSIS

On the Mendel-Morgan concept of heredity,[6] the heritable traits of an organism are conceived of as being controlled by a series of independently transmitted units, the genes. From Mendel's early experiments each gene was postulated to exist in one of two alternative forms (alleles), one being dominant to the other when both are present in the same diploid organism on homologous but different chromosomes. An allele was considered to arise by a rare change in one gene resulting in an observable modification of some specific character. The recognition of a gene is thus dependent upon the existence of its allele, since its behavior can then be observed in crossing experiments. For example, if A and a, B and b are alternative forms of two genes, a cross between two diploid parents carrying the combinations AB and ab will give rise to progeny in which the new combinations Ab and aB are observed. The frequency of such recombination is found to be constant for each pair of genes. If the numbers of recombinant progeny are less than those carrying the parental combinations, the genes are said to be linked. Linkage is thus indicated if the fraction of recombinants in the total progeny is less than 50%; the closer the linkage, the smaller the recombinant fraction becomes. If three genes are closely linked, the recombination frequencies between pairs of them show additivity; that is, if the recombinant fraction between A and B is 7% and that between B and C is 3%, then that between A and C will be either the sum (10%) or the difference (4%), from which it can be concluded that a linear relationship exists between these genes, and their order can be fixed as either ABC ($AC = 10\%$) or ACB ($AC = 4\%$). Each gene can thus be mapped at a characteristic position, termed its locus, with regard to other genes of the same linkage group, a set of such linkage groups being termed a linkage map. In higher organisms, these abstract linkage groups, constructed to rationalize the results of genetic analysis, are beautifully and intimately correlated with the cytologically observable chromosomes. During meiosis, the parental chromosomes pair, duplicate, and separate in a highly regulated way so as to segregate one complete haploid set of chromosomes to each of the resulting gametes. During this process there may be an exchange of parts between homologous chromosomes of the two parents, as a result of an event called "crossing over," so that the chromosomes of the haploid gametes carry new combinations of the parental genes. The frequency with which any two parental genes on the same chromosome are separated by recombination is found to be a measure of the linear physical distance between them. Linked genes can thus be regarded as those genes between which, at meiosis, there is an incidence of less than one such exchange by crossing over as the average of a large number of cells.

2. PSEUDOALLELES

Classical genetic studies are concerned largely with the recombination and interaction of different genes. Genes between which recombination did not occur were considered to be alternatives, or alleles of each other. This assumption that recombination did not take place within the functional unit implied that the units of function and recombination were equivalent. Early genetic research, however, soon revealed the existence of more than two forms or alleles of the same gene, which were recognized by the fact that when the two recessive alleles were present on different homologous chromosomes, the cell was phenotypically recessive, although the original (wild-type) gene was dominant to each allele. (If A is the wild-type gene, and a and α are two alleles both recessive to A, both A/a and A/α will show the wild phenotype, but a/α will show the recessive phenotype.)

In the early 1950's crosses of such mutants in *Drosophila* led to the conclusion that alleles defined by these functional tests did not behave as true alternatives, since recombination was observed between them. These pseudoalleles, as they were called, form a bridge between the classical studies and those that followed, and which stemmed largely from work with microbial systems.

One such set of pseudoalleles is illustrated by the lozenge (*lz*) gene of Green and Green,[7] in which three mutations involving eye pigmentation changes were studied. The mutants were recessive to the wild type and produced a recessive phenotype in combination with each other, and were thus defined as alleles by the functional criterion. In spite of this, recombination was found to occur between them, indicating distances of less than one-thousandth the total chromosomal length. Similar studies were reported by Green,[8] E. B. Lewis,[9] and Mackendrick[10] in *Drosophila*, and by Pontecorvo and his colleagues[11-13] in *Aspergillus*. One of the several explanations offered for this finding was that the various mutations might occur within the substructure of the gene controlling the lozenge function, between which recombination could occur.[13] This particular conclusion shortly received striking confirmation with the almost simultaneous publications in 1955, of Benzer[14] using T4 phage, and of Demerec and his colleagues[15, 16] in *Salmonella typhimurium*.

In general, genetic fine structure has been studied in the closest detail in bacteriophage ("running the map into the ground")[17] particularly by the elegant and fine experimental work of Benzer. In bacteria, the smallest details are similarly demonstrable and show striking analogies with the rather more precise phage data. This contribution will concentrate on those experiments which use bacteria as genetic material and which have the advantage of the greater opportunities of relating genetic structure to function (see Chapter 8).

B. THE CONCEPT OF A COMPLEX GENE LOCUS

1. ADVANTAGES OF MICROBIAL SYSTEMS

The investigation of intragenic structure requires not only the isolation of numerous mutants affecting the same function (pseudoalleles) but also the ability to detect rare recombinants in crosses between pairs of these mutants, which are not likely to occur more frequently than one in a thousand. The short generation time and size of bacteria permit facile accumulation and examination of populations many times the size of the total human world population—an obvious choice of material for the study of these rare mutational and recombinational events.

Moreover, in bacteria, the genetic characters accessible for study include those involving simple and fundamental biochemical functions. Thus, although morphological characters are few, mutations which affect a wide range of synthetic and catabolic activities can be investigated. These mutants have the great advantage of being open to selection, facilitating the isolation of both the rare mutant from the parental, and the recombinant from the nonrecombinant progeny of a cross. The use of these biochemical mutants was first employed in the now classical genetic studies of Beadle and Tatum using the mold *Neurospora crassa*.[18, 19] These experiments led to the idea that many genes function by controlling the activity of enzymes. An alteration of a single gene by mutation was envisaged as resulting in a loss of specificity in the enzyme controlled by that gene, thus leading to a metabolic or biochemical block in a particular synthetic pathway. This *one gene–one enzyme* relationship constituted a breakthrough in functional genetics, although the use of biochemical mutants as one of the main tools in the investigation of intermediary metabolism tended at first to overshadow the more fundamental genetic implications.

2. SELECTIVE METHODS AND TECHNIQUES

The bacteria which lend themselves most readily to the isolation of biochemical mutants are those termed "nonexacting," which grow well on a simple medium (minimal medium)[20] of inorganic salts together with a carbohydrate and energy source such as glucose. From these parental strains, mutants can be selected which have lost the ability to grow on this simple medium, most of them being deficient in a single enzymic activity present in the parental (wild-type) strain.[21] This deficiency can be overcome (in 85–95 % of mutants)[22] by the addition to the minimal medium of a single amino acid, vitamin, or purine-pyrimidine base, which is the growth factor whose synthesis is interrupted by the metabolic block brought about by the enzyme deficiency (see Fig. 1).

Such auxotrophic[23] mutants may arise spontaneously, or may be induced by treatment with a mutagenic agent such as irradiation with ultraviolet light,[24] which increases the over-all mutation rate 100-fold or more. Their frequency in populations is very low, however, and is often no more than 1 in 10^5 even in irradiated cultures. The introduction of the penicillin screening technique[25, 26] greatly facilitated the selection of these mutants. This technique makes use of the fact that penicillin is bactericidal only to growing cells. Incubation in minimal medium to which penicillin has been added thus destroys the *prototrophic*[23] wild-type bacteria, but not the mutants, and so effectively enriches the proportion of auxotrophic cells in the culture to more than 1 in 100. [More recent techniques[27-29] involve the use of chemical mutagens as, for example, ethyl methane sulfonate (EMS),[30] which yield as high a proportion of auxotrophic mutants as 1 in 100 and thus obviate the necessity for penicillin enrichment.]

These cultures, containing about 1 % mutants, are then diluted and plated on a complete medium such as nutrient agar, to produce isolated clones, some of which will be auxotrophic. The identification of these clones is much simplified by the replica plating technique introduced by the Lederbergs.[31] A print of the colonies on complete medium is taken by pressing over the surface a sterile pad of material such as velvet, having a "pile." This print can now be used to inoculate a plate of minimal medium and another of complete medium. Auxotrophic clones are recognized by their failure to grow on the minimal medium. These auxotrophic colonies are picked from the complete medium and inoculated to a template pattern on a similar medium. After growth, a further replication to minimal media plates, supplemented with one of a variety of growth factors, permits the identification of the specific growth factor. As an intermediate step, the use of amino acid pools[20, 32] reduces the number of operations and also preserves those mutants having more complex growth requirements (see next section).

3. TRANSDUCTION IN *Salmonella typhimurium*

a. Techniques. This system of genetic transfer, first discovered by Zinder and Lederberg[33] using the temperate phage P22 (see Chapter 2), was put to effective use in fine genetic analysis by Demerec and his collaborators working at the Laboratory of the Carnegie Institution of Washington's Department of Genetics at Cold Spring Harbor.

A large number of independent auxotrophic mutants responding to a single amino acid or purine were isolated and characterized by the Cold Spring Harbor School. The nomenclature used by Demerec,[34] which has formed the basis for a suggested uniform notation within microbial genetics,[35] is to designate each mutant with a triletter symbol denoting the growth requirement, e.g., *try* for tryptophan, *pro* for proline requirement. This is followed by a serial number depending merely on the order of isolation of the mutant. Some auxotrophs were found to require more than a single supplement, of which most were found to result from a single mutation that produced a metabolic block preceding the branching of the synthetic pathway into two or more directions.[36] These mutants, which in general required two growth factors, were designated by a four-letter symbol (e.g., *phty* denotes a requirement for phenylalanine plus tyrosine) to differentiate them from mutants with a requirement for two growth factors as a result of two independent mutations (e.g., *phe.tyr* denotes a mutant with a requirement for phenylalanine plus tyrosine derived by a second mutation from either a *phe* or a *tyr* mutant).

Each class of mutant was then further examined for its ability to utilise known precursors of the growth supplement, for cross-feeding or syntrophy,[36] and in some instances for the accumulation of such precursors in the culture as could be identified by paper chromatography. By these preliminary, rather crude biochemical tests, the probable metabolic block involved in each mutant could be identified.[37-44] The extension of these preliminary studies by more refined techniques involving the isolation and characterization of the associated enzymes has been effected in some instances.[45, 46]

By these methods, each group of mutants responding to a single growth factor was divided into subgroups, within which all mutants show the same response to various precursors of the growth factor, and the same accumulations and synthrophisms. These phenotypically identical mutants thus have identical biochemical blocks and were considered to arise by mutation in the same functional gene leading to inactivation of the same specific enzyme. To their designation could thus be added a letter denoting the phenotype, e.g., the tryptophan-requiring mutants were subdivided into four phenotypic groups *tryA*, *tryB*, *tryC*, and *tryD* from the results of biochemical tests shown in Table I, conforming to the metabolic pathway of Fig. 1.

TABLE I

RESPONSE OF TRYPTOPHANLESS AUXOTROPHS OF *Salmonella typhimurium* TO INTER-
MEDIATES OF THE TRYPTOPHAN PATHWAY AND THE RESULTS OF
CROSS-FEEDING TESTS[a]

Phenotypic group	Growth response to			Cross-feed mutants of group[c]
	Anthranilic acid[b]	Indole	Tryptophan	
A	+	+	+	None
B	−	+	+	A
C	−	+	+	A,B
D	−	−	+	A,B,C

[a] Data of Brenner.[37]
[b] Supplements added to minimal agar at 20 μg./ml.; growth after 24 hr. at 37°C.
[c] From parallel streaking on minimal agar after 48 hr. at 37°C.

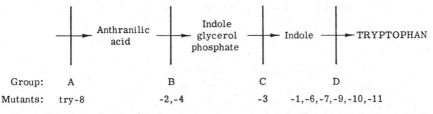

FIG. 1. Diagram showing biochemical sequence in tryptophan biosynthesis. A, B, C, and D indicate the positions of the biochemical blocks with the associated mutants. After Brenner.[37]

The wild-type *Salmonella* and each of its auxotrophs are sensitive to the phage P22. Phage lysates containing about 10^{11} particles per milliliter were prepared from cultures of each mutant, which could then be concentrated by high-speed centrifugation and suspended in buffer. A cross of two strains is effected by the use of one strain in the form of a bacterial culture (recipient), which is infected with a bacteria-free phage preparation of the other strain (donor). By this means, the genetic specificity of the donor is introduced by the phage vector into the recipient cells. The infected cells are plated on minimal medium on which neither donor nor recipient, being auxotrophic, can grow, but on which cells arising from recombination to reconstitute the wild-type genome can be selected from the background growth of nonrecombinant cells.

When one considered the disparity in the amount of genetic material as DNA (see below) in a bacterial cell[5] and in a P22 phage particle,[47] it is obvious that the bacterial DNA must be broken down into fragments less than one-hundredth the size of the total chromosome in order to be accommodated within a normal-sized phage particle. Thus, unless the mutations of donor and recipient are separated by less than one-hundredth total map length, it is unlikely that those fragments carrying the wild-type marker,

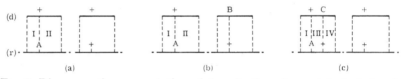

FIG. 2. Diagrammatic representation of transduction of a recipient strain, A, by phage grown on (a) wild-type donor; (b) donor with unlinked marker B; and (c) donor with linked marker C; (r) represents parts of the recipient chromosome; and (d) represents fragments of the donor chromosome.

corresponding to the recipient mutation, will also carry the mutation of the donor (see Fig. 2b). Thus, the frequency of wild-type recombinants will be the same as when a wild-type donor is used (crossing over in regions I and II, Fig. 2a and b). However, when the donor and recipient mutations are very closely linked so as to be carried on the same small fragment (Fig. 2c), the frequency of recombination will be reduced and will be proportional to the distance between the markers, since recombination is now proportional to the crossing over in regions I and III. The nearer the mutational sites (region III) the smaller the probability of recombination. When the two sites are identical, or separated by a region within which exchange does not occur, there will be no recombination.

b. Preliminary Results. As was found by Zinder and Lederberg,[33] auxotrophic recipients crossed with a wild-type donor, or with donors of different phenotype, gave several hundred prototrophic clones per plate spread with about 10^8 infected cells. However, in nearly all crosses between strains of identical phenotype some prototrophic clones were produced, in numbers significantly greater than those obtaining when uninfected recipients, or recipients infected with phage grown on the same strain (homologous crosses), were plated. Table II shows typical early results[15] obtained from crosses between seven *cysB* mutants and two mutants of a phenotypically similar, but nonidentical, group, *cysD*. The ability to produce prototrophic recombinants in a cross is taken to indicate genetic nonidentity of the mutations. In *cysB*, the demonstration of at least seven nonidentical mutations, all separable by recombination, makes unlikely one of the alternative hypotheses to account for similar pseudoalleles,[13]

TABLE II

NUMBERS OF PROTOTROPHIC RECOMBINANT CLONES ARISING FROM PLATING VARIOUS CYSTEINELESS AUXOTROPHS OF *Salmonella typhimurium* AFTER INFECTION WITH P22 PHAGE PROPAGATED ON OTHER CYSTEINELESS AUXOTROPHS[a]

Recipient[b]	Donor (source of phage)								
	cysB-10	*cysB-12*	*cysB-14*	*cysB-15*	*cysB-16*	*cysB-18*	*cysB-24*	*cysD-11*	Wild-type (control)
cysB-10	0	47	42	65	26	29	29	1157	1115
cysB-12	28[c]	0	43	83	33	36	2	2351	2104
cysB-14	29	38	0	33	2	4	6	2220	1792
cysB-15	76	95	107	0	54	88	61	1019	954
cysB-16	15	19	2	34	0	2	3	1223	979
cysB-18	5	20	1	23	3	0	3	856	771
cysB-24	25	47	14	84	10	8	0	528	1617
cysD-23	1879	791	2296	1399	951	860	1616	742	1592

[a] Data of Demerec *et al.*[16]

[b] One milliliter of an overnight culture of the recipient (ca. 10^9 cells/ml.) is infected with P22 phage (grown on donor) at a multiplicity of 8, and 0.1-ml. samples spread over minimal agar.

[c] Each figure represents the sum of the prototrophic clones appearing on a total of three plates after incubation of 48 hr. at 37°C.

namely, that there are at least seven distinct genes within this region all concerned with cysteine biosynthesis. In addition, the table shows that the numbers of prototrophs produced by these *cysB* × *cysB* crosses are always less than when a *cysB* mutant is crossed with a *cysD* mutant or with a wild-type donor. This reduction in recombination suggested that these seven distinct mutations occurred very close to each other and were clustered within a very small region of the chromosome. The more likely interpretation made by Demerec *et al.*,[15] therefore, was that the functional unit of *cysB* extended over a segment of chromosome, rather than having a point location, and that the integrity of many points on this segment was necessary for *cysB* enzyme production and wild-type activity. At many sites on this segment, therefore, mutations could occur, each leading to loss of this integrity and loss of *cysB* enzyme activity, and thus the production of mutants with identical phenotype. Between these sites, however, recombination to reconstitute the genome as found in the wild-type strain was possible. For chromosomal regions such as that responsible for the determination of the *cysB* enzyme, Demerec retained the term "gene locus," the presence of many sites of mutation within this structure leading to the term "complex gene locus," the various mutants being termed "nonidentical alleles" (cf. pseudoalleles, heteroalleles).[48]

c. Complex Gene Loci in Salmonella. This early work has been extended by analysis of well over a thousand independent mutants[38, 39, 41-44, 49-52, 54-57] which have been allocated to over fifty phenotypic groups each containing at least two mutants (up to a maximum of over one hundred), as summarized in Table III. Crosses have been carried out between most members of each group, resulting in the majority of instances in the production of prototrophs, with a yield considerably less than when mutants of nonidentical phenotypic groups are crossed. The conclusion reached was that "non-identical allelism (complex structure of loci) is not a special feature of certain gene loci but a general property of all."[56]

4. Complex Gene Loci in *Escherichia coli*

Subsequent to the work of Demerec and his colleagues, many complex loci have been demonstrated in *Escherichia coli*. Study of these loci has in most instances been undertaken because the enzymes involved are readily isolated and manipulated, so that correlated biochemical and genetic studies can be carried out. The details of some of the more characteristic of these systems are summarized in Table III and below.

a. Lac Loci and β-Galactosidase. Wild-type *E. coli* strain K12 can utilize a series of carbohydrates in addition to glucose, as a sole energy and carbon source, among these being the disaccharide lactose. Strains of K12 can be selected that have lost the ability due to the mutation $lac^+ \rightarrow lac^-$. A series of these *lac* markers were found to be located in the same chromosomal region.[58]

The transfer of genetic material from an Hfr donor to a recipient (F⁻) strain of *E. coli*, by means of conjugation (see Chapter 1) is a highly efficient process, so that if an Hfr strain is chosen which transfers the *lac* region as an early marker, a large proportion of the recipient cells will receive this marker. Pardee *et al.*[59, 60] have isolated large numbers of *lac* mutants in F⁻ strains, as well as in Hfr strains. The *lac* loci can be shown as the result of transfers using HfrH to be located as in Fig. 3,* the order of genes being *thr-leu-pro-lac-ade-gal.* Among these *lac* mutants, a group can

* See page 266.

be recognized in which the mutation has led to the loss of the enzyme β-galactosidase, responsible for the hydrolysis of lactose into the two hexoses glucose and galactose. These phenotypically identical *lac* mutants have been termed *z* mutants.[59-61]

Crosses in which the Hfr and F⁻ strains carry independent z^- mutations can be made, of the type Hfr z_A^- . ade^+ . str-s . × F⁻ z_B^- . ade^- . str-r (Fig. 4a) and the reciprocal cross in which the z markers are reversed (Fig. 4b). In both crosses, selection is made for ade^+ . str-r recombinants which are then scored for z^+ and z^- phenotype. The relative order of z_A and z_B can be concluded from frequencies of z^+ recombinants in the reciprocal crosses; if it is greater in the first cross (a) than in the second cross (b) the order of the markers is z_A-z_B-ade since, as shown in Fig. 4,* for z^+ . ade^+ . str-r recombinants, crossovers would be necessary in regions I and III in the first cross (a), and in regions I, II, and III in the second cross (b), thus requiring an additional crossover in region II. As indicated in Fig. 3, the crossover frequency in this *lac–ade* region is 22 %, and so in general the frequency of z^+ recombinants in one cross will be four to five times higher than in the reciprocal. In crosses of both types, the ratio of z^+ . ade^+ . str-r recombinants to ade^+ . str-r recombinants is a measure of crossing over within region I and thus a measure of the distance between two z mutations. Thus the relative order and the distances between a series of z mutant sites can be made with accuracy. As can be seen from Fig. 3, at least 38 independent mutational sites have been recognized and mapped within the z locus as shown.[62, 63]

b. Gal Loci. The transduction of these loci by defective phage particles, λ*dg* (see Chapter 2), is yet another highly efficient process of genetic transfer. This transduction is restricted to a cluster of bacterial markers concerned solely with galactose fermentation, which can be located by standard Hfr × F⁻ crosses at a region very near to the site of the λ prophage locus on the K12 chromosome.[58, 64, 65] From the wild K12 strain, which is able to break down D-galactose to provide a source both of energy and of carbon, mutants which have lost this ability (*gal⁻*) can be recognized by plating on a nonselective medium, such as eosin methylene blue or tetrazolium medium, on which *gal⁺* and *gal⁻* clones are differentiated by color.[20, 58]

A recipient K12 strain transduced with λ*dg* becomes diploid for this small region on which the *gal* markers are located, and is termed a syngenote (which may be either a heterogenote if the *gal* markers differ, or a homogenote if the *gal* marker of the fragment is genetically identical to that of the recipient strain).[66, 67]

When a gal_x^- recipient is infected with a high-frequency transducing (HFT) lysate from a *gal⁺* strain, the heterogenote gal_x^-/λ . gal^+ results (see Fig. 5). These heterogenotes (A) which are phenotypically *gal⁺*, segregate

* See page 266.

TABLE III
COMPLEX GENE LOCI IN BACTERIA

Biochemical pathway	Sequence of biochemical steps →	Clustered loci, with gene order and numbers of mutants	Interallelic complementation groups	References*
	Salmonella typhimurium			
Histidine (*his*)†	G-E-A-H-F-B-C-B-D-D	E - F - A - H - B - C - D - G 13 37 25 2 34 35 61 11	E(-a-b-c-d) B(-a-b-c-d) D(a-b)	38, 46, 52, 53, 54, 54a, 100, 113, 119, 152, 207
Tryptophan (*try*)‡	A-B-(C,D)	A - B - D - C 1 4 6 17	None	29, 37, 45, 50, 49, 55
Threonine (*thr*)	(D,C)-A-B-E	D - C - A - B 6 5 14 16 E(1)	None	43
Isoleucine (*ile*) and isoleucine plus valine (*ilva*)	*ileA-ilva*(A,D)*-ilvaB-ilvaC*	*ileA-ilvaA-ilvaD-ilvaB-ilvaC* 12 6 1 7 2	None	43
Leucine (*leu*)	A	A (107)	4	43, 111
Cysteine (*cys*)§	C - D - A - B - E (?)	C - D 107 84	C - D a - b - e - d - c 34 30 73 38 46	28, 40, 51, 57, 93
		A (62)	a - b - c 43 8 11	118
		cysB(26) - *try*(A-B-C-D)§	c - b - a—(*try*) 4 18 4	15, 16
		E (7)	a - d 4 3	
Methionine (*met*)	A - B - C - (E,F) (?)	A (15) B(12)—F(4) C(10) E(6)		44

	$adth(A,C,D)$-$ade(C,E)$-$adeB$	$adthA$ $adthD$ $adthC$-$adeC$ $adeB$ $adeE$		
Adenine (ade) and adenine plus thiamine ($adth$)				39, 117
Proline (pro)	D - (A,B) - C	(A,B) - C D		42
Escherichia coli				
Lactose (lac)‖		i - o - z - y	z (2 Groups)	58, 58a, 59, 60, 62, 63, 112, 174, 175, 199
Galactose (gal)#	k - t - e	k-o-t or k-t-o-e or k-t-e-o	None	64-69, 154, 173, 216-218, 219
Arabinose (ara)**	A - B - D	D - A - B - O		78-87, 215
Alkaline phosphatase (P)††		P	2 Groups	70, 71, 150, 169, 167, 178, 178a, 181, 182, 209-211
Tryptophan (try)§§	D - C - (A,B)	D - C - A - B		72-77, 110, 183, 206

* General references 34, 35, 56, 61, 92, 115, 171, 172, 195, 205
† Tables IV and VII, Figs. 9 and 10.
‡ Table I and Fig. 1.
§ Table II.
‖ Table VII, Fig. 3.

Figure 5.
** Figure 8.
†† Table VII and Fig. 5.
§§ Table VII, Figs. 1 and 7.

265

rare gal^- cells which can be shown to be of two genotypes; the haploid gal_x^- (C) and homogenotic $gal_x^-/\lambda.gal_x^-$ (B). These homogenotic clones are recognized by their ability to produce gal^+ papillae when replicated to a lawn of gal_y^- bacteria, after irradiation and incubation, and are capable of transducing gal_x^- at high frequency.[67, 68] Thus when a phage lysate of a $gal_x^-/\lambda.gal_x^-$ homogenote is applied to a gal_y^- recipient (D), heterogenotic $gal_y^-/\lambda.gal_x^-$ clones result. These clones may be initially either gal^+ or gal^-

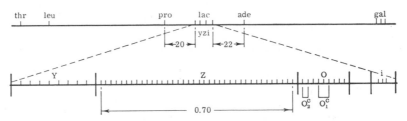

Fig. 3. Genetic map of the *lac* region in *E. coli* K12. The upper line represents the location of the *lac* region with respect to other linked markers. The lower line represents an enlargement of the linked *lac* loci showing the two structural genes *z* and *y*, the operator region *o*, and the regulator gene *i*. Recombination frequencies are shown below each line. After Jacob and Monod.[62, 63]

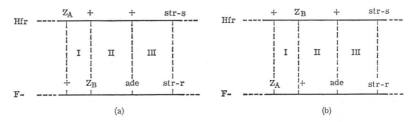

Fig. 4. Diagrammatic representation of crosses between two *lac*⁻ strains of *E. coli* K12. (a) shows the cross of Hfr $z_A^-.ade^+.str\text{-}s \times$ F⁻ $z_B^-.ade^-.str\text{-}r$; (b) shows the reciprocal cross Hfr $z_B^-.ade^+.str\text{-}s \times$ F⁻ $z_A^-.ade^-.str\text{-}r$. The upper line represents a part of the Hfr chromosome and the lower line the corresponding part of the F⁻ chromosome. The relative order of markers is assumed to be z_A-z_B-*ade*-*str*.

The gal^+ clones result from complementation (see p. 298) when the two gal^- mutations involve different functions, so that the heterogenote produced ($gal_y^-.gal_x^+/\lambda.gal_y^+.gal_x^-$ or $-+/+-$) has a wild (gal^+) phenotype (E). Gal^- clones are found when the two gal^- mutations involve the same function since here there is no complementation (F).[68, 69] When these gal^- heterogenotes are further incubated, gal^+ papillae arise from recombination events leading to the production of the two *cis*-heterogenotes, G ($--/$ $++$) and H ($++/--$) (both of which are phenotypically gal^+) from the original *trans*-heterogenote $-+/+-$. The process of crossing over is assumed to be due to mitotic recombination within the small diploid region. Morse has used this recombination as a measure of the distance between the two *gal⁻* mutations, and by this means has mapped 17 mutations arising in three adjacent *gal* loci.[69]

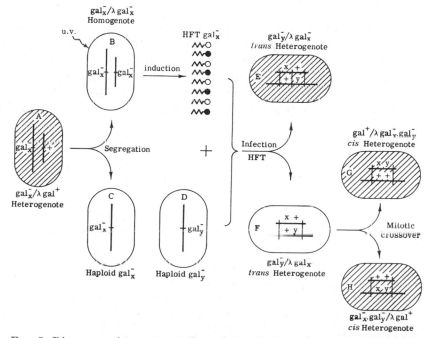

FIG. 5. Diagrammatic representation of complementation and recombination within the *gal* region of *E. coli* K12 strains infected with defective λ*dg* phage. Phenotypically *gal⁺* cells are crosshatched, phenotypically *gal⁻* cells are unhatched. On the left, the heterogenote (A), formed by infection of a *gal⁻ₓ* recipient with phage from the U V irradiation of a *gal⁺* cell lysogenic for λ, is allowed to segregate. Among the segregants, the rare *gal⁻* homogenotes (B) are isolated and HFT*gal⁻ₓ* lysates prepared by UV induction, producing equal numbers of active nontransducing phage (wavy line with ○) and defective transducing phage (wavy line with ●). Complementation is investigated by infecting nonidentical *gal⁻ᵧ* recipients (D) with this HFTλ. If the two *gal⁻* mutations (*x* and *y*) involve different functional units, then the *trans*-heterogenotes formed will be phenotypically *gal⁺* (E). If, however, different functional units are involved, the *trans*-heterogenotes will be *gal⁻* (F). These heterogenotes will undergo mitotic crossing over, some of the products being the phenotypically *gal⁺* *cis*-heterogenotes (G and H) which show up as *gal⁺* papillae on further incubation. The frequency with which these arise is a measure of the distance between the two *gal⁻* mutational sites (see Lederberg[68] and Morse[69]).

c. *Alkaline Phosphatase (P) Locus.* The enzyme, alkaline phosphatase, present in *E. coli* K12, can be detected by plating bacterial cultures for single colonies on a medium of low phosphate concentration and spraying with the substrate *p*-nitrophenyl phosphate (NPP) which turns yellow when dephosphorylated by this enzyme.[70] Wild-type (P^+) colonies turn yellow within a few seconds of spraying, whereas mutants having lost this activity $(P^-$ mutants) remain white. Garen et al.[70, 71] have isolated P^- mutants by this method after UV irradiation and have subjected them to an intensive biochemical and genetic scrutiny.

Most mutants were stable and were crossed by conjugation in all combinations. A cross of each pair of mutants (e.g., Hfr Cavalli $thr^+.leu^+.P_1^-$ $str\text{-}s \times F^- thr^-.leu^-.P_2^-.str\text{-}r$) was compared in each case with the reciprocal cross (Hfr $P_2^- \times F^- P_1^-$] and the two control crosses in which both Hfr and F^- strains carried either P_1^- or P_2^- (Hfr $P_1^- \times F^- P_1^-$; Hfr $P_2^- \times F^- P_2^-$), to evaluate the level of protrophic P^+ colonies due to reversion rather than

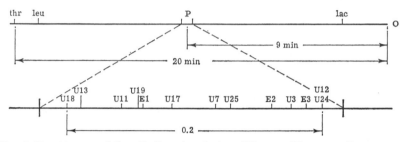

FIG. 6. Genetic map of the alkaline phosphatase (P) gene. The upper line represents the part of the chromosome transferred in the first 20 minutes at 37°C. by Hfr Cavalli starting at the origin, O, with the relative order of markers measured by timing of interrupted matings as indicated immediately below. The lower line represents an enlargement of the P region showing the relative order of P^- mutations fixed by frequency of P^+ recombinants in crosses of two P^- mutants. The bottom line shows recombination frequency between the two extreme P^- markers (see A. Garen[70] for details).

recombination. The parental cultures were mixed, and plated after 90 minutes on minimal medium containing streptomycin in which glycerophosphate was the sole source of phosphorus, the only cells capable of growth on this medium being those of genotype $thr^+.leu^+.P^+.str\text{-}r$. As a control, the same parental mixtures were plated on standard minimal medium containing streptomycin on which $thr^+.leu^+.P^-.str\text{-}r$ cells are selected, so that the percentage of P^+ recombinants can be expressed as a fraction of the $thr^+.leu^+$ recombinants.

The location and order of the various P^- mutations can therefore be made in a way entirely analogous to the mapping of $lac.z^-$ mutants. A hundred different P^- mutants tested in this way were in most instances shown to result from mutations at distinct sites, closely linked in a linear array. A preliminary map of some 13 mutational sites is shown in Fig. 6.[70, 71]

d. Transduction of the Tryptophan Synthetase Locus. A large number of tryptophanless auxotrophs of *E. coli* K12 have been studied genetically using transduction with P1 phage.[72] The final step in tryptophan biosynthesis in *E. coli* has been shown to be controlled by the enzyme, tryptophan synthetase. The step is complex and appears to involve the three reactions:

(1) Indole + L-serine → L-tryptophan
(2) Indole glycerol phosphate ⇌ indole + triose phosphate
(3) Indole glycerol phosphate + L-serine → L-tryptophan + triose phosphate

of which the latter reaction appears to be the most important physiologically.[72] Among the tryptophanless auxotrophs studied, a group of phenotypically similar mutants can be isolated which are unable to perform any one of these three reactions and are thus deficient in tryptophan synthetase. On isolation, this enzyme was found to separate on chromatographic columns into two stable protein components, A and B, neither of which independently had more than 2 to 3 % normal activity in any of the three component reactions, but when combined were found to reconstitute the normal level of activity. A large proportion of the mutants were found to have only one of these protein components inactivated.[72] A genetic analysis of mutants has been made[73-77] using P1 transduction (Chapter 2). This system of "general" transduction is essentially similar to the *Salmonella*-P22 system, the crosses being carried out by infecting one mutant with P1 phage grown on others, and selecting for tryptophan-independent recombinants on minimal medium. The more recent crosses have concentrated on mutants within the *A* region. Most of the crosses involve doubly auxotropic $try_x^-.his^-$ recipients and tryptophanless donors $try_y^-.$[72, 73] Since the *try* and *his* markers are not linked closely enough to be carried on the same transducing fragment,[76] the measurement of the ratio try^+/his^+ transductants gives a measure of recombination within the *try* region, with an internal correction for such various experimental variations as the efficiencies of the donors and recipients, which can normally produce extensive day-to-day experimental fluctuations. The frequencies of recombination between two *try* markers are thus expressed as a proportion of the transduction for the *his* marker, and a value of 5 % was found as the maximum between two *A* mutants of the *try* region.[72, 73] However, since the wild-type his^+ marker is found to be transduced with only half the efficiency of the try^+ marker, a more accurate value for recombination within the *try* region was obtained by the ratio $\frac{1}{2} try^+/his^+$, the maximum value found between two *try* markers in the *A* region being now corrected to 2.5 %.[74, 77] The minimum values were found to be limited by reversions of try^- to try^+. Thus, for mapping closely linked clusters of markers, triple auxotrophs $try_x^-.cys^-.his^-$ [74] were used (the *cys* and *try* markers being linked and carried on the same transducing fragment). Using a try_y^- strain as donor, the re-

cipients were plated on minimal media containing histidine (selecting for
$try^+ . cys^+$ transductions) and on minimal medium plus histidine and tryptophan (selecting cys^+ transductants). The recombination between try_x and
try_y is now found from the ratio $try^+ . cys^+/cys^+$. All reversions $try_{\bar{x}}$ to try^+
will still be cys^- and thus not interfere with the ratio, while contaminants
are not likely to require histidine. A sensitive selection method is thus ensured.[74]

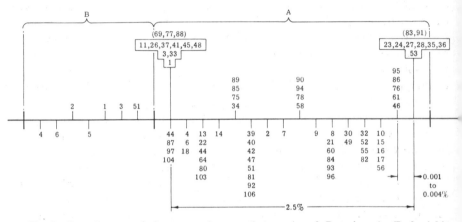

FIG. 7. Genetic map of the tryptophan synthetase A and B regions in *Escherichia
coli*. The heavy horizontal line represents a part of chromosome in the *try* region. Mutants in the B region form normal A protein, mutants in the A region form normal B
protein. Mutants listed above the map form an altered A-CRM (or B-CRM) (cross-
reacting material) protein, whereas those below are unable to form either an A or a
B protein. The mutants are clustered in groups between which there is less than 0.1%
recombination (between 25 and 100 nucleotides). Other mutants shown in boxes do
not show any recombination (less than 0.0002%) consistent with a location less than
one or a few nucleotides apart. Mutants shown at the same levels within the boxes
form proteins identical in stability to heat or to acid precipitation. The recombination
frequencies are shown on the lower lines. From C. Yanofsky *et al.*[72-75, 77]

It has been shown that most of the crosses yield try^+ cells in low yields,
consistent with a clustering of the mutational sites of the auxotrophs.
Crosses of two mutants in which the A function is affected give rise to less
recombinants than $A \times B$ crosses, as do $B \times B$ crosses. The values for
recombination are roughly additive, and led to the location of B mutants
to one side and A mutants to the other side of the locus as shown in Fig.
7.[72-74, 77]

e. Ara Loci in Escherichia coli B. A series of L-arabinose nonfermenting
mutants (ara^-), obtained from the wild (ara^+) strain of *E. coli* B have been
isolated on eosin-methylene blue medium in an analogous way to the

nonfermenting *lac⁻* and *gal⁻* mutants.[78] Similar mutants in *E. coli* K12 show that an *ara* locus maps between the *thr* and *leu* genes[79] (controlling threonine and leucine biosynthesis, respectively). This location, first mapped by conjugation experiments, was confirmed by the observation of linked transduction with phage P1 of the three markers *thr*, *ara*, and *leu* by Lennox.[80] Englesberg *et al.*[81-87] showed that these *ara* mutations are concerned with genes that control the three enzymes, L-arabinose isomerase, L-ribulokinase, and L-ribulose 5-phosphate 4-epimerase (see Fig. 8). The mutations were mapped by infecting $thr^-.leu^-$ recipients with P1 phage grown on $thr^+.leu^+$ donors, the various *ara* markers being introduced into the donor and recipient strains.[78] The crosses can thus be represented as $thr^-.ara_a^-.leu^- \times thr^+.ara_b^-.leu^+$ and selection is made for ara^+ recombinants by plating on a minimal medium in which L-arabinose is the sole carbon source. The ara^+ recombinants can then be analyzed for the associated transfer of the thr^+ and leu^+ markers. If the order of the markers is $thr\text{-}ara_a\text{-}ara_b\text{-}leu$, this particular cross will be expected to show more transfer of thr^+ (no recombination between ara_a^+ and thr^+) and less of leu^+ (recombination between ara_a^+ and leu^+), than will the reciprocal cross $thr^-.ara_b^-.leu^- \times thr^+.ara_a^-.leu^+$ (where recombination is required between ara_a^- and thr^+ but not between ara_a^+ and leu^+); whereas if the order were reversed, viz., $thr\text{-}ara_b\text{-}ara_a\text{-}leu$, the first cross would show less thr^+ and more leu^+ than the second. Thirty-eight of these ara^- mutants were precisely ordered in this way (the latter crosses analyzing only leu^+).[85, 87] The sites of mutation were shown to be closely linked and were arranged in a linear order between the *thr* and *leu*, forming four functionally and genetically distinct groups, *ara-A*,-*B*,-*C* and -*D*,[78, 84, 87] as shown in Fig. 8.[85, 87]

5. Complex Loci in Other Bacteria

Within recent years, evidence of complex loci has been emerging from studies of transformation. In the classical transformation of *Pneumococcus*, Lacks and Hotchkiss[88] have demonstrated close linkage of eight mutants deficient in the enzyme amylomaltase, whose sites are clustered on the same molecule of DNA.

The transformation system of *Bacillus subtilis* discovered by Spizizen[89] has the advantage that this organism is nutritionally nonexacting. Thus, a variety of auxotrophic mutants analogous to these of *E. coli* and *Salmonella* can be isolated and investigated by a method enabling direct manipulation of the purified genetic material. Preliminary studies in this system have revealed a cluster of nine *his* mutants, of which six appear to be concerned with an early step in histidine biosynthesis (*his-A* or *his-H* of the *Salmonella* pathway shown in Fig. 10) and between which recombination occurs, but never more than 30 %.[90] Several markers affecting a func-

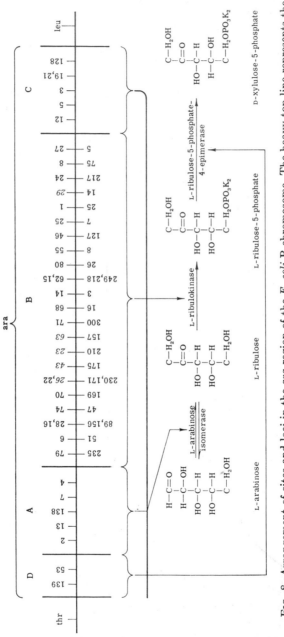

FIG. 8. Arrangement of sites and loci in the *ara* region of the *E. coli* B chromosome. The heavy top line represents the chromosome, with single site mutants shown immediately above. Within the *B* locus, the sites are shown above the line and represent the order of the mutants, none of which form measurable amounts of L-ribulokinase; the figures below the line show the levels of L-arabinose isomerase formed by each of these mutants. (Wild-type isomerase level is 70 μmoles of ribulose/hr./mg. protein.) Mutants shown in italics (*-26*, *-43*, *-23*, *-63*, and *-29*) are those forming CRM. Each capital letter represents one gene locus. Below is a diagram of the first three steps in the pathway of arabinose fermentation. The thick horizontal line indicates the absence of all three enzymes in mutants of the *C* locus. Data of Englesberg and colleagues.[78, 85, 87]

tion similar to that of tryptophan synthetase of *E. coli* have also been shown to be closely linked.[91]

6. STRUCTURE OF THE COMPLEX GENE LOCUS

The complex gene locus of Demerec[15, 16, 56] is equivalent ot the classical gene, as defined as a unit of function. When complex loci were first demonstrated, the use of the term "gene" was avoided because of its previous classical connotations with allelism. In its place terms such as "cistron"[17] or "complementing unit"[52] were taken up because of the apparent simplicity of their definition. Complications have arisen all too quickly, however, in the unambiguous use of these terms (see Section III,B,2) so that there seems at the moment good reason to rehabilitate the term "gene," provided its use is restricted to the functional genetic unit and it is acknowledged that this unit is capable of subdivision by both mutation and recombination.

a. Single Site and Multisite Mutants. When a series of phenotypically identical mutants are crossed, although the majority of crosses give rise to recombinant wild-type cells, a minority of the crosses are nonproductive and fail to produce recombinants. It is assumed, that such crosses involve mutants whose sites either are identical, or overlap. Two types of mutant have been recognized. The first type involves a number of mutants which fail to produce recombinants when crossed together, but which produce recombinants with any of a series of other mutants which themselves recombine in any combination. These mutants usually revert to the wild phenotype at a frequency of the same order as the forward mutation and, provided the sensitivity of the genetic system is adequate, it is assumed that they are produced by mutations arising at the same localized site. Examples of such mutants are shown by the *his-F* mutants *-71*, *-114*, and *-232* (Fig. 9), the *P⁻* mutants *U-12* and *U-24* (Fig. 6) and in the tryptophan synthetase *A* locus, mutants *-1*, *-3*, *-11*, *-26*, *-33*, *-37*, *-41*, *-45*, *-46* (Fig. 7).

With certain notable exceptions,[28, 51, 58a, 93] the second type of mutant is rather less frequent than the first,[28, 92] and fails to produce recombinants with a series of other mutants which themselves behave as a closely linked group. Such mutants usually fail to revert, and it is concluded that the mutational damage extends over a region of the chromosome on which the sites of all the mutants with which it fails to recombine are situated. Such multisite mutants are demonstrated in the *his-F* mutants *-612*, *-135*, *-41*, *-152*, *-644*, *-55*, *-666* and *-703* (Fig. 9). and the *his* mutants *EF-135*, *F-486*, *FA-703*, *AH-134*, *HB-22*, *GO-203*, *(E)F-41*, *(F)A-517*, *A-484*, *CDGO-63*, *FA-55*, *A-481*, *CDG(O)-538*, *FAHBCD-152*, *EFAH(B)-612*, *BCDGO-57*, *EFAHBCD-712*, and *FAHBCDG(O)-644*, extending in some cases over eight adjacent gene loci (Fig. 10). Multisite mutants are suggested to arise by some form of chromosomal aberration such as "looping."[93]

b. *Linearity and Continuity of the Gene and Chromosome.* From studies of higher organisms, it is evident from the additivity of genetic distances and the correlation of many genetic changes with microscopically observable chromosomal lesions[94] that there exists a one-dimensional structure over relatively long genetic distances. It is of interest to know whether such linearity exists also at the intragenic level, and whether the subelements of the gene form a continuous and one-dimensional structure. From the results of isotopic labeling of chromosomes, it has been suggested that the genes may be arranged on secondary chromosomal structures which are attached to the primary linear chromosome.[95, 96] This would be expected to give the appearance of a linear arrangement between two genes situated on different branches (observable structure) and also between two genes situated on the same branch (intragenic structure), but not between two genes on the same branch and another gene on a different branch. Fine genetic studies could be expected to throw light on this situation.

The first problem of intragenic linearity has been defined more precisely by Benzer[97] as a question of "topology" (i.e., whether the subelements of the gene are connected in a continuous way) rather than as involving the additivity of genetic distances, which are subject over these short regions to large variations imposed by such factors as negative interference.[12, 98] The conclusions of this author from studies of T4 coliphage, reached by a consideration of "deletion" mutants,[99] or what have been termed more conservatively in bacteria, multisite mutants,* are that the subelements of the T4-rII gene are in fact arranged on a linear structure.[97]

In an entirely similar manner, crosses of a series of bacterial mutants of the *hisF* gene of *Salmonella typhimurium* involving eight such multisite mutants can be plotted in the form of a "recombination matrix" as shown in Table IV, so that the unproductive crosses form an unbroken series (arranged in "dictionary order"). This is compatible only with a continuous arrangement, which can be adequately represented by a one-dimensional structure corresponding to that shown in Fig. 9. It seems likely, therefore that over very short distances (within a single gene locus) as well as over much larger chromosomal regions, as the results of timing experiments of

---

* From crosses between two T4 double rII mutants, in which the same deletion mutation is present in both parents, the other mutational (single) site being located at one side of the deletion in one parent and on the opposite site in the other parent (e.g., $rII_a.rII_{a1}.rII^+ \times rII^+.rII_{a1}.rII_b$), it was found that recombination between rII_a and rII_b was less than in the corresponding cross of the single mutants $rII_a \times rII_b$, suggesting a true deletion. Unfortunately this does not correlate with the measurement of DNA in deletion mutants; consequently the term "multisite" mutant will be used rather than deletion. (See Nomura and Benzer.[99])

TABLE IV

Recombination Matrix of 19 *his-F* Mutants of *Salmonella typhimurium*
Arranged to Form an Unbroken Sequence of Nonproductive Crosses[a]

his-F recipient	*his-F* donor																		
	-612	-135	-41	-58	-152	-42	-45	-71	-114	-232	-644	-93	-55	-73	-95	-666	-99	-703	-6
-612	0	0	0	0	0	0	0	0	0	0	0	0	0	0	0	0	0	0	0
-135	0	0	0	0	0	0	1	1	1	1	1	1	1	1	1	1	1	1	1
-41	0	0	0	0	0	0	0	0	0	0	0	0	0	0	1	1	1	1	1
-58	0	0	0	0	1	1	1	1	1	1	1	1	1	1	1	1	1	1	1
-152	0	0	0	1	0	0	0	0	0	0	0	0	0	0	0	0	0	0	0
-42	0	0	0	1	0	0	1	1	1	1	1	1	1	1	1	1	1	1	1
-45	0	1	0	1	0	1	0	1	1	1	1	1	1	1	1	1	1	1	1
-71	0	1	0	1	0	1	1	0	0	0	1	1	1	1	1	1	1	1	1
-114	0	1	0	1	0	1	1	0	0	0	1	1	1	1	1	1	1	1	1
-232	0	1	0	1	0	1	1	0	0	0	1	1	1	1	1	1	1	1	1
-644	0	1	0	1	0	1	1	1	1	1	0	0	0	0	0	0	0	0	0
-93	0	1	0	1	0	1	1	1	1	1	0	0	1	1	1	1	1	1	1
-55	0	1	0	1	0	1	1	1	1	1	0	1	0	0	0	0	0	0	0
-73	0	1	0	1	0	1	1	1	1	1	0	1	0	0	1	1	1	1	1
-95	0	1	1	1	0	1	1	1	1	1	0	1	0	1	0	1	1	1	1
-666	0	1	1	1	0	1	1	1	1	1	0	1	0	1	1	0	0	0	0
-99	0	1	1	1	0	1	1	1	1	1	0	1	0	1	1	0	0	1	1
-703	0	1	1	1	0	1	1	1	1	1	0	1	0	1	1	0	1	0	0
-6	0	1	1	1	0	1	1	1	1	1	0	1	0	1	1	0	1	0	0

[a] Data of Hartmann.[100] Nonproductive crosses are indicated by 0;
productive crosses are indicated by 1.

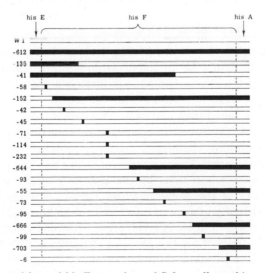

FIG. 9. Relative positions of *his-F* mutations of *Salmonella typhimurium* corresponding to the data expressed in Table IV.

interrupted matings in *E. coli* K12 show (see Chapter 2), the structure is continuous and linear. The possibility of a linear chromosome on which are arranged short side arms carrying several adjacent genes has not so far been excluded, although this seems less likely when multisite mutants extending over six or seven adjacent loci are considered (see Fig. 10).

Evidence of the type presented by Jacob and Monod,[62, 63] in which events leading to recombination between sites within the gene can be related to recombination between sites separated by about one twentieth of the total chromosomal length, appear, however, to exclude the existence of a branched chromosomal structure. In crosses shown in Fig. 4a and b, the numbers of z^+ recombinants from both crosses are found not to be equivalent, thus permitting the order of the two *lac* z^- mutations to be fixed relative to *ade*. These crosses demonstrate the continuity of the z_A-z_B-*ade* segment with the order of the two markers with respect to *ade* as shown. Similar crosses of the type Hfr $thr^+ . leu^+ . z_A^- . str$-$s$ $\times$ F- $thr^- . leu^- . z_B$-. str-r, demonstrate the continuity and the order of the markers thr-leu-z_A-z_B .[61] The unambiguous order of the markers thr-leu-lac-ade follows from similar crosses, restricting the only compatible structure to the linear arrangement thr-leu-z_A-z_B-*ade*, in which the intragenic *lac* structure forms an unbroken continuous structure with that of the *thr*, *leu*, and *ade* markers, a configuration whose dimensions are about a one-twentieth part of the total chromosomal distance.[61-63]

C. INTEGRATION OF GENETIC STRUCTURE WITH PHYSICOCHEMICAL DATA

1. DNA AS GENETIC MATERIAL

A turning point in the history of genetics was the recognition of the part played by the nucleic acids in the determination of heredity. It had long been recognized that these compounds formed a main constituent of the nuclei of animal cells, but protein was for many years the most favored candidate as the hereditary material. The demonstration by Avery *et al.* in 1944[101] that the transformation of pneumococcus discovered by Griffith[102] could be mediated by chemically purified, protein-free deoxyribonucleic acid (DNA) was of such elegance and refinement as to be almost irrefutable. This was followed, in 1952, by the discovery by Hershey and Chase[103] that the heredity of the bacterial virus T2 was determined solely by its DNA, which virtually alone was injected into the host cell.

The advance of genetics was given great impetus by the model proposed by Watson and Crick[104] for the physical structure of DNA, integrating as it did the biochemical data of Todd[105] and of Chargaff[106] with the dimensions and arrangements suggested by the X-ray crystallographic studies of Wilkins and co-workers.[107] This model offered a simple explanation of

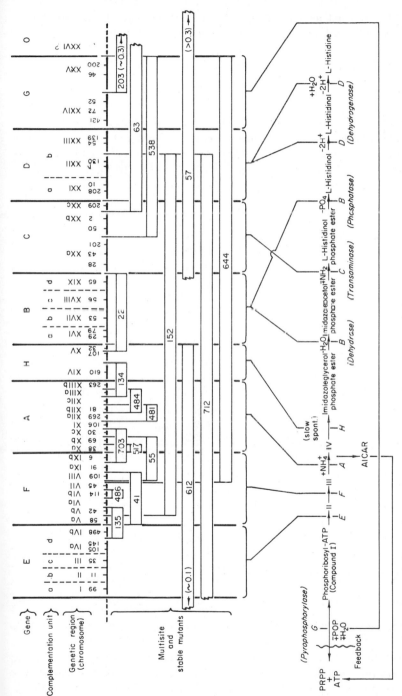

FIG. 10. Map of histidine region of the chromosome of *Salmonella typhimurium*. The dark horizontal line represents the chromosome. Multisite (deletion) mutants are represented by bars beneath the chromosome. The location of a few of the single site mutants is shown immediately above the chromosome. Roman numerals refer to segments of the *his* region defined by the various multisite mutants or by complementation studies. Below is a diagram of the biochemical pathway of histidine synthesis in *Salmonella*. From Ames and Hartman.[54]

how DNA could act as a reservoir of information, how it was capable of self-replication, and how mutation could occur.

2. Watson-Crick Model of DNA

The model of Watson and Crick[104] proposes that DNA is a double-chain polymer, each chain comprised of alternating deoxyribose-sugar and phosphate molecules. To each sugar is attached a nitrogenous base of which there are two types; the two purines, adenine (A) and guanine (G), and the two pyrimidines, cytosine (C) and thymine (T). The units of base-sugar-phosphate, termed nucleotides, are joined together through the sugar-phosphate backbone to produce a single polynucleotide chain. The DNA is comprised of two such chains, joined by hydrogen bonding between the purine and pyrimidine bases which face inward, the sugar-phosphate chains forming an outside backbone, and which are wound helically around each other. To be accommodated within the dimensions given by the X-ray data, there must be specific base pairing such that a purine is always paired to a pyrimidine. The position of the hydrogen bonds can only satisfy this arrangement when adenine is specifically paired with thymine (A-T), and guanine to cytosine (G-C). No restriction is placed on the order of bases along one chain.

The genetic information is suggested to be carried in the sequence of bases in one of the chains;[108] since the arrangement of bases on the two chains is complementary, one chain or strand can act as a template for the assembly of components (nucleotides) to produce the other, the self-replication of DNA being suggested to arise in this way. From the work of Fuerst et al.[109] it seems likely that the chromosome of an E. coli cell consists of about 10^7 nucleotide pairs. This correlates well with independent chemical estimations of DNA per nucleus and it has been concluded that the chromosome of such a bacterium is in the form of a continuous DNA double helix of length about 10^7 nucleotide pairs.[5]

Mutation was suggested to arise by occasional tautomeric shifts in the position of the hydrogen atoms involved in base pairings, resulting in rare temporary, and nonstandard base pairs, stabilized at the next replication by pairing to a standard base, thus finally resulting in a base substitution, and hence a change in base sequence.[104]

3. Physical Structure and Dimensions of the Gene

Genetic crossing experiments show that the chromosome is a linear, unbranched structure which can be subdivided on a functional basis into segments that have been called genes or gene loci, each segment controlling a single specific function. It is assumed that in bacteria this linear structure exists physically as an unbroken, unbranched double helix of DNA composed of about 10^7 nucleotide pairs. Within the structure of the gene, it has been shown that a number of mutations can arise which are located at different sites, from which the gene must be regarded as a segment of DNA embracing a considerable number of nucleotides. The deoxynucleotide pairs can be inferred to be the physical equivalents of the mutational sites. It has also been possible, using the techniques of microbial genetics, to evaluate the numbers of nucleotide base pairs that go to form a single gene, and to be reasonably certain that recombination can take place at many points on the chromosome by an exchange between almost any adjacent pair of nucleotides. Moreover, since chemical analysis of DNA has not so far reached a stage sophisticated enough to determine chemically the arrangement of bases, it has been the more recent challenge and interest of fine genetic analysis to deduce by indirect means the chemical nature of the mutational events and from this, the base sequence. These experiments integrate closely with others focused on the central biological problems of how DNA is able to perform its own replication (autocatalysis) and how it can dictate the structure of enzymes, the ultimate instruments of cell function (heterocatalysis).

a. Size of the Gene. The size of the gene as the unit of function has been estimated by several methods, some of which give a lower limit to the dimensions, whereas others set an absolute value. A value of several hundred to several thousand nucleotide pairs is consistent with most calculations.

i. Maximum number of mutable sites. Hartman,[52] on the basis of the probability of isolating duplicates, has estimated the maximum number of mutable sites within a gene. This method is thus dependent upon sufficient resolution to separate mutations at all possible sites. Clearly, since changes in the sequence of bases do not always lead to detectable alterations in function,[110] this method gives a minimum value which may have to be multiplied by a considerable factor to determine the total number of nucleotide pairs. Moreover, if most mutation extend over distances greater than single base pairs (which is not likely)[110] or if they do not occur with equal frequencies at all points (which seems to be probable),[17] the value will also be minimized. The estimates, which are based on the frequency with which mutations arise at identical sites gives values for seven histidine loci in *Salmonella typhimurium* as *hisA*,676; *hisB*,385; *hisC*,613; *hisD*,620; *hisE*,196; *hisF*,456; and *hisG*,121. A similar estimation[43] is based on the fact that within what was thought of as the unique *leu* locus in the same organism, 52 mutants were crossed without finding any site duplicated. This suggests a minimum value of 300–2000 (within confidence limits of 1–50%, respectively). More recent evidence,[111] however, indicates that this segment may represent four adjacent *leu* loci, reducing the value to 75 to 500 sites.

ii. Ratio of maximum to minimum recombination. Pontecorvo[22] has used the ratio of maximum to minimum recombination between any two mutants within the gene to give a minimal estimate of gene size. This assay depends upon the probability that enough mutations are studied so that at least two occur at adjacent nucleotide pairs, and that some are found toward the outside limits of the locus. Unless very large numbers of mutants are used, the method will of course also tend to give low estimates. Other perturbations are likely to arise from the fact that some mutations give rise to over-all higher recombination frequencies than do the majority of mutants;[52] with yet others, low recombination values with all other mutants are found.[52, 74] This type of estimation is, however, of value in cases such as transduction, when the total map length cannot be measured. The maximum to minimum recombination rates calculated for various loci are: *E. coli lac z* [62] (conjugation) 1400 $(0.72:0.0005\%)$[112]; *E. coli* alkaline phosphatase (also by conjugation),[71] 40 $(0.2\%:0.005\%)$; *Salmonella typhimurium hisA*[38] (by P22 transduction), 147 (1760:12) and for the *E. coli* tryptophan synthetase gene *"A"* (by P1 transduction)[74] 625 to 2500 $(2.5\%:0.004\%$ to $2.5\%:0.001\%)$.

iii. Ratio of the map length to the maximum intragenic recombination. This estimation has been used in *E. coli* K12; it is perhaps the most reliable and suffers from fewer limitations than other methods. From interrupted mating experiments, it appears that the transfer of the whole chromosome, which proceeds at an even speed, takes about 100 minutes at 37°C.[5] The measurement of the relative times of entry of a series of markers, and the extent of recombination between them were used by Jacob and Wollman[5] to calculate that 1 minute of transfer at 37°C. corresponds to 20% recombination. The total map length is thus fixed as 2000 units which is, therefore, equivalent to 10^7 nucleotide pairs. The maximum recombination frequency found between two z^- mutants is 0.7%[62] which corresponds therefore to a distance of 3500 nucleotide pairs (cf. minimal value of 1400 above). In the *P* gene, the maximum frequency is 0.2 map units or 1000 nucleotide pairs.[17]

b. The Unit of Recombination and Resolving Power. In order to maintain the absolute number of nucleotide pairs, and to avoid the introduction of sequence errors by addition or loss of bases, recombination should take place between adjacent base pairs. Since all base-to-base bonds along the DNA chain are of the same chemical nature,[105] it might be expected that recombination can occur between all adjacent base pairs, in which case mutation at different sites (base pairs) could always be resolved by recombination. If, however, there were regions over which recombination could not occur, mutations within this region could not be resolved. The measurement of minimum recombination frequencies allows a decision between these two possibilities.

In *E. coli*, one cell nucleus contains about 10^7 nucleotide base pairs and corresponds to a map distance of 2000,[5] so that there is an average of approximately 20 crossovers per 10^7 nucleotides per zygote. If crossing over could occur between each of these 10^7 pairs, the minimum frequency of crossing over expected (neglecting all complications of negative interference and other factors) would be 2 in 10^6 or 0.0002 %. If, however, crossing over was only possible between, say, 1 out of every 10 adjacent base pairs at, for example, every turn of the helix, there would be an average of 20 crossovers per 10^6 competent nucleotide pairs; the minimum crossing over measured would then be 2 in 10^5 or 0.002 %, since an increase in the size of the smallest possible unit would result in an increase of its fraction of the total.

In crosses by conjugation, a chosen marker is readily transferred to 1–2 % of zygotes, provided a suitable Hfr is used, so that one recombinant per 2.5–5×10^7 cells plated would be expected for a recombination frequency of 0.0002 %, which is well within the resolving power of the system and could be easily detected. The minimal experimental values so far reported are of 0.0005 % between *lac z⁻* mutants,[112] so corresponding to 2–3 nucleotide pairs, and a value 10 times as large (0.005 % — 25 nucleotide pairs) from alkaline phosphatase mutants.[71] However, since these figures are derived from a study of about a hundred mapped $z⁻$ sites and probably fewer $P⁻$ sites, the probability that two of these mutations will be at adjacent sites is small. (The fact that in both these systems several sites have been found to be unresolvable might suggest that they are likely to be more than one nucleotide apart if one assumes random probability of mutation at all sites. However, in the system investigated in the greatest detail, the T4-*rII* system, this randomness is not apparent, and sites of very frequent mutation (hot spots) are found.)[17]

In transduction, there is no direct way to measure the numbers of vectors in a phage population and thus no way of measuring absolute recombination frequencies.[92] It has already been shown that in *E. coli*, the size of the *lac* gene may be calculated as 3500 nucleotide pairs and the *P* gene as 1000. If the tryptophan synthetase *A* gene is assumed to be intermediate in size, it will contain about 2000 nucleotide pairs. Within this gene, Maling and Yanofsky[74] have measured recombination values of 1/2500 to 1/625 that of the recombination over the whole *A* gene, from which it can be inferred that recombination occurs at a maximum between every base pair to a minimum of between one out of four. From later evidence, (see Section III,D,2), Yanofsky *et al.*[110] have concluded that the size of the *A* gene is nearer to 800 nucleotide pairs, making it more likely that this smallest recombination value represents a probability of recombination between mutations at *any* adjacent base pair. This conclusion has also been reached by Benzer from studies in the bacteriophage T4.[14] It therefore seems likely that recombination is not restricted to special points, but can occur between any pair of nucleotides within the gene. Providing therefore that the resolving power of the system is adequate to detect this level of recombination, a lack of recombination can be taken as evidence of identity of sites. When the resolving power cannot be directly measured, as in transduction, it can however be assumed to be adequate if the sensitivity of the system can be increased without increasing the resolution. This can be demonstrated in the transduction, by phage P22, of certain markers, particularly those in the *his* region. When 2×10^7 recipient *his* cells, infected at a multiplicity of 2.5 with phage grown on nonidentical *his* cells were plated on minimal medium, a small number of crosses did not produce *his*⁺ recombinants, whereas other crosses gave a minimum of 10 *his*⁺ clones. When 2×10^8 cells were plated at a multiplicity of infection of 10, the level of these minimal *his*⁺ producing crosses was increased tenfold to produce 100 *his*⁺ clones, while the unproductive crosses remained unproductive.[38] All productive crosses, even those giving rise to the smallest numbers of recombinants, can thus be detected in this system. These results, however, cannot in themselves establish that recombination occurs between all adjacent base pairs.

With the conclusion that in *E. coli*, both in the tryptophan synthetase "*A*" gene[110] and the *lac z* locus,[112] crossing over occurs at least at every other base pair, the assumption is generally made that crossing over is in fact possible between almost all adjacent pairs, in both bacteria, and phage, and that lack of recombination in a system such as that of *his* transduction, does in fact restrict the mutations involved to identical (or overlapping) sites.

c. The Unit of Mutation. The unit of mutation (or "muton" in Benzer's terminology),[17] the smallest unit capable of independent mutation, is suggested to be a base pair by the Watson-Crick model. In order to establish its size and identity by genetic analysis, a triad of special mutants whose sites are located at three contiguous base pairs is needed. Two of the three possible crosses between these mutants would then be expected to give a value equivalent to one nucleotide, while the third cross would be expected to give no more than twice this value. The difference would give the size of the muton. To obtain three such mutants at the many thousands of possible sites in one locus requires rather extensive and exhaustive mutant isolations and crosses, and has so far not been realized. In T4 bacteriophage, a value of not more than five nucleotides has been achieved.[17] In bacteria, the variations in measurements of recombination of this size are subject to fluctuations too large to make this method a practical one, so that other approaches must be made. An alternative attack can be made on this problem through mutation, via the concept that base pair substitutions at a single site would be expected to be more limited if this site were one base pair, than if larger numbers of base pairs were involved in most mutations. The four alternative bases limit mutations by substitution at the same base pair to three, which might be expected to express their genetic individuality through their rates of mutation back to the wild phenotype, or possibly by phenotypic differences.

In many loci in bacteria, nonidentical mutations have been located at the same site. For example, in the *his* region of *Salmonella*, the sensitivity of transduction has been assumed to be adequate to resolve all mutations at nonidentical sites. Even so, four pairs of mutants (*his-12* and *-24*; *-40* and *-47*; *-60* and *-90*; and *-65* and *-143*) give no evidence of recombination between pairs as does the trio of mutants *his-133*, *-78*, and *-54*.[52] When the effects of a series of mutagens on the reversion of these strains are observed, the first three pairs behave identically to mutagenic treatment and are thus assumed to be duplicate isolations of the same mutational event. However, *his-65* and *-143*, and *his-133*, *-78*, and *-54* all give different patterns of reversion frequencies with the mutagens, from which it is concluded that at any one site there exist at least three alternative arrangements to the wild type, all of which are revertible at different frequencies, and thus conform to the prediction made, assuming this site to be a single nucleotide pair.[113]*

The numbers of distinct phenotypes recognized among a larger number of mutants mapping at the same site, also appears to be limited to three. Nine independent tryptophan synthetase A mutants have been mapped by Yanofsky *et al.*[77] at the same site which is probably a single base pair (see Fig. 7). One mutant (*A1*) forms a protein which is slightly more heat-labile than the wild type; two others (*A3* and *A33*) form proteins which are more heat-stable than wild protein, and six others (*A11*, *26*, *37*, *41*, *45*, and *48*) form protein of wild-type heat stability, but which is precipitated at a pH (4) where the wild protein remains in solution. It is of interest that the two mutants *A3* and *A33* appear to differ, *A3* reverting, while *A33* cannot apparently revert. *A3* would thus appear to be a point mutant (single base pair substitution), whereas *A33* could be due to either a small inversion or a rather special small deletion which is still able to form protein.

D. MUTATION

On the assumption that the genetic information resides in the sequence of nucleotide bases in the DNA,[108] a mutation can be defined as an altera-

* A similar conclusion has been drawn for the T4*rII* mutants, where at a certain "hot spot," at least 78 independent mutants fall into three distinct genetic groups based on their frequencies of reversion.[114]

tion in that sequence which has as its consequence a modification of the function controlled by the region in which the change takes place. We can thus limit our concepts of mutation to those alterations which cause sequence changes, and which will include the substitution of one base pair for another, additions or deletions of single base pairs, and additions, deletions, translocations of blocks of adjacent base pairs.

Substitutions, additions, and deletions restricted to a single base pair can be regarded as molecular mutations, ("single-site" mutations) all of which appear to result spontaneously and which also frequently occur as secondary mutations within a mutant strain, causing reversions to the wild phenotype.

In distinction, mutational events involving more than one base pair may be less frequent; certainly mutations extending over large segments of chromosome occur rarely.[28, 92] These latter mutations are invariably associated with an inability to regain the wild phenotype by reversion at any observable frequency, and it has been assumed (but so far unproved) that all mutations involving more than a single base pair are unlikely to revert to a measurable extent. Extensive "multisite" mutants are suggested to arise therefore as a result of chromosomal mutations, due more likely to mechanical or physical events rather than chemical ones.[28, 51, 92, 93]

1. FORWARD AND REVERSE MUTATIONS

Mutations produced as a result of simple base sequence changes, are not only likely to produce a recessive (or "mutant") phenotype from the wild type, but may also bring about a reversal of phenotype, producing a wild phenotype from the mutant. This reversal in phenotype can be most simply accomplished by a restitution of the original sequence; alternatively, changes are possible at the original site which do not restore the original sequence or, even more indirectly, reversal can arise by the occurrence of a secondary mutation at some alternative site to the first, to produce in effect a double mutant, which may in some way mimic or restore the wild-type activity. Such secondary mutations at sites distinct from the first are defined as suppressors.[56, 115] Thus, any mutation causing reversal of phenotype may be termed a reversion, which can be specified as a suppressor if it is known to occur at a site distinct from the primary mutation. Clearly, except where a system of high genetic resolution is available, it is not always possible to differentiate revertants due to closely linked suppressors from a secondary mutation at the same site as the first, which we now must assume to occur at the same base pair.*

* A practice open to criticism is the differentiation of suppressors and back mutants on a phenotypic rather than a genetic basis. For instance, when auxotrophic mutants are plated for phenotypic reversal, clones smaller than the wild type have sometimes

For most mutants, secondary mutations which restore the wild phenotype can be found, and these mutations lead either to partial or to complete restoration of wild-type activity.[115] On genetic analysis, these mutations have been shown sometimes to be linked[41] and sometimes unlinked.[117-119] They may be completely allele-specific,[117, 119] and have no effect on any other mutations within the same locus. Alternatively, they may affect several, but not all, sites within the same locus (and on occasion they may affect sites in apparently unrelated loci). In some instances they may even be completely nonallele-specific and equally affect all sites within the locus.[41, 118] It is only when direct evidence of detailed physical changes of function is available, such as the structural changes in the enzymes that are involved, that any attempt can be made to identify the mode of suppression. One of the first analyses along these lines showed that the effect of an unlinked suppressor was to remove a normal cellular component that inhibited the activity of a mutant.[120] Other such analyses will be discussed later.

2. CHEMICAL MUTAGENESIS

The natural, spontaneous mutation rate was found some years ago to be enhanced by various irradiation treatments,[24, 121, 122] which have been used with great effect as a pretreatment before attempted mutant isolation. Treatment with certain chemicals was first shown by Auerbach and coworkers[123, 124] also to result in an increase in the mutation rate, and indeed it was later found that many chemicals tend to increase mutation, although the effect of most is small.[125] In recent years, use of these chemical mutagens has increased rapidly since they overcome one of the drawbacks of irradiation, from which lethality is a more common end result than mutation. With certain chemical mutagens, however, mutation rates can be increased as high as a millionfold[126] without any great viability effects.

Early studies with mutagens suggested that they induce an over-all, nonspecific increase in mutation, which in general does not favor mutation in one particular functional unit over another.[127] However, when a large number of allelic mutations induced by chemical mutagenesis were mapped in phage T4, it was found that the coincidence of mutational sites produced by different mutagens was low, and suggested that mutations at distinct sites, in contrast to gene loci, react very specifically to certain mutagens.[128, 129] It seems very likely that this specificity reflects the variations in the

been assumed to be due to suppressor mutations, whereas normal sized colonies have been assumed to be due to back mutation. From the work of Yanofsky and his collaborators[110, 116] it can be seen that some back mutations at the original mutational site can lead only to partial activity, whereas certain suppressors can give restoration of normal wild type activity.

substituent groups of the nucleotide bases, which are more readily susceptible to attack by some mutagens than by others. The way in which these purine and pyrimidine bases interact with certain chemical mutagens has thus been the subject of much experimentation and speculation. This has led to promising approaches to the identification of base pairs occurring at specific sites, with the ultimate goal of base sequence determination by this method.

Much of the work with chemical mutagens has so far been restricted to bacteriophage, particularly to the production of mutants in the T4-*rII* region, where mutational changes can be rapidly and precisely located.[128, 129] Preliminary experiments involved the isolation and mapping of mutants produced in this gene locus by certain mutagens. More recent approaches concentrate on the ability of chemical mutagens to produce revertants of spontaneous or mutagen-induced primary mutants, for which a system is required such as T4-*rII*, which is capable of differentiating back mutation from closely linked suppression. The sensitivity of certain sites to specific mutagens will then favor certain bases. For instance, the base guanine would be specified if the forward mutation could be caused by a mutagen producing $G \rightarrow A$ change which is back mutated only by mutagens acting on A and T sites.

3. Mutation by Base Substitution

The simplest change in base sequence results from the alteration of a single base pair, particularly by substitution. Base substitutions have been classified into two kinds by Freese[130]: transitions, which involve purine/purine or pyrimidine/pyrimidine substitutions (e.g., $A/T \rightleftharpoons G/C$) and transversions involving purine/pyrimidine substitutions and vice versa (e.g., $A/T \rightleftharpoons C/G$). Three main groups of chemical mutagens which appear to produce these type of changes have been the object of much study.

a. Base Analogs. These are close structural analogs of the natural nucleotide bases which can be incorporated into DNA without destroying its capacity for auto- or heterocatalysis. Due to the difference in substituent groups which affect the position and stability of the hydrogen bonds, the pairing of these analogs is not entirely specific, and produces a tendency for "improper" pairing. Two analogs extensively used are 5-bromouracil (Bu), an analog of thymine, and 2-aminopurine (Ap), which acts as an analog of adenine. The chemical structure of bromouracil and of its nucleoside, bromodeoxyuride (Bdu), makes it likely to pair with adenine, and much less frequently with guanine.[130, 131]

b. Substances Modifying Nucleic Acid Bases. These produce modifications such that the specific pairing is altered. A much utilized mutagen, particularly in the production of mutants of RNA plant viruses, is nitrous acid which acts by deamination of the bases. It is also mutagenic for free bacteriophage,[132-134] isolated DNA,[135] and purified ribonucleic acid (RNA).[136] Chemical indications are that deamination of adenine (producing hypoxanthine) will lead to its pairing with cytosine, and cytosine, which is itself deaminated to uracil, will pair specifically with adenine. Deamination of guanine, however, will produce xanthine which would maintain its pairing with cytosine; whereas thymine, having no amino group, will be unaffected. Thus, nitrous acid might be expected to produce the changes $A/T \rightarrow G/C$ or $C/G \rightarrow T/A$ or both transitions. Mutants of tobacco mosaic virus are produced by nitrous acid to first-order kinetics, suggesting that deamination of a single amino group is sufficient to produce a mutation.[136] Hydroxylamine,[137-139] also the subject of much research, appears to react primarily with cytosine to produce pairing with adenine and thus to induce $C/G \rightarrow T/A$ transitions.

c. Substances Removing Bases from the DNA. These include alkylating agents such as ethyl ethanesulfonate (EES)[140, 141] and ethyl methanesulfonate (EMS),[30, 140, 141] which have been suggested to react primarily on guanine to release it from its sugar bond. Exposure to low pH's[139] appears to remove both purine bases, as does heat treatment.[142] These various agents do not attack the DNA backbone, so that the removed base can subsequently be replaced by another, making possible both transitions and transversions.

d. Possible Mechanisms of Base Substitution. These stem from early work involving base analogs, which revealed that mutants produced by these bases could also be induced to revert by base analogs.[131] The changes likely to be produced by Bu have been elaborated by Freese.[130] Since Bu is proposed to pair with adenine on most occasions, and only rarely with guanine, mutation could result from one of two pathways. The first would arise where Bu paired with A in place of T (as occurs with most incorporations of Bu). This A/Bu pair would produce on most replications a T/A and a Bu/A pair, but very rarely a *mistake in replication* would give rise to T/A and Bu/G. This latter pair would then produce A/Bu and G/C pairs at the next replication, the clone inheriting G/C being then mutant, since this has now replaced the original A/T pair. The alternative mechanism would arise by a *mistake in incorporation* where Bu happens very rarely to be incorporated to pair with G instead of with A. This rare Bu/G mistake would in virtually all cases produce A/Bu and G/C pairs at the next replication, the A/Bu pair replicating to T/A and Bu/A at the subsequent replication, so effecting a $G/C \rightarrow A/T$ change. It was suggested by Freese that the effect of both Bu and Ap mutagens was to produce the transitions $G/C \rightleftharpoons A/T$, in both directions, thus accounting for their ability to revert mutations initially produced by either mutagen.

Freese[130, 131] and his colleagues[134, 137, 139, 140, 141] have investigated extensively the interaction of a series of chemical mutagens on the same series of mutants, from which a reasonably consistent model of base substitution brought about by these mutagens can be built up. The results of many of these experiments are summarized in Table V, from which it can be seen that the main predictions from the chemistry of interaction of bases and mutagens are vindicated. Both Bu and Ap are suggested to produce transitions in both directions $G/C \rightleftharpoons A/T$. However, with Bu, the change $G/C \rightarrow A/T$ is likely to be more favored from the similarity of results with this mutagen to those with hydroxylamine (Ha) which seems from chemical

TABLE V

THE REVERTIBILITY OF rII MUTATIONS INDUCED BY VARIOUS CHEMICAL MUTAGENS[a]

Mutations induced by	Proportion of mutations reverted by					Base pair substitution inferred
	Bu	Ap	NA	Na	EES	
Bu	±[131]	++[131]	++[134]	−*[137]	−[140, 141]	$G/C \rightleftharpoons A/T$
Ap	++[131]	±[131]	++[134]	+†[137]	+[140, 141]	$A/T \rightleftharpoons G/C$
NA	+[130]	+[130]	++[134]			$A/T \rightleftharpoons G/C$
Ha	+[139]	++[139]		−‡[137]		$G/C \rightarrow A/T$
EES	+[140]	+[140]			±[140]	$G/C \rightarrow A/T$
						$G/C \rightleftharpoons C/G$
						$G/C \rightarrow T/A$

KEY: ++, virtually 100% reversion; +, majority reverted; ±, minority reverted; −, virtually no reversion; Bu, 5-bromouracil or 5-bromodeoxyuridine; Ap, 2-aminopurine; NA, nitrous acid; Ha, hydroxylamine; EES, ethyl ethanesulfonate.

[a] Collected data of Freese[130, 131] and colleagues.[134, 137, 139-141]

* Only 7 Bu mutants tested.

† Five out of 9 mutants reverted.

‡ Only 4 Ha mutants tested.

considerations to induce the change $C/G \rightarrow T/A$. With Ap it is concluded that the opposite change $A/T \rightarrow G/C$ predominates. Nitrous acid, as expected, acts as though capable of initiating both these transition changes to the same extent.*

Champe and Benzer[143] have treated a large number of phage T4rII mutants with the three mutagens Bu, Ap, and Ha. Of 339, 125 responded to one or more of the mutagens and were classified as reverting by transitional changes. Of these 125 mutants, 69 reacted unambiguously in the following ways from which certain nucleotide pairs of the wild-type strain

* From a recent survey by Kreig[143a] of mutagenesis in T4-rII by ethyl methanesulfonate, it has been concluded that this mutagen is considered unlikely to produce transversions.

were assigned. Two main types of *rII* mutants could be distinguished, one revertible by Ap, Bu, and Ha, and the other revertible by Bu and Ha only. It was concluded that Ap effected the changes A/T $\rightleftharpoons$ G/C, whereas the substitutions brought about by Bu and Ha were in one direction only, (G/C $\rightarrow$ A/T). A wild-type A/T pair was thus assigned to Bu revertible mutants on the assumption that the original mutation was produced by an A/T $\rightarrow$ G/C transition which could thus be reverted by the opposite transition G/C $\rightarrow$ A/T, shown by its revertibility by either Bu or Ha. Similarly, G/C pairs were assigned to the wild type at those sites where the susceptibility of the mutant to reversion by Ap alone was shown, the assumption in both cases being that reversion was produced by a restitution of the original base sequence.

It will be later shown that reversions occur which do not restore the wild-type sequence and which may yet produce the wild phenotype and, moreover, which occur by suppressors at sites very closely linked (within one or two nucleotide bases) to the original mutation. Even were the site of reversion to be identified at the original mutational site, other base sequences apart from the original may still produce the wild phenotype.[110] Thus, of the four alternative bases possible at any site, it is no longer certain that only one will give rise to the wild phenotype. Definitive conclusions as to base sequence cannot therefore be made until more precise data are available that these reversions in fact produce restitutions of the original base pair.

The experiments so far discussed apply only to phage T4 and the *rII* segment. In bacteria, we are not yet at the stage of being able to verify all the predictions made with regard to the specificity of the base substitutions with different mutagens. Therefore, perhaps it is not altogether surprising that the results emerging from treatment of bacterial mutations with base analogs indicate a more complex picture (particularly when it is borne in mind that in the T phage DNA the pyrimidine base hydroxymethylcytosine is substituted for cytosine). Strelzoff[144, 145] has investigated six auxotrophic mutants of the thymine-requiring strain, 15T⁻ of *E. coli*, four produced by Ap and two by Bu. These mutants conform to Champe and Benzer's restrictions, all six being revertible by Ap, but only three of the four Ap mutants and neither Bu mutant being reverted by Bu. Strelzoff proposed that from Bu-induced mutations, mistakes in replication (A/T $\rightarrow$ G/C) could be differentiated from mistakes in incorporation (G/C $\rightarrow$ A/T) by virtue of the fact that the former, involving the change A/Bu $\rightarrow$ Bu/G, is likely to occur with the same low probability at every replication after the incorporation of Bu, whereas the latter, involving the rare G/Bu incorporation, will give rise after two further replications to a stable transition. Thus an incorporation of Bu in Bu/A would result in mutants liberated at each replication after the removal of Bu, whereas each incorporation of Bu in Bu/G will produce one single crop of mutants which will no longer be produced when Bu is removed.[146, 147] By diluting and distributing the Bu-treated auxotrophs (after washing, and permitting one replication) to a series of tubes in which the number of further divisions was controlled by the amounts of growth factor (thymine) added, the number of tubes producing mutations after one, two, and three replications could be calculated from the number of tubes without revertants. It was found that two of the Bu-induced mutants gave rise to a constant number of reversions after one, two, and three replications, whereas another Bu-induced mutant produced reversions which increased with each replication. This latter was consequently assumed to be due to a $A/T \rightarrow G/C$ change and the others to a $G/C \rightarrow A/T$ change, supporting Freese's suggestion that both Ap and Bu can produce either transition $A/T \rightleftharpoons G/C$. It seems probable, therefore, that in bacteria both $G/C \rightleftharpoons A/T$ transitions can occur at the same order of frequency after Bu incorporation.*

In a study of a series of *his* mutants of *Salmonella*, Kirchner[113] found that a minority (20–25 %) were base analog revertible and there was little overlap in mutants responding to either of the mutagens Bu or Ap. Also, in contrast to other findings, most (11/12) Ap-induced mutants were revertible by Bu and only 3/12 by Ap itself. The small sample size may account for the fact that in Balbinder's reversion studies of *try* auxotrophs of *Salmonella*,[29] the majority of spontaneous mutants (9/15) were base analog revertible and responded equally well to either Ap or Bu.

It is thus concluded that both $A/T \rightleftharpoons G/C$ transitions are probably produced by Bu or Ap, but there is a variability in the response to one or another mutagen, depending presumably on the neighboring base pairs. Again, only close identification of the site and nature of the reversion will permit unequivocal extrapolations as to the nature of the wild-type nucleotide pair.

4. Mutations Due to Unitary Deletions and Additions

Mutations produced by treatment with a variety of acridines have been widely used in bacteriophage.[129, 149] So far, no mutants produced by acridines have been reported in bacteria, although abortive attempts have been made.[150] These particular mutants, however, are suggested to produce changes of such a specific nature as would be of great value in fine structure study, and for this reason, acridine-induced phage mutations will be discussed.

* Lysozymeless mutants of the bacteriophage T4 have recently been found to be produced by growth in bromouracil. Some of these mutants are produced by replications subsequent to removal of the mutagen, whereas others occur only in the presence of Bu. (See Terzaghi *et al.*[148])

In T4-*rII* mutants, of those mutations occurring spontaneously, 14% are revertible by base analogs. Of the remaining 86%, most are revertible by acridines.[149] It is inferred that the majority of the natural mutational events which revert spontaneously (and are thus assumed to be restricted to single nucleotide pairs) fall into two types, the base analog revertible and the acridine revertible.

A whole series of acridine-induced mutations have been mapped in the T4-*rII* segment, together with base analog-induced and spontaneous mutants.[129] The acridine-induced mutants were shown not to be reverted by base analogs, and acridines were without effect on the base analog mutants.[130, 131] These two nonoverlapping classes were explained by Freese[131] by assuming that base analogs produce transitions (A/T $\rightleftharpoons$ G/C) whereas acridines produce transversions (A/T $\rightleftharpoons$ C/G, T/A $\rightleftharpoons$ G/C), since a transition cannot be reversed by a transversion and vice versa. However, it was later pointed out[149] that there were no sites within the *rII* segment that were common to mutations produced both by base analogs and by acridines, as would be expected on this explanation, and led to the suggestion that acridines function as mutagens in some altogether different way. It was proposed that acridines produce insertions or deletions of base pairs. This hypothesis, encouraged by work on the physical association of DNA and acridine,[151] was supported by a series of ingenious experiments to be described later, which depend on the fact that acridine-induced mutants can spontaneously revert to produce the wild phenotype. It was thus suggested that either loss or insertion of base pairs is a frequent, if not predominant, source of spontaneous mutations in phage.

5. BLOCK DELETIONS AND TRANSLOCATIONS

In higher organisms, deletions, inversions, and translocations of segments of chromosome can be observed cytologically.[94] These types of mutational events, in contrast to those already described, which are considered as molecular events, are interpreted as due to chromosomal aberrations. Similar mutations arising in bacteria may be classified as follows.

a. Multisite Bacterial Mutants. These mutants, in which the mutational defect extends over a segment of chromosome covering many sites marked by other single site reverting mutants, are characterized by their inability to revert.[28, 51] They are suggested to arise as a result of block deletions and in general comprise about 4% of all mutations in *Salmonella*, although in some instances they are produced in greater numbers.[92] The further investigation of such regions, in which the probability of multisite mutants can be as high as 40% of the total mutants, led Demerec to propose that they may be determined by the presence in the DNA of regions which appear rather unusual in being devoid of mutant sites.[93] When two such regions are closely linked it is suggested that they have sufficient similarities so as to tend to synapse, with the consequent formation of a loop of chromosome, which in the process of subsequent replication is unrecognized, and the segment between the two nonmutating regions becomes "deleted" in the progeny. As discussed earlier, such deletion mutants have value in demonstrating the linearity and continuity of the genetic map. They have also been used with great effect in the mapping of new mutants, localizing them within a very small region with very few crosses. This technique, promoted by Benzer, has been of great value in *rII* mapping, particularly of mutagen-induced strains and of their revertants and suppressants. In *Salmonella*, the accumulation of sufficient multisite mutants is beginning to be of value in the mapping of new *his* mutants. Crosses with a series of multisite mutants (which can be achieved as spot tests, since the result need indicate only presence or absence of any number of prototrophs in excess of the reversion rate of the new mutant) permit a new *his* mutant to be located within a circumscribed region of the locus. For example (see Fig. 10), a mutant (such as *his*-58) giving prototrophs when infected with phage grown on all the multisite *his* mutants except *his-135*, *-41*, *-612*, and *-712* could be immediately located in region FVa.

b. Translocations. Translocations have been recognized in *E. coli* K12 after treatment with nitrogen mustard, in which large segments, comprising some 20 % or so of the whole chromosome, are rearranged at a different location on the linkage map.[152] These translocations may be associated with deletions, which can be as large as 1 % of the total chromosome.[153]

c. Inversions. Inversions, or local chromosomal rearrangements, may be fairly common in bacteria. It appears that in various sublines of *E. coli* K12 in which extensive genetic exchange in a small region has taken place as a result of repeated crosses, the arrangement of the genes may differ. Such conclusions may be reached with regard to the cluster of *gal* genes which appear in three lines of strains to have contrasting arrangements.[69, 154]

III. Translation of Genetic Information and Biochemical Function

The existence of a specific gene can be inferred in one or two ways; either genetically, by the isolation of a mutant of that gene, followed by the genetic location of its mutational site and hence that of the gene; or chemically, by the isolation of its specific enzyme, the absence of this enzyme in a derivative strain being indicative of mutation. The examination of fine genetic structure can thus be made from two angles, and the greatest detail is likely to be revealed by taking cognizance of these two complementary aspects. This is forcefully illustrated by certain mutants recently examined by Yanofsky and his colleagues,[110] by whose hands this two-pronged attack has been most vigorously prosecuted. These mutants have a normal phenotype and a normal level of enzyme activity. When the structure of the enzyme is examined, however, it is found to differ by a single amino acid substitution from the wild type. It is presumed, but so far undemonstrated, that there is a correlated difference in the genetic structure of the strains; an example of a heritable genetic change, but one which does not lead to a classical mutation, and which cannot be recognized except by protein structural studies.

A. GENES AND ENZYMES

Until quite recently, a lack of appropriate experimental data has ensured an abundance of models and speculation. This has no doubt been of enormous value in stimulating experimentation designed to support some of the more fancied theories. Some of these experiments are now yielding conclusions so that the choice of alternative models of the way in which genetic information may be translated into gene action is now a decreasing one.

The way in which genes might act was anticipated by Garrod[155] who regarded "inborn errors of metabolism" as due to mutations. This principle was extended in the 1940's to fungal genetics, particularly of *Neurospora*, by Beadle and Tatum[18, 19] making use of such metabolic disturbances resulting from mutation.

1. ONE GENE-ONE ENZYME HYPOTHESIS

Beadle and Tatum[18, 19] proposed that the majority of genes function by specifying the production of an enzyme, a change in the structure of the gene by mutation leading to a related change in the structure, hence in specificity and thus frequently to loss of activity of the specific enzyme. It is ironical that this reasoning was based, at least in part, upon the conclusion that genes were probably proteins, so that a gene-enzyme relationship would be anticipated by analogy with other protein-protein structural interactions such as that of antigen to antibody. This one gene-one enzyme hypothesis waited 17 years before its absolute confirmation by Ingram[156] with the demonstration that human genetic changes, behaving as though controlled by a single gene, resulted in the substitution of a single amino acid by another at a particular location in the structure of the hemoglobin molecule. Previously, the hypothesis had been indirectly verified by experiments such as those of Horowitz,[157] who showed that a mutant strain of *Neurospora* produced an enzyme with an altered temperature optimum. Suskind *et al.*[158] later showed that although enzyme activity was usually lost by mutation, nevertheless a protein, retaining immunological similarity to the enzyme, was often still produced by the mutant. Such enzymically inert (or low activity) protein was identified by its ability to cross-react immunologically with antiserum to the enzyme, and was termed cross-reacting material (CRM). This material can usually be isolated by the same methods as those which result in the isolation of the enzyme. However, it appears that protein structures can be elaborated which do not cross-react immunologically, but can be detected by other biological methods, such as complementation.[159]

2. SEQUENCE HYPOTHESIS

This extension of Beadle and Tatum's hypothesis elaborated by Crick[108, 160] proposes that the mode by which genes determine the structure of proteins is by way of the sequence of the nucleotide bases in the DNA, which is reflected in the sequence of amino acids in a polypeptide chain, then spatially arranged to form the enzyme. It is thus necessary to assume that each amino acid is determined by a certain arrangement of adjacent nucleotides. Which nucleotides specify which amino acids is termed the "genetic code," the coding ratio being the number of nucleotides necessary to code for one amino acid; a coding unit (or codon) is defined as a set of nucleotide bases which determines one amino acid.

3. THE CODING PROBLEM

The way in which a sequence of four nucleotide bases may determine the order of twenty different amino acids has been treated theoretically to produce a wide variety of alternative hypotheses.[161] The first, proposed by Gamov,[162] has "the distinction so far of being the only one that can be conclusively eliminated." This proposed an "overlapping" triplet code, in which a sequence of three nucleotides determined each amino acid. In order to accommodate the similarity in molecular dimensions of nucleotide and amino acid, a 1:1 physical relationship was suggested, requiring therefore that each nucleotide influence the choice of three adjacent amino acids. (A nucleotide code $ABCDABCD$ .... would thus be "read" to indicate the amino acids coded for by $ABC - BCD - CDA - DAB - ABC$....) This code was shown to be impossible by Brenner,[163] since all such overlapping codes would demand certain restrictions in the sequence of amino acids which were not found in known protein structures. More recently it has been shown that in many organisms a single mutation results in the alteration of one amino acid only.[110, 164, 165] Overlapping codes would be expected to produce two or more such amino acid changes per nucleotide change. Another restraint, widely accepted for some time, was that the code was nondegenerate, that is, each amino acid was thought to be coded by one specific nucleotide sequence only.[108, 160, 161] This has since proved unlikely, and currently a degenerate code in which each amino acid can be specified by one of a series of alternative nucleotide sequences is thought to be more plausible.[161] Whether the code is completely degenerate so that all sequences of nucleotides can code for some amino acid, or only partly degenerate, where certain "nonsense" sequences of nucleotides do not specify any amino acid, is not so far certain, but partial degeneracy has been favored[166] and nonsense sequences claimed.[159, 167] Degeneracy is also a convenient way of reconciling the disturbing results that many organisms with widely differing base ratios $(A+T/G+C)$, were nevertheless found to have similar amino acid ratios within the total cell proteins[168] (see Chapter 9).

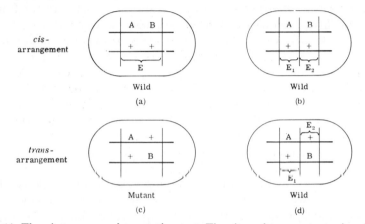

FIG. 11. The *cis-trans* complementation test. The sites of two mutants A and B are located in the *cis*-position in cells (a) and (b), (both mutational sites on the same chromosome, the homologous chromosome being wild-type); and in the *trans*-position in (c) and (d), (A being located on one chromosome and B on its homolog). The *cis*-arrangement has a wild phenotype whether A and B are located in the same (a) or in different (b) functional units (the enzymes E or $E_1 + E_2$ being found, respectively). The *trans*-arrangement will, however, have a mutant phenotype (c) if A and B are in the same functional unit (enzyme E being inactivated in both chromosomes), whereas when A and B are in different functional units (d) the cell will also have a wild phenotype (enzyme E_2 being produced by the $A.+$ chromosome and enzyme E_1 by the $+.B$ chromosome.

The solutions to most of these problems depend upon the integration of fine structure genetics and sequence analysis of related enzymes. The extent to which bacterial fine genetic structure has contributed is considered briefly below and in greater detail in Chapter 8.

B. FUNCTIONAL ANALYSIS AND COMPLEMENTATION

The complementation test devised by Lewis[9] compares the phenotypes of two alternative arrangements of mutant alleles. In the *cis*-arrangement (see Fig. 11a and b), the two mutations are located on the same chromosome, the homologous chromosome being wild-type. This arrangement

$(--/++)$ produces the wild phenotype and acts as the control. The essence of the test is whether the alternative *trans*-arrangement $(+-/-+)$, when the two mutations are carried one on one chromosome and the other on the homolog, shows a mutant or a wild phenotype. When the mutations are in different genes, the wild phenotype would be expected (d), whereas when they involve the same gene, the cell should lack an intact gene and so should show the mutant phenotype (Fig. 11c). Thus, lack of complementation is a demonstration of identity of function, whereas a complementing *trans*-heterozygote indicates nonidentity of the functions involved. This phenomenon is used as a test for functional allelism and has been most commonly termed the *cis-trans* or *complementation* test.*

There is a very strong tendency, particularly in bacteria, for genes controlling related functions to be closely linked (see Section IV, A_λ,1). The evidence for this, and its possible interpretation, will be more fully developed in the succeeding section. As an example, a series of genes concerned with histidine biosynthesis in *Salmonella* can be shown to be arranged in a contiguous array (see Fig. 10). With this arrangement it becomes necessary to be able to functionally differentiate very closely linked sites, since mere evidence of close linkage and similarity of phenotype is no longer adequate. A test such as the *cis-trans* test provides this evidence of functional identity or nonidentity, without any foreknowledge of what these functions might be. While it is true that the ultimate biochemical goal is the identification of the independent reactions, followed by the isolation of the purified enzymes, a simple test of complementarity, such as is provided by the *cis-trans* test, enables a rapid and preliminary classification of mutants on a functional basis.

This particular test, used first in heterozygotes, has also been shown to apply to fungal heterokaryons[169] when the two chromosomes are in distinct haploid nuclei, within the same cell. In bacteria, similar arrangements have been shown to mimic these conditions, as also in bacteriophage when two phage particles infect the same cell.[14] Complementation tests appear to be more sensitive indicators of low levels of activity than enzyme assays, complementation having been demonstrated between two mutants, one of which lacks an enzyme (imidazoleacetol phosphate ester transaminase) and the other having only a few per cent of the wild-type level.[53]

1. FUNCTIONAL TESTS IN BACTERIAL SYSTEMS

a. Abortive Transduction in Salmonella. This results in a partially diploid cell, in which *cis-trans* relationships can be observed. The phenomenon of "trails" of colonies observed during experiments on the transduction of

---

* The test employed is really a *trans* functional test, the *cis* arrangement being merely a control which is frequently omitted.

motility characters was suggested by Stocker et al.[170] to be due to an "abortive" transduction, in which the fragment of bacterial DNA introduced by the phage vector into the recipient cell was not integrated in the recipient genome, as occurred in the normal, stable transduction, but was able to persist in the recipient cell in a nonreplicating functional form (see Chapter 2).

Such a fragment, it was suggested, would be transmitted to only a single cell at each division, giving rise to a system of unilinear inheritance. This cell, being motile, would migrate, whereas the sibling cell, not inheriting the fragment, would remain in situ to produce a colony. Successive siblings of the motile cell would thus produce a series of colonies, and could satisfactorily account for the trail phenomenon. In studies of transduction of nutritional characters, Ozeki[171] invoked a similar system of unilinear inheritance arising from abortive transductions to account for the phenomenon of minute colony production. These minute colonies were observed, in addition to the normal sized prototrophic colonies (which resulted from stable transductions), when recipients were treated with phage from wild-type donors. The use of abortive transduction as a complementation test was recognized by Ozeki when it was found that minute colonies also resulted from crosses of a recipient with a mutant donor which was a functionally distinct on the basis of nutritional tests. Similar colonies were not, however, produced when the donor was a mutant functionally identical with the recipient, although, of course, normal prototrophic clones were produced, albeit at a low frequency. The production of minute colonies was later shown to fulfill the requirements of a complementation test for a wide variety of functional loci.[172] The application of abortive transduction is, however, restricted to those loci in which minute colonies can be clearly observed, which require certain minimal growth rate differences between the majority of the cells of the minute colony and the background cells with which they are genotypically identical. The various complementation groups recognized as a result of this technique are indicated in Table III.

b. *Minute Colony Formation in P1 Transduction.* This can also be used as a complementation test in *E. coli.* It was first observed in this system by Gross and Englesberg,[78] who found in the case of the three distinct *ara* loci, -*A*, -*B*, and -*C*, that *ara-C* recipients produced minute colonies with all donors except other *ara-C* mutants. Minute colonies were not, however, observed using *ara-A* and -*B* recipients, even with wild-type donor controls.

In the tryptophan synthetase mutants of *E. coli*, minute colonies have been reported in all $A \times B$ crosses, which occur irrespective of whether either mutant is able to form a protein, cross-reacting immunologically with the enzyme. Intergenic *A* or *B* crosses have not so far been extensively investigated.[72]

c. Gal Heterogenotes Produced by the Transducing Phage λdg. Gal heterogenotes result when a lysate from a homogenotic $(gal_x^-/\lambda \cdot gal_x^-)$ is applied to a
gal_y^- recipient, the heterogenote $gal_y^- . gal_x^+/\lambda . gal_y^+ . gal_x^-$ (or more simply
$-+/+-$) being formed (see Fig. 5 and p. 267). This is a *trans*-heterogenote
which would be expected to be phenotypically wild type $(+)$ when the
two *gal⁻* mutants concern different functions, and phenotypically mutant
$(-)$ when the mutations are within the same functional locus. Complementing heterogenotes which are *gal⁺* can clearly be distinguished from
the noncomplementing *gal⁻* type by a simple spot test, as a result of which
all *gal* mutants transducible with λ*dg* can be segregated into four groups:
-A, -B, -C, and *-D*.[68] *A, B,* and *D* do not complement mutants within the
same group, but complement all other mutants. Group *C* mutants, however,
are noncomplementary with groups *A* and *B* mutants and complement
only with *D*. These groups correlate to some extent with enzymes of the
galactose pathway which are:

1. Kinase. The reducing group of D-galactose is phosphorylated to
galactose-1-phosphate by a galactokinase.

2. Transferase. Galactose-1-phosphate is incorporated into a nucleotide,
uridino-diphospho-galactose, by an exchange reaction with UDP (uridine
diphosphate)-glucose catalyzed by the UDP-glucose transferase.

3. Epimerase. The 4-hydroxyl group of the hexose moiety of the nucleotide is epimerized by the UDP-galactose-4-epimerase to regenerate UDP-
glucose.

Gal-A mutants lack kinase activity, *gal-B* lack transferase,[68] and *gal-D*
mutants appear to lack epimerase;[173] whereas *gal-C* lack (or show low levels
of) kinase, transferase, and epimerase.[68]

d. "Sexduction" or F-Duction.[174] Sexduction has been used with great
effect to observe functional relationships in *E. coli* K12.[175] From various
Hfr donor strains, intermediate donors (F' strains) can be isolated, in
which chromosomal segments carrying known markers are incorporated
into the sex factor (see Chapter 4). These modified sex factors are infective,
and are transmitted with relative ease into F⁻ recipient cells, which in
addition to becoming F⁺ males, become diploid for the chromosomal region
carried by the sex factor, and can be regarded as functionally similar to
syngenotes produced by phage λ*dg*. Thus, when an *Flac⁺* factor (a sex
factor carrying the *lac* region from a *lac⁺* cell) is introduced into an F⁻
lac_a^- cell, the resultant cell is heterogenotic $(lac_a^-/Flac^+)$ and is phenotypically *lac⁺*. These cells also segregate *lac⁻* cells which can be shown to be
either haploid *lac⁻*, or more rarely the homogenotes $lac_a^-/Flac_a^-$. These
homogenotes transfer $Flac_a^-$ factors, so that when introduced into $F^- lac_b^-$
cells they yield heterogenotes of the type $lac_b^- . lac_a^+/Flac_b^+ . lac_a^-$, a *trans*-
heterogenote, which will be *lac⁺* if the two mutants are functionally identi-

cal or *lac⁻* if the mutations are in the same functional unit.[174] The many *lac⁻* mutants have been classified into three complementation groups by this method which correlate with parallel enzyme studies as follows[175]:

1. y^- mutants are unable to synthesize galactoside permease (acetylase) and are generally complemented by z^- but not by other y^- mutants.

2. z^- mutants are unable to synthesize β-galactosidase. These are always complemented by y^- mutants and fall into two groups on the basis of complementation with other z mutants.[112]

3. o^0 mutants are unable to synthesize either permease or galactosidase and complement neither mutants of the same group nor y nor z mutants.

Complementation of o mutants will be discussed in Section IV,B.

2. THE GENE, THE CISTRON, AND GENETIC FUNCTION

The word "gene," in classical terms, was defined as an entity that was not only the elementary unit of function, but was supposed to be indivisible by recombination. With the advent of more sophisticated notions of genetic structure, however, its continued use to denote a unit of function was considered to be semantically confusing. As a result, the term "cistron," coined by Benzer,[14] was widely adopted since it originally appeared to assume no more than was capable of being defined by a *cis-trans* test. To quote Benzer, "a group of non-complementary mutants falls within a limited segment of the genetic map. Such a map segment . . . will be referred to as a cistron." Unfortunately, the term cistron anticipated simpler interrelationships from the results of complementation tests than actually ensued in practice. For many groups of mutants, the allocation into cistrons is consistent with a series of nonoverlapping functional segments. In contrast, many cases are known where, among a series of mutational sites, all blocking synthesis of a single enzyme, and all mapping together within a single locus, some complement one another and form active enzyme, while others do not.[176, 177] This phenomenon is referred to as interallelic (or intergenic) complementation and can be illustrated by the results of the *his-B* mutants of *Salmonella*.[52, 54] Of the 34 alleles of this locus (which controls the activity of an enzyme converting imidazole glycerol phosphate ester to imidazoleacetol phosphate ester), 18 fall into four complementation groups, 2 in group *a*, 2 in group *b*, 4 in group *c*, and 10 in group *d*, the members of each group being noncomplementary, but complementing mutants in the other groups. Of the remaining 16, 10 complement members of one or two of the groups *a*, *b*, *c*, *d*, but do not complement the others; the 6 remaining mutants do not complement any mutant within the *hisB* complex. The sites of mutants in the four groups *a*, *b*, *c*, and *d* are located in specific regions in the genetic map of the locus. The noncomplementary mutants however are scattered throughout the locus. Moreover, since all are single-site reverting mutants, their complementation behavior is not explicable on the basis of deletion mutants.

The occurrence of complementation within the functional unit (interallelic complementation) has been correlated in most instances with a low level of enzyme activity (usually less than 25% wild type). It has been shown in the *am* locus of *Neurospora* by Fincham[177] that the enzyme produced is abnormal, and that for complementation to occur the individual mutants must each be able to produce a protein similar to the enzyme. Fincham has suggested that these conditions may be common to all cases of interallelic complementation, and further, that this phenomenon may be observed only when the enzyme concerned consists of a number of identical, polymerized subunits. In interallelic complementation, then, two different kinds of mutant subunits would thus be produced, so that hybrid molecules could form in which the structural defect in each kind of subunit could to some extent be corrected by the other. Common defects such as unstable configurations could be stabilized by a subunit defective in a different part of its structure.[177a] This picture is consistent with complementation within the *lac z* locus, where interallelic complementation is found, and where the enzyme β-galactosidase is known to consist of six identical polypeptide chains;[62] and within the *P* locus, where the enzyme is a dimer[70, 71] and complementation within the locus is also found.[159]

Levinthal *et al.*[178] have produced evidence of hybrid molecule formation in this alkaline phosphatase enzyme. The protein monomers can be separated by reduction and can then be reactivated to form the dimer with restoration of enzyme activity. When two physically distinctive enzymes are reduced, mixed, and allowed to reactivate together, hybrid molecules are shown to be formed. It remains to produce enzymically active hybrid molecules from two inactive proteins or to show that active enzyme, formed by complementation, preserves the distinct mutational defects of the proteins from which it is formed.*

C. Mutation and the Phenotype

1. Protein Structure and Its Implications

The elegant researches of Perutz[179] and of Kendrew[180] threw new light on the obscurities of protein structure. For genetics, perhaps the most far-reaching conclusion was that the actual sequence of amino acids in the polypeptide chain was alone sufficient to determine the tertiary and quaternary structure (cross linking and folding), to form the three dimensional structure of the protein; the secondary structure of the α-helix being deter-

---

* The production of enzymically active hybrid dimers from monomers of two inactive, CRM-forming mutants has recently been achieved.[178a]

mined by the succession of CO—NH peptide bonds between each amino acid. A linear sequence of nucleotides therefore seemed capable of determining the complete structure and activity of an enzyme, by defining its amino acid sequence. Moreover, it appeared that many amino acids could be substituted for others without either structural or functional changes. Certain other amino acids, however, were highly specific; for example, proline appeared to be responsible for bending of the α-helix. Replacement of such amino acids therefore would be likely to result not only in loss of structure but loss of activity.

2. Mutation by Base Substitution

If the code is not completely degenerate, the substitution of certain bases would lead to a coding unit unable to specify any amino acid. The mutations that might result in such substitution have been called "nonsense" mutations to distinguish them from "missense" mutations, in which the mutation would result in the replacement of one amino acid by another.[108] Nonsense mutations might be expected to result in a gap in the polypeptide chain, with a resulting lack of protein synthesis; whereas a missense mutation might in most instances lead to a protein similar in structure to the enzyme, but with loss of biological activity. Such protein should be isolated by methods designed to isolate the enzyme, and would also be expected to cross-react immunologically.* Assuming a completely nondegenerate triplet code, the nonsense-to-missense ratio for base substitution mutations would be expected to be about 2:1, since out of 64 possible triplets from 4 bases, only about 20 can code for an amino acid. The fact that many spontaneous mutations may be deletions which would not be likely to produce a protein, and the insensitivity of the tests for detecting such biologically inactive protein as CRM,[159] would both tend to increase the size of the ratio.† In the P gene, the ratio of non-CRM-producing mutants to CRM producers is 12:17 for EES-induced mutants;[181]

---

* Equally well, certain "missense" mutations could result in an amino acid substitution having a gross effect on the structure of the protein (for example, the replacement or the insertion of proline) as to make it both incapable of immunological cross reaction and unlikely that it would be isolated by procedures isolating the enzyme. In either event production of a protein of this nature would be difficult to differentiate from the lack of synthesis of a protein having structural similarities to the enzyme.

† It has been reported that interallelic complementation can occur with mutants that do not produce any detectable CRM. If one presumes that such complementation requires the formation of hybrid molecules it must be assumed that some "missense" mutants produce protein which is not detectable as CRM.[159] Since the code appears to be partly degenerate, this ratio should be even smaller, and present a more significant divergence than the 2:1 ratio, supporting the idea of degeneracy of the code.

in the tryptophan synthetase A gene, the ratio is 39:18 for spontaneous mutants;[77] and in the *lac z* gene, a majority of the z mutants are said to synthesize a protein capable of cross-reacting immunologically.[182] These values tend to suggest a nonsense-to-missense ratio of less than 2 to 1 and hence a degeneracy of the code.

a. Effect of Reversions. A remarkable correlation of the genetic mapping of reversions of several tryptophan synthetase A protein mutants and the consequent alterations in the protein structure has been revealed by Yanofsky *et al.*[110] The theoretical implications of such secondary mutations have been summarized as follows.

i. Reversions at the same nucleotide pair. Such reversions may be divided into those that restore the original base pair (the only true back-mutant) and those that replace the mutated base pair with a third alternative. The original base pair will, of course, restore the original amino acid sequence and full wild-type activity. An alternative base pair could, if the code were degenerate, restore the original amino acid, or it could specify an alternative amino acid, which would produce a protein with either partial or even full activity, depending on the tolerance of the protein structure for amino acid substitution.

ii. Reversion within the same coding unit. This type of reversion could occur at a nucleotide base pair different from that involved in the first mutation. If the coding ratio is three, the mutational site will be located only one or two nucleotide pairs distant from the original site and would thus be hard to resolve except in the most sensitive systems. If the code is degenerate, this mutation could again lead to a restoration of the wild-type amino acid and full activity, or alternatively a further amino acid could be specified, which again might lead to partial or complete restoration of wild-type activity.

iii. Reversion within the same gene. Reversion within the same gene would affect an amino acid other than that substituted by the first mutation. A double amino acid substitution might conceivably lead to a partial restoration of activity. For example, if the first mutation involved the replacement of a neutral amino acid by a basic one, the second mutation could involve the replacement of a basic amino acid with a neutral one, or a replacement of a neutral amino acid with an acidic one.

Two mutations, $A23$ and $A46$, affecting the same amino acid[183] (and thus within the same coding unit) of the A gene of tryptophan synthetase have both been found to be due to presumptive "missense" mutations since both produce CRM.[74] Proteins from the two mutants, as well as from four revertants of $A46$, have been analyzed and the amino acid sequences compared to the wild type.[110] Many of the theoretical types are found; two have a restoration of the original amino acid sequence, and two more have different alternative amino acid substitutions, yet show full enzyme activity, indicating a large measure of tolerance of both structure and activity to amino acid sequence, particularly since the only other reversion substituting yet another alternative amino acid gives partial activity. All these secondary mutations occur at the same site or within one or two nucleotides from the original site. Of particular interest is one partial revertant in which the second mutation is about one-tenth the extent of the A gene from the first (about 100 nucleotide pairs) and in which a second amino acid substitution counterbalances in some unknown way the effect of the first. Moreover, by itself, the second amino acid substitution is found to produce a mutant phenotype. A similar change has been reported in a mutation of the alkaline phosphatase gene, which is separated about 700 nucleotide pairs from the primary mutation.[71]

b. *Suppressors outside the Gene Locus—Translational Mutants.* In general most external suppressors found in bacteria tend to be allele-specific. Interest in suppressors of this type was quickened by the suggestion by Yanofsky and St. Lawrence[115] that a possible suppression mechanism might reside in other elements of the protein-synthesizing system apart from the gene. In the tryptophan synthetase locus both of *Neurospora* and *E. coli*, suppressed mutants usually were found to have an enzyme activity less than the wild type, and were thought to produce the mutant protein together with small amounts of the wild-type protein. This suggested a mechanism capable of correcting the mutant amino acid substitution in some of the gene products. It was proposed that if either the specific amino acid-activating enzyme, or the specific acceptor RNA (sRNA), were to mutate so that its specificity was no longer absolute, but allowed in a small proportion of syntheses, the attachment of the original amino acid, instead of the mutant amino acid, this would result in a low level of effective, wild-type protein being produced together with the mutant protein. Too great a loss in specificity would, of course, reduce the activities of all other cell proteins, but a loss of about 5–10 % in the majority of proteins could be offset by an absolute gain from zero to 5–10 % of activity of the mutant protein.

Suppressors of this type now appear to have been isolated in several systems. Of great interest, and underlining the universality of genetic mechanisms, is the demonstration of the similar effects of the same suppressors, on both the bacterial gene controlling alkaline phosphatase,[159] and on the T4 bacteriophage *rII* gene.[167] Benzer and Champe[184] had previously defined a subset of the *rII* mutants (subset I) as ambivalent, in that these mutants behaved as wild *r+* strains in a different bacterial host, whereas the remainder of the *rII* mutants retained the *rII* phenotype. The mutants of this subset were all believed to be due to nonsense mutations. It was suggested that the bacterial host in which they were active possessed a suppressor gene producing an acceptor RNA (sRNA), which coded for the base sequence of the mutant codon, and which was, moreover, specific for the amino acid encoded in unsuppressed strains by the original codon. This sRNA would not, of course, be present in an unsuppressed strain (and thus would suggest that the code was not completely degenerate). The suppressed strain could thus synthesize some enzyme with the wild-type amino acid sequence.[167]

Garen and Siddiqui[159] obtained results of a similar nature with alkaline phosphatase mutants of *E. coli*. It was found that 15 out of 220 P^- mutations isolated in an Hfr strain, in which they completely repressed the formation of both active enzyme and CRM, produced from 3–100 % enzyme activity when they were transferred into an F^- strain. In one case, the presumptive suppressor in the F^- strain which restored the P^+ phenotype was mapped and found to be located far from the P locus itself. The ability to produce 100 % activity was offered as confirmation of the nonsense nature of the original mutation, since a missense correction of such sRNA would be expected to affect all other proteins, mostly in a deleterious way. The suppressor is therefore suggested to function, not by producing mistakes, but by "converting nonsense into sense." When Benzer and Champe[167] tested their *rII* mutants in the Hfr and F^- strains used by Garen and Siddiqui, the F^- strain was found also to be capable of activating subset 1 mutants. It seems likely therefore that genes exist which control sRNAs, and that mutation within these genes can overcome primary mutations in many other genes by extending the degeneracy of the code. The result also encourages belief that the *rII* region is concerned with protein synthesis. The amino acid interfered with in both these particular classes of P^- and *rII* mutants would appear to be the same, which would indicate that the extent of nondegeneracy is therefore small, and that few coding units are unable to specify an amino acid.

3. MUTATION BY SIMPLE DELETIONS AND ADDITIONS

The addition or deletion of a single base pair would be expected to throw out the sequence of all the coding units read after it; (for example, a sequence read as *ABC, ABC, ABC,* . . . would read as *ACA, BCA, BCA,* . . . if the first *B* were removed), or in the words of Crick *et al.*[166] "a shift in reading frame" would be produced, resulting in what Benzer[167] has termed "gibberish," where even if the code were completely degenerate, the entire amino acid sequence following the mutation would be changed, with a resulting loss of protein structure in most instances when considerable numbers of amino acids were involved. The suggestion was made that acridines produced this type of mutation in bacteriophage, obtained from the fact that acridine mutants were not found in regions where a structural protein was required, as, for instance, in "head" and "tail" protein mutants.[149] Moreover, although lysozyme mutants produced by base analogs were nearly always "leaky" (indicating of a low level of enzyme activity, presumptively due to the presence of an altered protein), acridine-induced lysozyme mutants were always completely inactive (and were assumed not to elaborate a structural protein in any way similar to the enzyme).[185] Finally, physical evidence suggested that acridines were bound to DNA and were of such dimensions that one molecule could take up the position of a nucleotide base, and thus might be expected to give rise to deletions or additions.[149, 151] This hypothesis was used in an ingenious way by Crick et al.[166] to determine the coding ratio. Thus, if a mutational site produced by acridine happened to be a unitary deletion, spontaneous reversions must be due to similar unitary additions to restore the reading frame, and vice versa. It was found that these spontaneous reversions could result from one of a whole series of secondary mutations at sites distinct from the first (suppressor mutations), which could be located a distance of many nucleotide pairs from the original site. This suggested that although the reading frame may be corrected by the suppressor mutation, a complete change in sequence remains between the two sites. These suppressed mutants, however, give rise to a wild or semiwild (pseudowild) phenotype, and implied an extensive degeneracy of the code, together with a lack of gross effect of a considerable number of adjacent amino acid substitutions on either the structure or the activity of the putative rII enzyme. As expected, when the suppressor mutation was separated by recombination from the original mutation, it gave rise to the rII mutant phenotype, and could itself be similarly suppressed. These suppressors of suppressors, when separated, also gave rII phenotypes and could themselves be suppressed. Clearly if the first mutation were supposed a deletion ($-$), the first suppressors would be additions ($+$) and their suppressors again deletions ($-$), so that a series of single mutants of opposite types could be isolated. It was found that although the wild phenotype was given by the double mutant ($+-$ or $-+$), by the suppression of the original mutation, the double deletion ($--$) or double addition ($++$) mutants were mutant in phenotype. The triple type ($+++$ or $---$), however, again produced the wild phenotype. This suggested that three additions (or three deletions) had no effect on the reading frame, so that this frame must itself be of three nucleotide pairs (or a multiple of three if the addition and deletions were not of one but of several bases). The conclusions from these experiments were that the code is apparently extensively degenerate; that there is a high degree of tolerance to even a large number of adjacent amino acid substitutions in the structure and activity of the rII product, assumed to be protein; and the code is probably a triplet code (or some multiple of three). The ultimate proof must await, of course, the demonstration that these particular effects are also found in loci that are known to produce a protein (the *rII* function still awaits definition) and in particular, the identification that in the phenotypically wild, double mutants (+ − and − +) and in the triple mutants (+ + + and − − −), the protein with wild-type activity carries a changed amino acid sequence between the two extreme mutational sites.

4. MUTATION BY MULTISITE DELETION

Multisite mutants, if assumed to be deletions, would be expected to result in the complete loss of activity of any enzyme produced by a gene whose structure was implicated in such a deletion. This feature has been demonstrated with mutants of a whole series of linked *his* genes in *Salmonella*[46] and *try* genes in *E. coli*.[76] In the *his* region illustrated in Fig. 10, the

TABLE VI

SPECIFIC ACTIVITIES OF HISTIDINE BIOSYNTHETIC ENZYMES IN VARIOUS MUTANT STRAINS OF *Salmonella typhimurium* GROWN ON FORMYL HISTIDINE[a]

Strain	Enzymic block	Specific activity enzyme units/mg. protein			
		Dehy-drase	Trans-aminase	Phos-phatase	Dehydro-genase
Wild type	None	0.54	0.73	1.1	0.12
hisB-40	Dehydrase	<0.04	0.26	0.60	1.0
hisC-201	Transaminase	3.5	<0.01	16.6	0.81
hisD-1	Dehydrogenase	1.7	8.2	5.8	<0.04
hisFAHBCD-152	Multiple	<0.05	<0.01	<0.07	<0.04
hisGD-63	Multiple	0.23	<0.03	0.35	<0.04
hisG-203	Multiple (*o°*)	<0.14	<0.16	<0.06	<0.04

^a Data of Ames *et al.*[46]

multisite mutants exhibit a corresponding loss of enzymes, as shown in Table VI, characteristic of deletions. An inversion, on the other hand, might be expected to retain activity for those regions inverted intact, by analogy with the maintenance of functional activity by fragments introduced into the abortively transduced cell. Moreover, since multisite mutants, e.g., *his-152*, are able to grow with a single supplement (histidine in this case), the existence of other functionally essential material within this region is rendered highly unlikely.

D. COLINEARITY, THE CODING RATIO, AND THE GENETIC CODE

1. COLINEARITY

The sequence hypothesis would be verified if a series of mutational sites arranged in a specific linear order were shown to result in a series of amino acid substitutions, occurring in the same order within the protein. This has so far not been achieved, although in both the alkaline phosphatase and tryptophan synthetase systems of *E. coli*, individual amino acid substitutions in the proteins produced by various mutants have been identified. In the former system, two closely linked mutations have been shown to result in disturbances of the same peptide fragment (which is composed on average of some half-dozen amino acids) when this protein is subjected to tryptic digestion. The two mutations *E26* and *U24* are 0.005 map units apart (see Fig. 6), corresponding to about 25 nucleotide pairs. *E26* produces an altered enzyme whose tryptic digest shows the absence of a peptide normally present in the wild type enzyme digests. *U24* does not produce CRM, but it reverts to produce an altered enzyme. The revertant site is less than 0.0003 recombination units from the original *U24* site and so the sites are separated by one nucleotide or less; on digestion, the revertant protein is seen also to have missing the same peptide.[71]

In the tryptophan synthetase *A* gene, the two mutations *A23* and *A46*, whose sites map within one or two nucleotides of each other (see Fig. 7), have been shown to effect a substitution of the same amino acid[110] (out of a total of 280). Thus, although colinearity has not so far been demonstrated, there appears to be a close correlation between the distance apart of the mutational sites and the separation of the amino acids coded by these sites on the polypeptide chain.

2. THE CODING RATIO

If the sequence hypothesis be assumed, it is of obvious interest as a preliminary to decoding, to determine the coding ratio; that is, the number of nucleotides that make up each coding unit which ultimately results in the specification of a single amino acid. From successive, spontaneous mutational events leading to suppression of an originally acridine-induced mutation, Crick *et al.*[166] have suggested a ratio of 3 (or less likely 6, or 9, p. 305). An alternative, and so far less precise method is to obtain the ratio of the number of nucleotides forming a gene to the number of amino acids specified by that gene. The number of nucleotides is assayed by measuring the maximum recombination within the gene, and comparing this with the total map length. This ratio has been calculated for several loci shown in Table VII. In systems studied by transduction, the absolute recombination frequency is difficult to determine. Yanofsky *et al.*[110] have thus used another approach. Two mutants (*A23* and *A46*) are found, which undergo recombination at a frequency 1/625 to 1/2500 of the maximum occurring within the *A* gene. These mutations are shown to result in the substitution of the same amino acid, the number of amino acids in the A protein being 280. If these mutations are assumed to be one nucleotide apart, the total number of nucleotides in the A gene is between 625 to 2500 and the coding ratio would be between about 2 and 9. Each of these estimations shown in Table VII is of course subject to several sources of error and implicit assumptions. A coding ratio of 2 or 3 would, however, not be incompatible with these results.

3. THE GENETIC CODE

A variety of attacks is converging on the detailed solution of the code. Three main lines of evidence appear to hold out an early chance of decoding.

TABLE VII

MAXIMUM AND MIMIMUM RECOMBINATION FREQUENCIES WITHIN CERTAIN STRUCTURAL GENES OF *Escherichia coli* TOGETHER WITH SIZE OF THE PROTEIN SPECIFIED AND ESTIMATED CODING RATIO

Structural gene	(a) Maximum recombination within gene (%)	(b) Estimated gene size in nucleotides (a/2000 × 10^7)	(c) Minimum recombination between any two sites within gene (%)	(d) Estimated size of minimum crossing-over distance in nucleotides (bc/a)	(e) Number of amino acid residues in monomer	(f) Coding Ratio (b/e)
lac z	0.7[62, 63]	3500*	0.0005[112]	2.5[112]	1025[193]	ca. 3 (3.4)
Alkaline phosphatase (*P*)	0.2[71]	1000*	0.005[71]	25[71]	380[71]	ca. 3 (2.6)
Tryptophan synthetase *A*	2.5k†[74]	625–2500‡[110]	0.001k–0.004k†[110]	1§[74, 110]	280[11]	ca. 2–9

* Based upon the assumption that the DNA of one cell is a polynucleotide chain of 10^7 base pairs and the total map length is 2000.[5]

† The figures represent the relative frequency of crossing over compared to the total crossing over permitted in a single transduced fragment; in this case a tryptophan-carrying fragment, but in previous publications, histidine, giving twice the values. They must be multiplied by a constant k to convert to absolute recombination frequencies.[73, 74]

‡ Based upon the assumption that the minimum recombination figures represent crossing over between mutations on two adjacent base pairs (a/c).[110]

§ Assumed.[74, 110]

First, from the study of the changes produced by chemical mutagens, it has in some instances been possible to assign certain nucleotide bases at specific points on the genetic map.[143] Second, the ability of *in vitro* systems utilizing synthetic polynucleotides of known composition to elaborate artificial polypeptides has permitted a direct correlation between nucleotide sequences and the ability to polymerize certain characteristic amino acids.[161, 186-191] As a result, a possible sequence of nucleotides in the RNA determining each amino acid has been proposed. Third, in several cases, including the tryptophan synthetase and alkaline phosphatase systems of *E. coli*, study of mutations and reversions, involving the same amino acid, has established a series of amino acid substitutions which are effected by presumptive single nucleotide pair substitutions. So far these substitutions are completely compatible with the sequences inferred from artificial polypeptide syntheses.[104, 110, 189-192] Degeneracy is, however, an obvious complication in assigning the coding units in the DNA.

IV. Genetic Interactions

The ability of a single gene to determine the specific structure of one particular protein is now firmly established. However, other activities of genes are still relatively unexplored, particularly the way in which the activity of a gene is modified or specified by its position on the chromosome, and the way in which it may be itself integrated in greater units which Goldschmidt[194] has called "hierarchies of higher field orders." A study of genetic interaction may be made at many levels. Most of those considered so far involve the modification of the structure either of the gene, or of its product, the enzyme. There remains the relatively unexplored effects of gene-to-gene interaction and the possible existence of families of genes concerned with related functions, where the activity of one gene is integrated with that of others.

A. STRUCTURAL ASSOCIATIONS

1. LINKED LOCI CONTROLLING RELATED BIOCHEMICAL FUNCTIONS

In early transduction experiments, it was noted that when a certain class of auxotrophs, such as all those requiring tryptophan, were examined, not only did mutants of each phenotypically identical group show very close linkage, but many mutants of phenotypically related but nonidentical groups also behaved as though their sites formed a close cluster. In general, any *try* X *try* cross gave rather less than the expected number of prototrophs compared with crosses using the wild-type donor, and some crosses involving phenotypically nonidentical mutants gave as few recombinants as did those between identical mutants.[49, 50] It seemed likely therefore that all the *try* mutants sites were closely linked.

It has already been noted that the bacterial chromosome must be broken down to probably more than a hundred fragments in order that information may be transferred via P22 transducing vectors.[92] Only when two markers are separated by a distance of less than one-hundredth the chromosomal length, will there be any chance of their being situated on the same transducing fragment, and it is only under these conditions that linkage will be observed in transduction. Two close markers, which are not close enough to be transferred on the same fragment will show no more linkage than two very distantly located markers. Linkage of the type invariably associated with mutants of identical phenotype is demonstrated by a limitation in the crossing over between the sites, resulting in a reduction in the prototrophic yield, as exemplified in Table II. With two markers of different phenotype, however, linkage can be demonstrated by other methods. First, in a mutant × mutant cross, transductants of donor phenotype can often be selected, in addition to the wild-type recombinants, by plating on minimal medium enriched with the donor growth factor. For example, in Fig. 12a, where the recipient is A^+B^- and the donor A^-B^+, and plating is made on minimal medium containing growth factor A, A^-B^+ cells will be found in addition to the expected A^+B^+ cells when A and B are closely linked, the two genotypes being separated by replica plating on unsupplemented minimal medium. Alternatively, when the double auxotroph A^-B^- is available (Fig. 12b), close linkage can be demonstrated by the ability to isolate clones of A^+B^+ (in addition to those of A^-B^+ and A^+B^- which can be isolated whether linkage is present or not).

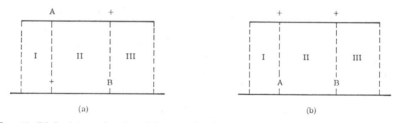

Fig. 12. Linked transduction. The two horizontal lines represent fragments of the donor chromosome (top) and the corresponding parts of the recipient chromosome (bottom). A and B are markers specifying different growth factors. Linked transduction in demonstrated by the ability to isolate donor type transductants either (a) as A^-B^+ cells due to a I–III crossover from a mating of an A^+B^- recipient with an A^-B^+ donor, or in (b) as wild-type A^+B^+ cells, also from a similar I–III crossover from mating an A^-B^- recipient with an A^+B^+ donor.

During the early work on phage P22 transduction, such linkage experiments were carried out in all possible pairwise combinations of mutants requiring different growth factors with, by and large, negative results. One of the very few positive combinations came from crosses of *tryB* auxotrophs and mutants of a certain cysteine-requiring phenotype, *cysB*. It was later shown that mutants of each of the four *try* groups A, B, C, and D were linked to any of several *cysB* mutants, but not to mutants of any other cysteine group. It seemed clear, therefore, that all four *try* loci and the *cysB* locus were closely linked.[49-51]

The relative order of the loci can be readily established by three point tests, as for example, by crossing a *tryD.cysB* recipient and a *tryB* donor. In such a cross the phenotype of the donor (*tryB*) can be selectively differentiated from the *try* phenotype of the recipient (*tryD*) by its ability to grow on indole. This cross is represented in Fig. 13, which shows three alternative arrangements of the loci; which of these is correct can be inferred from the relative numbers of the various transductional classes. Demerec had previously brought evidence to show that whatever the mechanism of information transfer in transduction, it must allow parts, in addition to the whole, of the information on one fragment to be transmitted to the progeny. This was suggested to occur by a mechanism akin to crossings over, which in order to incorporate information from a fragment and preserve the complete genome must always be of an even number. The likely assumption was made that the genotypes created by quadruple crossing over would be expected to be less frequent than those requiring merely a double crossover.[49] It can be seen that the quadruple crossover

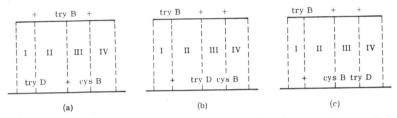

(a)   (b)   (c)

FIG. 13. Representations of the cross of a *tryD.cysB* recipient with a *tryB* donor, depending upon the arrangements of the three markers. The two horizontal lines represent fragments of the donor chromosome (top) and the corresponding parts of the recipient chromosome (bottom). The correct order is indicated by the quadruple crossover class (I–II–III–IV) being very much smaller than other crossover classes. The results obtained with this cross show that the quadruple class from order (a) (wild type) is less than that from order (c) (*tryB.cysB*). The quadruple class from order (b) (*tryB.tryD*) cannot be selected from other classes of the same phenotype (e.g., *tryD.*). The order can thus be assumed as either (a) or perhaps (b). However, in the reciprocal cross of a *tryB* recipient with a *tryD.cysB.* donor, the quadruple class (*cysB*) from order (b) is found at the same frequency as double classes such as *tryB*, so that the order is not likely to be (b). From the two crosses, order (a), viz., *tryD-tryB-cysB*, is thus indicated.

class (I-II-III-IV) in (a) would be the wild type, in (b) *tryB.tryD*, and in (c) *tryB.cysB*. When the actual cross is performed, the numbers of *tryB.cysB.* colonies are 657 compared to 16 of the wild type, from which it is assumed that the order shown in (c) is excluded. Similarly it can be shown with other *try* combinations that the *cysB* markers lie outside the cluster of the four *tryA, B, C*, and *D* loci.[49, 50]

From a consideration of a large number of *his* × *his* crosses, it seemed likely that all the *his* mutants were similarly clustered in four loci, *hisA, B, C*, and *D*, linked with no other known markers.[38] The accumulation of further numbers of *his* mutants has shown that there are probably eight or nine distinct *his* loci, all closely linked in the order shown in Fig. 10. This particular order has been reached by crosses with the 24 multisite mutants shown in the figure, more rigorously confirming the close linkage suggested by the two point crosses.[52, 54]

The finding that genes controlling biochemical functions in the same metabolic sequence tend to be closely linked within a cluster, and are not separated by functionally unrelated sites or genes, is a common one in *Salmonella*.[56, 92] This feature, as shown in Table III, is a not uncommon finding in many bacterial systems.[56, 195, 195a, b] In higher organisms, on the contrary, no such groupings occur, although there appears to be several examples of close linkage of certain markers in loci which have been assumed to be distinct but functionally related.[22] However, the functional distinction between these markers is based upon complementation tests, which in some instances, at least, is due to interallellic complementation,[196, 197] so that it is not therefore clearly demonstrated that in higher organisms there are any more linkage associations than is expected by chance. It is certainly clear that the linkage relationships existing in bacteria represent a more frequent association and involve larger numbers of genes which are distinct and yet functionally related. Moreover, in other organisms such as *Neurospora*, where these same pathways involving similar enzymes have been investigated, there are no such associations of these particular genes.[198]

2. Sequential Order of Gene Loci

When three point tests were used to investigate the order of the *try* loci in *Salmonella*, as shown in Fig. 13, not only were they found to be closely clustered, but the genetic sequence *tryA-tryB-tryC-tryD* was found to reflect the sequence of the reactions which appeared at that time to be under their control (Fig. 1.) Since then, the biochemical pathway has been found in *Salmonella*[45] (as in *E. coli*)[72] to be more complex than imagined, the last two reactions being carried out by one enzyme composed of the two proteins, whose structure is determined by genes *tryC* and *tryD* (and which are equivalent to the *E. coli* tryptophan synthetase *A* and *B* genes). Further genetic analysis based on larger numbers of mutants has modified the order to *tryA-tryB-tryD-tryC*,[55] which conforms precisely with the order previously established in *E. coli* from a study of multisite mutants and which is still correlated with the biochemical sequence *tryA-tryB-(tryC,tryD)*.[76]

As is shown in Fig. 10, the histidine loci are arranged in the genetic order *E-F-A-H-B-C-D-G*, while the biochemical sequence is G → (E, F, A, H) → B → C → B → D → D. The relative order of the reactions controlled by loci *E*, *F*, *A* and *H* is so far unestablished, and the enzymes controlled by *his-B* and *his-D* have dual functions. The only gene locus that appears to be out of sequence is thus *his-G*, which is at the opposite end of the genetic sequence to that expected from the biochemistry.[54]*

In clusters of other loci investigated in *Salmonella*, a close correspondence has been reported in genetic and biochemical sequence (see Table III). In four loci governing threonine synthesis, the genetic order is D-C-A-B and the biochemical sequence is either $D \to C \to A \to B$ or $C \to D \to A \to B$;[43] in a group of five isoleucine-valine loci, the genetic order *ileA* - *ilvaA* - *ilvaD* - *ilvaB* - *ilvaC* corresponds to the biochemical sequence *ileA* $\to$ (*ilvaA* , *ilvaD*) $\to$ *ilvaB* $\to$ *ilvaC*.[43] However, it is pointed out that these genetic sequences are based on two point tests and are therefore only approximate. Four proline loci, found to be arranged biochemically in the order $D \to (AB) \to C$, show genetic linkage of the *pro-A*, *-B*, and *-C* loci only, so that no correlated sequences are possible with this pathway.[42] However, in *E. coli*, Englesberg finds the biochemical sequence of a series of *ara* loci $A \to B \to D$,[81, 82, 85] to contrast with the genetic order *araD-araA-araB*, which was found by a precise ordering by three point tests.[78]

In general, therefore, there is a strong tendency for some, if not all, of the genes in a pathway to be ordered in the same sequence as the reactions under their control, although until more information is available on the threonine and isoleucine-valine mutants, the correspondence may not be as complete as was at one time thought.[56, 92, 195] In any event, a distinction should be drawn between linkage of related loci, of which there are numerous well-documented examples, and for which at least one plausible explanation can be offered,[62, 63, 199] and sequential order, in which there may not be a complete genetic and biochemical correspondence and for which no explanation, plausible or otherwise, has so far been put forward.

The association of related genes (and their possible sequential order), first demonstrated in *Salmonella*, was unexpected.[38, 49, 50] Where the corresponding genes have been demonstrated in other organisms, particularly in *Neurospora*, they are not found to be linked, and are frequently located even on separate chromosomes.[198] It is generally accepted that these linkages are not due to vestigial evolutionary arrangements, but reflect positive selective advantages.[92] There seems no reason to believe that this is due to the peculiar lability of the gene products,[200] or to the possibility that protein synthesis in bacteria has a chromosomal location, as was at one

---

* More recent evidence of Ames and Hartman[54a] has now shown that the enzymic sequence in histidine biosynthesis is $G \to E \to A \to H \to F \to B \to C \to B \to D \to D$. In this system, therefore, which has been studied in the greatest detail both biochemically and genetically, it can be seen that the genetic and biochemical sequences, although similar, do not in fact correspond. These authors have proposed that the genetic sequence may represent a gradient of enzyme levels, the G enzyme produced in the greatest, and the E enzyme in the least amount.

time suggested,[22] and is contrary to current evidence and views on ribosomal protein synthesis.[201-204] The advantage is obviously one which differentiates bacteria from other microörganisms. It has been proposed that
this difference may be genetic, and may reflect the fragmentary nature of
genetic transfer in bacteria, under which circumstances the ability to
transfer blocks of genes controlling a complete synthetic pathway may be
of value. In organisms where the complete genome is transferred, these
linkage blocks would have no such advantage.[195] An alternative explanation has been offered by Jacob and Monod,[62, 63] who muster a compelling
case for a system of genetic regulation and control of metabolic pathways
in bacteria, and which will be considered in detail in the following section.

B. Regulatory Systems

1. Regulatory and Structural Genes

In a consideration of mutants leading to the lac^- phenotype, Jacob and
Monod[62, 63] found two standard types of mutants. One type, defined as
z^-, results in a loss of the enzyme β-galactosidase, others, called y^-, show
a loss of galactoside-permease activity, and are mostly identified with the
inability to synthesize an active acetylase enzyme. The z and y mutants
map in two contiguous clusters. Moreover, y mutants do not complement
each other but complement all z mutants, and although some pairs of z
mutants can complement, the level of this complementation is low, and
can be ascribed to interallelic complementation.[182] Most z mutants produce
a protein (Cz), cross-reacting immunologically from 1 to 100 % with antisera
to β-galactosidase, while z^+/z_1^- heterogenotes, formed by sexduction and
diploid for this region, produce both normal enzyme and Cz_1. Thus, there
is good reason to believe that the two chromosomal segments z and y
carry structural information for the two enzymes, and can thus be defined
as structural genes. Both the enzymes β-galactosidase and acetylase are
inducible, being normally produced in very small amounts, which are increased several hundredfold on the addition of the substrate lactose, or a
similar galactoside, all of which thus act as inducers.

In contrast to z^- and y^- mutations, other mutations (termed i^-) in this
region lead to the production of both enzymes constitutively (at high levels
in the absence of inducers). In heterogenotes such as $i^+.z_1^-/F\ i^-.z^+$, both
enzyme and Cz_1 remain inducible, indicating that the factor i^+ is dominant
to i^-. This suggests that the i gene governs the expression of the y and z
genes, and since it is active in the *trans*-position, it must function through
a cytoplasmic component, which is then inactivated in the presence of
inducer. The i^+ is proposed to be the active form of the gene, which was
confirmed by the finding that deletions covering the i region produce

constitutive effects. The i gene was suggested to produce either an enzyme which destroys an endogenous inducer or a repressor. The distinction was made by the study of another mutant in this region termed i^s. This mutant does not synthesize either z or y enzymes, and is not a deletion since it gives rise to z^+ and y^+ recombinants in crosses with z^- and y^- mutants. Moreover, in i^s/i^+ diploids, i^s is dominant. Reversions of i^s to constitutivity were found, of which 50 % were found to be i^-. These findings sug gest that the i^s mutation involves an alteration (rather than a loss) of the i product, so as to make it incapable of being inactivated by the inducer. The product of the i gene was later shown to be uninhibited under conditions restricting protein synthesis. It was thus concluded that in distinction to the y and z genes, whose activity is directed to forming the structure of a protein, the i^- gene does not form any protein, and its function is to produce a cytoplasmic repressor regulating the activities of both the z and y genes, so that neither enzyme is produced. This nonprotein cytoplasmic repressor may be inactivated by the inducer, so that both enzymes begin to be synthesized. Mutations of the i gene to i^- result in loss of repression and lead to constitutive enzyme formation; mutations to i^s produce a repressor which is stable to the inducer (super-repressor) so that under all conditions the activities of both z and y genes are constantly repressed.

2. THE OPERATOR AS THE SITE OF REPRESSOR ACTION

The chromosomal site at which the repressor acts is defined as an operator, whose configuration, if assumed to be complementary to the repressor, must be genetically determined. It should therefore be possible to isolate mutants in which the affinity with the operator is impaired. Such mutants would produce a constitutive phenotype, but one which could be differentiated from the i^- constitutive mutants in two ways. Operator mutations should be genetically distinct and thus situated in a separate locus and fully complementary with all i^- mutants. Moreover, since a repressor-insensitive operator would produce enzymes constitutively, whether or not a repressor-sensitive operator were present in the same cell, they would be dominant-constitutive mutants, whereas the i^- mutants are recessive-constitutive. Mutants of this type (called operator-constitutive or o^c mutants) were looked for, and found by Jacob and Monod, by selecting for constitutive mutants from homozygous i^+/i^+ cells, and were mapped in a separate o region as shown in Fig. 3. The interpretation of o^c mutants and i^s mutants is confirmed by their interaction, since it is found that the repressor synthesized by i^s does not repress an o^c mutant, in the *cis-* or in the *trans*-position, viz., $i^s.o^+/F\ i^+.o^c$ forms both the enzymes β-galactosidase and acetylase constitutively.

3. The Operon Concept

The operator o^c mutations result in a constitutive expression only of those structural genes located in a *cis*-position, i.e., on the same chromosome. For instance, the heterogenote $o^+.z^-.y^+/F\ o^c.z^+.y^-$ produces β-galactosidase constitutively but acetylase is produced only on induction. The operator has thus no independent cytoplasmic expression and controls the activity of the chromosomal zy segment as an integrated unit. This integrated unit responsive to the operator, and the operator itself, constitute the operon, which thus behaves as a "genetic unit of co-ordinate expression."[62, 63] This concept would predict that some mutations in the operator (operator-negative or operator-defective) might permanently repress the z and y activities, even in the absence of repressor. Such o^o mutants have been found and can be differentiated from the similar i^s (super-repressor) mutants by the fact that since these latter act via cytoplasmic repression, they are dominant to the i^+ and o^+ mutants ($i^s.o^+.z^+/F\ i^+.o^+.z^+$ will produce no β-galactosidase), whereas o^o mutants are recessive to i^+ and o^+ ($i^+.o^o.z^+/F\ i^+.o^+.z^+$ produces β-galactosidase on induction). Both i^s and o^o mutants are still recessive to o^c, $i^s.o^+.z^+/F\ i^+.o^c.z^+$ and $i^+.o^o.z^+/F\ i^+.o^c.z^+$ producing β-galactosidase constitutively. The sites of o^o mutants are found within the same region as that giving rise to the operator constitutive (o^c) mutants (see Fig. 3). The presence of these o^o and o^c mutants within this same region having the properties as shown strongly support the concept of the operon.

4. Inducible and Repressible Systems

The greater appeal of the operon concept is that it is not restricted to inducible-enzyme systems, but appears to offer explanations of inducible temperate phage systems and also of repressible enzyme systems. Enzyme repression,[205] like induction, involves a sequence of enzymes mediating successive metabolic steps, but in the presence of the end product, the synthesis of each enzyme is repressed. Repressible systems have been revealed in the synthesis of tryptophan,[206] histidine[207] and other amino acids. The kinetics of repression appear to be analogous but opposed to those of induction, derepression being similar to induction. Repression involves a simultaneous and quantitively similar reduction in the synthesis of a series of enzymes, "coordinate repression," which is to be distinguished from "feedback inhibition"[208] in which the product of a series of enzymes inhibits the activity of an early enzyme, but does not interfere with its synthesis. Derepressed, constitutive mutants can be found, in which a series of originally repressible enzymes lose their repressibility. These mutations are found at sites within a regulator gene which is distinct and unlinked to the structural genes subjected to derepression. This gene is suggested to produce a cytoplasmic repressor which when activated by the repressing metabolite (corepressor) can then act on the operon to restrict further enzyme synthesis and is thus analogous to the i gene. It should be emphasized that the linkage of the i gene to the o^-, z, and y genes is gratuitous, and is not required of the concept.

5. CONTROL MECHANISMS IN BACTERIA

The operon concept envisages the operator and its genes as structurally associated to form the operon. Such a unit is present in the *lac* segment shown in Fig. 3, and it is suggested that those clusters of structural genes, particularly in *Salmonella* and *E. coli*, such as the *his* and *try* loci, could be examples of other operons.[199] In both these two systems, coordinate repression has been demonstrated.[206, 207] The extent to which other criteria of the operon apply in this and other systems has been the subject of much speculation and research, much outside the scope of this paper. The main features of some systems in which genetic analysis has figured are considered below.

a. Alkaline Phosphatase. The alkaline phosphatase enzyme of *E. coli* K12, being controlled by a single gene[70, 71], cannot be considered as part of an operon but is nevertheless of interest within the terms of regulation systems. This enzyme is repressed in the presence of high concentrations of orthophosphate,[209] and derepressed mutants can be isolated. These mutants, however, map in two distinct loci, R_1 and R_2.[210] The function of R_1 is proposed to be the synthesis of an endogenous inducer, permitting the cell to attain high levels of alkaline phosphatase synthesis. This inducer is then converted by the R_2 gene at high phosphate concentrations into a repressor. Thus R_2 acts as a normal regulator gene, whereas mutants in the R_1 gene show dual effects, being derepressed, but at the same time having a low enzyme level which cannot be increased by lowering the level of phosphate.[211] Regulation may thus involve the interplay of several regulator genes.*

b. Arginine Biosynthetic Pathway. This pathway has been studied in several coliform organisms and at least seven enzymes have been recognized. These enzymes are repressed in the presence of the terminal product of the pathway, arginine.[212-214] This repression appears to be controlled by a regulator gene, mutations of which result in constitutivity of at least five or six of these enzymes. However, in the two organisms *E. coli* B and *E. coli* K12, where it has been possible to map many of the structural

---

* According to a recent publication,[211a] mutations in either the R_1 or the R_2 regulator genes can be suppressed by the same gene which is capable of suppressing "nonsense" alkaline phosphatase mutants.[159] It is concluded that the repressor for alkaline phosphatase may thus be a protein molecule.

genes controlling these enzymes, it has been found that these genes are scattered over several regions of the linkage map.[215, 216] A series of separate operators, perhaps more than four, would thus be required to conform to the operon concept as it stands. Clearly, however, noncoordinate repression does not necessarily depend upon the contiguous linkage of the structure genes concerned.

   c. *Histidine Biosynthesis.* Histidine biosynthesis is controlled in *Salmonella* by seven or eight clustered gene loci (Fig. 10), producing a series of enzymes, at least seven of which have been identified, and which can be accurately assayed.[46, 54 54a] These enzymes are coordinately repressed in the presence of histidine, and it has been suggested that the *his* region constitutes an operon.[54, 152] No regulator mutants showing derepression have so far been isolated, nor have derepressed, dominant, o^c-type mutants.* Of the 600 or so *his* mutants examined, three are suggested to have a phenotype characteristic of o^o mutants.[54, 152] All three mutants are, however, deletion mutants (*G-203, DG-63,* and *CDG-57*) which extend across the terminal gene, *hisG,* and cover all single site mutants located at the *G* extremity of the histidine gene cluster (see Fig. 10).[54] The deletions, however, do not extend over those genes controlling most of the enzymes which are deficient in these mutants (see Table VI)[46] which constitutes the main evidence of operator mutations. However, among the 600 or more *his* mutants examined, no o^o point mutants which might have been expected to have been isolated without bias during the normal selection of histidineless mutants, have so far been recognized.†

   d. *Arabinose Fermentation.* Arabinose fermentation, as investigated by Englesberg and his colleagues in *E. coli* B, involves three distinct enzymes, which appear to be controlled by the three linked structural genes *araA, -B,* and *-D* (see Fig. 8).[78, 81, 82, 84] A fourth series of mutants, *araC,* appears to have lost the ability to synthesize all three enzymes, and it had been proposed that these are o^o mutations of an operator gene, the four genes *A, B, C,* and *D,* constituting an operon.[85] However, it has been found that some mutations have a dual effect on both the structure of one enzyme (producing a CRM), and also on the inducible level of another enzyme.[82] It should also be noted that both in the *lac* operon[62, 63] and in the *his* cluster there is some tendency of structural mutants of one gene to increase the levels of

---

   * A more recent paper reports the isolation of two genetically distinct classes of derepressed mutants, one of which is suggested to comprise regulator and the other o^c-type mutants.[54a]

   † Moreover, other mutants (polar mutants) resembling o^o mutants have been isolated at various sites throughout the histidine cluster, and it is proposed that no clear distinction exists between polar and o^o mutants.[54a] The evidence from o^o mutants cannot therefore be used in defining a specific operator region. These authors suggest elaborations of the operator model to accommodate these and other embarrassing[214a] findings.

enzymes from other genes (Table VI). Moreover, the genetic arrangement of these loci, *araD-araA-araB-araC*, although showing contiguous linkage, do not correspond with the sequential order of the biochemical reactions ($A \rightarrow B \rightarrow D$). However, the evidence that these genes constitute an operon appears less likely from more recent investigations.[83, 86] Initial experiments demonstrating that *araC* mutants can complement *araA* and *araB* mutants by the formation of minute colonies after transduction[78] have now been confirmed by a complementation test based on conjugation.[83] The transfer of the *ara* region from either *araA* or *araB* Hfr donors into *araC* recipients has shown that the resulting transient diploid zygotes are able to carry out the *araA* and *araB* functions to produce isomerase and kinase, respectively.[83] Moreover, some *araC* mutants are now found to produce detectable levels of isomerase.[215]

It is thought unlikely that *araC* produces a permease,[215] in which case its function must be related to a system of regulation of the three structural genes that does not conform to the operator model. This is supported by later experimental evidence on the dualism of the *araB* locus. It has been shown in 25 *araB* mutants that the inducible levels of both epimerase and isomerase correspond to the levels of kinase CRM found in these mutants. It is suggested that the *araB* gene may be self-regulating and contains information both for the structural determination of the kinase enzyme as well as controlling in a coordinated fashion the other two enzymes involved in L-arabinose metabolism.[86, 87]

e. Galactose Fermentation. Galactose fermentation in *E. coli* K12 appears to be controlled by a number of genes, of which most appear to be clustered in the chromosomal region which can be transduced by defective λ particles (λ*dg*).[68] Three enzymes have so far been identified: a kinase (*k*), a transferase (*t*), and an epimerase (*e*) which appear to act sequentially in the order $k \rightarrow t \rightarrow e$. Five groups of mutants have been recognized by complementation tests, one of which, *galE*, does not appear to be part of the cluster. Of the other four groups, three have been associated with the structural genes controlling the three enzymes, *galA* mutants lacking kinase, *galB* lacking transferase,[68] and *galD* lacking epimerase.[173] Mutants of the fourth gene, (*galC*) are usually deficient both in kinase and transferase and sometimes, but not always, epimerase. Mutants of *galA*, *galB* and *galD* groups form standard complementation groups, whereas *galC* mutants do not complement either *galA* or *galB* mutants.[68] This evidence has been used to support the claim that *galC* mutants are o^o mutants of an operator controlling the *galA* and *galB* genes.[154, 216] The three enzymes are coinducible with galactose,[216, 217] and mutants with constitutive levels of all three enzymes have been isolated which map in a region distinct from the *gal* cluster, suggested to be a regulator locus.[216] From this it appears that the operon may include *galD*, since the epimerase enzyme is also constitutive in these mutants, although its ability to complement presumed operator mutants is a departure from the original concept. Moreover, some genes show pleiotropic effects, kinase (*galA*) mutants producing transferase constitutively.[217, 218] Finally, there is some lack of agreement on the genetic ordering of these four genes. From mitotic crossing over within heterogenotes (see Fig. 5), Morse has concluded from a study of *galA* (*k*), *galB* (*t*), and *galC* (*o*) mutants that the arrangement is kinase - operator - transferase (*k-o-t*), no *galD* (*e*) mutants being investigated,[69] From mapping by transduction with P1 phage, Adler and Kaiser,[219] using a series of *gal* mutants including two *o°* mutants, have proposed the order *k - t - o - e*. Buttin, however, from a study of Hfr × F⁻ crosses using mutants of which one was an *oᶜ* mutant, suggests the order *k - t - e - o*, in which the operator locus is situated terminally, and the polarality of the *gal* operon corresponds to that of the *lac* operon, both being situated distal to the chromosomal markers, *thr* and *leu* (Fig. 3).[154] It thus seems possible that the sequence may be *k - t - o° - e - oᶜ*, which would be consistent with the physiology of the system, since the *oᶜ* mutant produces constitutive levels of all three enzymes, whereas the *o°* mutants are deficient in kinase and transferase only, and may thus be of the polar type as described by Ames and Hartman.[54a]

In conclusion therefore, whereas the operon as a single unit of genetic transcription comprising a cluster of related genes concerned in a biochemical sequence, appears to have validity,[220] the existence of a distinct operator region appears to be in some doubt. The recent accumulation of facts which the operon model cannot accommodate[54a, 86, 87, 214a, 221] thus appears to require some modification and elaboration of the model as originally proposed.

REFERENCES

[1] W. Hayes, *Symposium Soc. Gen. Microbiol.* **10,** 12 (1960); A. Kleinschmidt, D. Lang, and R. K. Zahn, *Z. Naturforsch.* **166,** 730 (1961); J. Cairns, *J. Mol. Biol.* **3,** 756 (1961); *ibid.* **6,** 208 (1963).

[2] J. Lederberg, *Genetics* **32,** 505 (1947).

[3] R. C. Clowes and D. Rowley, *J. Gen. Microbiol.* **11,** 250 (1954).

[4] L. L. Cavalli-Sforza and J. L. Jinks, *J. Genet.* **54,** 87 (1956).

[5] F. Jacob and E. L. Wollman, *Symposia Soc. Exptl. Biol.* **No. 12,** 75 (1958).

[6] T. H. Morgan, "The Theory of the Gene." Yale Univ. Press, New Haven, Connecticut, 1926.

[7] M. M. Green and K. C. Green, *Proc. Natl. Acad. Sci. U. S.* **35,** 586 (1949).

[8] M. M. Green, *Proc. Natl. Acad. Sci. U. S.* **40,** 92 (1954).

[9] E. B. Lewis, *Cold Spring Harbor Symposia Quant. Biol.* **16,** 151 (1951).

[10] M. E. Mackendrick and G. Pontecorvo, *Experientia* **8,** 390 (1952).

[11] J. A. Roper, *Nature* **166,** 956 (1950).

[12] R. H. Pritchard, *Heredity* **9,** 343 (1955).

[13] G. Pontecorvo, *Advances in Enzymol.* **13,** 121 (1952).

14 S. Benzer, *Proc. Natl. Acad. Sci. U. S.* **41**, 344 (1955).
15 M. Demerec, I. Blomstrand, and Z. E. Demerec, *Proc. Natl. Acad. Sci. U. S.* **41**, 359 (1955).
16 M. Demerec, *Am. Naturalist* **86**, 5 (1955).
17 S. Benzer, *in* "The Chemical Basis of Heredity" (W. D. McElroy and B. Glass, eds.), p. 70. Johns Hopkins Press, Baltimore, Maryland, 1957.
18 G. W. Beadle and E. L. Tatum, *Proc. Natl. Acad. Sci. U. S.* **27**, 499 (1941).
19 G. W. Beadle, *Physiol. Revs.* **25**, 643 (1945).
20 J. Lederberg, *Methods in Med. Research* **3**, 5 (1950).
21 E. L. Tatum, *Cold Spring Harbor Symposia Quant. Biol.* **11**, 278 (1946).
22 G. Pontecorvo, "Trends in Genetic Analysis." Columbia Univ. Press, New York, 1959.
23 F. J. Ryan and J. Lederberg, *Proc. Natl. Acad. Sci. U. S.* **32**, 163 (1946).
24 A. N. Promptov, *J. Genet.* **26**, 59 (1932).
25 J. Lederberg and N. D. Zinder, *J. Am. Chem. Soc.* **70**, 4267 (1948).
26 R. D. Davis, *Proc. Natl. Acad. Sci. U. S.* **35**, 1 (1949).
27 G. C. Meynell, *J. Gen. Microbiol.* **28**, 169 (1961).
28 M. Demerec, *Proc. Natl. Acad. Sci. U. S.* **46**, 1075 (1960).
29 E. Balbinder, *Genetics* **47**, 546 (1962).
30 A. Loveless, *Nature* **181**, 1212 (1958).
31 J. Lederberg and E. M. Lederberg, *J. Bacteriol.* **63**, 399 (1952).
32 R. Holliday, *Nature* **178**, 987 (1956).
33 N. D. Zinder and J. Lederberg, *J. Bacteriol.* **64**, 679 (1952).
34 M. Demerec, *Carnegie Inst. Wash. Publ.* **No. 612**, 1 (1956).
35 M. Demerec, *Microbial Genetics Bull.* **16**, 38 (1958).
36 B. D. Davis, *Experientia* **6**, 41 (1950).
37 S. Brenner, *Proc. Natl. Acad. Sci. U. S.* **41**, 862 (1955).
38 P. E. Hartman, *Carnegie Inst. Wash. Publ.* **No. 612**, 35 (1956).
39 T. Yura, *Carnegie Inst. Wash. Publ.* **No. 612**, 63 (1956).
40 R. C. Clowes, *J. Gen Microbiol.* **18**, 140 (1958).
41 K. Hashimoto, *Genetics* **45**, 49 (1960).
42 T. Miyake and M. Demerec, *Genetics* **45**, 755 (1960).
43 E. V. Glanville and M. Demerec, *Genetics* **45**, 1359 (1960).
44 D. A. Smith, *J. Gen. Microbiol.* **24**, 335 (1961).
45 T. Yura, *in* M. Demerec, H. Moser, R. C. Clowes, E. L. Lahr, H. Ozeki, and W. Vielmetter, *Carnegie Inst. Wash. Yearbook* **55**, 308 (1956).
46 B. N. Ames, B. Garry, and L. A. Herzenberg, *J. Gen. Microbiol.* **22**, 369 (1960).
47 N. D. Zinder, *J. Cellular Comp. Physiol.* **45**, Suppl. 2, 23 (1955).
48 H. Roman, *Cold Spring Harbor Symposia Quant. Biol.* **21**, 175 (1956).
49 M. Demerec and Z. E. Demerec, *Brookhaven Symposia in Biol.* **8**, [BNL 350 (C22)], p. 75 (1956).
50 M. Demerec and Z. Hartman, *Carnegie Inst. Wash. Publ.* **No. 612**, 5 (1956).
51 R. C. Clowes, *J. Gen. Microbiol.* **18**, 154 (1958).
52 P. E. Hartman, J. C. Loper, and D. Šerman, *J. Gen. Microbiol.* **22**, 232 (1960).
53 P. E. Hartman, Z. Hartman, and D. Šerman, *J. Gen. Microbiol.* **22**, 354 (1960).
54 B. N. Ames and P. E. Hartman, *in* "The Molecular Basis of Neoplasia" (M. D. Anderson Hospital Symposium, Houston). Univ. of Texas Press, Austin, Texas, 1962.
54a B. N. Ames and P. E. Hartman, *Cold Spring Harbor Symposia Quant. Biol.* **28**, 349 (1963).

[55] E. Balbinder, *Genetics* **47**, 469 (1962).

[56] M. Demerec and P. E. Hartman, *Ann. Rev. Microbiol.* **13**, 377 (1959).

[57] K. Mizobuchi, M. Demerec, and D. H. Gillespie, *Genetics* **47**, 1617 (1963).

[58] E. Lederberg, *Genetics* **37**, 469 (1952).

[58a] A. Cook and J. Lederberg, *Genetics* **47**, 1335 (1962).

[59] A. B. Pardee, F. Jacob, and J. Monod, *Compt. rend. acad. sci.* **246**, 3125 (1958).

[60] A. B. Pardee, F. Jacob, and J. Monod, *J. Mol. Biol.* **1**, 165 (1959).

[61] F. Jacob and E. L. Wollman, "Sexuality and the Genetics of Bacteria," p. 228. Academic Press, New York, 1961.

[62] F. Jacob and J. Monod, *J. Mol. Biol.* **3**, 318 (1961).

[63] F. Jacob and J. Monod, *Cold Spring Harbor Symposia Quant. Biol.* **26**, 193 (1961).

[64] E. M. Lederberg and J. Lederberg, *Genetics* **37**, 469 (1953).

[65] E. L. Wollman, *Ann. inst. Pasteur* **84**, 281 (1953).

[66] M. L. Morse, E. M. Lederberg, and J. Lederberg, *Genetics* **41**, 142 (1956).

[67] M. L. Morse, E. M. Lederberg, and J. Lederberg, *Genetics* **41**, 758 (1956).

[68] E. M. Lederberg, *Symposium Soc. Gen. Microbiol.* **10**, 115 (1960).

[69] M. L. Morse, *Proc. Natl. Acad. Sci. U. S.* **48**, 1314 (1962).

[70] A. Garen, *Symposium Soc. Gen. Microbiol.* **10**, 242 (1960).

[71] A. Garen, C. Levinthal, and F. Rothman, *J. chim. phys.* **58**, 1068 (1961)

[72] C. Yanofsky, *Bacteriol. Revs.* **24**, 221 (1960).

[73] C. Yanofsky and I. P. Crawford, *Proc. Natl. Acad. Sci. U. S.* **35**, 1016 (1959).

[74] B. Maling and C. Yanofsky, *Proc. Natl. Acad. Sci. U. S.* **47**, 551 (1961).

[75] D. R. Helinski and C. Yanofsky, *Proc. Natl. Acad. Sci. U. S.* **48**, 173 (1962).

[76] C. Yanofsky and E. S. Lennox, *Virology* **8**, 425 (1929).

[77] C. Yanofsky, D. R. Helinski, and B. D. Maling, *Cold Spring Harbor Symposia Quant. Biol.* **26**, 11 (1961).

[78] J. D. Gross and E. Englesberg, *Virology* **9**, 314 (1959).

[79] L. L. Cavalli, E. M. Lederberg, and J. Lederberg, *J Gen. Microbiol.* **8**, 89 (1953).

[80] E. S. Lennox, *Virology* **1**, 190 (1955).

[81] E. Englesberg, *J. Bacteriol.* **81**, 996 (1961).

[82] E. Englesberg, R. L. Anderson, R. Weinberg, N. Lee, P. Hoffee, G. Huttenhauer, and H. Boyer, *J. Bacteriol.* **84**, 137 (1962).

[83] R. B. Helling, and R. Weinberg, *Genetics* **48**, 1397 (1963).

[84] H. Boyer, E. Englesberg, and R. Weinberg, *Genetics* **47**, 417 (1962).

[85] N. Lee and E. Englesberg, *Proc. Natl. Acad. Sci. U. S.* **48**, 335 (1962).

[86] N. Lee and E. Englesberg, *Proc. Natl. Acad. Sci.* **50**, 696 (1963).

[87] R. Cribbs and E. Englesberg, *Genetics*, **49**, 94 (1964.)

[88] S. Lacks and R. D. Hotchkiss, *Biochim. et Biophys. Acta* **39**, 508 (1960).

[89] J. Spizizen, *Proc Natl. Acad. Sci. U. S.* **44**, 1072 (1958).

[90] E. Ephrati-Elizur, P. R. Srinivasan, and S. Zamenhof, *Proc. Natl. Acad. Sci. U. S.* **47**, 56 (1961).

[91] C. Anagnostopoulus and I. P. Crawford, *Proc. Natl. Acad. Sci. U. S.* **47**, 378 (1961).

[92] M. Demerec, *Cold Spring Harbor Symposia Quant. Biol.* **21**, 113 (1956).

[93] M. Demerec (unpublished results).

[94] M. Demerec and U. Fano, *Proc. Natl. Acad. Sci. U. S.* **27**, 24 (1941).

[95] J. H. Taylor, *Am. Naturalist* **91**, 209 (1957).

[96] J. H. Taylor, P. S. Woods, and W. L. Hughes, *Proc. Natl. Acad. Sci. U. S.* **43**, 122 (1957).

[97] S. Benzer, *Proc. Natl. Acad. Sci. U. S.* **45**, 1607 (1959).

[98] M. Chase and A. H. Doermann, *Genetics* **43**, 332 (1958).

[99] M. Nomura and S. Benzer, *J. Mol. Biol.* **3**, 684 (1961).

[100] P. E. Hartmann (personal communication).

[101] O. T. Avery, C. M. Macleod, and M. McCarty, *J. Exptl. Med.* **79**, 137 (1944).

[102] F. Griffith, *J. Hyg.* **27**, 113 (1928).

[103] A. D. Hershey and M. Chase, *J. Gen. Physiol.* **36**, 39 (1952).

[104] J. D. Watson and F. H. C. Crick, *Cold Spring Harbor Symposia Quant. Biol.* **18**, 123 (1953).

[105] A. R. Todd, reviewed by D. M. Brown and A. R. Todd, *in* "Nucleic Acids" (E. Chargaff and J. N. Davidson, eds.), Vol. I, Chapter 12, p. 409. Academic Press, New York, 1955.

[106] E. Chargaff, *in* "Nucleic Acids" (E. Chargaff and J. N. Davidson, eds.), Vol. I, p. 307. Academic Press, New York, 1955.

[107] M. H. F. Wilkins, A. R. Stokes, and H. R. Wilson, *Nature* **171**, 738 (1953).

[108] F. H. C. Crick, *Symposia Soc. Exptl. Biol.* **No. 12**, 138 (1958).

[109] R. Fuerst, F. Jacob, and E. L. Wollman, *Compt. rend. acad. sci.* **243**, 2162 (1956).

[110] C. Yanofsky, U. Henning, D. Helinski, and B. Carlton, *Federation Proc.* **22**, 75 (1963).

[111] P. Margolin, *Genetics* **44**, 525 (1959); *ibid.* **48**, 441 (1963).

[112] F. Jacob (unpublished results).

[113] C. E. J. Kirchner, *J. Mol. Biol.* **2**, 331 (1960).

[114] C. Yanofsky and P. St. Lawrence, *Ann. Rev. Microbiol.* **14**, 311 (1960).

[115] C. Yanofsky, *Cold Spring Harbor Symposia Quant. Biol.* **28**, 581.

[116] T. Yura, *Carnegie Inst. Publ.* **No. 612**, 77 (1956).

[117] S. Howarth, *Genetics* **43**, 404 (1058).

[118] P. Starlinger and F. Kaudewitz, *Z. Naturforsch.* **116**, 317 (1956).

[119] S. R. Suskind and L. I. Kurek, *Proc. Natl. Acad. Sci. U. S.* **45**, 93 (1959).

[120] A. J. Muller, *Proc. Natl. Acad. Sci. U. S.* **14**, 714 (1928).

[121] M. Demerec and R. Latarjet, *Cold Spring Harbor Symposia Quant. Biol.* **11**, 38 (1946).

[122] C. Auerbach and J. M. Robson, *Nature* **157**, 302 (1946).

[123] C. Auerbach, J. M. Robson, and J. R. Carr, *Science* **105**, 243 (1948).

[124] M. Westergaard, *Experientia* **13**, 224 (1957).

[125] A. Loveless and S. H. Howarth, *Nature* **184**, 1780 (1959).

[126] M. Demerec, G. Bertani, and J. Flint, *Am. Naturalist* **85**, 119 (1951).

[127] S. Benzer and E. Freese, *Proc. Natl. Acad. Sci. U. S.* **44**, 112 (1958).

[128] S. Brenner, S. Benzer, and L. Barnett, *Nature* **182**, 983 (1958).

[129] E. Freese, *J. Mol. Biol.* **1**, 87 (1959).

[130] E. Freese, *Proc. Natl. Acad. Sci. U. S.* **45**, 622 (1959).

[131] I. Tessman, *Virology* **9**, 375 (1959).

[132] V. W. Vielmetter and H. Schuster, *Biochem. Biophys. Research Communs.* **2**, 324. (1960).

[133] E. Bautz-Freese and E. Freese, *Virology* **13**, 19 (1961).

[134] R. M. Litman and H. Ephrussi-Taylor, *Compt. rend. acad. sci.* **249**, 838 (1959).

[135] K. W. Mundry and A. Gierer, *Z. induktire Astammungs—u. Vererbungslehre* **89**, 614 (1958).

[136] E. Freese, E. Bautz, and E. Bautz-Freese, *Proc. Natl. Acad. Sci. U. S.* **47**, 845 (1961).

[138] H. Schuster, *J. Mol. Biol.* **3**, 447 (1961).

[138a] H. Schuster and H. G. Wittman, *Virology* **19**, 42 (1963).

[139] E. Freese, E. Bautz-Freese, and E. Bautz, *J. Mol. Biol.* **3**, 133 (1961).

[140] E. Bautz-Freese, *Proc. Natl. Acad. Sci. U. S.* **47**, 540 (1961).

[141] E. Bautz and E. Freese, *Proc. Natl. Acad. Sci. U. S.* **46**, 1585 (1960).

[142] S. Zamenhof, *J. Bacteriol.* **81**, 111 (1961).

[143] S. Champe and S. Benzer, *Proc. Natl. Acad. Sci. U. S.* **48**, 532 (1962).

[143a] D. R. Kreig, *Genetics* **48**, 561 (1963).

[144] E. Strelzoff, *Biochem. et Biophys. Research Communs.* **5**, 384 (1961).

[145] E. Strelzoff, *Z. Vererbungslehre* **93**, 301 (1962).

[146] R. Rudner, *Z. Vererbungslehre* **92**, 336 (1961).

[147] R. Rudner, *Z. Vererbungslehre* **92**, 361 (1961).

[148] B. E. Terzaghi, G. Streisinger, and F. W. Stahl. *Proc. Natl. Acad. Sci. U. S.* **48**, 1519 (1962).

[149] S. Brenner, L. Barnett, F. H. C. Crick, and A. Orgel. *J. Mol. Biol.* **3**, 121 (1961).

[150] W. Vielmetter (personal communication).

[151] L. Lerman, *J. Mol. Biol.* **3**, 18 (1961).

[152] B. N. Ames, P. E. Hartman, and F. Jacob, *J. Mol. Biol.* **7**, 23 (1963).

[153] F. Jacob and E. L. Wollman, "Sexuality and the Genetics of Bacteria," p. 166. Academic Press, New York, 1961.

[154] G. Buttin, *Compt. rend. acad. sci.* **255**, 1233 (1962).

[155] A. E. Garrod, "Inborn Errors of Metabolism," 2nd ed. Oxford Univ. Press (Med. Publ.), London and New York, 1923.

[156] V. M. Ingram, *Nature* **180**, 326 (1957).

[157] N. Horowitz, *Federation Proc.* **15**, 818 (1946).

[158] S. R. Suskind, C. Yanofsky, and D. M. Bonner, *Proc. Natl. Acad. Sci. U. S.* **41**, 577 (1955).

[159] A. Garen and O. Siddiqui, *Proc. Natl. Acad. Sci. U. S.* **48**, 1121 (1962).

[160] F. H. C. Crick, *Brookhaven Symposia in Biol.* **12**, (*BNL558-C29*) 35 (1959).

[161] F. H. C. Crick, *in* "Progress in Nucleic Acid Research" (J. N. Davidson and W. E. Cohn, eds.), Vol. 1, p. 163. Academic Press, New York, 1963.

[162] G. Gamov, *Nature* **173**, 318 (1954).

[163] S. Brenner, *Proc. Natl. Acad. Sci. U. S.* **43**, 687 (1957).

[164] A. Tsugita and H. Fraenkel-Conrat, *J. Mol. Biol.* **4**, 73 (1962).

[165] H. G. Wittman, *Virology* **12**, 609 (1960).

[166] F. H. C. Crick, L. Barnett, S. Brenner, and R. J. Watts-Tobin, *Nature* **192**, 1227 (1961).

[167] S. Benzer and S. P. Champe, *Proc. Natl. Acad. Sci. U. S.* **48**, 1114 (1962).

[168] A N. Belozersky and A. S. Spirin, *Nature* **182**, 111 (1958).

[169] G. W. Beadle and V. L. Coonradt, *Genetics* **29**, 291 (1944).

[170] B. A. D. Stocker, N. D. Zinder, and J. Lederberg, *J. Gen. Microbiol.* **9**, 140 (1953).

[171] H. Ozeki, *Carnegie Inst. Wash. Publ.* **No. 612**, 97 (1956).

[172] M. Demerec and H. Ozeki, *Genetics* **44**, 269 (1959).

[173] E. Jordan, M. B. Yarmolinsky, and H. M. Kalckar, *Proc. Natl. Acad. Sci. U. S.* **48**, 32 (1962).

[174] F. Jacob and E. A. Adelberg, *Compt. rend. acad. sci.* **249**, 189 (1960).

[175] F. Jacob, D. Perrin, C. Sanchez, and J. Monod, *Compt. rend. acad. sci.* **250**, 1727 (1960).

[176] D. G. Catcheside, *Symposium Soc. Gen. Microbiol.* **10**, 181 (1960).

[177] J. R. S. Fincham, *Brit. Med. Bull.* **18**, 14 (1962).

[177a] J. R. S. Fincham and A. Coddington, *J. Mol. Biol.* **6**, 361 (1963).

[178] C. Levinthal, E. R. Signer, and K. Fetherolf, *Proc. Natl. Acad. Sci. U. S.* **48**, 1230 (1962).

[178a] M. J. Schlesinger and C. Levinthal, *J. Mol. Biol.* **7**, 1 (1963).

[179] M. F. Perutz, M. G. Rossmann, A. F. Cullis, H. Muirhead, G. Will, and A. C. T. North, *Nature* **185**, 416 (1960).

[180] J. C. Kendrew, *in* "Biological Structure and Function" (T. W. Goodwin and O. Lindberg, eds.), Vol. 1, p. 5. Academic Press, New York, 1960.

[181] C. Levinthal, A. Garen, and F. Rothman, *Proc. 5th Intern. Cong. Biochem., Moscow, 1961* in press.

[182] D. Perrin, *Cold Spring Harbor Symposia Quant. Biol.* **28**, 529.

[183] U. Henning and C. Yanofsky, *Proc. Natl. Acad. Sci. U. S.* **48**, 183 (1962).

[184] S. Benzer and S. P. Champe, *Proc. Natl. Acad. Sci. U. S.* **47**, 1025 (1961).

[185] G. Streisinger (personal communication).

[186] M. W. Nirenberg and J. H. Matthaei, *Proc. Natl. Acad. Sci. U. S.* **47**, 1588 (1961).

[187] P. Lengyel, J. F. Speyer, and S. Ochoa, *Proc. Natl. Acad. Sci. U. S.* **47**, 1930 (1961).

[188] J. H. Matthaei, O. W. Jones, R. G. Martin, and M. W. Nirenberg, *Proc. Natl. Acad. Sci. U. S.* **48**, 667 (1962).

[189] J. F. Speyer, P. Lengyel, C. Basilio, and S. Ochoa, *Proc. Natl. Acad. Sci. U. S.* **48**, 63 (1962).

[190] J. F. Speyer, P. Lengyel, C. Basilio, and S. Ochoa, *Proc. Natl. Acad. Sci. U. S.* **48**, 441 (1962).

[191] E. L. Smith, *Proc. Natl. Acad. Sci. U. S.* **48**, 677 (1962).

[192] H. G. Wittmann, *Z. Vererbungslehre* **93**, 491 (1962).

[193] K. Wallenfels and A. Arens, *Biochem. Z.* **332**, 247 (1960).

[194] R. B. Goldschmidt, *in* "Theoretical Genetics." Univ. of California Press, Berkeley, California, 1955.

[195] R. C. Clowes, *Symposium Soc. Gen. Microbiol.* **10**, 92 (1960).

[195a] E. W. Nester, M. Schafer, and J. Lederberg, *Genetics* **48**, 529 (1963).

[195b] J. R. Beckwith, A. B. Pardee, R. Austrian, and F. Jacob, *J. Mol. Biol.* **5**, 618 (1962).

[196] M. E. Case and N. H. Giles, *Proc. Natl. Acad. Sci. U. S.* **46**, 659 (1960).

[197] J. R. S. Fincham and J. A. Pateman, *J. Gen. Microbiol.* **11**, 236 (1957).

[198] R. W. Barratt, D. Newmeyer, D. D. Perkins, and L. Garnjobst, *Advances in Genet.* **6**, 1 (1954).

[199] F. Jacob, P. Schaeffer, and E. L. Wollman, *Symposium Soc. Gen. Microbiol.* **10**, 67 (1960).

[200] G. Pontecorvo, *Biochem. Soc. Symposia (Cambridge, Engl.)* **4**, 40 (1950).

[201] M. B. Hoagland, M. L. Stevenson, J. F. Scott, L. I. Hecht, and P. C. Zamecnik, *J. Biol. Chem.* **231**, 241 (1958).

[202] M. B. Hoagland, *Brookhaven Symposia in Biol.* **No. 12**, (1959).

[203] S. Brenner, F. Jacob, and M. Meselson, *Nature* **190**, 576 (1961).

[204] F. Gros, H. Hiatt, W. Gilbert, G. C. Kurland, A. W. Riseborough, and J. D. Watson, *Nature* **190**, 581 (1961).

[205] H. J. Vogel, *in* "The Chemical Basis of Heredity" (W. D. McElroy and B. Glass, eds.), p. 276. Johns Hopkins Press, Baltimore, Maryland, 1957.

[206] J. Monod and G. Cohen-Bazire, *Compt. rend. acad. sci.* **236**, 530 (1953).

[207] B. N. Ames and B. Garry, *Proc. Natl. Acad. Sci. U. S.* **45**, 1453 (1959).

[208] A. Novick, *Ann. Rev. Microbiol.* **9**, 97 (1955).

[209] A. Torriani, *Biochim. et Biophys. Acta* **38**, 460 (1960).

[210] H. Echols, A. Garen, S. Garen, and A. Torriani, *J. Mol. Biol.* **3,** 425 (1961).

[211] A. Garen, and H. Echols, *J. Bacteriol.* **83,** 297 (1962).

[211a] A. Garen and S. Garen, *J. Mol. Biol.* **6,** 433 (1963).

[212] H. J. Vogel, *Cold Spring Harbor Symposia Quant. Biol.* **26,** 163 (1961).

[213] L. Gorini, W. Gunderson, and M. Burger, *Cold Spring Harbor Symposia Quant. Biol.* **26,** 173 (1961).

[214] W. K. Maas, *Cold Spring Harbor Symposia Quant. Biol.* **26,** 183 (1961).

[214a] I. Zabin, *Federation Proc.* **22,** 27 (1963); *Cold Spring Harbor Symposia Quant. Biol.* **28,** 431 (1963).

[215] E. Englesberg (personal communication).

[216] G. Buttin, *Cold Spring Harbor Symposia Quant. Biol.* **26,** 213 (1961).

[217] H. M. Kalckar, K. Kurahashi, and E. Jordan, *Proc. Natl. Acad. Sci. U. S.* **45,** 1776 (1959).

[218] H. M. Kalckar and T. A. Sundararajan, *Cold Spring Harbor Symposia Quant. Biol.* **26,** 227 (1961).

[219] J. Adler and A. D. Kaiser, *Virology* **19,** 117 (1963).

[220] R. G. Martin, *Cold Spring Harbor Symposia Quant. Biol.* **28,** 357 (1963).

[221] J. R. Beckwith, *Biochim. et Biophys. Acta* **76,** 162 (1963).

CHAPTER 7

Molecular Aspects of the Gene: Replication Mechanisms

ROBERT L. BALDWIN

I. Introduction

In the last ten years we have seen the beginning and rapid growth of research aimed at describing in purely chemical terms a basic biological problem, replication of the genes. The problem has two parts: determination of the chemical structures of genes and chromosomes, and definition of the reactions responsible for their replication. A major goal is to reproduce these reactions in the test tube: to isolate the necessary enzymes, find conditions where they function properly, and finally to synthesize *in vitro* biologically active nucleic acids.

Another major goal is to determine the mechanism of gene replication. The outlines of the problem are clear but an intensive study of mechanism is only beginning. In general terms the problem of how DNA (deoxyribonucleic acid) is replicated was analyzed correctly by Watson and Crick[1] on the basis of their structural model for DNA. Their proposal that each polynucleotide chain of the double helix serves as a template for fashioning a new chain of complementary base sequence has been confirmed by the enzymic studies of Kornberg and his co-workers (for a summary, see Kornberg[2]). Detailed studies of the mechanism of DNA synthesis have had to wait upon enzyme purification. Recently the DNA synthesizing enzyme from *Escherichia coli* has been purified to a stage approximating final purity and DNA polymerases from other sources have been highly purified. The enzymes necessary for synthesis of viral RNA's (ribonucleic acid) are being purified as this is written,* and RNA polymerases catalyzing the

---

* *Note added in proof:* See, for example, the section on "The Synthesis and Structure of RNA" in *Cold Spring Harbor Symposia Quant. Biol.* **28,** 59–109 (1963).

synthesis of specific RNA under the direction of a DNA template have been purified from several sources.

The purpose of this chapter is to discuss current problems, rather than to provide a complete survey of the literature. (Often a single reference will be given to some point although several workers have contributed to establishing it, and the basis for choosing this reference may be only that it contains a good summary of the evidence.) For other recent reviews, see the articles by Bessman[2a] and Bollum.[2b]

II. Structure and Chemistry of the Genetic Material

So far as is known now, bacterial and viral chromosomes are large molecules of nucleic acid. We begin, then, with the structure and chemistry of DNA and RNA and consider those aspects which are particularly relevant to the mechanism of replication. As compared to proteins, the structures of nucleic acids are characterized by great simplicity. However, the same terms needed to describe different levels of structural organization in proteins[3] are often applied to nucleic acids: these are primary, secondary, and tertiary structure. The primary structure is the covalent structure: the sequence of units in a polynucleotide chain, and the covalent bonds which link these units. Both RNA and DNA have been found to have simple linear structures, without branching. The secondary structure is the local conformation in which a nucleic acid is folded or coiled. For most DNA's this conformation is known to be the double helix proposed by Watson and Crick[4] which is formed from two DNA chains running in opposite directions. The tertiary structure is the arrangement in three-dimensional space of the entire molecule. Little is known about the tertiary structures of RNA and DNA but it is commonly assumed that, unlike proteins, most nucleic acids do not have fixed tertiary structures in solution but rather are displayed in space as randomly as the primary and secondary structures will allow. When nucleic acids are assembled into viruses and bacteriophages, regular packing of the nucleic acid moiety is very likely. For example, in coliphage T2 a DNA double helix whose extended length is about 50–70 μ is packed into a phage head whose diameter is only 0.1 μ.[5]

A. Covalent Structure of DNA and RNA

1. Primary Structure in Outline

The covalent structure of a DNA chain is shown diagrammatically in Fig. 1. The RNA chain differs only in that ribose replaces deoxyribose. For a recent summary of bond angles, bond distances, and proof of structure, see Steiner and Beers.[6] The positions of the glycosidic (base-sugar) linkages have been confirmed by synthesis and also the glycosidic linkage has been shown to be β. Chemical evidence that the phosphate linkage proceeds from the 3'-OH of one pentose ring to the 5'-OH of its neighbor (reviewed by Brown and Todd[7]) is confirmed by the results of enzymic hydrolysis of DNA and RNA to mononucleotides. Digestion either of RNA or DNA by venom diesterase gives nearly a quantitative yield of 5'-P mononucleotides (a nucleotide that has phosphate esterified to the 5'-hydroxyl group) while spleen diesterase, in conjunction with micrococcal endonuclease, gives complete conversion to 3'-P mononucleotides.[8-10]

The purine and pyrimidine bases which are commonly found in DNA

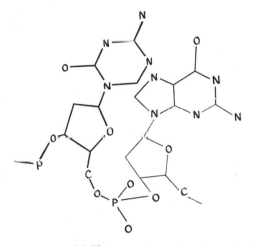

Fig. 1. Covalent structure of DNA: a section of a polynucleotide chain containing two bases, C and G. This is an artist's sketch of a brass rod model, built to show the bond angles and bond distances. The hydrogen atoms have been omitted and most of the carbon atoms are not labeled.

and viral RNA are shown in Fig. 2. Guanine, cytosine, and adenine are present both in RNA and DNA, while uracil usually occurs in RNA and thymine (5-methyluracil) is found in DNA. The names of these bases will be abbreviated to G, C, A, U, and T, respectively, in the rest of this chapter. Other bases are also present in certain cases. In the DNA's of coliphages T2, T4, and T6, 5-hydroxymethylcytosine completely replaces cytosine[11] and is found chiefly in the form of mono- and diglucosylated derivatives (for their structures, see Kuno and Lehman[12]).

Two *Bacillus subtilis* phages have partially glucosylated DNA's in which thymine is replaced by uracil and 5-hydroxymethyluracil, respectively.[13-15] Recently, Gold *et al.*[16] have found DNA-methylating enzymes which are distributed ubiquitously and which convert cytosine to 5-methylcytosine and adenine to 6-methylaminopurine. The base compositions of RNA and DNA from various sources are discussed by Sueoka in Chapter 9 of this book.

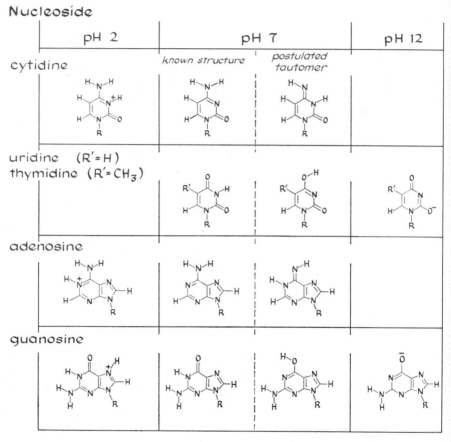

FIG. 2. Protonated forms of the bases in RNA and DNA; R = ribose and deoxyribose, respectively. Other resonance forms, in which the charges and the double bonds occupy other positions, also contribute but the protons are located in fixed positions, as shown here. The structure for A at pH 2 is taken from Cochran,[177] those for A, U, and T at pH 7 and 12 from Miles,[178, 179] and those for C[180, 180a] and G[181] from Miles and co-workers.

2. LOCATION OF PROTONS

The mechanism of base pairing in DNA and RNA by specific hydrogen bonding hinges on the location of the ionizable protons in the bases A, G, C, T, and U (see Fig. 4). When Watson and Crick[4] proposed the pairing of A with T and G with C in the DNA helix, it was probable but not certain that the four bases were present in their amino and keto, rather than imino and enol, forms. (In reference books of that period G was often written as the enol tautomer.) Since then infrared studies of model compounds in D_2O (especially the work of Miles with analogs in which a methyl group replaces the proton) have established the existence at neutral pH of the keto and amino forms shown in Fig. 2. In view of the suggestion by Watson and Crick[17] that spontaneous mutations may arise through mispairing of a base in its rare tautomeric form (cf. Fig. 4c), several methods have been tried for detecting these tautomers. Because the proportion which is in the rare tautomeric form is very small, it has been difficult to measure directly. However, Katritzky and Waring[17a] estimate, on the basis of acid-base properties of uracil analogs, that the frequency of the enol tautomer of N-methyluracil is about 10^{-3} to 10^{-4}, while in the corresponding 5-bromo compound it is some 10 times higher. Similar calculations[17a] for cytosine analogs[17b] allow the frequency of the imino tautomer of N-methylcytosine to be estimated at about 10^{-5}. These frequencies are much higher than some observed[18] rates of spontaneous mutation (10^{-7} – 10^{-8}) which may correspond to a transition from an AT to a GC base pair, or vice versa. For a more detailed comparison, one needs to know the reaction rates for interconversion of the tautomeric forms, as well as for the appropriate steps in the DNA polymerase reaction.

Near pH 4 protons are added to A, G, and C and near pH 10 protons are removed from G, T, and U. The structures which result are also shown in Fig. 2 (for a summary of pK_a values, see Steiner and Beers,[6] p. 25). The phosphate group in the backbone of a polynucleotide chain is a strong acid: the pK_a for the corresponding ionization in mononucleotides is below pH 1.[6]

3. CHEMICAL STABILITY

Depurination and diester bond breakage are the chief types of chemical damage suffered by DNA and RNA. In DNA strand breakage appears to follow depurination (see the discussion by Fiers and Sinsheimer[19]), and depurination is catalyzed by acid and by heat.[20] In the case of RNA, diester bond cleavage proceeds directly via a cyclic intermediate involving the 2'-OH group of ribose, and the reaction is strongly catalyzed by alkali. Alkaline hydrolysis at room temperature can give quantitative breakdown to mononucleotides. A thorough study of the rates of hydrolysis of RNA under different conditions has been made by Bacher and Kauzmann.[21] One may summarize by saying that RNA is unstable in acid and very unstable in alkali, whereas DNA is unstable in acid and fairly stable in alkali. Both become less stable at any pH as the temperature is increased. With materials isolated from natural sources or made enzymically, enzymic hydrolysis is often a problem.

Other types of chemical damage have also been demonstrated. For example, ultraviolet light promotes the hydration and dimerization of thymine (reviewed by Wierzchowski and Shugar[22]). Mechanical shear evidently will break covalent bonds in DNA if the molecule is sufficiently large (see Section II,C).

B. Physical Structure of the DNA Helix

1. Derivation of the Structure by X-Ray Diffraction

The structure of the DNA double helix (form B, the one believed to exist in solution) is shown in Fig. 3. Its principal features are well known. It has the form of a rope ladder twisted into a regular right-handed helix, in which the base pairs AT and GC are the rungs of the ladder and the sugar-phosphate chains are the two ropes. The sugar-phosphate backbone has polarity, since a phosphate connects the 3'-OH of one deoxyribose to the 5'-OH of the next; the two complementary strands have opposite polarities. There are ten base pairs per turn of the helix and they are spaced 3.4 A. apart, the van der Waal's contact distance between stacked purine and pyrimidine rings. The AT and GC base pairs have the structures shown in Fig. 4. Each base pair is rotated 36° about the helix axis from its neighbor. An important property of the structure is that the helix is regular: every base-sugar linkage is found at the same distance from the helix axis and is rotated, relative to its neighbors in the chain, by the same amount (36°). The ionized phosphate groups are on the outside of the helix, where they nevertheless produce a large electrostatic charge which tends to unfold the helix. Location of the water molecules around the helix is not shown. In fact, it is not known whether they occupy definite positions on the helix. Water probably plays a role in stabilizing the DNA structure since there is a change to another crystal form, the A form, when wet fibers of sodium DNA are taken to low humidity.[23]

Evidence for the structure shown in Fig. 3 comes both from X-ray diffraction patterns of DNA fibers and from model building. A chief purpose of building models is to exclude structures which require unusual bond angles or bond distances, or which necessitate placing two nonbonded atoms closer than the sum of their van der Waal's contact distances. Then, when the atomic coordinates of the model have been measured, atomic scattering factors are used in programing a computer to find the X-ray pattern which this structure would give. Comparison with the observed pattern then shows whether or not further adjustments of the model are needed. This was the procedure used by Langridge et al.,[24, 25] whose third model gives good prediction of the observed X-ray patterns. It retains the essential features of the original model proposed by Crick and Watson[26] but the

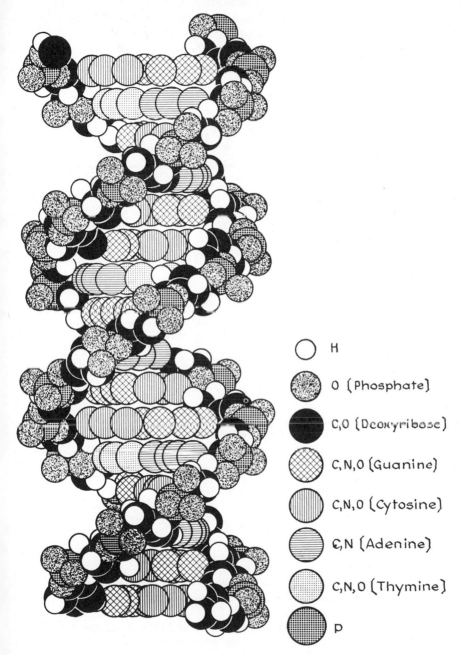

FIG. 3. Space-filling model of the DNA double helix, form B (modeled after the figure shown by Eigen[182] and the earlier figure of Feughelman et al.[183]).

coordinates of the atoms have been altered appreciably. The present structure is believed to be a close approximation to the final one.[25]

Three different crystal forms of DNA (the A, B, and C forms) have been

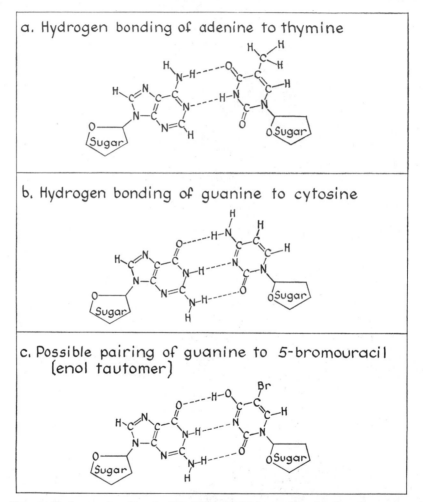

FIG. 4. Hydrogen bonding in the AT and GC base pairs (*a, b*) and an example
(*c*) of the mispairing that might occur when one base is present in a rare tautomeric
form: the possible pairing of G with the enol tautomer of 5-bromouracil.

reported in which there are obvious differences in the structure of the helix.
Evidence that the B form is the one present in solution rests chiefly on
finding the B form at high humidities when the DNA double helices are
separated from each other by large sheaths of water.[23] Also the mass per

unit length of DNA in solution has been measured by low-angle X-ray scattering[27] and agrees with the value predicted for the B form. A transition to the A form is observed in fibers of sodium DNA when the relative humidity is lowered below about 75%. Although a complete structure for the A form has not yet been reported, the work of Langridge et al.[28] confirms the suggestion of Crick and Watson[26] that the base pairs are tilted relative to the helix axis and displaced sideways, giving rise to a 30% shortening of the helix. Highly crystalline X-ray patterns are obtained readily from fibers of the A form of DNA, and consequently much of the early effort directed towards solving the structure of DNA was spent in analyzing these patterns. When Langridge et al.[28] found that the lithium salt of DNA would crystallize in the B form, they could then obtain sufficient information from the X-ray patterns of the B form to determine its structure in detail.

The C form of DNA is given by fibers of lithium DNA under special conditions of salt and low humidity. These conditions and a proposed structure for the C form have recently been given by Marvin et al.[29] The base pairs are tilted 6° relative to the helix axis and the two bases in a base pair are twisted 5° away from each other.

2. UNFOLDING OF THE DNA HELIX

The DNA helix is a highly ordered structure in which most of the possible rotations about single bonds have been frozen in place. One would expect from this that the separated polynucleotide chains possess more entropy than the helix and, since this will tend to unfold the helix, that there must be a favorable change in heat content (heat must be given off) on forming the double helix from the separated chains. These expectations have been confirmed by experiment. Recent studies on the formation of the RNA double helix rArU,* by mixing the RNA homopolymers of A and U, give $\Delta H = -8.7$ kilocalories per mole of base pairs and $\Delta S = -23$ entropy units per mole of base pairs.[30, 31] This value of $-\Delta H$ is larger than expected for merely forming two hydrogen bonds in aqueous solution.[30] Since the rArU homopolymer pair forms a double helix whose structure is similar to that of DNA[32] these values for ΔH and ΔS provide a guide to the behavior of DNA.

Granted that ΔH and ΔS both are negative, it follows that ΔG, the change in free energy for the transition from separated strands to helix, will become positive above a given temperature, $T_m(\Delta G = \Delta H - T\Delta S$; at $T_m \, \Delta G =$

---

* Here r is used to denote an RNA chain, d to denote a DNA chain; rArU stands for a complex formed from separate chains of rA and rU polymers while the RNA copolymer which contains A alternating with U will be written rAU and random copolymers as rA,U.

0 and $\Delta H = T_m \Delta S$). Above this temperature the DNA helix will unfold spontaneously. T_m is usually determined from the mid-point of the melting curve of absorbance vs. temperature, with the assumption that the degree of melting is equal to the percent of the final increase in absorbance.[33] The melting temperature of a DNA increases with its GC content[34] and this has been interpreted in terms of a different ΔH for AT and GC base pairs.[35] The use of melting curves to compare the stability of different helices, and also to characterize nucleic acids, is illustrated in Fig. 5.

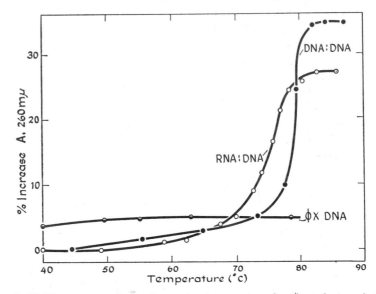

FIG. 5. Melting curves of absorbance vs. temperature for three forms of ϕX-174 DNA[174]: the native single-stranded DNA, the RNA:DNA hybrid made with the RNA polymerase from *E. coli*, and the double-stranded DNA (DNA:DNA) made with the DNA polymerase from *E. coli*. The solvent contains Na$_3$ citrate, 0.05 M in Na[+]. At this Na[+] concentration the native ϕX DNA is almost completely melted at 40°C., the lowest temperature shown.[66]

In addition to the increase in rotational entropy, another major factor tending to unfold the DNA helix is the charge repulsion between ionized phosphate groups, which is less in the separated strands. Consequently the helix can be stabilized* by adding a neutral salt (e.g. NaCl) which screens the phosphate charges or by neutralizing the phosphate groups with a cation such as Mg[++] which is bound strongly. The DNA helix also unfolds at acid or alkaline pH's (reviewed by Jordan[36]; see also Dove *et al.*[37]). At

---

* This explains the strong dependence of T_m on the type and concentration of the cation, and the consequent use of a standard solvent (e.g., 0.15 M NaCl, 0.015 M. Na$_3$ citrate[34]) to compare the stability of different DNA's.

these pH's,* certain hydrogen bonds between base pairs are broken by the addition or removal of protons; compare Figs. 2 and 4.

Since the DNA helix is formed by winding two chains about each other once every ten base pairs, this helix must be unwound as it is melted. For some time it was thought that the two strands would remain wound around each other after melting.[38] The first clear indication that they do come apart was obtained by Meselson and Stahl,[39] who studied a hybrid DNA (labeled for one generation of growth with a heavy isotope) and who found that the DNA dissociates into two subunits after melting. These can be separated by centrifugation in a density gradient. Later work has been aimed at finding whether the two subunits are in fact the two strands of the DNA helix (see Section III,B).

The mechanism of unwinding, and prediction of the time required for unwinding, have been the subject of much theoretical study.[40-43] This problem has a direct bearing on the mechanism of DNA replication[44] since recent evidence suggests that in many cases the entire DNA content of a bacterial or viral chromosome is a single molecule of nucleic acid (Section II,C). According to the semiconservative model for DNA replication, the two strands of a double helix must also be unwound during replication, each strand then becoming part of a new helix. The great length of these molecules raises certain questions. Given a fixed force which drives the unwinding of the helix, how long will the unwinding take? How much work is required to unwind the strands? The problem is that both the time and the energy required increase rapidly with the length of the helix. Depending on the mechanism of unwinding, the time required shows a dependence on helix length L varying from L^2 to L^3.[43] There are still few experimental studies in this field, but recent work by Freese and Freese[45] indicates that the time required to unwind the DNA of a bacterial chromosome may be comparable to the generation time (20 minutes or so) if the DNA is a continuous double helix. The time required to melt T2 DNA (molecular weight about 1.3×10^7) has been measured by Crothers[46] and agrees fairly well with the prediction of Fixman[43] for melting by unwinding from one end of the helix.

When thermally melted DNA is cooled rapidly, or alkali-melted DNA is quickly reneutralized, the DNA remains denatured. The viscosity is then greatly reduced, the molar absorbancy at room temperature is greater than that of native DNA and the absorbancy melting curve is spread out over a wide temperature range (cf. Fig. 12b). Amino groups of A, G, and C are more available for reaction with formaldehyde[47] or nitrous acid, and

---

* The pH at which titration and unfolding of a DNA occurs is different than that for titration of the mononucleotides, because the protons are held in hydrogen bonds in the helix.

the increased rate of reaction with these reagents can be used to distinguish denatured from native DNA. Also certain deoxyribonucleases distinguish native from denatured DNA. The best example is *E. coli* exonuclease I,[48, 49] crystalline preparations of which attack denatured DNA at a rate some 40,000 times greater than native DNA.

Recently Marmur, Doty, and co-workers have made the important discovery that the two complementary chains of a DNA helix can recombine after they have been separated by melting.[50-53a] Evidence for specific recombination* is given by recovery of transforming activity, formation of a structure which once more melts sharply at the T_m of the native DNA, and by the formation of hybrid molecules (labeled in one strand by heavy isotopes) which are resistant to breakdown by *E. coli* exonuclease I. There is not yet evidence that strand recombination can occur *in vivo* by such a mechanism.

3. SECONDARY STRUCTURE OF RNA AND ϕX DNA

The properties of most viral RNA's and also of ϕX DNA resemble those of denatured DNA more than native DNA and it seems probable that these molecules do not have any fixed and regular secondary structure, although elements of secondary structure are present. For example, the existence of some secondary structure in the RNA from tobacco mosaic virus is shown clearly by the work of Spirin and co-workers[54] on the viscosity-temperature curves of this RNA. The freshly prepared infectious RNA shows a sharp increase in viscosity over a temperature interval of about 10°C. Presumably the formation of some base pairs between A and U and between G and C provides the basis for the structure maintained at low temperatures. It has been shown by Fresco and Alberts,[55] from the analysis of mixing curves of the RNA homopolymer of U with a random copolymer of A and U, that an ordered structure will form with A paired to U and with "looping out" of the extraneous U residues from the rA,U copolymer, if its U content is not too large. As yet there is no case known in which an RNA must have a specific secondary structure to show its biological activity, although the definite possibility exists that this may be true of amino-acid acceptor RNA's.[56]

The X-ray diffraction patterns shown by natural RNA's are usually indistinct and have not been of much use in establishing secondary structure until recently. Spencer *et al.*[57] have obtained a fairly crystalline fiber pattern from a preparation containing yeast acceptor RNA and later Langridge and Gomatos[58] found that reovirus RNA, whose solution properties indicate that it has a large amount of secondary structure,[59] gives a clear X-ray

* The procedure used for strand recombination is "annealing" at a temperature about 25°C. below T_m in 0.3 M NaCl, 0.03 M Na$_3$ citrate.[53]

diffraction pattern of a similar type. Both resemble the crystalline pattern found by Davies[60] for the RNA homopolymer pair rIrC. The major point of interest is that the structure resembles the A form, rather than the B form, of DNA and although constructed from base pairs of the DNA type, they are tilted by about 10–15° from a perpendicular to the helix axis.[58]

Both electron microscopy[61] and low angle X-ray scattering from solution[62] indicate that RNA can form a rodlike structure in solution over short distances. The melting curves of absorbancy vs. temperature are broad for natural RNA's[63] indicating that melting is much less cooperative than in DNA. Also the absorbancy can be increased by reducing the salt concentration,[64, 65] unlike native DNA whose absorbancy remains quite constant.

That the DNA from phage ϕX-174 is single-stranded has been shown in many ways.[66] It was suggested by P^{32} suicide results.[67] The most direct demonstration was that the base composition does not obey the pairing rule for a Watson-Crick helix, in which A = T and G = C on a molar basis. The fact that the base composition does not follow the pairing rule means also that ϕX DNA is not an equal mixture of the two complementary strands, and presumably only one type of strand is present. Other indications of the single-stranded nature of ϕX DNA are that the absorbancy melting curve is broad and melting begins at low temperatures (cf. Fig. 5), the molar absorbancy at 20°C. is higher than that of a native DNA, and there is a significant rate of reaction with formaldehyde.[66]

C. BACTERIAL AND VIRAL CHROMOSOMES

1. "ONE CHROMOSOME, ONE NUCLEIC ACID MOLECULE"

As techniques have been developed for handling giant DNA molecules, the hypothesis has been greatly strengthened that viral and even bacterial chromosomes* are single molecules. This hypothesis was developed clearly by Levinthal[68] some years ago. The recognition that shearing forces developed in routine laboratory operations can break these giant molecules[68, 70] clarified earlier contradictory results. Thus, while early studies by P^{32} autoradiography suggested that the DNA from phage T4 contained one large piece of molecular weight 45×10^6 in addition to smaller pieces,[71] ultracentrifugal analyses[72, 73] seemed to show only small pieces. Later experiments with P^{32} autoradiography, which were designed to prevent shear breakage, showed that the entire DNA contents of the phage (about 130 million molecular weight) are present in a single molecule.[74, 75] The

---

* Since the chromosomes of plant and animal cells are highly complex structures, as seen by the electron microscope, Ris and Chandler[69] suggest that the term "chromosome" is inappropriate here and should be replaced by the term "genophore."

length of the T2 DNA molecule has also been measured directly by electron microscopy[5] and by tritium autoradiography[76] and these results indicate also that there is one DNA molecule per phage. Similar results have been obtained with other phage DNA's, for example ϕX-174,[66] T3,[77] and T7.[78] None of these results can exclude, of course, the possibility that some non-DNA material links different sections of the chromosome together.*

These conclusions have been anticipated for several years from genetic studies. All of the genetic markers of *E. coli* belong to a single linkage group.[80] Furthermore, this linkage group has physical continuity as shown by interrupted mating experiments: transfer of a chromosome from an Hfr to an F⁻ strain can be interrupted by shearing in a Waring Blendor. The number of genetic markers which enter a recipient cell is proportional to the time of mating before interruption (see Chapter 1 by Gross). Similarly, the genetic markers of phages such as λ and T4 have been shown to have single linkage groups.[81, 82]

2. CIRCULAR CHROMOSOMES

The question of whether bacterial and viral chromosomes are circular is presently being studied in several systems. The genetic map of *E. coli* can be represented by a circle.[80] On the other hand, Hfr strains of *E. coli* deliver their chromosomes to F⁻ cells in a mating experiment as if these chromosomes were linear. Very recently Cairns[83, 84] has been able to extract from *E. coli* chromosomes which in a few instances are intact and untangled, and to photograph them by tritium autoradiography (Fig. 6). His results suggest that both the Hfr and the F⁻ strains have chromosomes which are physically circular, and that circularity is maintained during replication. If this is true it is necessary, in order for the two daughter chromosomes to separate from each other after replication, that the continuity of the DNA double helix be interrupted by a "swivel" where free rotation can occur. The swivel could be simply a break in one DNA strand or some non-DNA material.

Preparations of the single-stranded DNA from ϕX-174 show two components in sedimentation velocity experiments.[66] Recent experiments[19, 85, 86] show that only the faster of these (which may be called native ϕX DNA) is active in transforming protoplasts. The native ϕX DNA is also resistant to attack by *E. coli* exonuclease I, an enzyme which readily attacks single-

* When controlled shear breakage is used as a tool for obtaining DNA fragments of defined length,[79] no weak points are found in T2 DNA. Calculations show that the shearing stress should be greatest in the middle of the molecule, and it is found that breakage does occur near the middle and that molecules below a critical size remain unbroken.

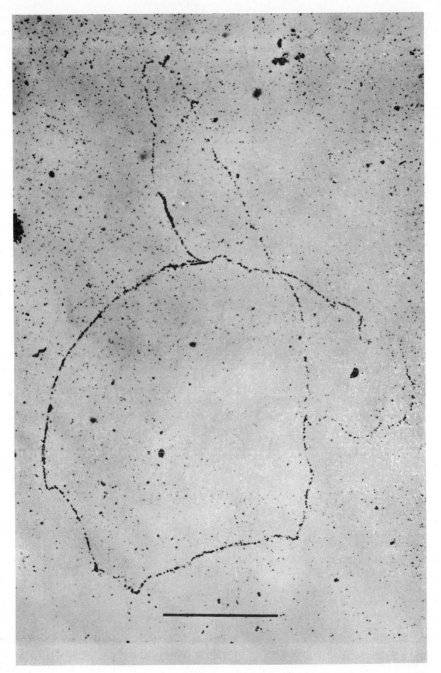

Fig. 6. Autoradiograph of the chromosome of *E. coli* K12 Hfr,[84] labeled with H[3]-thymidine for two generations. The scale shows 100 μ. One can see two circular structures (each 1100 μ in circumference) joined along a common segment.

stranded DNA but which requires a 3'-OH end group.[48] The first cleavage by an endonuclease (pancreatic deoxyribonuclease) reduces the sedimentation coefficient of the native DNA to that of the original slower moving component, and enables *E. coli* exonuclease I to act. Treatment with spleen diesterase indicates that native ϕX also lacks a free 5'-OH end group. These results could mean either that the molecule is circular or that the ends are blocked in some way. The fact that the first cleavage of native DNA by endonuclease gives a physically homogeneous product, as judged by sedimentation velocity experiments, argues for the ring structure: a linear molecule should be broken into two pieces of different sizes, if the attack is at random. The exonuclease I cannot hydrolyze the broken ring structure completely and seems to reach a block in the chain. Thus, native ϕX DNA behaves as if it were a circular molecule containing one unusual linkage.*

The chromosome of phage T4 is genetically circular.[87] Annealing experiments with pieces broken by shear[88] indicate that the base sequence is circularly permuted from one molecule to the next. This would be the result expected if a circular chromosome were broken at random either on extraction from the phage or before being packed into the phage. The existence of "terminal redundancy" heterozygotes in T4[87a] leads Streisinger *et al.* to suggest a model for circular permutation in which the physical structure is always linear.

Still a different case is presented by phage λ. Its genetic map is linear[81] and shear breakage of the extracted DNA breaks the genetic map roughly in half.[81, 89, 90] Thus the genetic map and the DNA are colinear. However the ends of λ DNA seem to be sticky. Hershey *et al.*[91] have found a folded form as well as dimers and trimers; Ris and Chandler[69] have found circular structures by electron microscopy, which can be produced at will[91a] using conditions established by Hershey *et al.*[91] There appears to be a change in the order of the phage genes when λ DNA is attached to the host chromosome in the lysogenic state.[91b,c]

These examples show that circularity is an important question in considering the structure and replication of bacterial and viral chromosomes, and that it is too soon to generalize.

---

* *Note added in proof:* The "replicative form" of ϕX DNA (see Section III,D,4), which has the properties of double-stranded DNA, has been purified and found to be circular by direct examination in the electron microscope [A. K. Kleinschmidt, A. Burton, and R. L. Sinsheimer, *Science* **142**, 961 (1963)]. Also, electron microscope pictures [W. Stoeckenius, *Proc. Natl. Acad. Sci. U.S.* **50**, 737 (1963)] of the DNA from polyoma virus (a small, animal virus) confirm the conclusion—based on physicochemical properties—that the DNA is double-stranded and circular [R. Dulbecco and M. Vogt, *Proc. Natl. Acad. Sci. U.S.* **50**, 236 (1963); R. Weil and J. Vinograd, *Proc. Natl. Acad. Sci. U.S.* **50**, 737 (1963)].

III. Replication of DNA

A. ENZYMIC SYNTHESIS OF DNA

1. COMPONENTS OF THE REACTION

The components needed for DNA synthesis *in vitro* are[92] (*1*) the DNA-synthesizing enzyme (DNA polymerase), (*2*) deoxynucleoside triphosphates of the four bases in DNA, or certain of their analogs, (*3*) Mg^{++}, and (*4*) a template DNA. The typical event in synthesis is the addition of a mononucleotide to the growing end of a DNA chain, which is illustrated

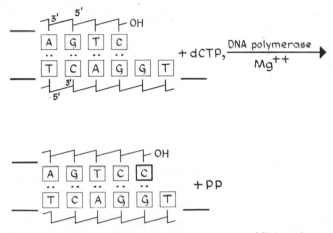

FIG. 7. The typical event in DNA synthesis *in vitro:* addition of a nucleotide at the 3'-OH end of a DNA strand, governed by base pairing of the added nucleotide to the complementary strand.

schematically in Fig. 7. The chain to which addition occurs is called the primer strand and the complementary one is called the template strand.[93] The presence of a free 3'-OH group, either at the end of the template strand or on the primer strand, greatly stimulates the reaction[93] but it is not yet known whether it represents an absolute requirement. Reversal of the synthetic reaction by pyrophosphorolysis can be demonstrated[92, 94] but its rate is negligible under the usual synthetic conditions.

Initial efforts to demonstrate DNA synthesis *in vitro* were hindered by the small amounts of DNA polymerase in the cell and by the action of deoxyribonucleases in cell extracts in breaking down DNA, including any DNA newly synthesized. These same two problems have made the purification of DNA polymerase a time-consuming project, requiring both large quantities of cells and patience. However the DNA polymerase from *E. coli* has now been purified to a point approaching final purity.[94,95] The degree of purification, starting from the initial extract, is about 2000-fold and the molecular weight of the *E. coli* polymerase is about 100,000.[94] If the activity per molecule of DNA polymerase is the same in the crude extract as in the purified product (when assayed with the dAT copolymer as template) then there are about 300 molecules of DNA polymerase per cell, assuming[95a] that the weight of protein per cell times Avogadro's number is 6×10^{10}. Other sources from which the enzyme has been highly purified include calf thymus,[96-98] extracts of T2-infected *E. coli*[99] and *B. subtilis*,[100] and these enzymes show the same basic requirements for catalyzing DNA synthesis.

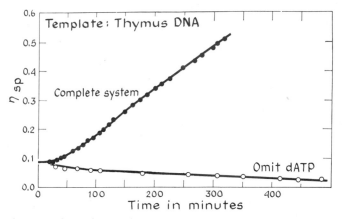

FIG. 8. An example of the requirement for all four triphosphates in DNA synthesis.[102] In the complete system, with calf thymus DNA as template, synthesis begins promptly and since the product has a high viscosity the reaction can be followed viscometrically. When dATP is omitted no synthesis occurs within the time of this experiment.

2. EVIDENCE THAT THE TEMPLATE IS COPIED

Two striking features of the enzymic reaction are the requirements for a template DNA and for the triphosphates of all four deoxynucleosides. The latter is shown in Fig. 8. Both requirements suggest that the template DNA is being copied enzymically. Stronger evidence comes from the observation that the newly synthesized DNA has the same base composition as the template when DNA's of widely differing AT contents are used as templates.[101, 102] Furthermore, the base composition of the product does not change when the relative concentrations of the four triphosphates are varied wide'y. A more stringent test of accurate copying is the distribution of dinucleotides or "nearest neighbors" (ApC, GpA, etc.) along the DNA chains. The same nearest neighbor frequencies were found using a samp!e of calf thymus DNA as with the use of an enzymically synthesized product present after 20-fold replication of this DNA.[103] When ϕX DNA and double-stranded ϕX DNA (made enzymically) were used as templates, the nearest neighbor frequencies obeyed the rules predicted from the base ratios for ϕX DNA (in which A $\neq$ T, G $\neq$ C) and for a double-stranded DNA (A = T, G = C), respectively.[104] Thus it seems definite that the enzymic synthesis of DNA *in vitro* is a reaction in which the base sequence of the template DNA is copied.

Less is known about the accuracy of copying at the macromolecular level. One would like to have the answers to the following questions. (*1*) Does the DNA polymerase produce *in vitro* a new complementary strand of exactly the same length as the template strand? (*2*) Is the newly synthesized strand an accurate copy of the template strand along its entire length? These are closely related to a third, more basic question. (*3*) Can the DNA polymerase initiate new chains, or must the *in vitro* reaction always proceed by addition to a 3'-OH group on the primer strand? Clearly, unless new chains can be started one cannot expect accurate copying of the length of a template strand. At present definite answers to these questions cannot be given; however, evidence which bears on them will be considered later in the chapter.

3. *De Novo* SYNTHESIS OF DNA POLYMERS

When the DNA polymerase from *E. coli* is incubated without a template DNA but in the presence of the triphosphates of A and T, or of G and C, there is no chemically measurable synthesis for several hours and then new polymers are made whose synthesis is rapid once it begins. The dAT copolymer[105] contains A and T in strictly alternating sequence while the dGdC homopolymer pair[106] contains complementary chains of G and of C. Synthesis begins promptly when the dAT copolymer or its analogs are added as template DNA's with the *E. coli* polymerase.

Little is known about the *de novo* synthesis of these polymers. Efforts to detect low-molecular-weight intermediates in the lag period of dAT synthesis were not successful.[107] Before any conversion of labeled triphosphates to an acid-insoluble form could be found, trace amounts of *macromolecular* dAT were detected, early in the lag period, by using aliquots from the reaction mixture to reduce the lag period in a second *de novo* synthesis. Evidence that this "lag-reducing activity" was of macromolecular size came from the rate at which the activity sedimented in a preparative ultracentrifuge. Recently it has been found that the octanucleotide p(AT)$_4$, synthesized chemically, will reduce the lag period of a *de novo* synthesis.[108]

It would be interesting to know why the synthetic polymer containing the AT base pair is an alternating copolymer while the GC base pair is built into a pair of homopolymer strands. A naturally occurring DNA containing chiefly alternating AT sequences has been found by Sueoka[109] (cf. Swartz et al.[104]) in crab testes.

The synthetic DNA polymers provide a strenuous test of the copying accuracy of DNA polymerase, since dAT and dGdC each contain only a single type of base pair. For example, if any G is incorporated during the synthesis of dAT one could detect it with great sensitivity by using radioactive dGTP and unlabeled dATP and dTTP. In such an experiment no incorporation of P^{32}-labeled dGTP into dAT was found by Trautner et al.[110]; the sensitivity of detection could be extended to 1 part in 500,000. However when dA$\overline{BU}$, an analog of dAT containing 5-bromouracil in place of T, was used as a template for further dA$\overline{BU}$ synthesis, an incorporation of G was detected at a level of one residue of G for every few thousand of A and BU. This fits the hypothesis that the mutagenic action of BU results from an occasional pairing of G with the enol tautomer of BU.[17, 111] However, analysis of the dinucleotide frequencies showed a considerable fraction of the G incorporated next to G. On the hypothesis just given, all the G should have been next to BU. Also, the incorporation of G found when other triphosphates were omitted suggests some end addition.

4. Base Pairing as the Mechanism of Copying

On the basis of their structure for DNA Watson and Crick[1, 17] suggested that copying of a template DNA could proceed by pairing A with T and G with C (Fig. 4). Studies with the purified DNA polymerase from E. coli confirm this and also indicate that the rate of DNA synthesis is negligible unless this base pairing can take place. (Thus, there is no initial synthesis in the absence of a template DNA nor incorporation of G or C when dAT is used as the template.) The first point to be made is that the copying mechanism will function without preexisting base pairs in the template since single-stranded DNA's will serve as templates. This is true not only of the natural DNA from phage ϕX-174 but also of the synthetic DNA homopolymers such as dC.[106] Thus, any mechanism is unlikely which uses the entire AT or GC base pair for copying, because then one would need a separate copying mechanism when single-stranded DNA's are used as templates.

Second, certain analogs of the natural substrates can be used in the enzymic synthesis.[112] * These include the deoxyribonucleoside triphosphates

* When triphosphates containing base analogs are tested with the DNA polymerases from B. subtilis or T2-infected E. coli, the same pattern of results is found as with the E. coli DNA polymerase,[93] suggesting that it is a general pattern for DNA synthesis.

of uracil, 5-bromouracil, 5-bromocytosine, and hypoxanthine. In each case the analog replaces only one of the natural bases, the one predicted from considerations of forming a hydrogen-bonded base pair with the same dimensions as the AT and GC pairs, and with equivalent positions for the glycosidic bonds. With one exception the substituted group appears on the outside of the helix. The exception is the replacement of G by hypoxanthine, which is a substitution of hydrogen for the 2-amino group of G and leaves intact the dimensions and two of the three hydrogen bonds of the GC base pair.

A third piece of evidence comes from a study of the *limited reaction*[113] which occurs when a template DNA is incubated with DNA polymerase in the absence of one of the triphosphates. It is found that one or a few nucleotides are added covalently to the 3'-OH end of each primer strand. When the limited reaction is studied using dAT as the template, the addition only of A or T can be detected, not of G or C.[105] This indicates that the limited reaction, like the usual synthetic reaction, proceeds only by specific base pairing.

Base pairing of the template with the newly synthesized DNA can be demonstrated in another way, from melting curves of hybrid DNA's containing complementary strands of dAT and dABŪ. Hybrid molecules can be made from a solution containing dAT and dABŪ by an annealing procedure.[114] In low salt the AT and ABŪ base pairs have markedly different thermal stabilities, so that one can follow the melting of dAT:dABŪ hybrid molecules in the presence of dAT:dAT and dABŪ:dABŪ, since the hybrid molecules melt in an intermediate temperature zone (Fig. 9b). Then, when dAT is used as a template for the enzymic synthesis of dABŪ or vice versa, it is found that the first product of synthesis melts in the hybrid melting zone (Fig. 9a).[115]

The energy of hydrogen bonding between bases is only a few kilocalories per mole of base pairs.[30, 116] What then accounts for the extraordinary accuracy of the DNA polymerase in placing A opposite T and G opposite C? One possibility is that steric factors are decisive: that a nucleoside triphosphate is accepted if it can fit into an active site which includes both the enzyme and the template DNA, so that the resulting base pair has the correct dimensions and positions for the glycosidic bonds. It is interesting that the DNA polymerase from *E. coli* will incorporate ribonucleoside triphosphates into a polymer in the presence of Mn^{++}.[117] Lee-Huang and Cavalieri[118] have reported that the RNA homopolymer pair rArU, which forms a double helix similar to the DNA helix[32] but whose diameter may be somewhat greater,[119] will serve as a template for DNA synthesis using the DNA polymerase from *E. coli*, and resulting in the synthesis of the DNA homopolymer pair dAdT.

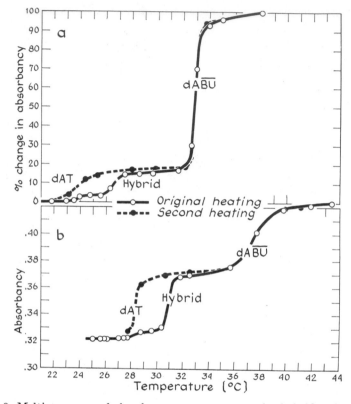

FIG. 9. Melting curves of absorbance vs. temperature for hybrid molecules containing dAT and dAB̄U, showing that melting curves can be used to demonstrate dAT:dAB̄U base pairs and that the physically and enzymically formed hybrid molecules melt alike. In the bottom figure the hybrid molecules were made physically by an annealing procedure.[114] In the top figure they were made enzymically by using dAB̄U as a template for dAT synthesis.[115] In both cases most of the dAT present melts in a hybrid melting zone 3°C. above the T_m for dAT. The dAB̄U which is released on melting the hybrid forms a dAB̄U:dAB̄U helix and then melts later when the dAB̄U melting zone is reached. (The second melting curves show that the dAT: dAB̄U base pairs do not re-form after melting and cooling in low salt. The T_m's differ in the two figures because of small differences in the Na⁺ concentration, but the relative T_m's for the three species are the same in both experiments.)

B. SEMICONSERVATIVE REPLICATION

In addition to suggesting base pairing as the mechanism for copying DNA, the Watson-Crick model[4] focused attention on the integrity of the DNA molecule. The question is whether the original helix remains intact after copying (conservative replication) or whether the strands separate during replication, each strand remaining intact (semiconservative replication), or whether the strands themselves are fragmented and rejoined during replication (dispersive replication). These terms were used by Delbrück and Stent,[44] who discuss some of their implications. Actually, examples of all three modes of copying DNA now are known: in the DNA-directed synthesis of RNA the DNA helix remains intact after copying (see Section III,E), while the replication of DNA itself appears to be semiconservative but often accompanied by fragmentation and rejoining of chains, especially in the case of the T-even phages.

1. THE MESELSON-STAHL EXPERIMENT

Meselson and Stahl[39] realized that if they could label the newly synthesized DNA chains with a lighter isotope, and then separate the DNA species of different densities, they could determine whether the parental DNA remains intact after replication. The method of centrifugation to equilibrium in a density gradient,[72] which was developed for this purpose, has since become one of the major tools of the nucleic acid chemist. In their experiment $E.$ $coli$ B was first grown on a synthetic medium containing $N^{15}H_4Cl$. After changing the medium to one containing N^{14} and allowing growth for various times, they lysed the cells with sodium dodecyl sulfate and examined the DNA in a CsCl density gradient (Fig. 10). For molecules of high molecular weight the technique is sufficiently sensitive to resolve components differing in density by less than 0.014 g./ml., which is the difference between N^{14}- and N^{15}-labeled $E.$ $coli$ DNA.

After one generation all the DNA had a hybrid density. After two generations half the DNA was hybrid, half light (Fig. 10). The results were exactly those predicted for semiconservative replication: Meselson and Stahl had shown that the DNA contained two equal subunits which separate on replication, and that each subunit remained intact through many generations. Further, they showed that the two subunits could be separated by heating at 100°C. At that time this was a surprising result: it was then widely believed that the two strands of a DNA helix are not disengaged after melting because they remain wound around each other. This belief was based on measurements by light scattering of the molecular weight before and after heating.[38] Since then, it has been found that there are serious technical problems in measuring the molecular weights of large DNA's, especially by light scattering.[51, 120, 121]

2. STRUCTURE OF THE HYBRID DNA

The Meselson-Stahl experiment gave results in complete agreement with the semiconservative replication of DNA, but their results could also fit a special type of conservative model for replication. Measurements of molecular weight and also of the kinetics of enzymic breakdown of DNA led

Cavalieri *et al.*[122] to suggest such a model. In their view each subunit of the Meselson-Stahl experiment is itself a double helix, the two double helices being held together by unspecified bonds which are broken when the DNA is copied at the next replication (for a summary of this and later work, see

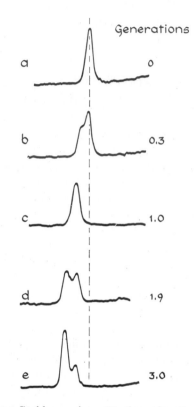

FIG. 10. The Meselson-Stahl experiment[39]: these density gradient patterns show the relative amounts of heavy, hybrid, and light DNA at various generation times after transferring *E. coli* grown in an N^{15} medium to an N^{14} medium. The existence of a hybrid DNA, its persistence during many generations, and the relative amounts of the three species at different generation times show that *E. coli* DNA contains two equal subunits which separate on replication, each subunit remaining intact.

Cavalieri and Rosenberg[123]). Several studies have been made to clarify this point, most of them concerned with the structure of the hybrid DNA and the nature of the bonds linking the subunits. If the two subunits of the hybrid DNA are the two strands of a DNA helix, then the Meselson-Stahl experiment establishes the semiconservative replication of DNA.

Rolfe[124] used sonic breakage to show that the subunits are not linked end to end. This treatment is believed to break across both strands of a DNA helix, and should yield some heavy and also some light DNA if the hybrid DNA is an end-to-end dimer. Schildkraut et al.[52] found that the two subunits separate just at the top of the thermal melting curve of absorbance vs. temperature. The same conclusion was reached by Frei-felder and Davison,[125] who fixed the degree of melting by reaction with formaldehyde and then studied the separation of subunits as a function of the degree of melting. Thus the conditions needed for separation of the hybrid subunits coincide with complete melting of the DNA helix, and with breaking the hydrogen bonds between base pairs. Moreover, the two subunits cannot melt independently of each other.[126] This was shown with hybrid DNA from E. coli labeled with BU in one subunit. DNA completely labeled with BU melts at a lower pH than unlabeled DNA (cf. Fig. 11a). Both subunits of the hybrid DNA were found to melt together, at an inter-mediate pH (Fig. 11b).

Also, the recombination experiments of Marmur, Doty and their co-workers (Section II,B) are most simply interpreted by assuming that the subunits are the individual strands. After heating the DNA at a tempera-ture where the subunits are separated, it is found that annealing conditions which give specific recombination of the subunits[52] also produce renatured DNA in which the original helical structure has been largely restored.[53]

Different methods of measuring the number of strands in DNA from actively dividing organisms have given conflicting results. Although electron microscope studies led Hall and Cavalieri[127] to conclude that much of the DNA is four-stranded, measurements of the mass per unit length by low-angle X-ray scattering[128] gave the value for a two-stranded helix on DNA samples prepared from resting and from actively dividing cells, including one sample prepared by Cavalieri.

Cairns' studies of DNA replication in E. coli[83, 84] based on autoradiogra-phy with tritium labeling, add to the evidence that replication is semi-conservative (see Section III,C). Replication of a more complex type of chromosome, that of the bean plant, was found to be semiconservative by Taylor et al.,[129] who used autoradiography. Sueoka[130] has shown that DNA replication in the alga Chlamydomonas follows the pattern seen in the Meselson-Stahl experiment.

3. In Vitro SYNTHESIS

It is of considerable interest to know whether DNA synthesis in vitro, using the purified DNA polymerase, will show semiconservative replica-tion. When the newly synthesized DNA is labeled in such a way that it

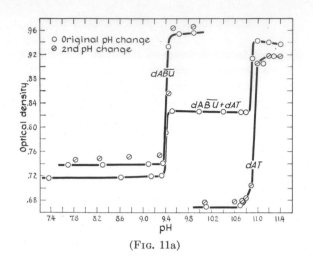

(FIG. 11a)

pH Melting of Hybrid DNA

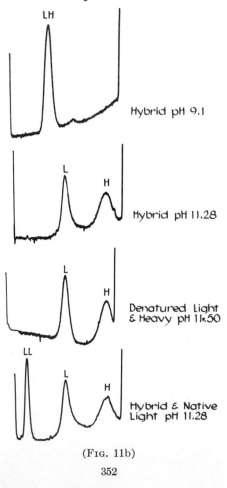

(FIG. 11b)

352

can be distinguished from the template, will the same stages of replication be found as in the Meselson-Stahl experiment? Is a stable hybrid formed and, after a second round of replication, does a new species appear, free from the original template and containing only newly synthesized DNA? The latter question bears on the problem, mentioned in Section III,A,2, of whether the DNA polymerase can initiate new chains. It also depends on whether unwinding of the parental helix will take place in an orderly fashion in the *in vitro* system, so that daughter molecules can separate when replication is complete. Thus far different systems have given different results. Before mentioning these, it might be well to review the evidence that the products of enzymic synthesis have high molecular weights and also physical properties like those of natural DNA's. The newly synthesized DNA's have high viscosities (cf. Fig. 8) and sedimentation coefficients[102, 131] and show sharp melting curves of absorbance vs. temperature (cf. Fig. 14). In the case of one enzymically synthesized DNA, the dAT copolymer, it has been shown that the X-ray pattern given by the B form (lithium salt) is like the ones given by natural DNA's, and shows the same helix dimensions.[132]

When samples are taken at different stages in the *de novo* synthesis of dAT, the size of the copolymer (judged by sedimentation coefficient and viscosity) is found to be the same at all times, although the size varies from one *de novo* synthesis to the next.[105] Since the kinetics of *de novo* synthesis[107] indicate that dAT is made by a template-copying process even before observable amounts of the polymer are made, this implies that the DNA polymerase does reproduce the length of the dAT template. When dAB̄Ū is used as a template for the synthesis of dAT, density gradient analyses show a broad hybrid band early in the synthesis (broad because it contains molecules with different ratios of dAT to dAB̄Ū) and then at later stages a sharp dAT band appears.[115] Melting curves show that the material in the hybrid band does indeed contain hybrid base pairs, i.e., complementary strands of dAT and dAB̄Ū. (The same type of result is obtained when dAT is the template and dAB̄Ū newly synthesized.) Since the final product, dAT, is free from the template, dAB̄Ū, it appears that

---

Fig. 11. pH melting curves for DNA containing 5-bromouracil. (a): Melting curves for the dAT and dAB̄Ū copolymers[184] (and for a mixture of the two copolymers) show that incorporation of BU into a DNA lowers the pH at which it melts. (b): This effect is used to show that the two subunits of *E. coli* hybrid DNA do not melt independently.[126] The bottom density gradient pattern shows a mixture of unlabeled *E. coli* DNA and a BU-containing hybrid DNA at pH 11.28. The unlabeled DNA has not begun to melt since it still has the buoyant density of native DNA; the density increases by 0.06 g./ml. on melting. On the other hand, the subunits of the hybrid DNA have separated at this pH and both are found to be completely melted, showing that the pH at which a subunit melts depends on the kind of DNA in the other subunit.

the DNA polymerase can initiate new chains in this system.* Furthermore, since one strand of the newly synthesized dAT must have come from a dA$\overline{\text{BU}}$:dAT hybrid molecule, according to the semiconservative model, synthesis evidently causes unwinding of the strands of the parental DNA, allowing the two daughter molecules to separate when replication is complete.

When the single DNA homopolymers dI and dC are used separately as templates for synthesis of the complementary DNA, the resulting homopolymer pair can be dissociated into separate bands of dI and dC[133] by density gradient centrifugation at alkaline pH. This indicates that the complementary strands are not linked by phosphodiester bonds and that the DNA polymerase can initiate new chains. Using a natural DNA as template (heat-denatured *B. subtilis* DNA) for the *E. coli* polymerase, Richardson *et al.*[93] found that part of the 1:1 hybrid formed after one round of replication did not dissociate and part did, upon density gradient sedimentation at alkaline pH. This indicates that at least some of the newly synthesized DNA was not linked to primer strands by phosphodiester bonds.† However, Bollum[98] has found that synthesis stops after one round and the newly synthesized DNA does not dissociate from the template after melting when calf thymus polymerase is used to replicate a denatured DNA template.

When the *E. coli* polymerase is used to replicate native DNA templates, a surprising result is found: the newly synthesized DNA melts reversibly. This is discussed in more detail in Section III,D,3. No band with the buoyant density of newly synthesized DNA is found, even after extensive replication, but only a broad hybrid band.[93, 95] These results, like those of Bollum[98] with calf thymus polymerase, indicate that DNA synthesis *in vitro* can follow a complicated course which is not yet understood.

Thus it is too soon to draw firm conclusions about the mechanism of DNA synthesis viewed at the macromolecular level. On the whole, studies with model polymers fit a simple picture of DNA replication, perhaps because the opportunities for the DNA polymerase to misbehave are more

* One might argue that the product has been freed from the primer by degradation of the primer, since the phosphocellulose fraction of DNA polymerase used in this work[115] is known to contain two exonucleases, one being the DNA phosphatase-exonuclease (see Section III,D,1). However, both exonucleases act at the 3'-OH end of a DNA chain and this is the growing end of a chain synthesized by DNA polymerase. The phosphocellulose fraction of *E. coli* DNA polymerase is essentially free from endonuclease.[94]

† In certain cases, failure to dissociate two strands after melting is not proof that they are covalently linked. Physically formed hybrid molecules of dAT and dA$\overline{\text{BU}}$, made by melting and slow cooling, dissociate slowly after thermal melting[114] and only partial dissociation is achieved by density gradient centrifugation at alkaline pH.[134]

limited. In the dAT-dA$\overline{\text{BU}}$ system a hybrid is formed first and then a species containing only newly synthesized DNA, as in the Meselson-Stahl experiment with *E. coli*. In the DNA with a hybrid buoyant density, the newly synthesized DNA is found to be hydrogen-bonded to the template. The DNA homopolymer pairs such as dGdC separate completely into chains of dG and dC on melting at alkaline pH, indicating that they are not linked by phosphodiester bonds. With natural DNA's as templates, the situation is more complex and different results have been obtained with DNA polymerases prepared from different sources, with native and denatured DNA templates, and even with polymerase preparations from the same source, but purified to different extents (cf. Section III,D,3). The phenomenon of reversible melting of the DNA synthesized from a native DNA template (Section III,D,1) suggests that this product differs in a fundamental manner from natural DNA's.

4. REPLICATION OF PHAGE DNA

In a typical cycle of infection, growth and lysis of the bacterial host, a single invading bacteriophage can produce 100 or more progeny and thus the parental phage DNA may undergo seven generations of replication ($2^7 = 128$). The first question is, of course, whether the parental DNA appears in the progeny at all. For T2 and T4 bacteriophages this has been answered by P^{32} transfer experiments[135, 136] which clearly show the presence of parental DNA in the offspring phage. The same is true of coliphage λ.[137]

Although infection with phage labeled with heavy isotopes yields some offspring with the buoyant density predicted for semiconservative replication of the DNA (phage T7, Meselson[138]; phage λ, Meselson and Weigle[137]), considerable dispersion of the parental DNA often occurs as well. In the case of the T-even phages dispersion of the parental DNA is so drastic that no semiconservative phages are found and the progeny containing parental DNA (labeled both with P^{32} and heavy isotopes) have buoyant densities only slightly greater than unlabeled phage. After extraction of the DNA and fragmentation by sonication[139, 140] DNA of hybrid density is found indicating that replication is semiconservative over short regions. A new DNA polymerase is produced after T2 infection[99] but it is not yet known whether the dispersive replication of T2 phages can be accounted for by the properties of this new polymerase.* When *E. coli* is mixedly infected with two strains of phage λ, carrying both genetic and density (isotopic or mutant) markers, genetic recombinants are found which contain

---

* *Note added in proof:* Experiments based on inhibition of protein synthesis by chloramphenicol lead Kozinski *et al.* to suggest that a new enzyme is responsible for the extensive recombination [A. W. Kozinski, P. B. Kozinski, and P. Shannon, *Proc. Natl. Acad. Sci. U.S.* **50,** 746 (1963)].

some parental DNA and have intermediate densities.[137, 141] It is not yet clear what the relation is between recombination and DNA replication.

C. SEQUENTIAL SYNTHESIS

By an elegant use of tritium autoradiography, Cairns[83, 84] has been able to observe directly the replication of DNA in *E. coli*. After providing a pulse of tritium-labeled thymidine to a thymine-requiring strain and ending the pulse by dilution with cold thymidine, growth is stopped with cyanide, the cells are lysed by 1% sodium dodecyl sulfate under controlled conditions, and the DNA is collected on a Millipore filter. The length of the chromosome (completely labeled by a 1-hour exposure to H^3-thymidine) is found to be 700–1100 μ. Several autoradiograms suggest that the chromosome is circular (cf. Fig. 6), although most of the ones examined were not circular and presumably were broken on extraction.

After a 3-minute pulse of label has been given two pieces of labeled DNA are found, each 60–80 μ long, and a 6-minute pulse produces labeled pieces twice this length. If growth is stopped immediately the two labeled pieces are found close to each other. If instead growth is allowed to continue in the presence of unlabeled thymidine, the two labeled pieces are found to be separated from each other. The density of the tritium label after a short pulse is half that of completely labeled λ or T2 DNA or of the fully labeled *E. coli* chromosome, after a 1-hour exposure to H^3-thymidine.

These experiments permit the important conclusion that synthesis is linear, proceeding continuously along the chromosome.* The rate of synthesis is 20–30 μ per minute. (1 μ = molecular weight 2×10^6 for a Watson-Crick helix.) Thus, chain propagation takes place at a rate of 3000 nucleotide units added per second. Sequential synthesis explains the absence of DNA bands of intermediate density, other than hybrid, in the Meselson-Stahl[39] experiment. The DNA molecules which they studied had molecular weights of the order of 10^7 while the entire *E. coli* chromosome is about 2×10^9 so that only two chromosomal fragments out of 200 would be expected to have light joined to heavy DNA and hence have a density other than heavy, hybrid, or light.[84] Also, the amount of tritium found per unit length of newly synthesized DNA adds to the evidence that DNA replication is semiconservative in *E. coli*. Finally, Cairns' experiments suggest that replication follows a "fork" mechanism in which both strands of the parental chromosome are used simultaneously as templates for the

---

* *Note added in proof:* The number of growing points per chromosome has recently been found to be one or perhaps two [F. Bonhoeffer and A. Gierer, *J. Mol. Biol.* **7**, 534 (1963)] by a technique based on pulse labeling, followed by breaking the chromosome into pieces of defined size and measuring the buoyant densities of the labeled pieces.

synthesis of new DNA, even though the phosphate-sugar backbone of each chain has opposite polarity in the two strands. The two daughter helices appear to be joined also at the other end of the fork, thus maintaining circularity during replication (cf. Fig. 6).

This evidence for a fork mechanism of replication, taken together with the opposite polarity of the DNA strands,[103] suggests that DNA synthesis might proceed in an additional way not yet demonstrated enzymically (see Fig. 12). Present results show clearly that *in vitro* DNA synthesis proceeds by reaction of a 3′-OH end group in a DNA chain with the 5′-PPP group of a deoxyribonucleoside triphosphate. However, these results do not rule out the possibility that the same DNA polymerase may catalyze the reverse reaction of a 3′-OH group of a deoxyribonucleoside triphosphate with

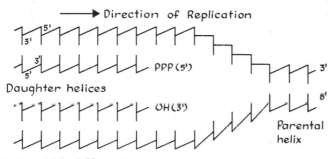

Fɪɢ. 12. A model for DNA replication in *E. coli* which fits the results of Cairns.[83, 8] (It should be noted that the existence of 5′-PPP ends on DNA chains has not yet been demonstrated.)

the 5′-PPP end of a DNA chain, when such ends are present. Studies of the limited reaction by Adler *et al.*[113] gave two types of evidence that the newly added mononucleotides were present at 3′-OH ends of DNA chains. (In these studies the template DNA—calf thymus DNA—probably did not contain significant amounts of 5′-PPP ended chains, since most of the ends were probably generated by chain breakage.) First, it was shown that spleen diesterase releases the added monomer chiefly as the *nucleoside*. This enzyme splits phosphodiester bonds to yield 3′-P mononucleotides, but leaves a nucleoside at 3′-OH end of a chain. Second, venom diesterase, which is believed to attack only the 3′-OH end of a chain,[113] liberated more than 90 % of the added monomer as 5′-P mononucleotides when less than 3 % of the total nucleotides had been released. If DNA synthesis *in vivo* proceeds by a fork mechanism as in Fig. 12, it is not unlikely that two enzymes (or two active sites on the same enzyme) are required to carry out the two types of addition, one to 3′-OH ended chains and the other to 5′-PPP ended chains.

Studies based on genetic markers add to the evidence that DNA synthesis is sequential and, moreover, may have a unique starting point on the chromosome and direction of replication. Using *E. coli* cells synchronized by a filtration technique, Nagata[142] finds that the λ prophage is replicated at a particular time after cell doubling in two Hfr strains, but not in an F⁻ strain. The same type of result is obtained when these strains are made doubly lysogenic with phages λ and 424. Yoshikawa and Sueoka[143] noted that if DNA is synthesized by a fork mechanism, and if there is a single direction of synthesis and a unique starting point, then a genetic marker which has just been replicated should be found twice as often (i.e., should appear in both daughter chromosomes) as one not yet replicated. Accordingly, they extracted the DNA from *B. subtilis* in exponential and stationary phases, and compared the relative concentrations of several genetic markers, as measured by transformation. These were found to be different in exponentially growing and resting cells, and lend support to the model of sequential replication.

Sequential DNA replication and the question of what determines the unique starting point are topics closely related to the subject of control of DNA synthesis,[144, 145] and will not be reviewed here.

D. Current Problems

1. Auxiliary Enzymes

During purification of the DNA polymerase from *E. coli*, two additional enzymic activities persist through many purification steps. One of these, a DNA phosphatase,[95] was found only when, after chromatography of the DNA polymerase on phosphocellulose had shown a single peak, rechromatography on hydroxylapatite gave resolution of a minor component, the DNA phosphatase-exonuclease. This new enzyme has been purified extensively from *E. coli* extracts and identified as a phosphatase, highly specific for a phosphate residue esterified to the 3′-OH terminus of a DNA chain. Unlike *E. coli* alkaline phosphatase, the DNA phosphatase requires a high-molecular-weight substrate. It has been useful in demonstrating that 3′-P end groups are powerful inhibitors of the DNA polymerases from *E. coli*, *B. subtilis*, and T2-infected *E. coli*.[93-95] This last point is illustrated in Fig. 13. When *E. coli* endonuclease is used to produce new 3′-OH and 5′-P end groups in the template DNA, the rate of DNA synthesis with *E. coli* polymerase is markedly increased. However, when 3′-P ends are produced, by use of spleen or micrococcal endonuclease, the rate of DNA synthesis is drastically decreased. Treatment of the altered DNA with DNA phosphatase removes the inhibition created by 3′-P groups and shows the increase in rate of DNA synthesis expected for production of 3′-OH groups. When template DNA's isolated from different sources are pretreated with DNA phosphatase, there is a 2- to 10-fold increase in the rate of DNA synthesis with the *E. coli* DNA polymerase.

These facts suggest a function for the DNA phosphatase *in vivo*, namely, to relieve inhibition of DNA synthesis produced by 3'-P groups. Although 3'-P termini may arise through physical breakage of the phosphodiester

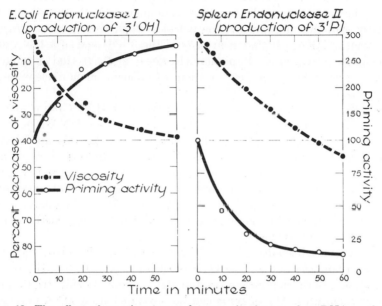

FIG. 13. The effect of creating new end groups in the template DNA on the rate of DNA synthesis *in vitro*.[95] *B. subtilis* DNA was incubated with either *E. coli* endo-nuclease, producing 3'-OH ends in the DNA chains, or with spleen endonuclease, producing 3'-P ends. Endonuclease action was followed by the decrease in relative viscosity of the DNA solution. Priming activity (the rate at which a given DNA template supports DNA synthesis, under fixed conditions) is expressed relative to untreated *B. subtilis* DNA.

bonds, at present no enzymic reaction is known which will produce these end groups in *E. coli*.

The DNA phosphatase also acts as an exonuclease, initiating its stepwise hydrolysis at a 3'-OH terminus and removing 5'-P mononucleotides, with a marked preference for double-stranded DNA.[95] Using the enzyme in this way it has been possible to remove part of a DNA chain starting from its 3'-OH end, presumably leaving intact the corresponding region of the complementary chain with its 5'-P end, and then to show that the DNA polymerase will again continue the DNA chain from the 3'-OH end, presumably restoring the missing segment.

The other enzymic activity which accompanies the *E. coli* polymerase during purification has not yet been dissociated from it. This is an exonuclease activity. Purification for this activity (exonuclease II[146]) yields essentially the same ratio of polymerase to exonuclease as does purification for the polymerase activity. The pH optima for the two activities are quite different. Thus the synthetic reaction can occur at a pH where there is only slight exonuclease action.[94] Some properties of the purified enzyme are (1) that it is essentially free from endonuclease activity, as judged by the very slow loss in transforming activity when it is used to hydrolyze transforming DNA, (2) that it attacks at the 3'-OH end of a DNA chain, successively liberating 5'-P mononucleotides; and (3) that it quantitatively degrades DNA chains to their component mononucleotides. Its function *in vivo* is obscure.

The DNA methylating enzymes recently described by Gold *et al.*[16] may play an important role in the function and replication of DNA. The demonstration that these enzymes are highly specific make this an intriguing hypothesis. Methylating enzymes from a given source do not, with one exception, significantly methylate the DNA from this same source. Different DNA's from other sources are methylated to different extents; the degree of methylation is small—of the order of 0.05 % of the nucleotides are methylated. Cytosine and adenine are methylated to give 5-methylcytosine and 6-methylaminopurine.

An enzyme has been described[147-149] which catalyzes the incorporation of a terminal ribonucleotide or deoxyribonucleotide at the 3'-OH end of a DNA chain. Both ribonucleoside and deoxyribonucleoside triphosphates serve as substrates. The enzyme can be separated from DNA polymerase and is inhibited rather than stimulated by the addition of the other three triphosphates. Its function *in vivo* is not yet known.

The inactivation of transforming DNA by ultraviolet light can be reversed in part by visible light and an enzyme partially purified from *E. coli* and from bakers yeast.[150-152]

2. Secondary Structure of the Template

Different preparations of DNA polymerase show different requirements for secondary structure in the template DNA. Despite the importance of the problem, few facts of general significance have emerged and the topic will be reviewed only briefly here. The first point to be made is that what seems to be an effect of secondary structure may turn out to be an effect of 3'-P or 3'-OH groups. Thus, the preliminary observation[153] that *E. coli* DNA is relatively inactive as a template for *E. coli* polymerase unless heated or pretreated with an endonuclease probably can be explained in this way. At any rate pretreatment with DNA phosphatase increases 2- to 10-fold the effectiveness of *E. coli* DNA as a template,[95] and now the native DNA is as good or better than heat-denatured DNA as a template for *E. coli* polymerase.[93] On the other hand, both calf thymus polymerase[154] and T2 polymerase[99] have been reported to require single-stranded or denatured DNA's as templates.

It seems clear that in *E. coli* the entire chromosome is not first separated into single DNA strands which are then replicated. The single strands would have the buoyant density of denatured rather than native DNA and the two are easily separated by centrifugation in a density gradient. If a large amount of the DNA in *E. coli* were single-stranded, this would have been observed in the experiments of Meselson and Stahl,[39] who examined whole cell lysates. It is possible that a short region of the chromosome just ahead of the point of replication is denatured before replication. This is discussed by Rolfe[155] who has found a minor band in the density gradient pattern for *E. coli* DNA which has certain properties of single-stranded DNA. He postulates that this is the actively replicating region of the chromosome. The mechanism which would convert the DNA to single strands in this region is not known. Since the double helix is likely to be the thermodynamically stable form,* more than an "unzipperase" is required. Combination of the DNA with a protein which has affinity for the purine or pyrimidine bases is one possibility. Felsenfeld *et al.*[155a] have made the interesting observation that when pancreatic ribonuclease combines with DNA, the DNA becomes denatured.

3. SYNTHESIS OF TRANSFORMING ACTIVITY

Using the *E. coli* polymerase and native transforming DNA from *B. subtilis*, Richardson *et al.*[95] failed to find transforming activity in the newly synthesized DNA which could not be ascribed to contamination with the original template DNA. Litman and Szybalski,[156] who used a less purified enzyme preparation† and denatured the template by heat, did find such activity. At the moment it is not clear which of these factors explains why the two groups found different results. In considering the negative results of Richardson *et al.*, the following points should be kept

---

* *In vitro*, DNA synthesis requires a Mg^{++} concentration high enough to maintain the melting temperature of *E. coli* DNA near 100°C.

† Litman and Szybalski used a DEAE fraction of *E. coli* polymerase, which contains some endonuclease as well as the DNA phosphatase-exonuclease, while Richardson *et al.* used the hydroxyl-apatite fraction which contains neither of these activities. Two other differences, one in procedure and one in results, should be noted: after synthesis, Litman and Szybalski found a small DNA band with the buoyant density of the final product, while Richardson *et al.* did not. Both groups used density labels to fractionate template from product but Richardson *et al.* could also measure template remaining in the product fractions by a tritium label, while Litman and Szybalski relied on the buoyant density alone to show that the product was free from the original template.

in mind. (*1*) Although trace amounts of endonuclease are known to inactivate transforming DNA rapidly, this is not likely to be the explanation here. Incubation of the template with hydroxyl-apatite polymerase (without substrate) results in only a very slow loss of transforming activity. (*2*) The failure to register transforming activity could be caused by the problem of getting the DNA into the cell: electron micrographs[93] indicate that there is some branching in the product. (*3*) The newly synthesized DNA` may be degraded in the host cell because the DNA lacks the host modification.[156a] It has been shown by Dussoix and Arber[156b] that when λ phages are grown on *E. coli* K12 and then allowed to infect *E. coli* B or K12 (P1), the phage DNA is degraded. Recent evidence[156a] indicates that specific methylation by host-cell methylating enzymes[16] is needed to protect the DNA from degradation. From this point of view one would not expect DNA synthesized *in vitro*, without the methylating enzymes, to function in transformation.

The DNA synthesized by *E. coli* polymerase from a native DNA template shows a curious property which may also be closely related to the lack of transforming activity: it melts reversibly. This was first noted on comparing absorbancy melting curves of product and template[93, 157] (cf. Fig. 14). Two other methods of measuring secondary structure give the same result: after heating and fast cooling the enzymically synthesized DNA regains its original buoyant density in a CsCl density gradient and also its resistance to attack by *E. coli* exonuclease I.[95] In contrast, the template DNA (*B. subtilis*) now has the buoyant density of denatured DNA and is digested by exonuclease I. Current theories of the melting and reformation of the DNA helix attribute reversibility to the presence of "nuclei": regions where complementary sequences remain in register after melting and permit the double helix to rewind promptly on cooling, without requiring the complementary strands to "find each other." Thus, DNA can be treated by reagents which are thought to cross-link the two strands and which cause the double helix to re-form rapidly on melting and fast cooling.[158] Cross-linking does not seem to be the explanation for reversible melting of enzymically synthesized DNA, since the template and the product separate after melting.[95] A second explanation for reversible melting could be the presence of complementary sequences within a single strand. For example the dAT copolymer, which contains the alternating sequence ATAT···, rapidly re-forms a helical structure after melting in low salt, whereas the DNA homopolymer pairs such as dGdC or dIdC may take days to re-form a helix after melting in very low salt.[134]

Meanwhile *phenotypic transformation* by RNA synthesized *in vitro* has been reported by Hurwitz *et al.*[159] (see Table I). They used native transforming DNA from *Diplococcus pneumoniae* and the RNA polymerase (cf. Section III,E) from *E. coli*. The DNA by itself will genotypically transform some of the *D. pneumoniae* cells from sulfonamide-sensitive to sulfonamide-resistant, and of course such colonies are easily detected. To show phenotypic transformation, the products of RNA synthesis were first treated with deoxyribonuclease, which then was destroyed by heating, and wild-type (nontransforming) DNA was added. The mixture was then cooled slowly from 60°C. in conditions which allow the formation of

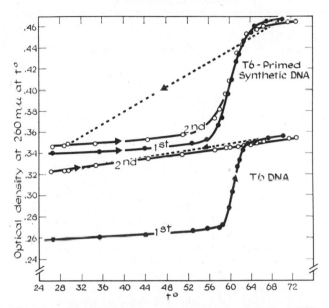

FIG. 14. The reversible melting of an enzymically synthesized DNA.[93] A native DNA from phage T6 was used as a template for extensive DNA synthesis by the *E. coli* DNA polymerase. Under the same conditions of melting and then cooling quickly in low salt, the newly synthesized DNA re-forms a helical structure, whereas the template DNA does not, as shown by the second melting curves.

RNA:DNA hybrids.[160] Without this step no transformants were registered, presumably because the RNA is taken up by the cells only as an RNA: DNA hybrid. Then unstable colonies were found, as expected for transformation by a substance which is not replicated and so is diluted out by cell division.

4. REPLICATION OF ϕX DNA

It has not yet been possible to study the complete replication of ϕX DNA at the enzymic level. The facts obtained from other types of studies are as follows: (*1*) ϕX DNA is single-stranded and probably circular (see Sections II,B,3 and II,C,2). (*2*) There is a "replicative form" which appears after phage infection and is multiplied 50-fold compared to the input DNA.[161] (3) None of the parental DNA is transferred to progeny phage.[162] (4) ϕX DNA does not form an RNA:DNA hybrid with the RNA produced *in vivo* after ϕX infection.[163] These observations raise many

TABLE I

EFFECT OF RNA POLYMERASE PRODUCTS ON SULFONAMIDE-SENSITIVE
Diplococcus pneumoniae[a]

Reaction mixture[b]	Treatment after reaction	Number of colonies per ml which are	
		Stable	Unstable
Complete system	Heated for 10 minutes at 60°C.	500	340
Complete system + DNase (0.1 μg.)	Heated for 10 minutes at 60°C.	<5	<5
Complete system + RNase (0.5 μg.)	Heated for 10 minutes at 60°C.	520	<5
Complete system	Add DNase (0.1 μg.), incubated for 10 minutes; heated at 60°C. for 10 minutes; slow cool	<5	<5
Complete system	Add DNase (0.1 μg.), incubated for 10 minutes; heated at 60°C. for 10 minutes; add wild-type *D. pneumoniae* DNA; slow cool	<5	360
Complete system + DNase (0.1 μg.)	Heated at 60°C. for 10 minutes; add wild-type *D. pneumoniae;* slow cool	<5	<5

[a] From Hurwitz *et al.*[159].

[b] Reaction mixture contained 10 mμmoles of *D. pneumoniae* DNA containing the sulfonamide-resistant marker in the RNA polymerase system. Heating was carried out in small volumes in a thermostatically controlled bath. Concentrations of wild-type DNA were added to provide approximately a 5-fold excess over RNA present and allowed to cool slowly from 60°C. to room temperature over a period of 3 hours where indicated.

interesting questions, especially in comparison with recent work on the replication of RNA viruses, but it seems premature to discuss them here.

E. COMPARISON WITH THE DNA-DIRECTED SYNTHESIS OF RNA

Synthesis of RNA from a DNA template evidently is part of transcription rather than replication of the genetic code. However, a comparison of the two copying mechanisms is helpful in trying to understand the replication of DNA. We will not be concerned with general properties of the synthesis, but only with those aspects which concern mechanism.

The components needed for the DNA-directed synthesis of RNA were established almost simultaneously by several workers, using different bacterial sources to purify the RNA polymerase.[164-166] These components are the four ribonucleoside triphosphates of A, U, G, and C, Mn^{++} or Mg^{++}, a DNA template, and the RNA polymerase. As in the case of DNA synthesis, the rate of RNA synthesis is negligible when one of the four triphosphates is left out. Both single-stranded and double-stranded DNA's function as templates.[167, 168]

Evidence that this RNA synthesis is a copying reaction and that copying proceeds by base pairing is analogous to that for DNA synthesis. The base composition of a double-stranded template is reproduced in the RNA synthesized and so is the distribution of dinucleotides, or nearest neighbors.[169, 170] When single-stranded ϕX DNA (which has A $\neq$ T and G $\neq$ C) is used as a template, the base composition of the product is *complementary* to that of the template but when double-stranded ϕX DNA (made enzymically) is used, then the base composition of the RNA synthesized is the same (replacing U for T) as that of the DNA.[167, 168] Consequently, in this *in vitro* system both of the DNA strands are copied.* Analogs of the natural triphosphates can be used. Each of these substitutes specifically for the natural triphosphate which has corresponding base-pairing properties.[171]

Several lines of evidence indicate that when a double-stranded DNA is used as a template for RNA synthesis it remains as double-stranded DNA. First, the transforming activity of pneumococcal DNA was found to be unchanged after RNA synthesis.[168] Second, examination of the products of reaction by density gradient analysis shows only DNA (with the buoyant density of native DNA) and RNA, not an RNA:DNA hybrid.[172-174] Also, when dAT is used as template for the synthesis of an alternating rAU copolymer, the melting curve of absorbance vs. temperature shows only two steps, with normal T_m's for dAT and rAU, without any hybrid melting zone.[173] Finally, when *E. coli* exonuclease I is present during RNA synthesis, the DNA template is not hydrolyzed, as would be expected if it were temporarily converted to a single-stranded form.[175]

On the other hand, when a single-stranded DNA is used as template, a stable RNA:DNA hybrid is formed[174, 176] (cf. Figs. 5 and 15). Its composition is close to 1:1, RNA:DNA.[174] The hybrid continues to function

---

* *Note added in proof:* Several groups of workers have recently obtained independent evidence that *in vivo* only one strand of the DNA is copied: see for example the section on "Messenger RNA" in *Cold Spring Harbor Symposium Quant. Biol.* **28**, 161–211 (1963).

as a template, and a newly synthesized RNA strand will usually displace the preceding one from the template.[174]

These facts present an interesting problem: since a stable RNA:DNA hybrid can be formed when single-stranded DNA is used, why does it fail

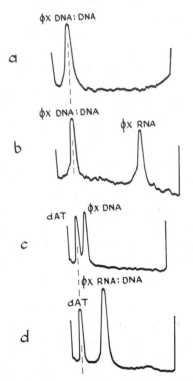

FIG. 15. Density gradient patterns showing the type of RNA product synthesized by *E. coli* RNA polymerase from double-stranded and from single-stranded ϕX DNA as templates.[174] The double-stranded ϕX DNA (*a*), which was made from single-stranded ϕX DNA by means of the *E. coli* DNA polymerase, gives only RNA (*b*) as a product. Synthesis from single-stranded ϕX DNA (*c*) as template gives first an RNA:DNA hybrid (*d*) and then RNA. (These materials were banded in a Cs_2SO_4 density gradient; dAT was added in (*c*) and (*d*) only as a density marker.)

to form when double-stranded DNA is used? One answer might be a lower stability of the RNA:DNA base pair, compared to DNA:DNA. Taking the T_m as a measure of base pair stability (for a very long helix), the results with ϕX DNA (Fig. 5[174]) indicate that the hybrid is somewhat less stable. Some other explanations are considered by Chamberlin and Berg.[174] One fact of significance for DNA replication emerges clearly: copying by base pairing does not necessarily result in a permanent separation of the two strands of a template DNA.

ACKNOWLEDGMENT

I am much indebted to Drs. A. Kornberg, I. R. Lehman, and C. C. Richardson for information and for discussions of the problems considered here; the responsibility for drawing conclusions in advance of the facts, as well as for any errors, is entirely my own.

REFERENCES

[1] J. D. Watson and F. H. C. Crick, *Nature* **171,** 964 (1953).

[2] A. Kornberg, "Enzymatic Synthesis of DNA." Wiley, New York, 1961.

[2a] M. J. Bessman, *in* "Molecular Genetics" (J. H. Taylor, ed.), Vol. I. Academic Press, New York, 1963.

[2b] F. J. Bollum, *in* "Progress in Nucleic Acid Research" (J. N. Davidson and W. E. Cohn, eds.), Vol. I, p. 1. Academic Press, New York, 1963.

[3] K. U. Linderstrøm-Lang, "Proteins and Enzymes" Lane Medical Lectures. Stanford Univ. Press, Stanford, California, 1952.

[4] J. D. Watson and F. H. C. Crick, *Nature* **171,** 737 (1953).

[5] A. K. Kleinschmidt, D. Lang, D. Jacherts, and R. K. Zahn, *Biochim. et Biophys. Acta* **61,** 857 (1962).

[6] R. F. Steiner and R. F. Beers, "Polynucleotides." Elsevier, New York, 1961.

[7] D. M. Brown and A. R. Todd, *in* "The Nucleic Acids" (E. Chargaff and J. N. Davidson, eds.), Vol. I, p. 409. Academic Press, New York, 1955.

[8] R. L. Sinsheimer and J. Koerner, *J. Biol. Chem.* **198,** 293 (1952).

[9] W. Cohn and E. Volkin, *J. Biol. Chem.* **203,** 319 (1953).

[10] L. A. Heppel, R. Markham, and R. J. Hilmoe, *Nature* **171,** 1152 (1953).

[11] G. R. Wyatt and S. S. Cohen, *Biochem. J.* **55,** 774 (1953).

[12] S. Kuno and I. R. Lehman, *J. Biol. Chem.* **237,** 1266 (1962).

[13] R. G. Kallen, M. Simon, and J. Marmur, *J. Mol. Biol.* **5,** 248 (1962).

[14] I. Takahashi and J. Marmur, *Nature* **197,** 794 (1963).

[15] I. Takahashi and J. Marmur, *Biochem. Biophys. Research Communs.* **10,** 289 (1963).

[16] M. Gold, J. Hurwitz, and M. Anders, *Proc. Natl. Acad. Sci. U.S.* **50,** 164 (1963).

[17] J. D. Watson and F. H. C. Crick, *Cold Spring Harbor Symposia Quant. Biol.* **18,** 123 (1953).

[17a] A. R. Katritzky and A. J. Waring, *J. Chem. Soc.* p. 1540 (1962).

[17b] G. W. Kenner, C. B. Reese, and A. R. Todd, *J. Chem. Soc.* p. 855 (1955).

[18] E. Freese, *in* "Molecular Genetics" (J. H. Taylor, ed.) Vol. I p. 207. (see Table V) Academic Press, New York, 1963.

[19] W. Fiers and R. L. Sinsheimer, *J. Mol. Biol.* **5,** 420 (1962).

[20] S. Greer and S. Zamenhof, *J. Mol. Biol.* **4,** 123 (1962).

[21] J. E. Bacher and W. Kauzmann, *J. Am. Chem. Soc.* **74,** 3779 (1952).

[22] K. L. Wierzchowski and D. Shugar, *in* "Progress in Photobiology." Elsevier, New York, 1961.

[23] R. E. Franklin and R. G. Gosling, *Acta Cryst.* **6,** 673 (1953).

[24] R. Langridge, D. A. Marvin, W. E. Seeds, H. R. Wilson, C. W. Hooper, M. H. F. Wilkins, and L. D. Hamilton, *J. Mol. Biol.* **2,** 38 (1960).

[25] R. Langridge, H. R. Wilson, C. W. Hooper, M. H. F. Wilkins and L. D. Hamilton *J. Mol. Biol.* **2,** 19 (1960).

[26] F. H. C. Crick and J. D. Watson *Proc. Roy. Soc.* **A223,** 80 (1954).

[27] V. Luzzati, A. Nicolaieff, and F. Masson, *J. Mol. Biol.* **3,** 185 (1961).

[28] R. Langridge, W. E. Seeds, H. R. Wilson, C. W. Hooper, M. H. F. Wilkins, and L. D. Hamilton, *J. Biophys. Biochem. Cytol.* **3,** 767 (1957).

[29] D. A. Marvin, M. Spencer, M. H. F. Wilkins, and L. D. Hamilton, *J. Mol. Biol.* **3**, 547 (1961).

[30] M. A. Rawitscher, P. D. Ross, and J. M. Sturtevant, *J. Am. Chem. Soc.* **85**, 1915 (1963).

[31] R. F. Steiner and C. Kitzinger, *Nature* **194**, 1172 (1962).

[32] A. Rich and D. R. Davies, *J. Am. Chem. Soc.* **78**, 3548 (1956).

[33] I. Tinoco, Jr., *J. Am. Chem. Soc.* **82**, 4785 (1960).

[34] J. Marmur and P. Doty, *Nature* **183**, 1427 (1959).

[35] H. De Voe and I. Tinoco, Jr., *J. Mol. Biol.* **4**, 500 (1962).

[36] D. O. Jordan, in "The Nucleic Acids" (E. Chargaff and J. N. Davidson, eds.), Vol. I, pp. 447–492. Academic Press, New York, 1955.

[37] W. F. Dove, F. A. Wallace, and N. Davidson, *Biochem. Biophys. Research Communs.* **1**, 312 (1959).

[38] S. A. Rice and P. Doty, *J. Am. Chem. Soc.* **79**, 3937 (1957).

[39] M. Meselson and F. W. Stahl, *Proc. Natl. Acad. Sci. U. S.* **44**, 671 (1958).

[40] C. Levinthal and H. R. Crane, *Proc. Natl. Acad. Sci. U. S.* **42**, 436 (1956).

[41] W. Kuhn, *Experientia* **13**, 301 (1957).

[42] H. C. Longuet-Higgins and B. H. Zimm, *J. Mol. Biol.* **2**, 1 (1960).

[43] M. Fixman, *J. Mol. Biol.* **6**, 39 (1963).

[44] M. Delbrück and G. S. Stent, in "The Chemical Basis of Heredity" (W. D. McElroy and B. Glass, eds.), p. 699. Johns Hopkins Press, Baltimore, Maryland, 1957.

[45] E. B. Freese and E. Freese, *Biochemistry* **2**, 707 (1963).

[46] D. M. Crothers, personal communication (1963).

[47] R. Haselkorn and P. Doty, *J. Biol. Chem.* **236**, 2738 (1961).

[48] I. R. Lehman, *J. Biol. Chem.* **235**, 1479 (1960).

[49] I. R. Lehman, to be published (1964).

[50] J. Marmur and D. Lane, *Proc. Natl. Acad. Sci. U. S.* **46**, 453 (1960).

[51] P. Doty, J. Marmur, J. Eigner, and C. Schildkraut, *Proc. Natl. Acad. Sci. U. S.* **46**, 461 (1960).

[52] C. L. Schildkraut, J. Marmur, and P. Doty, *J. Mol. Biol.* **3**, 595 (1961).

[53] J. Marmur and P. Doty, *J. Mol. Biol.* **3**, 585 (1961).

[53a] J. Marmur, R. Rownd and C. L. Schildkraut, in "Progress in Nucleic Acid Research" (J. N. Davison and W. E. Cohn, eds.) Vol. I, p. 231. Academic Press, New York, 1963.

[54] A. S. Spirin, *J. Mol. Biol.* **2**, 436 (1960).

[55] J. R. Fresco and B. M. Alberts, *Proc. Natl. Acad. Sci. U. S.* **46**, 311 (1960).

[56] M. Arca, C. Calvori, L. Frontali, and G. Tecce, *Biochem. Biophys. Research Communs.* **10**, 117 (1963).

[57] M. Spencer, W. Fuller, M. H. F. Wilkins, and G. L. Brown, *Nature* **194**, 1014 (1962).

[58] R. Langridge and P. J. Gomatos, *Science* **141**, 694 (1963).

[59] P. J. Gomatos and I. Tamm, *Proc. Natl. Acad. Sci. U. S.* **49**, 707 (1963).

[60] D. R. Davies, *Nature* **186**, 1030 (1960).

[61] N. A. Kisselev, L. P. Gavrilova, and A. S. Spirin, *J. Mol. Biol.* **3**, 778 (1961).

[62] S. N. Timasheff, J. Witz, and V. Luzzati, *Biophys. J.* **1**, 525 (1960).

[63] P. Doty, H. Boedtker, J. R. Fresco, R. Haselkorn, and M. Litt, *Proc. Natl. Acad. Sci. U. S.* **45**, 482 (1959).

[64] H. Boedtker, *J. Mol. Biol.* **2**, 171 (1960).

[65] R. A. Cox and U. Z. Littauer, *Biochim. et Biophys. Acta* **61**, 197 (1962).

[66] R. L. Sinsheimer, *J. Mol. Biol.* **1**, 43 (1959).

[67] I. Tessman, *Virology* **7**, 263 (1959).

[68] C. Levinthal, *in* "Conference on Genetics" (H. E. Sutton, ed.), Josiah Macy, Jr. Foundation, New York, 1960.

[69] H. Ris and B. Chandler, *Cold Spring Harbor Symposia Quant. Biol.* **28**, 1 (1963).

[70] P. F. Davison, *Proc. Natl. Acad. Sci. U. S.* **45**, 1560 (1959).

[71] C. Levinthal and C. A. Thomas, *Biochim. et Biophys. Acta* **23**, 453 (1957).

[72] M. Meselson, F. W. Stahl, and J. Vinograd, *Proc. Natl. Acad. Sci. U. S.* **43**, 581 (1957).

[73] J. B. Fleischman, *J. Mol. Biol.* **2**, 226 (1960).

[74] P. F. Davison, D. Freifelder, R. Hede, and C. Levinthal, *Proc. Natl. Acad. Sci. U. S.* **47**, 1123 (1961).

[75] I. Rubenstein, C. A. Thomas, and A. D. Hershey, *Proc. Natl. Acad. Sci. U. S.* **47**, 1113 (1961).

[76] J. Cairns, *J. Mol. Biol.* **3**, 756 (1961).

[77] I. Bendet, E. Schachter, and M. A. Lauffer, *J. Mol. Biol.* **5**, 76 (1962).

[78] P. F. Davison and D. Freifelder, *J. Mol. Biol.* **5**, 643 (1962).

[79] E. Burgi and A. D. Hershey, *J. Mol. Biol.* **3**, 458 (1961).

[80] F. Jacob and E. L. Wollman, *Symposia Soc. Exptl. Biol.* **No. 12**, 75 (1958).

[81] A. D. Kaiser, *J. Mol. Biol.* **4**, 275 (1962).

[82] G. Streisinger and V. Bruce, *Genetics* **45**, 1289 (1960).

[83] J. Cairns, *J. Mol. Biol.* **6**, 208 (1963).

[84] J. Cairns, *Cold Spring Harbor Symposia Quant. Biol.* **28**, 43 (1963).

[85] W. Fiers and R. L. Sinsheimer, *J. Mol. Biol.* **5**, 408 (1962).

[86] W. Fiers and R. L. Sinsheimer, *J. Mol. Biol.* **5**, 424 (1962).

[87] G. Streisinger, R. S. Edgar, and G. H. Denhardt, unpublished work.

[87a] J. Sechand, G. Streisinger, H. Lanford, H. Reinhold, and M. M. Stahl, unpublished work.

[88] C. A. Thomas, *Cold Spring Harbor Symposia Quant. Biol.* **28**, 395 (1963).

[89] C. M. Radding and A. D. Kaiser, *J. Mol. Biol.* **7**, 225 (1963).

[90] D. S. Hogness, to be published (1964).

[91] A. D. Hershey, E. Burgi, and L. Ingraham, *Proc. Natl. Acad. Sci. U. S.* **49**, 748 (1963).

[91a] L. A. MacHattie and C. A. Thomas, Jr., in press (1964).

[91b] E. Calef and G. Licciardello, *Virology*, **12**, 81 (1960).

[91c] A. M. Campbell, *Advances in Genetics* **11**, 101 (1962).

[92] M. J. Bessman, I. R. Lehman, E. S. Simms, and A. Kornberg, *J. Biol. Chem.* **233**, 171 (1958).

[93] C. C. Richardson, C. L. Schildkraut, and A. Kornberg, *Cold Spring Harbor Symposia Quant. Biol.* **28**, 9 (1963).

[94] C. C. Richardson, C. L. Schildkraut, H. V. Aposhian, and A. Kornberg, *J. Biol. Chem.* **239**, 222 (1964).

[95] C. C. Richardson, C. L. Schildkraut, H. V. Aposhian, A. Kornberg, W. Bodmer, and J. Lederberg, *in* "Informational Macromolecules" (H. J. Vogel, V. Bryson, and J. O. Lampen, eds.), pp. 13–26. Academic Press, New York, 1963.

[95a] S. E. Luria, *in* "The Bacteria" (I. C. Gunsalus and R. Y. Stanier, eds.), Vol. I, p. 1. Academic Press, New York, 1960.

[96] F. J. Bollum, *J. Am. Chem. Soc.* **80**, 1766 (1958).

[97] F. J. Bollum, *J. Biol. Chem.* **235**, 2399 (1960).

[98] F. J. Bollum, *Cold Spring Harbor Symposia Quant. Biol.* **28**, 21 (1963).

[99] H. V. Aposhian and A. Kornberg, *J. Biol. Chem.* **237**, 519 (1962).

[100] T. Okazaki and A. Kornberg, *J. Biol. Chem.* **239**, 259 (1964).

[101] I. R. Lehman, S. B. Zimmerman, J. Adler, M. J. Bessman, E. S. Simms, and A. Kornberg, *Proc. Natl. Acad. Sci. U. S.* **44**, 1191 (1958).

[102] I. R. Lehman, *Ann. N. Y. Acad. Sci.* **81**, 745 (1959).

[103] J. Josse, A. D. Kaiser, and A. Kornberg, *J. Biol. Chem.* **236**, 864 (1961).

[104] M. N. Swartz, T. A. Trautner, and A. Kornberg, *J. Biol. Chem.* **237**, 1961 (1962).

[105] H. K. Schachman, J. Adler, C. M. Radding, I. R. Lehman, and A. Kornberg, *J. Biol. Chem.* **235**, 3242 (1960).

[106] C. M. Radding, J. Josse, and A. Kornberg, *J. Biol. Chem.* **237**, 2869 (1962).

[107] C. M. Radding and A. Kornberg, *J. Biol. Chem.* **237**, 2877 (1962).

[108] A. Kornberg, L. L. Bertsch, J. F. Jackson, and H. G. Khorana, *Proc. Natl. Acad. Sci. U.S.*, **51**, 315 (1964).

[109] N. Sueoka, *Proc. Natl. Acad. Sci. U. S.* **48**, 1851 (1962).

[110] T. A. Trautner, M. N. Swartz, and A. Kornberg, *Proc. Natl. Acad. Sci. U. S.* **48**, 449 (1962).

[111] E. Freese, *J. Mol. Biol.* **1**, 87 (1959).

[112] M. J. Bessman, I. R. Lehman, J. Adler, S. B. Zimmerman, E. S. Simms, and A. Kornberg, *Proc. Natl. Acad. Sci. U. S.* **44**, 633 (1958).

[113] J. Adler, I. R. Lehman, M. J. Bessman, E. S. Simms, and A. Kornberg, *Proc. Natl. Acad. Sci. U. S.* **44**, 641 (1958).

[114] R. B. Inman and R. L. Baldwin, *J. Mol. Biol.* **5**, 185 (1962).

[115] R. G. Wake and R. L. Baldwin, *J. Mol. Biol.* **5**, 201 (1962).

[116] D. M. Crothers and B. H. Zimm, to be published (1964).

[117] P. Berg, H. Fancher, and M. Chamberlin, *in* "Informational Macromolecules" (H. J. Vogel, V. Bryson, and J. O. Lampen, eds.), pp. 467–483. Academic Press, New York, 1963.

[118] S. Lee-Huang and L. F. Cavalieri, *Abstr. Biophys. Soc.* WA9 (1963).

[119] A. Rich, *in* "The Chemical Basis of Heredity" (W. D. McElroy and B. Glass, eds.), p. 557. Johns Hopkins Press, Baltimore, Maryland, 1957.

[120] J. A. V. Butler, D. J. R. Laurence, A. V. Robins, and K. V. Shooter, *Proc. Roy. Soc.* **A250**, 1 (1959).

[121] D. Froelich, C. Strazielle, G. Bernardi, and H. Benoit, *Biophys. J.* **3**, 115 (1963).

[122] L. F. Cavalieri, B. H. Rosenberg, and J. F. Deutsch, *Biochem. Biophys. Research Commun.* **1**, 124 (1959).

[123] L. F. Cavalieri and B. H. Rosenberg, *Ann. Rev. Biochem.* **31**, 247 (1962).

[124] R. Rolfe, *J. Mol. Biol.* **4**, 22 (1962).

[125] D. Freifelder and P. F. Davison, *Biophys. J.* **2**, 249 (1962).

[126] R. L. Baldwin and E. M. Shooter, *J. Mol. Biol.* **7**, 511 (1963).

[127] C. E. Hall and L. F. Cavalieri, *J. Biophys. Biochem. Cytol.* **10**, 347 (1961).

[128] V. Luzzati, D. Luzzati, and F. Masson, *J. Mol. Biol.* **5**, 375 (1963).

[129] J. H. Taylor, P. S. Woods, and W. L. Hughes, *Proc. Natl. Acad. Sci. U. S.* **43**, 122 (1957).

[130] N. Sueoka, *Proc. Natl. Acad. Sci. U. S.* **46**, 83 (1960).

[131] H. K. Schachman, I. R. Lehman, M. J. Bessman, J. Adler, E. S. Simms, and A. Kornberg, *Federation Proc.* **17**, 1202 (1958).

[132] D. R. Davies and R. L. Baldwin, *J. Mol. Biol.* **6**, 251 (1963).

[133] E. Elson, unpublished work (1963).

[134] R. B. Inman and R. L. Baldwin, *J. Mol. Biol.* in press (1964).

[135] C. Levinthal, *Proc. Natl. Acad. Sci. U. S.* **42**, 394 (1956).

[136] G. S. Stent, G. H. Sato, and N. K. Jerne, *J. Mol. Biol.* **1**, 134 (1959).

[137] M. Meselson and J. Weigle, *Proc. Natl. Acad. Sci. U. S.* **47**, 857 (1961).
[138] M. Meselson, *in* "The Cell Nucleus" (J. S. Mitchell, ed.), pp. 240–245. Butterworths, London, 1960.
[139] A. W. Kozinski, *Virology* **13**, 124 (1961).
[140] A. W. Kozinski and P. B. Kozinski, *Virology* **20**, 213 (1963).
[141] G. Kellenberger, M. L. Zichichi, and J. Weigle, *Proc. Natl. Acad. Sci. U. S.* **47**, 869 (1961).
[142] T. Nagata, *Proc. Natl. Acad. Sci. U. S.* **49**, 551 (1963).
[143] H. Yoshikawa and N. Sueoka, *Proc. Natl. Acad. Sci. U. S.* **49**, 559 (1963).
[144] O. Maaløe and P. C. Hanawalt, *J. Mol. Biol.* **3**, 144 (1961).
[145] F. Jacob and S. Brenner, *Compt. rend. acad. sci.* **256**, 298 (1963).
[146] I. R. Lehman and C. C. Richardson, *J. Biol. Chem.* **239**, 233 (1964).
[147] J. S. Krakow, H. O. Kammen, and E. S. Canellakis, *Biochim. et Biophys. Acta* **53**, 52 (1961).
[148] J. S. Krakow, C. Coutsogeorgopoulos, and E. S. Canellakis, *Biochim. et Biophys. Acta* **55**, 639 (1962).
[149] H. G. Klemperer, J. S. Krakow, and E. S. Canellakis, *Biochim. et Biophys. Acta* **61**, 43 (1962).
[150] C. S. Rupert, S. H. Goodgal, and R. M. Herriott, *J. Gen. Physiol.* **41**, 451 (1958).
[151] C. S. Rupert, *J. Gen. Physiol.* **43**, 573 (1960).
[152] J. Marmur and L. Grossman, *Proc. Natl. Acad. Sci. U. S.* **47**, 778 (1961).
[153] A. Kornberg, *Science* **131**, 1503 (1960).
[154] F. J. Bollum, *J. Biol. Chem.* **234**, 2733 (1959)
[155] R. Rolfe, *Proc. Natl. Acad. Sci. U. S.* **49**, 386 (1963).
[155a] G. Felsenfeld, G. Sandeen, and P. H. von Hippel, *Proc. Natl. Acad. Sci. U.S.* **50**, 644 (1963).
[156] R. M. Litman and W. Szybalski, *Biochem. Biophys. Research Communs.* **10**, 473 (1963).
[156a] W. Arber, personal communication (1963).
[156b] D. Dussoix and W. Arber, *J. Mol. Biol.* **5**, 37 (1962).
[157] S. B. Zimmerman and A. Kornberg, unpublished work.
[158] E. P. Geiduschek, *Proc. Natl. Acad. Sci. U. S.* **47**, 950 (1961).
[159] J. Hurwitz, A. Evans, C. Babinet, and A. Skalka, *Cold Spring Harbor Symposia Quant. Biol.* **28**, 59 (1963).
[160] B. D. Hall and S. Spiegelman, *Proc. Natl. Acad. Sci. U. S.* **47**, 137 (1961).
[161] R. L. Sinsheimer, B. Starman, C. Nagler, and S. Guthrie, *J. Mol. Biol.* **4**, 142 (1962).
[162] R. L. Sinsheimer, personal communication (1962).
[163] S. Spiegelman and M. Hayashi, *Cold Spring Harbor Symposia Quant. Biol.* **28**, 161 (1963).
[164] S. B. Weiss, *Proc. Natl. Acad. Sci. U. S.* **46**, 1020 (1960).
[165] J. Hurwitz, A. Bresler, and A. Diringer, *Biochem. Biophys. Research Communs.* **3**, 15 (1960).
[166] A. Stevens, *Biochem. Biophys. Research Communs.* **3**, 92 (1960).
[167] M. Chamberlin and P. Berg, *Proc. Natl. Acad. Sci. U. S.* **48**, 81 (1962).
[168] J. Hurwitz, J. J. Furth, M. Anders, and A. Evans, *J. Biol. Chem.* **237**, 3752 (1962).
[169] S. B. Weiss and T. Nakamoto, *Proc. Natl. Acad. Sci. U. S.* **47**, 1400 (1961).
[170] J. J. Furth, J. Hurwitz, and M. Goldmann, *Biochem. Biophys. Research Communs.* **4**, 431 (1961).
[171] F. M. Kahan and J. Hurwitz, *J. Biol. Chem.* **237**, 3778 (1962).

[172] E. P. Geiduschek, T. Nakamoto, and S. B. Weiss, *Proc. Natl. Acad. Sci. U. S.* **47**, 1405 (1961).

[173] M. Chamberlin, R. L. Baldwin, and P. Berg, *J. Mol. Biol.*, **7**, 334 (1963).

[174] M. Chamberlin and P. Berg, *Cold Spring Harbor Symposia Quant. Biol.* **28**, 67 (1963).

[175] M. Chamberlin, unpublished work (1962).

[176] R. C. Warner, H. H. Samuels, M. T. Abbott, and J. S. Krakow, *Proc. Natl. Acad. Sci. U. S.* **49**, 533 (1963).

[177] W. Cochran, *Acta Cryst.* **4**, 81 (1951).

[178] H. T. Miles, *Biochim. et Biophys. Acta* **22**, 247 (1956).

[179] H. T. Miles, *Biochim. et Biophys. Acta* **27**, 46 (1958).

[180] H. T. Miles, *Proc. Natl. Acad. Sci. U. S.* **47**, 791 (1961).

[180a] H. T. Miles, R. B. Bradley, and E. D. Becker, *Science* **142**, 1569 (1963).

[181] H. T. Miles, F. B. Howard, and J. Frazier, *Science* **142**, 1458 (1963).

[182] M. Eigen, *Naturwiss.* **12**, 426 (1963).

[183] M. Feughelman, R. Langridge, W. E. Seeds, A. R. Stokes, H. R. Wilson, C. W. Hooper, M. H. F. Wilkins, R. K. Barclay, and L. D. Hamilton, *Nature* **175**, 834 (1955).

[184] R. B. Inman and R. L. Baldwin, *J. Mol. Biol.* **5**, 172 (1962).

Chapter 8

Gene-Enzyme Relationships

Charles Yanofsky

I. Introduction

Studies of intermediary metabolism over the years have established that most physiological reactions are enzyme-catalyzed. Genetic investigations performed to determine the relationship between enzyme-catalyzed reactions and the hereditary material of the cell have shown that such reactions are under strict genetic control. How the genetic material exerts its control over the enzymic machinery of the cell has been intensively studied in recent years and we now understand many aspects of the relationship between gene, enzyme, and biochemical reaction. The pioneering work in this area by Beadle, Tatum, and co-workers[1] demonstrated very clearly that single genetic changes generally result in the loss of ability to perform single biochemical reactions. Each loss of synthetic ability was subsequently correlated with the absence of a particular enzymic activity.[2]

Extensive investigations of the effects of gene mutations on specific enzymes have shown that there are several ways in which mutational alterations can affect the formation or activity of an enzyme. Since the methods used to select and detect mutants usually only require that there be a loss or reduction of a functional activity, it would be expected that all

---

* This article is based on material available to the author prior to its completion in August 1963.

genetic changes which could lead to such a loss would be recovered. The variety of effects that have been observed support this expectation and illustrate very clearly the complexities of a functioning cell and the interactions between different cell constituents.

This article will be primarily concerned with enzyme structure and function and their alteration by mutation. Our present understanding of some important genetic phenomena which involve interactions between various cell components will also be discussed. Certain aspects of gene-enzyme relationships will be omitted, such as the genetic control of enzymes associated with structural components of the cell and developmental control of enzyme formation. The author feels that at the present time our ignorance in these areas is so great it would be impossible to present more than a speculative discussion of these problems. Other aspects of the function of genetic material, such as its role in duplication and recombination and its participation in RNA (ribonucleic acid) synthesis, will not be discussed. In addition, the fine structure of genetic material and the process of mutation will only be considered in relation to the determination of protein structure. The reader is referred to other chapters in "The Bacteria" or to "Molecular Genetics" (J. H. Taylor, ed.)[2a] for articles dealing with the subjects that have been omitted.

The illustrative examples used in this review were frequently selected from studies performed in the author's laboratory. This selection does not reflect the absence of comparable examples from other studies; rather it indicates the preference of the author to deal with observations with which he has first-hand familiarity.

A. Current View of Protein Synthesis

On the basis of studies on the chemical nature and structure of genetic material,[3-6] the intermediary steps in protein synthesis,[7, 8] and the aforementioned gene-enzyme relationship,[2, 9] a concept has evolved of the role of genetic material in protein formation.

It is believed that a major function of the genetic material of each organism is to specify the amino acid sequences of the proteins formed by that organism. It is assumed that the nucleotide sequences in DNA (deoxyribonucleic acid) contain the information that is ultimately translated into the specific amino acid sequences of polypeptide chains.[10-13] A group of adjacent nucleotides in DNA, called a coding unit, presumably codes for each amino acid[14, 15] and a continuous sequence of coding units specifies a linear sequence of amino acids in a polypeptide chain.[12] It is believed that the translation of the nucleotide sequences of DNA into amino acid sequences does not take place directly at the site of DNA localization within each cell; rather, segments of one strand of the DNA double helix are translated into single-stranded messenger RNA's[16-19] and these messenger RNA's are involved directly in determining the amino acid sequence of proteins. The ribonucleotide sequence of each messenger RNA is presumably complementary to the nucleotide sequence of the DNA strand from which it was copied.[16-18] The translation of the nucleotide sequence of an RNA messenger into the amino acid sequence of a protein is accomplished in association with groups of ribonucleoprotein particles, the ribosomes.[8, 20-23] The amino acids are transferred to the ribosome-messenger RNA complex from specific amino acid carriers, called transfer RNA's.[7] Each amino acid is activated and attached to transfer RNA by an amino acid-specific activating enzyme.[7] The transfer RNA's are also amino acid-specific; however, there appears to be more than one transfer RNA species for some of the amino acids.[24-27] The transfer RNA molecule is believed to contain a nucleotide sequence that corresponds—presumably by complementarity—to a segment of the RNA messenger.[28] The amino acid carried by transfer RNA is linked by peptide bond formation to an amino acid of a growing polypeptide chain. It is believed that the translation of the information contained in the messenger RNA proceeds from the region corresponding to the amino terminal end of the polypeptide chain.[8, 29] The chain when complete is released from the messenger-polyribosome complex and then probably completes the folding process to form the native protein. The folding is assumed to be determined by the primary structure of the polypeptide chain.[30] If a polypeptide chain is a subunit of a multichain complex, it associates with the other chains of the protein and forms the native functional unit.[31-33] For a detailed description of the stages in protein synthesis see the reviews by Berg[7] and Schweet and Bishop.[8]

B. Enzyme Structure and Function

Since different regions of an enzyme may be responsible for different functions, it is necessary to inquire into the specific functions before attempting to interpret the relationships between gene and enzyme. At the present time it would appear that at least the following different functions can be ascribed to the same or different regions of some enzyme molecules: substrate and coenzyme binding; catalytic activity; stability; allosteric interactions; and specific association with other polypeptide chains.

1. Active Site Region

The portion of enzyme structure concerned with the binding and attack of the substrate is obviously of principal importance. These two seemingly related functions—catalytic activity and binding specificity—may often be performed by different specific regions of an enzyme, although most certainly these regions would be near one another in the folded molecule. This conclusion is based on several observations.[34] First, it has been found that substrate analogs will often compete with the substrate for the substrate binding site of an enzyme. The fact that such analogs are competitive inhibitors suggests that they may combine with the same region of the protein that binds the substrate. Since these analogs are not attacked by the enzyme it would appear that binding at the active site is not sufficient in itself to ensure attack by the enzyme. The distinction between binding site and catalytic site is also evident from other findings.[34] Several proteolytic enzymes, including trypsin and chymotrypsin, have very similar amino acid sequences in the vicinity of a particularly reactive serine residue.[35] This serine residue is believed to play an important role in the catalytic act. Although trypsin and chymotrypsin have similar sequences at the catalytic site and carry out the same type of reaction, they have very different specificities. Trypsin attacks bonds on the carboxy side of lysine and arginine, while chymotrypsin splits bonds on the carboxy side of phenylalanine, tyrosine, tryptophan, methionine, leucine, and several other amino acids. From these facts it would appear that amino acid sequences other than the one at the catalytic site are involved in determining binding specificity. Substrate binding is now believed to play a major role in enzyme activation.[34] According to the "induced fit" theory of Koshland[36] the combination of substrate with enzyme induces a conformational change in the protein. The protein in this form—and only in this form—is capable of attacking the substrate.

2. THE STRUCTURE OF THE ACTIVE SITE REGION

Although the substrates of many enzymes are small molecules and there is often only one substrate-combining site per protein molecule or protein subunit, it does not follow that only a small segment of the polypeptide chain of a protein constitutes the active site region. Proteolytic digests of enzymes are usually devoid of enzymic activity and this is also true of denatured proteins. Reduction of disulfide bonds often leads to chain unfolding and to loss of enzymic activity. These and other observations indicate that the correct amino acid sequence is insufficient to determine binding or catalytic activity unless it is held in the proper conformation. In studies on this subject with pancreatic ribonuclease, it has been found that removal of a 20-amino acid fragment from the amino terminal end of the protein, or removal of the last four amino acids at the carboxy-terminal end of the protein, leads to enzyme inactivity.[37, 38] In either case a conformational change is associated with the loss of a segment of the enzyme.[37] The residual protein lacking the 20-amino acid fragment from the amino terminal end can still bind substrate. Thus, although the residual protein is enzymically inactive it can assume the conformation necessary for substrate binding. Other treatments also inactivate the enzyme,[37] some involving the chemical modification of specific amino acids in the protein. It is likely, therefore, that portions of a protein molecule, although not directly concerned with combination or attack of the substrate, are important in establishing the native conformation of the active site region. On the other hand, there are examples in which a sizable segment of an enzyme can be removed without appreciable loss of enzyme activity.[39, 40] In such cases it is apparent that the entire structure is not necessary to establish a functional conformation of the active site region. Thus the active site region may constitute only a small segment of an enzyme molecule but many different regions along the polypeptide chain may participate directly or indirectly in establishing its native conformation. Considerable information is available on the relationship between primary structure and tertiary structure[41-44] and the forces responsible for maintaining the globular protein structure.[45]

3. ALLOSTERIC INTERACTIONS

In a number of cases substances that do not interact directly with substrates or products of a reaction and are not analogs of the substrate combine specifically with an enzyme. This combination may serve to inhibit or stimulate enzyme activity and is believed to be of major consequence in regulating enzyme activity. In the best-understood interaction of this type, the end product of a biosynthetic pathway combines with and inhibits the enzyme that catalyzes the first reaction unique to the pathway.[46] In such cases the enzyme must have a recognition site for the inhibitor. This type of specific interaction with nonsubstrate has been termed an allosteric interaction.[47] Allosteric interactions will be considered in somewhat greater detail later in this article.

4. SPECIFIC ASSOCIATION

Many enzymes consist of subunits of like or unlike polypeptide chains. In some cases, only the complex is the physiologically effective unit. For specific association of polypeptide chains to occur, a portion, or portions, of the structure of each polypeptide chain must be concerned with affinity for the other polypeptide chain, or chains. Furthermore, since many enzymes contain several polypeptide subunits it is likely that the structure of each subunit, and of the complex, must prevent nonspecific associations. The structure of each folded polypeptide chain and complex must therefore provide for specific associations and for buffering against nonspecific associations which could have detrimental effects on catalytic activity. Specific association may play a major role in localizing enzymes and other cell components in the proper cell structures. Allosteric interactions probåbly play an important role in specific association of polypeptide chains.[48, 49]

5. Enzyme Structure and the Regulation of Enzyme Formation

It is likely that whether or not an enzyme will be formed is in part determined by the interaction of specific DNA segments or messenger RNA segments with regulatory substances in the cytoplasm. Convincing evidence for the existence of DNA segments concerned with regulation, called "operator" regions, has been obtained in mutational studies with several enzyme systems.[50-53] In studies on the synthesis of β-galactosidase in *Escherichia coli* it has been shown that some mutations in the operator region also have an effect on the structure of the enzyme.[50] It is likely, therefore, that in this case a segment of the amino acid sequence of the enzyme corresponds to a DNA segment that is involved in the regulation of β-galactosidase synthesis and in the determination of the amino acid sequence of the protein.

II. Genetic Control of Protein Structure and Function

A. Mutational Alteration of Enzyme Activity

1. Introduction

Most studies of the effects of mutation on enzyme activity, formation, and structure have been performed with induced mutants. Since a mutation is a relatively rare event, selective conditions usually must be employed in the isolation of mutant strains. Therefore, the material that has been obtained for study generally reflects the selective conditions imposed during isolation. In microorganisms forward mutational alterations involving loss of function have usually been selected under conditions where only those strains with near complete loss of a given synthetic ability would be detected. Strains with a partial loss would rarely be recovered because they would be difficult to distinguish from members of the starting population. This restriction is not always imposed; with some systems detection methods permit the recognition of mutants under nonselective conditions (e.g., alkaline phosphatase, β-galactosidase). In recovering strains in which there is a gain in function as a result of mutation, selection is also employed since there is undoubtedly a minimum level of synthetic ability which is requisite for an organism to be distinguishable from the population that lacks the function. Thus strains with a restored enzyme that is only slightly active or in which only small amounts of active enzyme are formed might not be distinguishable from the original strain. It is probable, therefore, than many—if not most—of the protein alterations that do occur as a result of a change in the genetic material, go unnoticed.

2. QUALITATIVE ENZYME ALTERATIONS RESULTING FROM MUTATIONS

Fortunately, a wide variety of enzymes have been examined in mutational studies with microorganisms.[2, 9] Although selective conditions are usually employed in mutant isolation, nonselective conditions have been used in some cases.[54, 55] In studies of the effects of mutations within a single structural gene it has generally been observed that two major

TABLE I

EXAMPLES OF THE DIFFERENT TYPES OF PROTEIN ALTERATIONS THAT HAVE BEEN DETECTED IN STUDIES OF GENE-ENZYME RELATIONSHIPS

Enzyme	Alterations detected	Reference
Glutamic dehydrogenase (*Neurospora*)	CRMless, unusual substrate requirements, activation required, stability, inactive CRM	57, 72-74
β-Galactoside (*E. coli*)	CRMless, stability, ability to aggregate, affinity for galactosides	50, 55, 75-77
Tryptophan synthetase (*Neurospora*)	CRMless, inactive CRM, partially active enzyme, inhibitor-sensitive CRM	56, 54, 78-82
Tryptophan synthetase (*E. coli*) A protein	CRMless, partially active enzyme, stability, charge	59, 62, 63, 68, 83, 84
B protein	CRMless, partially active enzyme, inactive CRM	59, 85
Tyrosinase (*Neurospora*)	stability, charge	86, 87
Alkaline phosphatase (*E. coli*)	CRMless, inactive CRM, partially active enzyme	11, 54, 88

categories of mutant types are recovered.[52, 54, 56-59] Mutants in the first category produce an altered form of an enzyme, called CRM (serologically cross-reacting material), but the protein is inactive or has altered enzymic activity. Mutants in the second category appear to be totally devoid of this protein and the wild-type enzyme. Representatives of this second category —the so-called CRMless mutants—have been examined in a number of systems (see Table I), using a variety of criteria which might be expected to detect a protein related to the normal protein, or a fragment of this protein. As yet, in no case has such a protein, or protein fragment, been positively identified. With the alkaline phosphatase system, for example, isotopic labeling of the total protein of a CRMless mutant, followed by subsequent fractionation, failed to detect any protein that had the fractionation characteristics of the normal enzyme.[60] Similar analyses with several tryptophan synthetase A protein mutants also failed to detect an A protein in extracts of CRMless mutants. The production of an altered protein by some CRMless alkaline phosphatase mutants does seem likely, however, on the basis of complementation studies.[61] The alkaline phosphatase of *E. coli* is composed of two identical polypeptide subunits. Complementation studies carried out with CRM and CRMless mutants have shown that alkaline phosphatase activity is detectable in some cases in which a CRMless mutant is one partner in the complementation test.[61] Since a functional protein appears to be produced, it is likely that the CRMless mutant is capable of forming the alkaline phosphatase-polypeptide chain but that this chain cannot be recognized unless a chain with a different alteration is available for the formation of a complex.

In studies with tryptophan synthetase mutants of *E. coli* somewhat different criteria have been employed in the examination of extracts of CRMless mutants for a protein resembling the wild-type protein.[62] The tryptophan synthetase of *E. coli* consists of two separable protein subunits, designated A and B, each of which has slight activity in one of the reactions catalyzed at a rapid rate by the wild-type A-B complex.[33] If a protein were present in a CRMless extract, and it could combine with the normal second subunit, it could be detected by activity measurements or in competition studies. Experiments based on these detection methods have all been negative.[62] Indirect evidence obtained with certain CRMless tryptophan synthetase mutants also suggests that a protein is formed but it cannot be recognized. In reversion studies with one CRMless mutant it was shown that a genetic change at a second site within the gene restored a functional enzyme.[63] Although the enzyme activity could be demonstrated with cell suspensions, it was not possible to detect the protein in extracts. Thus the protein is probably present in both the original CRMless mutant and in the revertant but it is not recognizable.

Immunological studies with extracts of certain CRMless tryptophan synthetase mutants of *Neurospora* have led to the detection of a protein that blocks the precipitation reaction between the wild-type enzyme and antienzyme.[64] The nature of this protein, or protein fragment, has not been established so it cannot be stated that it represents an altered form of the enzyme. Of interest in this regard is the finding that tryptophan synthetase fragments obtained by proteolytic digestion of the enzyme also block the enzyme-antienzyme reaction.[65]

There are several explanations that may be considered for CRMless mutants. First, it is conceivable that a protein is formed but its structure is so altered that it cannot be recognized by the detection techniques employed. The complementing CRMless alkaline phosphatase mutants and the CRMless tryptophan synthetase mutants of *E. coli* mentioned above are probably of this type. Second, it is also conceivable that some amino acid substitutions affect protein stability so adversely that the protein is inactivated and destroyed soon after formation. A third possible explanation would depend on whether there are nucleotide sequences in DNA which do not code for specific amino acids, so-called nonsense sequences.[66] A mutational alteration at a particular nucleotide position in a gene could result in the change of a meaningful coding unit (corresponding to an amino acid) to a nonsense coding unit. If a nonsense coding unit were present in a gene it is conceivable that the corresponding nucleotide sequence in messenger RNA would prevent translation of the messenger into a continuous sequence of amino acids. This could lead to the formation of a fragment, or fragments, of the polypeptide chain rather than the intact polypeptide chain, or the polypeptide fragments might not be released from the template. If fragments are formed by some CRMless mutants it is not too surprising that they have not been detected. A fourth possibility is that the altered polypeptide chain cannot be released, or is released very slowly from the messenger-polyribosome complex. This possibility will be discussed in the section on the regulation of enzyme formation.

Most of the explanations mentioned above could apply in instances in which a mutation involved a single nucleotide substitution in DNA. In addition, alteration of DNA by the addition or deletion of a single nucleotide in a gene could have many of the same effects.[67] A single nucleotide addition or deletion in a gene could result in a shift of the coding unit reading frame with a consequent change of the amino acid sequence of a portion of the corresponding polypeptide chain. If a substantial portion of a polypeptide chain had a different amino acid sequence, it probably could not be recognized as being related to the unaltered protein. This explanation has been offered by Crick *et al.*[67] to account for genetic findings obtained with acridine dye-induced mutants of phage T4 and their revertants. Only a fraction of the CRMless mutants,[61, 63, 68] or any mutants[69-71] isolated following treatment with other mutagenic agents, would appear to be of this type since many are reverted by base analogs or alkylating agents.

Many different types of enzyme changes have been detected in studies with spontaneous and mutagen-induced mutants and revertants. Examples of the different effects of mutation on enzyme activity and properties are presented in Table I. In the examples cited, changes affecting the active site seem quite common; however, as was pointed out earlier, this is probably a reflection of the methods used in the isolation of the mutants. Other alterations affect enzyme stability, sensitivity to naturally occurring substances in the environment, the ability of subunits to associate to form an effective protein complex, the energy of activation of the enzyme, charge, etc. It is apparent from these varied effects on enzyme activity and structure that the proper conformation and amino acid sequences of many different regions of a protein are essential for physiological activity.

In only a few of the cases cited is it known whether the altered protein differs from the normal protein by a single amino acid substitution. In fact, even in those cases in which single amino acid changes have been detected, it is virtually impossible to prove that other changes did not occur. Nevertheless, in all cases that have been thoroughly investigated, single-step mutational events have been shown to be associated with single amino acid replacements. When dealing with naturally occurring variant proteins, such as some human hemoglobins,[10] and the tyrosinases of *Neurospora*,[86,87] it might be expected that several amino acid changes would be present in a variant protein. In the extensive studies performed with human hemoglobins[10] this does not appear to be the case.

3. CHANGES IN ENZYME LEVELS AS A RESULT OF MUTATIONAL ALTERATIONS IN STRUCTURAL GENES

In addition to alterations of protein structure resulting from mutation, effects on the formation of specific proteins are also observed. In some cases these effects are due to changes in genic regions that are not concerned with the primary structure of the protein, or proteins, that are affected. These will be considered in the section dealing with the regulation of enzyme formation.

In other cases it has been observed that mutations that affect protein structure, or are mappable within the region of the gene concerned with protein structure, affect the amount of enzyme that is formed. In addition, these mutations often affect the formation of related enzymes whose controlling genes are located nearby. For example, several mutations in the genes concerned with arabinose utilization in *E. coli* affect the levels of many enzymes concerned with the metabolism of this sugar.[89] Similarly, studies with β-galactosidase mutants (*E. coli*)[50, 90] and tryptophan synthetase mutants (*E. coli*)[59, 62, 83] have shown that the level of CRM formed is affected as well as the properties of the CRM. Furthermore, in both systems related enzymes controlled by neighboring genes were reduced in amount as a result of an alteration affecting β-galactosidase or tryptophan synthetase. It is clear that an alteration in a genic region concerned with structure can have a profound effect of the formation of the corresponding enzyme and on enzymes controlled by neighboring genes as well. Possible interpretations of these effects will be considered in the section dealing with the regulation of enzyme formation.

B. Genetic Changes and Their Effects on, and Relationship to, Protein Primary Structure

1. Protein Primary Structure Changes Associated with Mutations

If mutation is defined as "a heritable change in the genetic material of an organism," then several categories of possible events must be considered as mutations. At the nucleotide level mutations could involve substitution of one nucleotide for another, deletion of one or more nucleotides, or the addition of one or more nucleotides. Any of these changes would presumably be capable of affecting the structure of a protein. Other types of mutational alterations, such as translocations and inversions, would also be expected to have profound effects on protein structure.

In no case is the specific nucleotide change associated with a mutational alteration known with any degree of certainty. It is believed that a very simple event is responsible for most mutational changes—probably a single nucleotide substitution. The principal basis for this conclusion is the fact that the kinetics of mutant production following mutagen treatment indicate that single events are responsible for mutant formation.[69] Furthermore, only single amino acid changes are generally observed associated with mutational alterations that occur spontaneously or are induced by chemical mutagens,[13, 91-93] and often the changes are reversible.[13]

The amino acid differences that have been detected in studies with mutant forms of hemoglobin, tobacco mosaic virus, and the tryptophan synthetase A protein are summarized in Table II. In the latter case the mutational changes from active ⇌ inactive enzyme and stable ⇌ unstable enzyme appear to be associated with single amino acid replacements.[13, 95-97]

Among naturally occurring proteins that differ by one or more amino acid residues it is not known, of course, how many separate mutational events were responsible for each difference. Comparison of the amino acid replacements in naturally occurring variant forms of hemoglobin with those induced in tobacco mosaic virus protein and the tryptophan synthetase A protein indicates that several of the same amino acid changes are observed (Table II). This fact would tend to favor the view that single-step changes have been preserved in the hemoglobin variants.

As yet, primary structure changes have not been described in any instance in which an addition or deletion of a nucleotide is believed to have taken place, nor has it been demonstrated that a deletion leads to the alteration or loss of a segment of a protein. In studies with phage T4 an *rII* mutant has been isolated in which a deletion has removed segments of two functionally separate but adjacent regions of the *rII* gene.[98] The results of complementation and mutation studies with the strain bearing this deletion have been interpreted as indicating that the two presumed protein products of this genic region, which are believed to be distinct in non-

TABLE II

AMINO ACID DIFFERENCES BETWEEN THE NORMAL AND MUTANT FORMS
OF HEMOGLOBIN, TOBACCO MOSAIC VIRUS, AND TRYPTOPHAN
SYNTHETASE A PROTEIN[a]

Amino acid change	Protein	Amino acid change	Protein
Ala → Glu	TS	Gly → Val	TS
Arg → Lys	TMV	Gly → Cys	TS
Arg → Gly	TMV, TS	His → Tyr	Hb
Arg → Thr	TS	His → Arg	Hb
Arg → Ser	TS	Ileu → Thr	TMV
Asp → Ala	TMV	Ileu → Val	TMV
Asp → Gly	TMV	Ileu → Met	TMV
Asp → Ser	TMV	Leu → Arg	TMV
AspNH$_2$ → Lys	Hb, TMV	Leu → Phe	TMV
AspNH$_2$ → Arg	TMV	Pro → Ser	TMV
AspNH$_2$ → Ser	TMV	Pro → Leu	TMV
Glu → Gly	Hb, TMV, TS	Ser → Phe	TMV
Glu → Val	Hb, TS	Ser → Leu	TMV
Glu → Lys	Hb	Ser → Arg	TS
Glu → GluNH$_2$	Hb	Thr → Ileu	TMV, TS
Glu → Ala	TS	Thr → Met	TMV
GluNH$_2$ → Val	TMV	Thr → Ser	TMV
Gly → Asp	Hb, TS	Tyr → Cys	TS
Gly → Arg	TS	Val → Gly	TS
Gly → Glu	TS	Val → Ala	TS
		Val → Glu	TS

[a] Based on data tabulated by Jukes[94] and on references 12, 13, 101, 102.

KEY: Hb, human hemoglobin; TS, tryptophan synthetase A protein; TMV, tobacco mosaic virus protein.

mutants, are joined together to form one polypeptide chain.[98] This polypeptide chain would presumably lack the amino acid sequence corresponding to the deleted region. Since the *rII* proteins have not been isolated as yet, it is not possible to verify this interpretation. There are several cases in which polypeptide chains or proteins have sufficiently similar primary structures to be interesting subjects for comparison. This is particularly true of the different chains of human hemoglobins.[99] The alpha and beta chains have several similarities, and the gamma chain very closely resembles the β-chain. In view of the similarity of the amino acid sequences of these chains it seems likely that one or more were derived from a common single-chain ancestral molecule.[99] This presumably could come about by gene duplication followed by many mutational alterations, with the gradual development of a new hemoglobin type.

2. GENE AND PROTEIN FINE STRUCTURE RELATIONSHIPS

As mentioned previously, one of the basic assumptions in our thinking about the relationship between gene and protein is that there is a linear correspondence between the two structures. Examinations of this assumption must of necessity be indirect at the present time. Although it is possible to determine the positions of amino acid replacements in proteins that are associated with mutational events, it is not possible to determine the corresponding nucleotide changes in DNA, or their relative positions. This obstacle stems from the fact that it is not possible to isolate what could be considered a DNA fragment corresponding to a single gene. In attempting to test the concept of colinearity the best that can be done at the present time is to compare a fine structure genetic map with the primary structure of the corresponding protein. A number of gene-protein systems are being studied with this purpose in mind.[11, 12, 54, 100] The findings obtained to date demonstrate a direct relationship between the locations of alterations on a genetic map and the positions of amino acid substitutions in the corresponding protein,[11, 12, 95, 96] and establish the existence of a colinear relationship between gene structure and protein structure.[12]

In studies with the A protein of *E. coli* tryptophan synthetase several cases have been found in which there is a correspondence between the positions on the genetic map at which mutations occur and the positions in the protein at which amino acid replacements are detected (Fig. 1); i.e., alterations near one another on the genetic map lead to amino acid replacements near one another in the protein.[12, 95, 96] The same relationship has been demonstrated in studies with the alkaline phosphatase of *E. coli*.[11] In addition, one segment of the tryptophan synthetase A protein has been sequenced[12, 101, 102] (Fig. 1) and the order of the positions of amino acid replacements in this segment is the same as the order of the mutational sites in the *A* gene. Furthermore, if the known lengths of the *A* gene (3.7 recombination units) and the A protein (280 amino acid residues) are considered, the distances between the positions of amino acid replacements in the protein are in fair agreement with recombination data.[12, 101, 102] These findings provide strong support for the concept of colinearity of gene structure and protein structure.

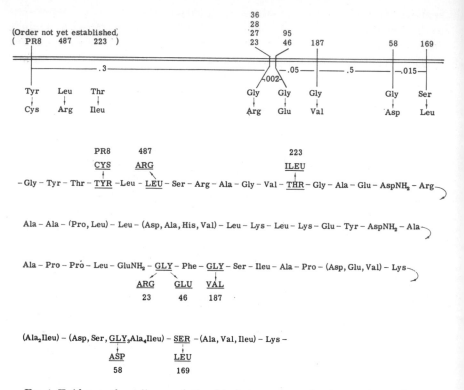

FIG. 1. Evidence of a colinear relationship between gene structure and protein structure. The genetic map of a segment of the *A* gene is presented above, with the amino acid replacement characteristic of each mutant. The corresponding segment of the A protein and the positions of the changes are shown below. Based on published[12, 95-97] and unpublished studies of Yanofsky, Carlton, Guest, Helinski, and Henning.

3. PRIMARY STRUCTURE CHANGES ASSOCIATED WITH REVERSION EVENTS

Reverse mutations have also been studied in examinations of the relationship between mutational changes and protein primary structure changes. Figure 2 presents the three possible types of reversion events that could involve single nucleotide substitutions. The substitution could be at the same position as the original nucleotide change, or at another nucleotide position in the same amino acid coding unit. In either case the amino acid responsible for inactivity of the corresponding mutant protein would be replaced. The substitution could also be in an amino acid coding unit other than the one changed by the original mutation. In the latter case it would be expected that the corresponding revertant protein would have two amino acid differences from the wild-type protein. It would have one change identical to that in the protein of the original mutant strain, and a second change elsewhere in the protein. This second alteration would presumably compensate in some way for the effects of the original amino acid replacement.

Reversion event	Wild-type sequence	Mutant sequence	Revertant sequence	
1. Nucleotide substitution	A	A	A	) Triplet
at original site	T	T	T	coding
	C ⟶	T ⟶	A	) unit
2. Nucleotide substitution	A	A ⟶	C	
at a different position	T	T	T	
in altered coding unit	C ⟶	T	T	
3. Nucleotide substitution	A	A	A	
in a second coding unit	T	T	T	
	C ⟶	T	T	
	.	.	.	
	.	.	.	
	.	.	.	
	.	.	.	
	.	.	.	
	.	.	.	
	.	.	.	
	T	T	T	
	A	A	A	
	G	G ⟶	C	

Fig. 2. The three types of reversion events resulting from single nucleotide substitutions.

In studies of reversion, inasmuch as the selective conditions employed simply require the restoration of a function lacking in a mutant, it would be expected that many different primary structure changes would be represented among revertant strains recovered from any one mutant. The amino acid changes that could occur would obviously be limited by the original mutational alteration, since only those new changes that could restore a functional protein would be detected. Furthermore, if each reversion event involved the substitution of only one nucleotide, the composition and sequence of that mutant coding unit would restrict the possible amino acid changes.

Extensive reversion analyses have been performed with two A protein mutants (tryptophan synthetase).[13, 63, 97] The amino acid replacements in the A proteins of these mutants are at the same position in the protein; either arginine (A-23) or glutamic acid (A-46) replaces glycine.[13, 95, 96] Strain A-23 has a very complex reversion pattern; it gives rise to revertants which are indistinguishable from the wild type (in terms of most of their properties) and several classes of revertants, called partial revertants, which form a functional A protein, but the protein is not as active catalytically as the wild-type A protein.[63, 68] Analyses of the A proteins of members of the first group have shown that in addition to reversions restoring the wild-type amino acid, glycine, arginine is replaced by serine[13, 97] (Fig. 3).

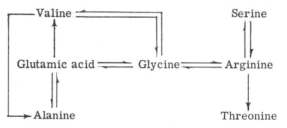

FIG. 3. Amino acid replacements at one position in the tryptophan synthetase A protein. The wild-type protein has glycine at this position. The A proteins with valine, alanine, serine, or threonine at this position are functional while the proteins with arginine or glutamic acid are inactive.

This serine-containing protein appears to be as active enzymically as the glycine protein. Many revertant proteins have been examined in these studies and only the two amino acids have been detected.[13] Only one member of the second group, the partial revertants, has been examined and the A protein of this revertant has a threonine residue instead of the arginine residue.[13] The other mutant examined, strain A-46, also has a complex reversion pattern (Fig. 3). It gives rise to two different partial revertant types and revertants which are indistinguishable from the wild type.[13, 63, 68] Analyses of the A proteins of members of this latter category have shown that either glycine or alanine can replace glutamic acid.[13, 97] The alanine protein appears to be similar to the glycine protein in functional activity. Representatives of the two partial revertant types have been analyzed; one type forms an A protein with valine instead of glutamic acid at the critical position in the A protein.[97] The valine protein is only slightly active enzymically. The second partial revertant type has been shown to have a primary structure change at a second position in the protein.[103] The original mutant change—glycine to glutamic acid—is still evident in the protein of this strain, but there is a second change, in a different peptide, of a tyrosine residue to a cysteine residue.[103] This cysteine residue must in some manner compensate for the effects of the presence of the glutamic acid residue elsewhere in the protein. Recombination experiments with this partial revertant have permitted the isolation of a strain with the genetic change responsible for the tyrosine → cysteine replacement but lacking the A-46 alteration; i.e., glycine rather than glutamic acid was present at the other relevant position in the protein. This protein was enzymically inactive. Thus, both changes must be present in the same protein molecule for activity. Amino acid replacement analyses were carried out with approximately 30 revertants from the glutamic mutant and only the four types of changes mentioned were detected.[13] Second-site reversion (reversion at a second position within a gene) has also been studied in relation to the mutagenic effects of acridine dyes.[67] The interpretation of these effects will be discussed presently.

The findings in the studies with the two A protein mutants illustrate very clearly the restrictions on reversion possibilities that are imposed by the composition of the mutant coding unit. Clearly, at least five amino acids—glycine, alanine, serine, threonine, and valine—are functional at one position in the protein but the alanine and valine coding units can only be derived from the glutamic acid coding unit, and the serine and threonine coding units can only be derived from the arginine coding unit. These findings suggest that each mutational change involves a single nucleotide change and, therefore, that the nucleotide composition and sequence of the critical coding unit in the mutant gene limits the reversion possibilities.

In one other system, the alkaline phosphatase of *E. coli*, evidence has also been obtained suggesting that an amino acid change at a second position in the protein compensates for the effect of the primary amino acid replacement.[11] Here, too, the second change leads to an inactive protein in an otherwise unaltered protein.

As mentioned previously, a mutational event might involve an addition or a deletion of a single nucleotide rather than a substitution. In such cases reversion would probably involve the opposite change—addition for deletion, and deletion for addition.[67] It is, of course, also conceivable that a deletion or addition near one end of a gene could be reversed by nucleotide substitutions in this region.

Genetic and physicochemical studies with acridine dyes suggest that acridine mutagenesis may involve the addition or deletion of single nucleotides.[67, 104] Furthermore, analyses of acridine-induced *rII* mutants of bacteriophage T4 and their revertants suggest that translation of mes-

rII Gene

(Hypothetical nucleotide
and amino acid sequence)

		1	2	3	4	5	6	7	8

Wild type

ABC ABC ABC ABC ABC ABC ABC ABC

Ala – Ala – Ala – Ala – Ala – Ala – Ala – Ala

Deletion mutant

	1	2.	3	4	5	6	7	8

ABC BCA BCA BCA BCA BCA BCA BCA
    ×

Ala – Gly – Gly – Gly – Gly – Gly – Gly – Gly

Addition revertant of
the deletion mutant

1	2	3	4	5	6	7	8

ABC BCA BCA BBC ABC ABC ABC ABC
    ×

Ala – Gly – Gly – Val – Ala – Ala – Ala – Ala

Wild type

1	2	3	4	5	6	7	8

ABC ABC ABC ABC ABC ABC ABC ABC

Ala – Ala – Ala – Ala – Ala – Ala – Ala – Ala

Addition mutant

1	2	3	4	5	6	7	8

ABC AAB CAB CAB CAB CAB CAB CAB

Ala – Ser – Leu – Leu – Leu – Leu – Leu – Leu

Deletion revertant of
the addition mutant

1	2	3	4	5	6	7	8

ABC AAB CAB ABC ABC ABC ABC ABC
      ×

Ala – Ser – Leu – Ala – Ala – Ala – Ala – Ala

FIG. 4. The effect of single nucleotide additions or deletions on the composition of the coding units in the *rII* gene of phage T4.[67] Subscript letter x indicates nucleotide deleted; underlined letter indicates nucleotide added; a bar under a number (1) refers to a coding triplet. In each case reversion restores the original triplets except for the region between the two changes, if the sequence is read from a fixed starting point.

senger RNA proceeds from a fixed starting point and that each sequence of three nucleotides corresponds to an amino acid.[67] On the basis of the interpretation of the results of these studies (Fig. 4) it would be expected that a single nucleotide addition or deletion in a gene would lead to a change in the amino acid sequence of a protein, starting from the position corresponding to the position of the nucleotide addition or deletion in the gene. Reversion would involve the opposite change, e.g., addition for deletion mutant, and would restore the normal amino acid sequence except for the region of the protein corresponding to the region between the sites of the nucleotide changes. Acridine-induced phage mutants that lack a functional lysozyme should be excellent material with which to test these expectations.

C. NUCLEOTIDE COMPOSITION AND SEQUENCE OF CODING UNITS

1. NUCLEOTIDE-AMINO ACID RELATIONSHIPS

The nature of the coding relationships between the nucleotides of DNA and the amino acids of proteins has been a subject of considerable theoretical and experimental attention over the past ten years. A number of codes have been proposed in which nucleotides on both strands of DNA are involved in specifying amino acid sequence information.[105] In view of recent studies,[8, 16-21] which suggest that the actual translation is performed on single-stranded messenger RNA's by the ribosomes, and that messenger RNA has the complementary structure of only one of the strands of DNA,[16-18] the coding problem would appear to be reduced to a consideration of possible sequences of nucleotides on one strand that could code for 20 different amino acids.

A code involving only two nucleotides per amino acid seems very unlikely. Twenty coding units are needed for the common amino acids in proteins and there are only 16 two-nucleotide combinations. Furthermore, the available data suggest that there is appreciable degeneracy of the code[106-109], i.e., there are several nucleotide sequences (coding units) for each amino acid. Nevertheless, a mixed code containing some coding units with two nucleotides is certainly not ruled out by any existing data. Triplet codes, i.e., codes with three nucleotides per amino acid coding unit, have been seriously considered by several investigators.[66, 67, 106-109] Overlapping codes involving three nucleotides were excluded[110] on the basis of the consideration that overlapping would restrict the amino acids that could be adjacent to one another. There does not appear to be any such restriction as far as can be determined from known amino acid sequences in proteins. This argument is no longer applicable, however, in view of the recent evidence which suggests that there is appreciable degeneracy of the code. With a degenerate overlapping code it would be possible to have many combinations of amino acids adjacent to one another. More convincing evidence that is inconsistent with overlapping codes has been obtained in mutational studies. In no case have adjacent amino acids in a protein been changed by a single mutational event.[13, 93, 111] Furthermore, in one study of mutational alteration of protein primary structure any one of seven different amino acids could occupy one position in a protein.[13] In each of these cases the amino acids on either side of this position in the protein were unchanged.[13, 112] Obviously not all of these changes could be due to mutational alterations at the same nucleotide position; nevertheless, there was no change of either of the adjacent amino acids. A code in which a nucleotide triplet codes for each amino acid and in which there is no overlapping of nucleotides in adjacent coding units would appear to be the simplest code that would provide sufficient combinations to specify several coding units for each of the 20 amino acids.

One serious problem which arises in nonoverlapping, degenerate triplet codes is the recognition of the separation between adjacent coding units. This problem was considered initially by Crick et al.[66] before evidence of degeneracy was presented, and it was proposed that there might be certain triplets, nonsense triplets, which did not code. Crick et al.[66] showed that if most triplets were of the nonsense type several triplet codes could be derived, each containing only twenty meaningful coding units. In each of these codes all overlaps of the twenty coding units were nonsense. An alternative, also proposed by Crick and co-workers,[67] which is consistent with degeneracy of the code, is that the nucleotide sequence in messenger RNA is read (translated) from a fixed starting point, three nucleotides at a time (Fig. 4). According to this interpretation it would be possible to have as many as 64 different meaningful triplets. Since the reading would start from a fixed point and involve three nucleotides at a time, each coding unit would be marked off from the preceding and succeeding ones. Codes involving four nucleotide coding units have also been considered.[113] With four nucleotides per amino acid, many more meaningful and nonsense nucleotide sequences could be written. It is obvious that there are many possible codes, and we do not yet know whether every amino acid is coded by the same number of nucleotides. Certainly, it would not be too surprising if there were something unusual about the coding units that correspond to the first or last amino acid in a protein.

An approach to deciphering the genetic code has recently been discovered in studies with synthetic messenger RNA's. Nirenberg and Matthaei,[114] while examining the effects of ribonucleic acids on the incorporation of labeled amino acids into proteins in vitro, observed that synthetic polyribonucleotides would stimulate the incorporation of labeled amino acids into a protein product. It was further noted that when polyuridylic acid was added phenylalanine was the predominant labeled amino acid that was incorporated into polypeptides.[114] This initial finding suggested that the RNA coding unit for phenylalanine involved some sequence of uridylic acid residues. Extension of this observation by Nirenberg and co-workers,[106, 108] and Ochoa and co-workers[107, 109, 115] has led to the designation of specific coding units for all of the amino acids (Table III). Using syn-

TABLE III

CODING UNITS DETECTED WITH SYNTHETIC POLYRIBONUCLEOTIDES[a]

Amino acid	Coding unit			
Alanine	UCG	UCG	ACG	—
Arginine	UCG	CCG	GAA	—
Aspartic acid	GUA	ACA	GCA	—
Asparagine	UAC	UAA	CAA	—
Cysteine	UUG	—	—	—
Glutamic acid	UAG	AAG	AAC	
Glutamine	UAC	AGG	AAC	—
Glycine	UGG	CGG	AGG	—
Histidine	AUC	ACC		—
Isoleucine	UUA	UAA	UAC	—
Leucine	UUU	UUA	UUC	UUG
Lysine	UAA	AAA	AAC	AAG
Methionine	UGA	—	—	—
Phenylalanine	UUU	UCU	—	—
Proline	UCC	CCC	CCA	CCG
Serine	CCU	CUU	UCG	ACG
Threonine	UCA	CAC	CAA	CGC
Tryptophan	UGG	UCG	—	—
Tyrosine	UUA	UCG	—	—
Valine	UUG	—	—	—

[a] Taken from the compilation by Jukes.[94]

thetic polyribonucleotides containing two or three of the nucleotide components of RNA, in different combinations, it was shown that the specificity of amino acid incorporation was markedly affected by the composition of the polymer that was provided. By employing polynucleotides with different ratios of two component nucleotides the relative incorporation of different amino acids was affected.[108, 115] The conclusion from these experiments was that the coding units corresponding to amino acids that were incorporated to a great extent contained two nucleotides of the major nucleotide component of the polyribonucleotide, while amino acids that were incorporated poorly were coded by sequences in which the minority nucleotide was the predominant component. It was not possible from these studies to establish the number of nucleotides corresponding to each amino acid, but the quantitative data on relative amino acid incorporation and relative base composition of the RNA messenger was most readily explained by a triplet code.[108, 115]

In these studies it was observed that polyribonucleotides containing different nucleotides frequently stimulated the incorporation of the same amino acid.[106-109] This finding led to the designation of several coding units for each of the amino acids and established that the code was degenerate in the *in vitro* system. At the present time most of the 64 theoretically possible triplet coding units have been identified.[106-109] As the list of identified coding units grew, an unanticipated relationship between different coding units for the same amino acid became apparent. In many cases two or more coding units for the same amino acid had two nucleotides in common.[106-109] This relationship has been interpretated in several ways,[94, 116] including the proposal[116] that the two shared nucleotides may occupy the same positions in different codings units, and that in the third position the two purines are equivalent in coding and the two pyrimidines are equivalent in coding. One possible implication of this suggestion is that a given transfer RNA may pair with two different messenger RNA triplets. Whether or not this interpretation is correct remains to be determined.

Evidence of a different nature also suggests that the code consists of triplet coding units (Fig. 4). In the previously mentioned studies by Crick and co-workers[67] with acridine-induced *rII* mutants of phage T4 it was observed that most of the revertants obtained from such mutants were second-site revertants; i.e., the reversion event occurred at a second site within the *rII* gene. Examination of the mutants and the second-site revertants led to two surprising findings; (*1*) phage with the second-site change free of the primary mutational alteration had the mutant phenotype, and (*2*) the original mutants and the revertants could be grouped into two categories. These were arbitrarily designated + and −. If a + alteration were combined with a − alteration, the phenotype of the doubly altered strain was often wild-type. Thus + and − appeared to represent two different types of alterations of the genetic material. As was mentioned previously, Crick *et al.*[67] interpreted these observations in terms of additions and deletions of single nucleotides. The + and − types would thus represent strains in which the mutation involved an addition or deletion of a nucleotide. If the code were triplet and read from a fixed starting point three nucleotides at a time, the effects of a single nucleotide deletion could only be reversed by adding a nucleotide at the original position or at another position in the same gene. The amino acids in between the two points of mutation in a + − strain would not necessarily be the same as those in the unmutated protein (Fig. 4). Since certain amino acid sequences would be essential for protein function, it would be expected that certain + − combinations would restore the wild-type phenotype while other combinations would not—and this is exactly what was found. Extension of these experiments to the synthesis of phage stocks in which three + or three − alterations in the *rII* region were combined led to the additional finding that such combinations could restore the wild-type phenotype.[67] The interpretation offered is that coding units are in fact composed of triplets for each amino acid and either the addition of three nucleotides or the deletion of three nucleotides restores the normal reading frame. In either case the only region of the corresponding protein which would differ from the wild-type protein would be the region between the positions corresponding to the extremes of the sites of nucleotide additions or deletions (Fig. 4). This explanation requires a great deal of degeneracy of the code since almost every triplet would have to be meaningful. The principal objection to the interpretation of these studies is that it depends on the existence of a protein product of the *rII* gene. Although this seems likely, no such protein has been detected to date.

Attempts have been made to deduce the relative nucleotide sequences in coding units by examining amino acid replacement data in relation to the coding units determined in studies with synthetic polyribonucleotides.[13, 93, 94, 111, 117] The assumption underlying this approach is a reasonable one, viz., that an amino acid change results from a single nucleotide change. If this assumption is correct, and the code is triplet, any amino acid that replaces a second amino acid must be coded by a coding unit that is identical at two positions to the coding unit of the original amino acid. The replacement data summarized in Table II and the coding units presented in Table III are consistent with these assumptions. However, in view of the extent of the degeneracy of the code which is evident from the studies with synthetic polyribonucleotide,[106-109] and the fact that nucleotide sequences are not known, it is perhaps not surprising that coding units can be selected that are consistent with amino acid replacement data. Because of degeneracy it is possible to relate the nucleotide positions in a group of coding units only in cases in which a series of changes are detected at the same position in a protein. There is one such series known, in the trytophan synthetase A protein, where any one of seven amino acids can occupy the same position in the protein.[13, 95-97, 112] These seven amino acids are related in that single mutational events were involved in each amino acid change.[13] Furthermore, the fact that most of these changes were observed repeatedly supports the view that each mutational change probably was a single event, possibly involving a single nucleotide substitution. The additional fact that many of the changes at this site in the tryptophan synthetase A protein were also observed following base analog mutagenesis also supports the nucleotide substitution hypothesis.[13] From data of this type, and the known coding units,[106-109] it was possible to deduce some information on the relative nucleotide sequences in the coding units for the seven amino acids.[13]

A direct approach to determining the sequences of nucleotides in coding units was described by Wahba *et al.*[118] Using polynucleotide phosphorylase, polyribonucleotides were prepared with known nucleotide sequences at one end. With these polyribonucleotides specific amino acid incorporation could be studied in the *in vitro* system.[114] It was found in this way[118] that poly-U containing G at the 5′-hydroxyl end stimulated the incorporation of cysteine as well as phenylalanine, while poly-U containing A at the 5′-hydroxyl end stimulated the incorporation of tyrosine and phenylalanine. These data, plus the finding that the tyrosine appeared to be at the carboxy-terminal end of the synthesized polypeptide, suggested that the sequences AUU and GUU corresponded to tyrosine and cysteine, respectively.[118] It is interesting that the conclusion from this experiment is consistent with amino acid replacement data since the tyrosine-cysteine change is a known amino acid replacement (Table II). Extensions of this approach will obviously yield considerable, if not complete, information on the sequence of nucleotides in the different coding units.

The relative order of the nucleotides in other coding units has been inferred from recombination experiments with the A-gene-A-protein system.[13, 97] If two *A* mutants with alterations in the same coding unit are crossed with one another, recombinants can only be recovered if different nucleotide positions were affected by the original mutations. This is illustrated in Fig. 5. If the same nucleotide position were involved in both coding unit changes it would not be possible to obtain any recombinants with coding units differing from those of the parental strain. However, if the nucleotide alterations were in different positions in the same coding unit it would be possible to obtain two new coding units by recombination. If either of these coding units corresponded to an amino acid that could restore activity to an enzyme, a wild-type-like recombinant would be detected. When this approach was applied to strains with amino acid replacements at the same position in the A protein, it was found that new amino acids did appear in the A proteins of recombinants from crosses. For example, in the cross of a valine strain by an arginine mutant, serine and glycine recombinants were recovered.[13, 97] This finding demonstrates that the specific valine and arginine coding units concerned differ in different nucleotide positions, and furthermore, that from these coding units it is possible to derive coding units for glycine and serine. By using a linked genetic marker in the same cross the genetic analyses gave some information concerning the relative positions of the different nucleotide alterations

1. Cross between mutants in which the mutations affected the same nucleotide position in one coding unit

Mutant 1 ACB
         ↑
Wild type ABB
         ↑
Mutant 2 AAB

Mutant 1 ACB
     ×   × ⟶ only the parental coding units
Mutant 2 AAB

2. Cross between mutants with nucleotide differences at two positions in the same coding unit

Mutant 1 ACB
     × ⟶ ACC + ABB (new coding units)
Mutant 2 ABC

3. Cross between mutants with nucleotide differences at three positions in the same coding unit

ACB
 × ⟶ ACC, AAC, BCB, BAB, AAB, BCC
BAC   (new coding units)

FIG. 5. Recombination within an amino acid coding unit.

on the genetic map.[13] This approach cannot give the nucleotide composition of the coding units but imposes restrictions on possible sequences within these coding units.[13]

2. NUCLEOTIDE COMPOSITION AND SEQUENCE OF NATURAL CODING UNITS

Although it seems very likely that it will be possible to determine the RNA nucleotide sequences corresponding to specific amino acids with the *in vitro* system that has been discussed, it ultimately will be necessary to confirm these sequences in DNA and to establish the existence of the assumed relationships between DNA, messenger RNA, transfer RNA, and amino acids. As mentioned previously, it is not possible to isolate or recognize a DNA segment corresponding to a single gene, nor is there a convenient procedure for the sequential analysis of the nucleotides in DNA. Furthermore, there is the additional complication in analyses with DNA that probably only one of the strands is involved in specifying the nucleotide sequence of messenger RNA. Thus the possibility of determining the nucleotide sequences in DNA that correspond to specific amino acids is remote at the present time. An indirect approach, which attempts to overcome these difficulties, involves the study of mutagenic agents which presumably cause specific nucleotide changes in DNA.[13, 69, 93, 111] If amino acid substitutions could be correlated with specific nucleotide changes, and if different nucleotide changes could be induced in the same coding unit, theoretically it would be possible to obtain *in vivo* evidence concerning the nucleotide composition of coding units corresponding to specific amino acids. In general, two types of mutagenic agents have been employed in studies of this type: (*1*) base analogs which can be incorporated into DNA and cause nucleotide changes due to errors in incorporation or pairing; (*2*) agents which can be used to chemically alter specific nucleotides, either in the intact organism, or free of the organism (transforming DNA, tobacco mosaic virus RNA) with the result that errors occur during replication. The presumed nucleotide changes caused by these agents have been summarized by Freese.[69]

This approach has been used in a few cases and the amino acid changes detected have been correlated with the nucleotides in the coding units assigned to the amino acids in *in vitro* studies.[13, 93, 111] Because of the degeneracy of the code, it is not too surprising that there is good agreement between the presumed specificity of the mutagen and the changes actually observed. Somewhat more impressive are the results of studies of the effect of nitrous acid treatment of synthetic polyribonucleotide on the incorporation of amino acids in the *in vitro* system.[119] The polyribonucleotides, poly-UA, poly-UG, and poly-UC, were treated with nitrous acid and the specificity of amino acid incorporation was determined with the chemically altered product. It was found that the treated poly-UA acquired the coding characteristics of poly-UG while the treated poly-UG and poly-UC lost the ability to stimulate the incorporation of serine and valine, respectively. These observations were consistent with the changes known to result from nitrous acid treatment.[69, 93, 120, 121] In spite of these convincing results, the use of mutagens leaves much to be desired in the ultimate objective of determining nucleotide composition and sequences. Nitrous acid treatment has been shown to produce deletions with high frequency in phage,[122] in addition to causing presumed single nucleotide changes. Furthermore, studies on the replication of DNA containing 5-bromouracil (dABŪ polymer) did not give the expected result, guanine being exclusively incorporated next to bromouracil.[123] Nevertheless, base analog mutagenesis and chemical treatments do show mutational specificity and thus the continued use of mutagens should contribute to our information on the nucleotide composition of coding units.

One of the most promising approaches to determining the nucleotide composition and sequences of natural coding units would appear to be the isolation and study of specific messenger RNA's. The development of techniques for the separation of messenger RNA's by hybrid formation with DNA,[124-126] and the use of RNA from RNA viruses in the *in vitro* amino acid incorporation system[127, 128] hold considerable promise. In fact, it has been shown with both tobacco mosaic virus RNA and the RNA of phage F2 that a protein associated with these viruses is formed when the corresponding RNA is added to the Nirenberg-Matthaei system.[127, 128] Only a fraction of the protein formed with tobacco mosaic virus RNA appears to correspond to the protein of tobacco mosaic virus.[127, 128] Therefore, much of the RNA of the virus must be concerned with coding for proteins that do not enter the mature virus. Mutational studies with TMV are consistent with these conclusions; only a fraction of the mutational alterations that affect the virus alter the viral protein.[93] It remains to be determined how many genes are represented in most messenger RNA's.

D. PRIMARY STRUCTURE CHANGES IN RELATION TO FUNCTION

Quite apart from their bearing on the genetic code, amino acid substitutions are of interest with regard to their effect on protein function. It is questionable to what extent the effects of single amino acid changes in a protein can be interpreted in the absence of information on the tertiary structure of the protein in solution. However, tertiary structures determined by crystallographic studies may be sufficiently representative of the structure in solution to permit the study of this question. As yet, information of this type is not available for mutationally altered proteins. In altered hemoglobins, the effects of some of the amino acid changes detected can be interpreted as a stabilization of the altered hemoglobin in the ferric form.[10] In altered tryptophan synthetase A proteins, substitution of a single uncharged residue by a residue with a charged side chain results in the complete loss of enzymic activity[95, 96] (Fig. 4). When such charged amino acids are replaced by amino acids with small neutral side chains such as in serine and alanine, the corresponding A proteins are fully functional.[13, 97] When the substituted amino acids have somewhat larger side chains, as in threonine and valine,[13, 97] the corresponding proteins are only slightly active catalytically. Thus the nature of a single side chain at a critical position in the protein markedly affects the activity of the protein. Single amino acid substitutions also have profound effects on the stability and other properties of specific proteins. Perhaps of even greater interest are cases in which an amino acid replacement at one position reverses the effects of a previous amino acid replacement in the same protein. As mentioned previously, instances of this type have been noted in studies with the alkaline phosphatase[11] and tryptophan synthetase A protein of *E. coli*.[103] In such cases there is obviously some interaction between different regions of the folded polypeptide chain.

Many amino acid changes can be tolerated in proteins, with little or no effect on activity. This is most obvious from comparisons of the structure of a protein that is present in different species.[129, 130] Furthermore, extensive chemical modifications of a protein can often be accomplished without appreciably affecting enzyme activity.[37, 131, 132] In addition, as mentioned previously, it is possible to remove large segments of the polypeptide chains of certain enzymes without destroying catalytic activity.[39, 40] These observations indicate that not all of an enzyme's structure is essential for catalytic activity. The complexity of protein structure would appear to make the task of interpreting single amino acid replacements a formidable one.

III. Gene Interactions and Enzyme Formation and Activity

In recent years studies with microorganisms have provided insight into the regulatory mechanisms used to control the cellular levels and activities of many enzymes.[133] The regulatory mechanisms employed permit the cell to respond efficiently to changes in the environment and also to maintain enzymic processes in balance. Studies on the genetic control of the regulation of the synthesis of specific enzymes have shown that regulatory systems are quite complex. There appear to be some genic regions that are responsible for the production of cell substances, repressors, that are concerned with determining whether or not a given enzyme is formed. In addition, there appear to be genic regions that respond to these substances by permitting the synthesis or preventing the formation of specific enzymes. The various mechanisms that are believed to be involved in the regulation of microbial syntheses have been reviewed in Volume III, Chapter 12, and elsewhere,[133] and will not be dealt with in detail here. A few examples will be given, however, to illustrate the general types of observations that have been made, and the interactions that occur between regulatory genes and genes determining protein structure.

A. REGULATION OF PROTEIN SYNTHESIS

Studies on the regulation of β-galactosidase synthesis in *E. coli*[50, 55] have shown that a gene, designated i, is concerned with the formation of a cell substance, a repressor, that is involved in regulating the synthesis of β-galactosidase. This repressor is believed to prevent the release or formation of messenger RNA concerned with the structure of β-galactosidase. The mechanism of repression is assumed to involve the interaction of the repressor substance with a specific receptor region in the genetic material, the "operator region."[50, 55] When the repressor substance is combined at the operator region the cell is believed to be incapable of producing messenger RNA for β-galactosidase. If an inducer is added from the environment it presumably stimulates enzyme formation by preventing the repressor from combining at the operator region. The chemical nature of the repressor substance is not known. The studies with this system have shown that the β-galactosidase operator region and specific repressor not only control β-galactosidase formation, but also control the production of the products of at least two other genes.[50, 55] These genes are immediately adjacent to the β-galactosidase structural gene and are concerned with the formation of a galactoside permease and a galactoside transacetylase.[50, 55, 134] A complex of genes controlled by one operator region, and including this region, has been termed an "operon."[50, 55, 135] Similar interactions between operator regions, repressor genes, structure-determining genes, and groups of structure-determining genes concerned with related reactions have been observed in other systems.[51-53, 133, 136, 137] Mutational alterations with very different effects have been detected in the operator region controlling the β-galactosidase operon.[50, 55] One type of operator mutation, O^c, results in the synthesis of high levels of β-galactosidase and the other enzymes controlled by the same operon, in the absence of an exogenous inducer. This type of alteration has been interpreted as a change in the operator region which prevents combination with the repressor substance. A second type of operator mutation, O^o, prevents the cell from forming enzyme in response to the substrate or other inducers. This type of mutation has been interpreted as an alteration in the operator region which results in the inability of the inducer to prevent the repressor from inhibiting messenger RNA formation. This could be due to increased affinity of the repressor substance for the operator region, or to the inability of the operator region to interact with the inducer.

An important question which may be asked concerning the operator region is whether it is within the primary structure-determining region of the gene for β-galactosidase. Although examination of the β-galactosidase produced by some of the operator mutants did not reveal any gross protein structure differences, as mentioned previously, revertants obtained from some O^o mutants appeared to form structurally altered enzymes.[50, 55] It would seem, therefore, that at least a portion of the operator region concerned with the synthesis of β-galactosidase (and the other enzymes controlled by the same operon) also codes for a segment of the primary structure of β-galactosidase. This, of course, would not be true of the other enzymes controlled by the same operator region. These observations indicate that a segment of the β-galactosidase protein may correspond to a nucleotide sequence with an important function in regulation. Regulatory genes, perhaps analogous to the i gene, that are not linked to the structural gene, or genes, they control, have been demonstrated in studies with other enzymes; e.g., the alkaline phosphatase[137] and tryptophan synthetase of

E. coli,[138] the tyrosinase of *Neurospora*,[87, 139] and the histidine enzymes of *Salmonella*.[136]

Once messenger RNA leaves its site of synthesis it presumably combines with ribosomes and serves as a template for the synthesis of specific polypeptide chains. Studies on the life of messenger RNA suggest that it functions in the synthesis of a very few protein molecules,[16, 19] and then is degraded. Exceptions are apparent in animal systems—the most notable one involves the presumed messenger RNA for hemoglobin which appears to be used repeatedly.[8] If all messenger RNA's have a very short life in microbial systems, it would not be necessary to regulate the translation of the messenger. Regulation of the synthesis of messenger RNA would be sufficient to control protein formation. However, if some messengers have a long life, regulatory mechanisms at the RNA translation level would probably also be necessary. Studies of the effect of regulatory mutations and induction on the formation of specific messengers have shown very clearly that the rate of specific messenger synthesis is controlled.[140, 141]

It was mentioned previously that certain structural gene mutations affect the rate of synthesis of the corresponding protein in addition to altering protein structure. In some cases mutations of this type also lead to a reduced rate of synthesis of other enzymes controlled by the same operon.[50, 52, 83, 136, 142] Often the activities of all the enzymes controlled by genes on one side of the mutated gene are low. Mutations of this type, called "polarity mutations,"[50] have been detected in several systems.[50, 52, 136, 142] In studies of the histidine operon of *Salmonella*, 20 of 39 mutants examined showed significant polarity effects.[136] The levels of all the enzymes controlled by genes on the side of the mutated gene away from the operator gene were low, while the enzymes controlled by genes between the operator and the mutated gene were present in normal amounts. Thus some mutations can disturb the coordinated synthesis of enzymes controlled by the same operon.

There are two levels at which these observations could be explained. A structural gene mutation could affect the rate of synthesis or release of messenger RNA's from DNA, or it could affect the rate of synthesis or release of a polypeptide chain from the messenger RNA-polyribosome complex. Of the two explanations the first seems less likely because it would require that many single nucleotide substitutions in DNA would influence the rate of translation of DNA into RNA.[136] If, in fact, certain coding units in messenger RNA correspond to minority transfer RNA molecules, as has been suggested,[136] the rate of synthesis of each protein could in part be governed by the make-up of the corresponding RNA. On this basis, quantitative effects on enzyme formation associated with structural gene mutations would be due to the availability of different specific transfer RNA molecules. To explain polarity within an operon it would have to be further asssumed that each messenger RNA molecule corresponds to an operon and that translation of the messenger proceeds from one end to the other. Recent studies by Martin[143] suggest that there is a single messenger for the entire histidine operon and other studies suggest that the messenger RNA may be quite large.[17, 19] It is also conceivable that the folding of each polypeptide chain may influence its rate of release from the messenger RNA-polyribosome complex. Amino acid replacements that make specific folding of the polypeptide chain less likely might decrease the rate of protein synthesis. If the translation is oriented, polarity effects could be observed.

The preferential translation of certain segments of an RNA messenger is clearly evident from studies with an RNA phage.[127, 144] It was shown that the principal protein product formed in response to phage RNA was the coat protein. Therefore, despite the fact that information specifying other proteins was present in the RNA, one region was preferentially translated into polypeptide chains.

It would appear from the data that are available that there are several levels at which regulation of specific protein synthesis is accomplished.

B. Regulation of Enzyme Activity

In addition to regulatory mechanisms which operate at the level of RNA and protein synthesis, regulation of metabolic activities is also accomplished, and more rapidly, by the interaction of small molecules with enzymes.[46, 47] Nonspecific environmental conditions, e.g., pH, ionic strength, etc., influence enzymic activity, but of greater significance are specific interactions between an enzyme and substances which in one way or another are affected by the functioning of the enzyme. One of the most interesting groups of enzymes which are affected by low molecular weight metabolites are the so-called "feed-back" enzymes.[46] These enzymes can combine with the end product of the pathway in which they participate and are inactive or less active under such conditions. The particular enzyme in a biosynthetic pathway which is generally subject to feed-back inhibition by the end product of the pathway is the enzyme catalyzing the first unique step in the pathway.[46, 47] This mechanism of enzyme inhibition has the obvious advantage to the cell of blocking a pathway if an excess of the end product of the pathway is present. Furthermore, feed-back inhibition can probably instantaneously stop a reaction while regulatory mechanisms that operate at the level of RNA and protein synthesis could not. Feed-back inhibition is therefore particularly important during stages of active metabolic activity.

Whenever the sole available carbon or nitrogen source is the substrate of an enzyme that is susceptible to feed-back inhibition, feed-back inhibition would be expected to prevent the utilization of the substrate. In studies of biochemical reactions that are involved in both synthetic and degradative pathways it has been found that two distinct enzymes are produced, only one of which is subject to feed-back inhibition. This situation has been most clearly documented with the L-threonine deaminases of *E. coli*.[46, 145] One threonine deaminase is inhibited and its formation repressed by an end product of threonine metabolism, isoleucine, while the second deaminase is insensitive to isoleucine inhibition and its synthesis is induced by threonine. With two distinct enzymes, subject to different regulatory controls, the bacterial cell can cope with this seemingly difficult problem.

A second interesting situation encountered in microorganisms illustrates the use of feed-back inhibition in dealing with a difficult regulatory problem. Metabolic reaction sequences generally branch as they near the small molecular weight biosynthetic end products. This presents the organism with the problem of regulating enzymic reactions that are common to the synthesis of two or more end products. If feed-back inhibition of a common enzyme were obtained with either end product, the synthesis of both end products would be blocked. Studies of one situation of this type in *E. coli*,[146] involving a reaction that is common to the synthesis of both lysine and threonine (aspartic acid $\rightarrow$ aspartyl phosphate), have shown that two aspartokinases are produced. One of the enzymes is inhibited (and repressed) by threonine but not by lysine, while the other enzyme has the opposite sensitivities. In this case, an excess of either end product only partially inhibits a common biosynthetic step.

The mechanism of feed-back inhibition of enzyme activity has been studied with several enzyme systems. With both threonine deaminase[46, 147] and aspartic transcarbamylase,[148] the feed-back inhibitor lowers the affinity of the enzyme for its normal substrate. This lowers the rate of the reaction at any given substrate concentration. With aspartic transcarbamylase, as the aspartate concentration is increased the inhibition by the feed-back inhibitor, cytosine triphosphate, is relieved.[148] This indicates that under physiological conditions the activity of the enzyme is probably regulated by the concentrations of several substances.

Studies on the mechanism by which the feed-back inhibitor alters the ability of an enzyme to combine with its substrate suggest that conformational changes of the enzyme, affecting the active site region, are associated with the attachment of inhibitor. It has been possible to desensitize an enzyme with respect to feed-back inhibition without affecting the substrate-combining site by relatively mild treatments such as gentle heating.[46, 47, 147-149] In addition, mutation can also reduce the sensitivity of an enzyme to a feed-back inhibitor,[136, 150] and to different extents.[47] In one case, involving the feed-back-sensitive enzyme PRPP-ATP-PPase (phosphoribosyl-ATP pyrophosphorylase) Martin has found that the desensitized enzyme still binds the feed-back inhibitor, histidine.[149] It seems likely, therefore, that desensitization may involve protein structure changes which prevent combination with an inhibitor from altering the conformation of an essential site of substrate binding. Gerhart and Pardee[148] have in fact shown that the sedimentation coefficient of desensitized aspartic transcarbamylase is 5.9 as compared to a value of 11.6 obtained with the native enzyme. This suggests that in this case desensitization involves the separation of protein subunits. It would appear, therefore, that native aspartic transcarbamylase is composed of subunits and that specific association between these subunits is essential for feed-back inhibition. The observations mentioned suggest that different regions of a protein are concerned with substrate binding and feed-back-inhibitor binding and that each combination results in a different conformational change.

In addition to the substrate and end product, other substances apparently can specifically combine with an enzyme and affect its activity. For example, the inhibition of aspartic transcarbamylase by cytosine triphosphate is relieved by ATP[148] and the inhibition of threonine deaminase by isoleucine is antagonized by valine.[151] Gerhart and Pardee[148] have interpreted the ATP effect in the following way: when the ATP concentration is exceptionally high the cell needs additional pyrimidine nucleotides for nucleic acid synthesis. By relieving the cytosine triphosphate inhibition of the transcarbamylase, ATP would permit an increase in the internal concentration of cytosine triphosphate.

Metabolites have been shown to have effects on enzyme activity which cannot be ascribed to relief of inhibition. Acetyl-CoA-carboxylase has been found to be activated by citrate or fluorocitrate, compounds which do not participate in the reaction catalyzed by this enzyme.[152, 153] Activation requires incubation of enzyme with citrate at physiological temperatures.[152] These observations suggest that there is a slow, temperature-dependent, modification of enzyme structure in the presence of citrate. Sucrose-gradient sedimentation studies demonstrated that there was a marked change in the sedimentation coefficient when the enzyme was activated.[153] The inactive enzyme had an S value of 18.8 while the S value for the activated enzyme was about 43. This finding indicates that citrate activation involves the association of several subunits. Apparently the complex is the only enzymically active unit. Aggregation of subunits has also been shown to play a major role in enzyme activation in studies with beef liver glutamic dehydrogenase.[49, 154-158] In the presence of coenzyme, $NADH_2$ (reduced diphosphopyridine nucleotide), the enzyme dissociates into four subunits of approximate molecular weight of 250,000. In this form the enzyme is considerably less active and, in fact, appears to function as an alanine dehydrogenase.[156] NAD and ADP can prevent the dissociation induced by $NADH_2$. A variety of nonsubstrates can disaggregate glutamic dehydrogenase, including many estrogens and thyroxine.[156, 158] The disaggregation induced by steroids can be reversed by several amino acids, including L-leucine, L-isoleucine, and L-methionine. The site of leucine binding appears to be distinct from the site of glutamate oxidation, indicating again that an interaction site may be distinct from the substrate binding site.[156] In fact, Frieden has concluded that the disaggregation caused by pyridine nucleotides is due to binding at sites other than the coenzyme binding site at the active center.[49, 159] It is clear that the structures of many proteins contain sites which bind nonsubstrates and are used to control enzyme activity. Other examples and other aspects of allosteric interactions are discussed in detail by Monod, Changeux, Jacob.[47]

C. INTERALLELE COMPLEMENTATION

One of the standard tests employed in the past with *Neurospora* to determine whether or not two mutant genes were alleles was to prepare a heterocaryon containing both types of mutant nuclei in the same cytoplasm, and to examine the phenotype of the resultant culture.[160] If the two mutants were altered in different genes the heterocaryon was expected to form all essential functional end products, and therefore to exhibit the wild-type phenotype. If both mutants produced defective forms of the same end product, the heterocaryon was expected to have the mutant phenotype. This test seemed adequate for many years. However, when extensive allelism testing was carried out, exceptions were noted.[73, 161-165] In fact, exceptions have been detected in many organisms in which it is possible to have different allelic forms of a gene in the same cytoplasm. This type of interaction which gives a phenotype approaching that of the wild type is termed "interallele complementation." Not all the alleles at a particular locus are capable of complementation.[165-171] Furthermore, not every combination of complementing alleles results in the wild-type phenotype.[165] Complementation tests have been conducted with large numbers of mutants to detect all possible complementing pairs. On the basis of such tests maps have been constructed which relate the mutants in terms of their ability, or lack of ability, to complement.[165] Complementation maps are usually represented in the following way: If two mutants are incapable of complementing with one another, they are represented by overlapping bars. If they do complement the bars are not overlapping. If two strains complement one another but a third mutant does not complement with either, the bar representing the third mutant overlaps the bars corresponding to both of the other mutants. Each bar represents a defective region, in terms of the complementation test. In most cases complementation maps prepared as described are linear. Furthermore, complementation maps sometimes show fair linear correspondence with fine-structure genetic maps prepared with the mutants used in the complementation tests.[167] There are some notable exceptions where circular[172] or spiral complementation maps[173] appear to best describe the data and in which the genetic and complementation maps do not correspond.

Enzyme analyses performed with extracts of heterocaryons formed from complementing mutants have shown that the enzymic activity is present that is specifically lacking in the two mutants.[82, 165, 168, 172, 174] Thus the two mutant genes, or their products, interact to form a functional protein. In several cases the functional product was distinguishable from the wild-type enzyme.[77, 162, 168] The interaction between the two mutant alleles could involve messenger RNA's and/or polypeptide chains, during or after synthesis, but most of the existing evidence favors interaction between polypeptide chains as the mechanism of complementation. Since many proteins are composed of two or more subunits it is reasonable to expect that random association would give some proteins with nonidentical subunits.[162] If the subunits were defective in different regions the associated complex might exhibit enzyme activity. Direct support for this mechanism of complementation has been obtained from the observation that complementation can be accomplished *in vitro* by mixing extracts of complementing mutants under prescribed conditions.[174-176] In *in vitro* studies with highly purified CRM's from alkaline phosphatase mutants, for example, Schlesinger *et al.*[176] clearly demonstrated that the active protein that is produced is a dimer composed of one subunit of each of the CRM types. In this case no simple correlation exists between the genetic map and the complementation map.[176] With proteins that consist of more than two subunits it would be expected that several complementation enzymes could be produced. Recent studies by Fincham and co-workers suggest that this is the case when certain mutant forms of *Neurospora* glutamic dehydrogenase are employed in *in vitro* complementation experiments.[168]

Whether the mechanism of complementation observed *in vitro* is the exclusive mechanism that operates *in vivo* is not known. The condition that is most effective in dissociating protein subunits *in vitro* is mild acidification. Certainly such conditions do not prevail *in vivo*, but it has been suggested that *in vivo* the formation of the complementation aggregate may take place at the site of synthesis of one of the polypeptide subunits.[177] Since, in a heterocaryon or the equivalent, the synthesis of each polypeptide chain probably occurs in an environment of completed polypeptide chains of a second type, the formation of a mixed aggregate may take place readily.

In instances of *in vivo* complementation the level of enzyme activity that is observed varies with each pair of mutants and generally is considerably less than the wild-type level.[165, 174] The low levels are not due to an effect on specific protein synthesis since immunological studies indicate that the protein is produced but there is less activity associated with it.[77, 178] The different activity levels observed probably reflect the structure of the aggregate, if subunit association is responsible for activity, and the extent to which the different subunits can interact to form a semifunctional active site.[168] This will depend on many factors, including the affinities of the subunits for each other, the number of subunits in the aggregate, the number of active sites in the aggregate and the number of different polypeptide chains that comprise the aggregate. Proteins are known where the aggregate consists of two identical subunits, two nonidentical subunits, two pairs of nonidentical subunits, four identical subunits, etc., and in which the aggregate shows different degrees of dissociability into subunits. It seems likely that in most cases complementation depends on these properties of the enzyme being studied.

D. Suppressor Mutations

In reversion studies with mutant strains it is frequently found that some of the genetic changes responsible for the restoration of the wild-type phenotype do not occur in the mutant gene.[9] Genetic changes of this type, which reverse the effects of a mutation in another gene, are termed "suppressor mutations." Since suppressor mutations are recognized by the restoration of the wild-type phenotype, it would be expected that a variety of mechanisms would be responsible for the phenotype change. Of principal interest with regard to mechanisms of gene action is the question: Do some suppressor mutations lead to an alteration of the structure of the protein product of some other gene, or do all suppressor mutations indirectly circumvent a specific enzymic defect?

In cases of suppression the nature of the original mutational damage is of major importance. If the initial alteration resulted in metabolic imbalance, suppressor mutations could restore a more normal condition. If the original mutation caused some defect in the regulation of the formation of some enzyme, suppressor mutations might compensate for the defect by altering one of the cell constituents involved in regulation. If the original alteration resulted in the loss of an enzymic activity as a result of a primary structure change, suppression might involve relief of inhibition of an altered enzyme, activation of a by-pass of the blocked reaction, or restoration of a functional primary structure, if any of these are possible by suppressor mutation.

Instances representing many of the mechanisms mentioned have been found in studies of suppression with various microorganisms. In one well-analyzed case in *Neurospora*[179, 180, 181] it was shown that the primary mutational alteration in one mutant resulted in the production of an enzyme that was unusually susceptible to inhibition by trace amounts of divalent cations. A suppressor mutation permitted this strain to grow without a specific nutritional supplement and to produce a functional enzyme. When this enzyme was examined it was found to be indistinguishable from the mutant enzyme, particularly with respect to metal sensitivity. These findings have been interpreted as indicating that in the intact organism the suppressor mutation results in the exclusion of the natural inhibitor. This suppressor gene, as would be expected, affects only one of many other alleles at the same locus.[78] Thus the particular protein alteration of the suppressible mutant was the major factor determining the suppressor mutation that was detected. In other cases suppressor mutations affect most mutants altered at the same locus, and, as well, mutants blocked at different steps in the same pathway.[182-184] Suppressors of this type are most readily interpreted in terms of the activation of an alternate biosynthetic pathway.

Another example of suppressor gene action, illustrating the interdependence of different biosynthetic pathways, has been discovered in studies with pyrimidine mutants of *Neurospora*.[185, 186] Members of one class of pyrimidine mutants are suppressed by a gene which appears to have its primary effect on ornithine transcarbamylase, an enzyme participating in arginine synthesis. In strains with the suppressor gene the specific activity of ornithine transcarbamylase is reduced to 2–3% of the wild-type level. This reduction limits arginine synthesis but not to the extent that it limits growth. Since carbamylphosphate is involved in the synthesis of both arginine and pyrimidines it seems likely that some change affecting the utilization of this compound is responsible for the suppression of the pyrimidine requirement. The suppressor gene-pyrimidine mutant interactions are still under investigation.

One of the most commonly encountered types of suppressor mutation is allele-specific, and restores a functional enzyme.[78, 187-190] The allele-specificity of these suppressors establishes that the mutated suppressor gene cannot carry the structural information for the missing enzyme. If it did all mutants at one locus would be suppressed by the same suppressor gene. Allele-specific suppressor genes have been detected that affect CRM-forming mutants[59, 78] and others that suppress CRMless strains.[59, 61, 63] Enzyme activity measurements with extracts of suppressed CRM and CRMless mutants indicate that, although enzymic activity is restored, the level is generally very low.[59, 78] In studies of suppressor mutations affecting CRM-forming tryptophan synthetase mutants of *E. coli*, the level of activity detected was less than 10% of that expected on the basis of the total A or B protein that was present.[78, 190] In suppressed CRMless mutants, the level of restored activity was also low, but in such cases the enzyme appeared to be fully active.[59] These observations indicate that whatever the suppressor mechanism is, it does not restore normal amounts of fully active enzyme. Exceptions to this general result have been found in studies with an inducible enzyme, the alkaline phosphatase of *E. coli*.[61] The proposed explanation for this finding will be considered later in this section.

The low level of enzyme activity detected in suppressed CRM formers could be associated with enzyme molecules which are only slightly active catalytically. Alternatively, small amounts of a fully active protein could be produced by the suppressed mutant. Investigations with extracts of several suppressed CRM-forming mutants have demonstrated the presence in suppressed mutants of a fully active protein that resembles the wild-type protein in every property examined.[190, 191] The CRM protein is still formed by suppressed mutants and is indistinguishable from the CRM of the parental mutant.[190] The CRM protein and the suppressor-associated protein have been isolated from one suppressed A protein mutant and the primary structures examined.[190] It was found that the fully active A protein and the CRM protein had different amino acids at one position in the protein. The active protein had the same amino acid that was present at this position in the wild-type protein while the CRM protein had the same amino acid that was present in the CRM of the unsuppressed mutant. Active proteins restored as a result of suppression of CRMless mutants have been studied in several systems and the protein resembles the wild-type protein in its properties.[59, 61] However, primary structure studies have not been reported in any of these cases.

Since many of the allele-specific suppressor mutations that have been described restore a functional protein, and in the one case cited cause a primary structure change, it is reasonable to consider as a mechanism of suppression the alteration of some component involved in the incorporation of amino acids into proteins.[61, 68, 190, 192] There are several known cell components that participate in translating DNA information into protein primary structure including messenger RNA, transfer RNA's, and amino acid-activating enzymes. Presumably any one of these could be altered by a suppressor mutation with the result that either of two amino acids could be inserted at specific locations in the proteins of suppressed mutants. Specific nucleotide positions in some messenger RNA molecules could be modified enzymically with the result that the triplet with the modified nucleotide would be translated into a different amino acid than the unmodified triplet. Alteration of a specific transfer RNA or activating enzyme could lead to partial loss of specificity with the result that either of two amino acids could be inserted at the same position in a protein. If the suppressor mutation led to an alteration of a species of transfer RNA or an amino acid-activating enzyme it would be expected that the same change that restored a functional protein in one case could have a detrimental effect on other enzymes. Thus a functional enzyme would be formed at the expense of the alteration of a fraction of most other protein molecules. This may, in fact, be responsible for the finding that allele-specific suppressors often affect growth rate[193, 194] and restore only low levels of a functional protein. The one notable exception, as mentioned previously, is a suppressor of one class of alkaline phosphatase mutants.[61] This suppressor restores high levels of enzyme in CRMless mutants. This case has been interpreted in the following way:[61, 195] The mutants concerned are CRMless because of a change from sense to nonsense in one coding unit. The suppressor mutation results in a new species of transfer RNA which can recognize the nonsense sequence and transfer an amino acid to the growing polypeptide chain. The same interpretation of this type of suppressor mutation has been offered on the basis of studies with rII mutants of phage T4.[192, 195] In fact, the same suppressor gene interacts with presumed nonsense triplets in the rII gene and the alkaline phosphatase gene. The most convincing evidence suggesting that this type of suppressor mutation does affect nonsense sequences comes from studies with rII mutants. It was shown by Benzer and Champe[195] that an rII mutation that is suppressed by the presumed nonsense-triplet suppressor converts a complementing region of the rII locus into a noncomplementing region. This result would be expected if the mutational change were from a sense triplet to a nonsense triplet.

At the present time there appear to be more questions than answers on the subject of suppressor gene action. The mechanism of primary structure alteration by allele-specific suppressors remains to be elucidated and the question of "nonsense-mutation" suppressors must be clarified. In addition, there are some unexplained suppressor mutations, the so-called "super-suppressors," that are only relatively specific and affect many alleles at different loci.[196, 197] These could be "nonsense-mutation" suppressors, suppressors that have a mutator action on messenger RNA, or suppressors with some other mechanism of action. Equally difficult to explain is the finding in one study of suppression that six nonallelic suppressor genes restore functional enzyme to a particular allele.[198] Another observation that appears to be inconsistent with any of the mechanisms of allele-specific suppression mentioned is the fact that extensive studies with adenylosuccinase and glutamic dehydrogenase of *Neurospora* failed to detect suppressor mutations. If allele-specific suppression is accomplished by the alteration of one of the cell components involved in messenger RNA translation, it would be expected that all genes involved in protein structure determination would be subject to the same suppressor mutations. One possible explanation can be offered for the inability to recover suppressors; it is conceivable that in these cases the enzyme concerned consists of several identical subunits and the complex of normal subunits is the only enzymically active form. Thus if an inactive mutationally-altered enzyme contained four identical polypeptide subunits and the suppressor gene led to the modification of 10% of the polypeptide chains, the likelihood of forming a complex containing four suppressor-modified subunits would be too low to be of any significance with regard to supporting growth. On the other hand "nonsense-mutation" suppressors should be detectable in these cases.

It is apparent that considerably more attention should be given to the mechanism of action of suppressor genes since suppression promises to reveal many interesting interactions that occur between different cell components involved in primary structure determination.

VI. General Conclusion

Initially, studies of the biochemical genetics of many organisms led to the elucidation of the intricate pathways of intermediary metabolism. Subsequently, investigations of gene and protein alterations associated with mutations contributed to our understanding of the many aspects of the gene-enzyme relationship that are reviewed here. It is certain that the mutational approach will continue to be informative, and will reveal those aspects of protein structure, function, and localization that are physiologically significant in a growing cell.

REFERENCES

[1] G. W. Beadle and E. L. Tatum, *Proc. Natl. Acad. Sci. U. S.* **79,** 499 (1950).
[2] J. R. S. Fincham, *Advances in Enzymol.* **22,** 1 (1960).
[2a] J. H. Taylor, ed., "Molecular Genetics," Part 1. Academic Press, New York, 1963.
[3] J. D. Watson and F. H. C. Crick, *Cold Spring Harbor Symposia Quant. Biol.* **18,** 123 (1953).
[4] E. Chargaff, *Federation Proc.* **10,** 654 (1951).
[5] S. Benzer, *Proc. Natl. Acad. Sci. U. S.* **45,** 1607 (1959).
[6] S. Benzer, *Proc. Natl. Acad. Sci. U. S.* **47,** 403 (1961).
[7] P. Berg, *Ann. Rev. Biochem.* **30,** 293 (1961).
[8] R. Schweet and J. Bishop, in "Molecular Genetics" (J. H. Taylor, ed.), Part 1, p. 353. Academic Press, New York, 1963.
[9] C. Yanofsky and P. St. Lawrence, *Ann. Rev. Microbiol.* **14,** 311 (1960).
[10] C. Baglioni, in "Molecular Genetics" (J. H. Taylor, ed.), Part 1, p. 405. Academic Press, New York, 1963.

11 A. Garen, C. Levinthal, and F. Rothman, *J. chim. phys.* **58**, 1068 (1961).
12 C. Yanofsky, see discussion following paper by W. Gilbert. *Cold Spring Harbor Symposia Quant. Biol.* **28**, 297, 1963.
13 C. Yanofsky, *Cold Spring Harbor Symposia Quant. Biol.* **28**, 581 (1963).
14 M. W. Nirenberg, O. W. Jones, P. Leder, B. F. C. Clark, W. S. Sly, and S. Pestka, *Cold Spring Harbor Symposia Quant. Biol.* **28**, 549 (1963).
15 J. F. Speyer, P. Lengyel, C. Basilio, A. J. Wahba, R. S. Gardner, and S. Ochoa, *Cold Spring Harbor Symposia Quant. Biol.* **28**, in press (1963).
16 E. Volkin, *in* "Molecular Genetics" (J. H. Taylor, ed.), Part 1, p. 271. Academic Press, New York, 1963.
17 S. Spiegelman, *in* "Informational Macromolecules" (H. J. Vogel, V. Bryson, and J. O. Lampen, eds.), p. 27. Academic Press, New York, 1963.
18 J. Marmur, C. M. Greenspan, E. Palecek, F. M. Kahan, J. Levine, and M. Mandel, *Cold Spring Harbor Symposia Quant. Biol.* **28**, 191 (1963).
19 F. Gros, S. Naono, C. Woese, C. Willson, and G. Attardi, *in* "Informational Macromolecules" (H. J. Vogel, V. Bryson, and J. O. Lampen, eds.), p. 387. Academic Press, New York, 1963.
20 P. A. Marks, E. R. Burka, and D. Schlessinger, *Proc. Natl. Acad. Sci. U. S.* **48**, 2163 (1962).
21 J. R. Warner, P. Knopf, and A. Rich, *Proc. Natl. Acad. Sci. U. S.* **49**, 122 (1963).
22 A. Gierer, *J. Mol. Biol.* **6**, 148 (1963).
23 G. Spyrides and F. Lipmann, *Proc. Natl. Acad. Sci. U. S.* **48**, 1977 (1962).
24 J. Apgar, R. W. Holley, and B. H. Merrill, *J. Biol. Chem.* **237**, 796 (1962).
25 U. Lagerkvist and P. Berg, *J. Mol. Biol.* **5**, 139 (1962).
26 P. Berg, U. Lagerkvist, and M. Dieckmann, *J. Mol. Biol.* **5**, 159 (1962).
27 N. Sueoka and T. Yamane, *Proc. Natl. Acad. Sci. U. S.* **48**, 1454 (1962).
28 F. H. C. Crick, *Symposia Soc. Exptl. Biol.* **No. 12**, 138 (1958).
29 H. M. Dintzis, *Proc. Natl. Acad. Sci. U. S.* **47**, 247 (1961).
30 C. B. Anfinsen, E. Haber, M. Sela, and F. H. White, Jr., *Proc. Natl. Acad. Sci. U.S.* **47**, 1309 (1961).
31 H. A. Itano and S. J. Singer, *Proc. Natl. Acad. Sci. U. S.* **44**, 522 (1958).
32 H. S. Rhinesmith, W. A. Schroeder, and L. Pauling, *J. Am. Chem. Soc.* **80**, 3358 (1958).
33 I. P. Crawford and C. Yanofsky, *Proc. Natl. Acad. Sci. U. S.* **44**, 1161 (1958).
34 D. E. Koshland, Jr., J. A. Yankulov, Jr., and J. A. Thoma, *Federation Proc.* **21**, 1031 (1962).
35 J. A. Cohen, R. A. Oosterbaan, H. S. Jansz, and F. Berends, *J. Cellular Comp. Physiol.* **54**, Suppl. 1, 231 (1959).
36 D. E. Koshland, Jr., *in* "The Enzymes" (J. B. Sumner and K. Myrbäck, eds.), Vol. 1, Chapter 7. Academic Press, New York, 1959.
37 H. A. Scheraga and J. A. Rupley, *Advances in Enzymol.* **24**, 161 (1962).
38 F. M. Richards and P. J. Vithayathil, *J. Biol. Chem.* **234**, 1459 (1959).
39 R. L. Hill and E. L. Smith, *J. Biol. Chem.* **231**, 117 (1958).
40 O. Nylander and B. Malmström, *Biochim. et Biophys. Acta* **34**, 196 (1959).
41 C. J. Epstein and C. B. Anfinsen, *J. Biol. Chem.* **237**, 2175 (1962).
42 C. J. Epstein, C. B. Anfinsen, and M. Sela, *J. Biol. Chem.* **237**, 3458 (1962).
43 D. Wellner, H. I. Silman, and M. Sela, *J. Biol. Chem.* **238**, 1324 (1963).
44 H. F. Perutz, "Proteins and Nucleic Acid." Elsevier, New York, 1962.
45 H. A. Scheraga, "Protein Structure." Academic Press, New York, 1961.
46 H. E. Umbarger, *Cold Spring Harbor Symposia Quant. Biol.* **26**, 301 (1961).

[47] J. Monod, J. P. Changeux, and F. Jacob, *J. Mol. Biol.* **6**, 306 (1963).

[48] G. M. Tomkins, K. L. Yielding, and J. F. Curran, *J. Biol. Chem.* **237**, 1704 (1962).

[49] C. Frieden, *J. Biol. Chem.* **238**, 146 (1963).

[50] F. Jacob and J. Monod, *Cold Spring Harbor Symposia Quant. Biol.* **26**, 193 (1961).

[51] G. Buttin, *Compt. rend. acad. sci.* **255**, 1233 (1962).

[52] N. Lee and E. Englesberg, *Proc. Natl. Acad. Sci. U. S.*, **48**, 335 (1962).

[53] B. N. Ames, P. E. Hartman, and F. Jacob, *J. Mol. Biol.* **7**, 23 (1963).

[54] C. Levinthal, *Brookhaven Symposia in Biol.* **No. 12** 76 (1959).

[55] F. Jacob and J. Monod, *J. Mol. Biol.* **3**, 318 (1961).

[56] S. R. Suskind, C. Yanofsky, and D. M. Bonner, *Proc. Natl. Acad. Sci. U. S.* **41**, 577 (1955).

[57] J. R. S. Fincham, *J. Mol. Biol.* **4**, 257 (1962).

[58] S. R. Suskind, *J. Bacteriol.* **74**, 308 (1957).

[59] C. Yanofsky and I. P. Crawford, *Proc. Natl. Acad. Sci. U. S.* **45**, 1016 (1959).

[60] A. Garen and C. Levinthal, *Biochim. et Biophys. Acta* **38**, 470 (1960).

[61] A. Garen and O. Siddiqi, *Proc. Natl. Acad. Sci. U. S.* **48**, 1121 (1962).

[62] B. Maling and C. Yanofsky, *Proc. Natl. Acad. Sci. U. S.* **47**, 551 (1961).

[63] M. K. Allen and C. Yanofsky, *Genetics* **48**, 1065 (1963).

[64] S. R. Suskind, M. L. Wickham, and M. Carsiotis, *Ann. N. Y. Acad. Sci.* **103**, 1106 (1963).

[65] M. D. Garrick and S. R. Suskind, *Ann. N. Y. Acad. Sci.* **103**, 793 (1963).

[66] F. H. C. Crick, J. C. Griffith, and L. E. Orgel, *Proc. Natl. Acad. Sci. U. S.* **43**, 416 (1957).

[67] F. H. C. Crick, L. Barnett, S. Brenner, and R. Watts-Tobin, *Nature* **192**, 1227 (1961).

[68] C. Yanofsky, D. R. Helinski, and B. D. Maling, *Cold Spring Harbor Symposia Quant. Biol.* **26**, 11 (1961).

[69] E. Freese, *in* "Molecular Genetics" (J. H. Taylor, ed.), Part 1, p. 207. Academic Press, New York, 1963.

[70] E. Balbinder, *Genetics* **47**, 545 (1962).

[71] R. Rudner, *Z. Vererbungslehre* **92**, 336 (1961).

[72] J. R. S. Fincham, *Biochem. J.* **65**, 721 (1957).

[73] J. R. S. Fincham, *Proc. Intern. Congr. Genet. 10th Congr., Montreal* **1**, 355 (1959).

[74] J. R. S. Fincham and J. A. Pateman, *J. Genet.* **55**, 456 (1957).

[75] D. Perrin, A. Bussard, and J. Monod, *Compt. rend. acad. sci.* **249**, 778 (1959).

[76] D. Perrin, F. Jacob, and J. Monod, *Compt. rend. acad. sci.* **251**, 155 (1960).

[77] D. Perrin, *Ann. N. Y. Acad. Sci.* **103**, 1058 (1963).

[78] C. Yanofsky and D. M. Bonner, *Genetics* **40**, 761 (1955).

[79] S. R. Suskind and E. Jordon, *Science* **129**, 1614 (1959).

[80] J. A. DeMoss and D. M. Bonner, *Proc. Natl. Acad. Sci. U. S.* **45**, 1405 (1959).

[81] C. Yanofsky, *Bacteriol. Revs.* **24**, 221 (1960).

[82] M. Rachmeler and C. Yanofsky, *J. Bacteriol.* **81**, 955 (1961).

[83] C. Yanofsky, *in* "Cytodifferentiation and Macromolecular Synthesis" (M. Locke ed.), p. 15. Academic Press, New York, 1963.

[84] U. Henning and C. Yanofsky, *J. Mol. Biol.* **6**, 16 (1963).

[85] I. P. Crawford and L. M. Johnson, *Genetics* **48**, 725 (1963).

[86] N. H. Horowitz and M. Fling, *Genetics* **38**, 360 (1953).

[87] N. H. Horowitz, M. Fling, H. L. MacLeod, and N. Sueoka, *Genetics* **44**, 516 (1959).

[88] F. Rothman and R. Byrne, *J. Mol. Biol.* **6**, 330 (1963).

[89] E. Englesberg, R. L. Anderson, R. Weinberg, N. Lee, P. Hoffer, G. Huttenhauer, and H. Bayer, *J. Bacteriol.* **84**, 137 (1962).

90 A. B. Pardee and J. R. Beckwith, *in* "Informational Macromolecules" (H. J. Vogel, V. Bryson, and J. O. Lampen, eds.), p. 255. Academic Press, New York, 1963.

91 A. Tsugita and H. Fraenkel-Conrat, *J. Mol. Biol.* **4**, 73 (1962).

92 A. Tsugita, *J. Mol. Biol.* **5**, 284 (1962).

93 H. G. Wittmann, *Z. Vererbungslehre* **93**, 491 (1962).

94 T. H. Jukes, *Am. Scientist* **51**, 227 (1963).

95 D. R. Helinski and C. Yanofsky, *Proc. Natl. Acad. Sci. U. S.* **48**, 173 (1962).

96 U. Henning and C. Yanofsky, *Proc. Natl. Acad. Sci. U. S.* **48**, 183 (1962).

97 U. Henning and C. Yanofsky, *Proc. Natl. Acad. Sci. U. S.* **48**, 1497 (1962).

98 S. P. Champe and S. Benzer, *J. Mol. Biol.* **5**, 288 (1962).

99 V. Ingram, *Federation Proc.* **21**, 1053 (1962).

100 G. Streisinger, F. Mukai, W. Dryer, B. Miller, and S. Horiuchi, *Cold Spring Harbor Symposia Quant. Biol.* **26**, 25 (1961).

101 B. Carlton and C. Yanofsky, manuscript in preparation.

102 J. Guest and C. Yanofsky, unpublished results.

103 D. Helinski and C. Yanofsky, *J. Biol. Chem.* **238**, 1043 (1963).

104 L. S. Lerman, *Proc. Natl. Acad. Sci. U. S.* **49**, 94 (1963).

105 G. Gamow, A. Rich, and M. Ycas, *Advances in Biol. and Med. Phys.* **4**, 23 (1956).

106 O. W. Jones, Jr. and M. W. Nirenberg, *Proc. Natl. Acad. Sci. U. S.* **48**, 2115 (1962).

107 A. J. Wahba, R. S. Gardner, C. Basilio, R. Miller, J. F. Speyer, and P. Lengyel, *Proc. Natl. Acad. Sci. U. S.* **49**, 116 (1963).

108 M. W. Nirenberg and O. W. Jones, Jr., *in* "Informational Macromolecules" (H. J. Vogel, V. Bryson, and J. O. Lampen, eds.), p. 451. Academic Press, New York, 1963.

109 A. J. Wahba, R. S. Miller, C. Basilio, R. S. Gardner, P. Lengyel, and J. F. Speyer, *Proc. Natl. Acad. Sci. U. S.* **49**, 880 (1963).

110 S. Brenner, *Proc. Natl. Acad. Sci. U. S.* **43**, 687 (1957).

111 A. Tsugita and H. Fraenkel-Conrat, *in* "Molecular Genetics" (J. H. Taylor, ed.), Part 1, p. 477. Academic Press, New York, 1963.

112 B. C. Carlton and C. Yanofsky, *J. Biol. Chem.* **238**, 2390 (1963).

113 G. W. Golomb, L. R. Welch, and M. Delbruck, *Kyl. Danske Videnskub. Selskub. Biol. Medd.* **23**, 1 (1958).

114 M. W. Nirenberg and J. H. Matthaei, *Proc. Natl. Acad. Sci. U. S.* **47**, 1588 (1961).

115 S. Ochoa, *in* "Informational Macromolecules" (H. J. Vogel, V. Bryson, and J. O. Lampen, eds.), p. 437. Academic Press, New York, 1963.

116 R. V. Eck, *Science* **140**, 477 (1963).

117 E. L. Smith, *Proc. Natl. Acad. Sci. U. S.* **48**, 859 (1962).

118 A. J. Wahba, C. Basilio, J. F. Speyer, P. Lengyel, R. S. Miller, and S. Ochoa, *Proc. Natl. Acad. Sci. U. S.* **48**, 1683 (1962).

119 C. Basilio, A. J. Wahba, P. Lengyel, J. F. Speyer, and S. Ochoa, *Proc. Natl. Acad. Sci. U. S.* **48**, 613 (1962).

120 O. H. Schuster and G. Schramm, *Z. Naturforsch.* **136b**, 697 (1958).

121 H. Schuster, *Biochem. Biophys. Research Communs.* **2**, 320 (1960).

122 I. Tessman, *J. Mol. Biol.* **5**, 442 (1962).

123 T. A. Tratner, M. N. Swartz, and A. Kornberg, *Proc. Natl. Acad. Sci. U. S.* **48**, 449 (1962).

124 B. D. Hall and S. Spiegelman, *Proc. Natl. Acad. Sci. U. S.* **48**, 137 (1961).

125 E. K. F. Bautz and B. D. Hall, *Proc. Natl. Acad. Sci. U. S.* **48**, 400 (1962).

126 E. T. Bolton and B. J. McCarthy, *Proc. Natl. Acad. Sci. U. S.* **48**, 1390 (1962).

[127] N. D. Zinder, *in* "Informational Macromolecules" (H. J. Vogel, V. Bryson, and J. O. Lampen, eds.), p. 239. Academic Press, New York, 1963.

[128] A. Tsugita, H. Fraenkel-Conrat, M. W. Nirenberg, and J. H. Matthaei, *Proc. Natl. Acad. Sci. U. S.*, **48**, 846 (1962).

[129] T. H. Jukes, *in* "Informational Macromolecules" (H. J. Vogel, V. Bryson, and J. O. Lampen, eds.), p. 485. Academic Press, New York, 1963.

[130] F. Sorm, *Advances in Enzymol.* **24**, 415 (1962).

[131] F. M. Richards and P. J. Vithayathil, *Brookhaven Symposia in Biol.* **13**, 115 (1960).

[132] J. SriRam, M. Bier, and P. H. Maurer, *Advances in Enzymol.* **24**, 109 (1962).

[133] See *Cold Spring Harbor Symposia Quant. Biol.* **26**, (1961).

[134] I. Zabin, A. Kepes, and J. Monod, *J. Biol. Chem.* **237**, 253 (1962).

[135] F. Jacob, D. Perrin, C. Sanchez, and J. Monod, *Comp. rend. acad. sci.* **250**, 1727 (1960).

[136] B. Ames and P. E. Hartman, *Cold Spring Harbor Symposia Quant. Biol.* **28**, 349 (1963).

[137] A. Garen and H. Echols, *Proc. Natl. Acad. Sci. U. S.* **48**, 1398 (1962).

[138] G. Cohen and F. Jacob, *Compt. rend. acad. sci.* **248**, 3490 (1959).

[139] N. H. Horowitz, M. Fling, H. L. MacLeod, and N. Sueoka, *J. Mol. Biol.* **2**, 96 (1960).

[140] M. Hayashi, S. Spiegelman, N. C. Franklin, and S. E. Luria, *Proc. Natl. Acad. Sci. U. S.* **49**, 729 (1963).

[141] G. Attardi, S. Naono, J. Rouvière, F. Jacob, and F. Gros, *Cold Spring Harbor Symposia Quant. Biol.* **28**, 363 (1963).

[142] N. C. Franklin and S. E. Luria, *Virology* **15**, 299 (1961).

[143] R. G. Martin, *Cold Spring Harbor Symposia Quant. Biol.* **28**, 357 (1963).

[144] D. Nathans, G. Notani, J. H. Schwartz, and N. D. Zinder, *Proc. Natl. Acad. Sci. U. S.* **48**, 1424 (1962).

[145] M. Freundlich and H. E. Umbarger, *Cold Spring Harbor Symposia Quant. Biol.* **28**, 505 (1963).

[146] E. R. Stadtman, G. N. Cohen, G. LeBras, and H. de Robichon-Szulmajster, *J. Biol. Chem.* **236**, 2033 (1961).

[147] J. P. Changeux, *Cold Spring Harbor Symposia Quant. Biol.* **26**, 313 (1961).

[148] J. C. Gerhart and A. B. Pardee, *J. Biol. Chem.* **237**, 891 (1962).

[149] R. G. Martin, *J. Biol. Chem.* **238**, 257 (1963).

[150] H. S. Moyed, *J. Biol. Chem.* **235**, 1098 (1960).

[151] J. P. Changeux, *J. Mol. Biol.* **5**, 220 (1962).

[152] D. B. Martin and P. R. Vagelos, *J. Biol. Chem.* **237**, 1787 (1962).

[153] P. R. Vagelos, A. W. Alberts, and D. B. Martin, *J. Biol. Chem.* **238**, 533 (1963).

[154] C. Frieden, *J. Biol. Chem.* **234**, 809 (1959).

[155] C. Frieden, *J. Biol. Chem.* **237**, 2396 (1962).

[156] G. M. Tomkins and K. L. Yielding, *Cold Spring Harbor Symposia Quant. Biol.* **26**, 331 (1961).

[157] G. M. Tomkins, K. L. Yielding, M. Talal, and J. F. Curran, *Cold Spring Harbor Symposia Quant. Biol.* **28**, 461 (1963).

[158] J. Wolff, *J. Biol. Chem.* **237**, 236 (1962).

[159] C. Frieden, *Biochim. et Biophys. Acta* **47**, 428 (1961).

[160] G. W. Beadle and V. L. Coonradt, *Genetics* **29**, 291 (1944).

[161] J. A. Pateman and J. R. S. Fincham, *Heredity* **12**, 317 (1958).

[162] J. R. S. Fincham, *J. Gen. Microbiol.* **21**, 600 (1959).

[163] J. R. S. Fincham and J. A. Pateman, *Nature* **179**, 741 (1957).

[4] N. H. Giles, C. W. H. Partridge, and N. J. Nelson, *Proc. Natl. Acad. Sci. U. S.* **43**, 305 (1957).

[165] D. O. Woodward, C. W. H. Partridge, and N. H. Giles, *Proc. Natl. Acad. Sci. U. S.* **44**, 1237 (1958).

[166] M. E. Case and N. H. Giles, *Proc. Natl. Acad. Sci. U. S.* **46**, 659 (1960).

[167] M. E. Case and N. H. Giles, *Cold Spring Harbor Symposia Quant. Biol.* **23**, 119 (1958).

[168] J. R. S. Fincham and A. Coddington, *J. Mol. Biol.* **6**, 361 (1963).

[169] D. G. Catcheside and A. Overton, *Cold Spring Harbor Symposia Quant. Biol.* **23**, 137 (1958).

[170] P. E. Hartman, Z. Hartman, and D. Serman, *J. Gen. Microbiol.* **22**, 354 (1960).

[171] A. M. Lacy and D. M. Bonner, *Proc. Natl. Acad. Sci. U. S.* **47**, 72 (1962).

[172] S. R. Gross, *Proc. Natl. Acad. Sci. U. S.* **48**, 922 (1962).

[173] A. M. Kapuler and H. Bernstein, *J. Mol. Biol.* **6**, 443 (1963).

[174] D. O. Woodward, *Proc. Natl. Acad. Sci. U. S.* **45**, 846 (1959).

[175] J. C. Loper, *Proc. Natl. Acad. Sci. U. S.* **47**, 1140 (1961).

[176] M. Schlesinger, A. Torriani and C. Levinthal, *Cold Spring Harbor Symposia Quant. Biol.* **28**, 539 (1963).

[177] D. Zipser and D. Perrin, *Cold Spring Harbor Symposia Quant. Biol.* **28**, 533 (1963).

[178] M. Rachmeler and C. Yanofsky, *J. Bacteriol.* **81**, 955 (1961).

[179] S. R. Suskind and L. I. Kurek, *Science* **129**, 1068 (1959).

[180] S. R. Suskind and L. I. Kurek, *Proc. Natl. Acad. Sci. U. S.* **45**, 193 (1959).

[181] S. R. Suskind, *in* "The Chemical Basis of Heredity" (W. McElroy and B. Glass, eds.), p. 123. Johns Hopkins Press, Baltimore, Maryland, 1957.

[182] J. Lein and P. S. Lein, *Proc. Natl. Acad. Sci. U. S.* **38**, 44 (1952).

[183] B. S. Strauss and S. J. Pierog, *J. Gen. Microbiol.* **10**, 221 (1954).

[184] S. Howarth, *Genetics* **43**, 404 (1958).

[185] R. H. Davis, *Genetics* **47**, 351 (1962).

[186] R. H. Davis and V. W. Woodward, *Genetics* **47**, 1075 (1962).

[187] N. H. Giles, *Cold Spring Harbor Symposia Quant. Biol.* **16**, 283 (1951).

[188] P. Starlinger and F. Kaudewitz, *Z. Naturforsch.* **116b**, 317 (1956).

[189] T. Yura, *Carnegie Inst. Wash. Publ.* **No. 612**, 77 (1956).

[190] S. Brody and C. Yanofsky, *Proc. Natl. Acad. Sci. U. S.* **50**, 9 (1963).

[191] I. Crawford and C. Yanofsky, *Proc. Natl. Acad. Sci. U. S.* **45**, 1280 (1959).

[192] S. Benzer and S. P. Champe, *Proc. Natl. Acad. Sci. U. S.* **47**, 1025 (1961).

[193] C. Yanofsky, *Proc. Natl. Acad. Sci. U. S.* **38**, 215 (1952).

[194] N. H. Giles and C. W. H. Partridge, *Proc. Natl. Acad. Sci. U. S.* **39**, 479 (1953).

[195] S. Benzer and S. P. Champe, *Proc. Natl. Acad. Sci. U. S.* **48**, 1114 (1962).

[196] D. C. Hawthorne and R. K. Mortimer, *Genetics* **48**, 617 (1963).

[197] A. Campbell, *Virology* **14**, 22 (1961).

[198] C. Yanofsky and D. M. Bonner, *Genetics* **40**, 602 (1955).

CHAPTER 9

Compositional Variation and Heterogeneity of Nucleic Acids and Protein in Bacteria

N. SUEOKA

I. Introduction

Interrelationship among the three biological macromolecules, DNA (deoxyribonucleic acid), RNA (ribonucleic acid), and protein, has been a central subject of biological and biochemical investigations for the last decade. The achievements obtained so far from such studies are truly remarkable. Fundamental questions of genetics involving gene structure, action, replication, mutation, recombination, and transmission are now at least partially understood in molecular terms. Enzymic steps involved in the biosynthesis of the macromolecules have been discovered and fairly well characterized. The conceptual connection of the three macromolecules is understood as the flow of genetic information stored in DNA to protein.

Variation and heterogeneity in the over-all base composition of DNA and RNA in the amino acid composition of protein are statistical averages of each system and by themselves do not directly define a mechanism. Nevertheless, a systematic knowledge of compositional information is important. It helps to grasp the entire picture, allows interpretation of specific cases relative to this total picture, and suggests theories which may open new experimental approaches.

In the present chapter, the accumulated data on the base composition of DNA will first be presented in detail. Then, the base composition of RNA and the amino acid composition of protein will be discussed in relation to the base composition of DNA. Our primary purpose will not be to make an exhaustive compilation of existing data, but to present an over-all picture of the problem. For further information, appropriate review articles may be consulted.[1-6]

Several aspects of the compositional studies of DNA, RNA, and protein are listed below.

1. Structural regularities of the macromolecules inferred from compositional regularities.

2. Comparative aspects (variation) of composition among different organisms.

3. Compositional heterogeneity among the DNA molecules of an organism.

4. Compositional correlation between different macromolecules.

5. Genetic interaction and similarity of DNA base composition between different organisms.

6. Compositional change of the macromolecules.

These aspects of the compositional studies of macromolecules have played a number of initiating roles in the development of present-day molecular biology. A couple of examples will be enough to illustrate the point. Equimolarity of adenine and thymine, and of guanine and cytosine, in DNA, which had been deduced from data on the chromatographic base analysis[7, 8] provided essential information for the formulation of the Watson-Crick structure of DNA.[9] The first physical evidence of the existence of messenger RNA was in the similarity of its base composition to that of DNA.[10]

II. DNA Base Composition

Overwhelming data have been accumulated on the average base composition of double-stranded DNA, which show the equimolar contents of guanine (G) with cytosine (C), and adenine (A) with thymine (T).[1] Consequently, in this review the composition will be expressed as the percentage of guanine plus cytosine (GC-content; Doty et al.[11]). The base composition of DNA has two basic features: the variation of the mean DNA base composition in different organisms, and the heterogeneity of the base composition of the DNA molecules within an individual or a species. These two features will be described in the following sections.

A. Variation

A compilation of existing data on species difference of the average base composition is presented in Table I from which the following features are apparent:

1. Lower forms of life have more variability in the DNA base composition.

Higher organisms definitely tend to have a narrower range of variation in the DNA base composition (Table I) when one organism is compared to another. However, higher organisms possess a larger compositional heterogeneity within the DNA of a single organism. We shall return to this point later.

2. The range of DNA base composition is approximately between 25 and 75% GC.

The mean of DNA GC-contents of bacteria and protozoa is found in the range of 25 to 75%, and this extends over the range of the mean DNA GC-content of higher organisms. The absence of natural DNA outside this range (with one exception noted below) may suggest that the genetic information necessary for the survival of an organism cannot be stored by adenine and thymine or guanine and cytosine alone.

3. Phylogenetic relations are reflected in the mean GC-content.

This point was first raised by Lee et al.[23] from their analysis of the base composition of bacterial DNA. Belozersky and Spirin[24] added further evidence. Among bacterial species there are several cases in which taxonomically related bacteria have similar values of GC-content. For example, some genera of the Enterobacteriaceae, Escherichia, Salmonella, and Shigella, have similar GC-contents of their DNA. A number of such examples have been discussed in their papers.[23, 24] Moreover, both groups of authors have suggested that reclassification may be made for some species of bacteria according to the DNA base composition. In higher organisms, the feature is even more evident. For example, all forms of vertebrates so far tested have a mean GC-content of 40 to 44% (Table I). Examples found in protozoa and algae give more examples supporting the idea (Table I). The mean DNA GC-content of various strains of Tetrahymena pyriformis lies within a narrow range (25–31%), and yet the difference in the GC-content is rather uniform among the molecules.[18, 25] A similar situation is found in other species of protozoa.[19] A comprehensive treatment of this issue has recently been provided by Marmur et al. [6]

B. Heterogeneity

Early evidence of compositional heterogeneity of DNA was based on salt fractionations of DNA molecules from its complex with basic proteins of various kinds, and on chromatographic analysis of base composition of fractionated DNA. Thus Chargaff et al.[26] succeeded in separating calf thymus DNA into fractions containing 35 to 50% GC. Brown and Watson[27] report compositional fractionation of calf thymus DNA by using a histone-kieselguhr column. Further fractionation was applied to the DNA of pig liver, human spleen, and coliphage T6 by Crampton et al.[28] Except in the coliphage DNA, existence of heterogeneity was demonstrated.

The nature of the heterogeneity became much clearer when two properties of DNA, hyperchromicity and density, were found to be dependent on

TABLE I

Base Composition of DNA of Various Organisms[a]

GC (%)	Viruses	Bacteria	Protozoa	Fungi	Algae	Higher plants	Invertebrates	Vertebrates	GC (%)
20			21, 29						20
22			12						22
24			1, 2, 3, 4, 6, 8						24
26		72	5, 7, 9						26
28	12	74	11, 22, 23						28
30		18, 32, 41, 49	10, 24, 26						30
32		17, 19, 26, 51, 52, 75, 76	25, 28						32
34	2, 3	11, 29, 40, 64, 65, 66, 68, 69, 77, 78	27	2	2	10[b]	9		34
36	1	14, 38, 44, 70, 73, 79, 80							36
38		12, 23, 28, 39, 81, 82, 83, 84, 85, 86					10,[c] 11		38
40	4, 14	44, 87, 88			1, 3	3, 5,[b] 6,[b] 7,[b] 8,[b] 11[b]	(5), 6, 7	1, (1)	40
42	11	13, 53, 89			(15)	2	(2), 8[c]	3,[d] 4, 5,[d] (6), 7,[d] 9, 10, 11,[d] 12, (14), (16)	42
44	9, 13, 18	50, 71, 90		3		4, 12	(1), (4), 12[c]	2, 6, 8, 13, (15), (17)	44
46			13				(3)		46
48	5, 7, 17	20, 91, 92			(20)	1, 9[b]			48
50	6, 8, 10	36, 37, 54, 55, 56, 57, 63, 93, 94, 95, 96		4					50
52		21, 25, 97, 98, 99, 100, 101, 102, 103, 104			(12), (14), (17)				52
54		8, 24, 43, 57, 58, 62, 105, 106, 107	18, 19	1	7, (16*)				54
56		5, 10, 108			(18*), (19)				56
58		5, 6, 9, 15, 16, 22, 27, 35, 61, 109, 110	15, 16, 17		6, 10, (21)				58
60		111, 112, 113	20		9, (11*), (13)				60
62		114, 115, 116	14		5				62
64		46, 60, 117, 118, 119, 120, 121, 122, 123			4				64
66		7, 33, 45, 125, 126, 127, 128, 129, 130, 131, 132			(8)				66
68		34, (47), 48, 59, 45, 133			(22)				68
70									70
72		30, 31, 42, 60							72
74	15, 16	1, 2, 3, 4, 67							74
76									76
78									78
80									80

[a] Each figure corresponds to organisms given. Use of parentheses indicates analysis by CsCl density gradient centrifugation.

VIRUSES: 1. Bacteriophage T2; 2. T4; 3. T6; 4. T5; 5. T1; 6. T3; 7. T7; 8. λ virus; 9. Salmonella Al; 10. P22; 11. φX 174; 12. PBS2; 13. α; 14. vaccina virus; 15. herpes simplex virus; 16. pseudorabies virus; 17. polyoma virus; 18. bacteriophage SP8 (contains hydroxymethyluracil instead of thymine).

References: Organisms 1-11 (cited in ref. 4); 12 (ref. 12); 13 (ref. 13); 14 (ref. 14); 15, 16 (ref 15); 17 (ref 16); 18 (ref. 17).

BACTERIA: 1. Actinomyces globisporus flaveolus; 2. Actinomyces globisporus streptomycini; 3. Actinomyces griseus; 4. Actinomyces viridochromogenes; 5. Aerobacter aerogenes; 6. Agrobacteria tumefaciens; 7. Alcaligenes faecalis; 8. Azotobacter agile; 9. Azotobacter chroococcum; 10. Azotobacter vinelandii; 11. Bacillus cereus; 12. Bacillus megaterium; 13. Bacillus subtilis; 14. Bacillus thuringiensis; 15. Bifidibacterium bifidum; 16. Brucella abortus; 17. Clostridium bifermentans; 18. Clostridium perfringens; 19. Clostridium valerianicum; 20. Corynebacterium acnes; 21. Corynebacterium diphtheriae; 22. Corynebacterium parvum; 23. Diplococcus pneumoniae; 24. Erwinia carotovora; 25. Escherichia coli; 26. Fusiformis fusiformis; 27. Fusiformis polymorphus; 28. Hemophilus influenzae; 29. Micrococcus asaccharolyticus; 30. Micromonospora coerulea; 31. Micrococcus lysodeikticus; 32. Micrococcus pyogenes; 33. Mycobacterium phlei; 34. Mycobacterium tuberculosis; 35. Mycobacterium vadosum; 36. Neisseria gonorrhoeae; 37. Neisseria meningitidis; 38. Pasteurella aviseptica; 39. Pasteurella boviseptica; 40. Pasteurella tularensis; 41. Plectridium saprogenes; 42. Proactinomyces citreus; 43. Proteus morganii; 44. Proteus vulgaris; 45. Pseudomonas aeruginosa; 46. Pseudomonas fluorescens; (47) Pseudomonas saccharophila; 48 Pseudomonas tabaci; 49. Ramibacterium ramosum; 50. Rickettsia prowazeki; 52. Ristella clostridiformis; 53. Ristella insolit; 54. Salmonella enteritidis; 55. Salmonella gallinarum; 56. Salmonella paratyphi; 57. Salmonella typhimurium; 58. Salmonella typhosa; 59. Sarcina flava; 60. Sarcina lutea; 61. Serratia marcescens; 62. Shigella dysenteriae; 63. Shigella paradysenteriae; 64. Staphylococcus pyogenes; 65. Streptococcus faecalis; 66. Streptococcus foetidus; 67. Streptococcus griseus; 68. Streptococcus pyogenes; 69. Streptococcus zymogenes; 70. Veillonella parvula; 71. Vibrio cholerae; 72. Welchia perfringens; 73. Micoplasma gallisepticum (PPLO A5969). 74. Spirillum linum; 75. Flavobacterium aquatile; 76. Cytophaga johnsonii; 77. Leptospira pomona; 78. Sporocytophaga myxococcoides; 79. Streptococcus faecium; 80. Treponema pallidum; 81. Streptococcus bovis; 82. Streptococcus cremoris; 83. Streptococcus viridans; 84. Streptococcus sanguis; 85. Cytophaga fermentans; 86. Cytophaga aurantiaca; 87. Leptospira biflexa; 88. Pseudomonas cruciviae; 89. Vibrio metschnikovi; 90. Saprospira grandis; 91. Flavobacterium acidificum; 92. Spirillum serpens; 93. Shigella dispar; 94. Shigella sonnei; 95. Salmonella abony; 96 Erwinia rhapentica; 97. Erwinia milletiae; 98. Erwinia chrysanthemi; 99. Erwinia nimipressuralis; 100. Klebsiella aerogenes; 101. Klebsiella edwardsii; 102. Klebsiella allatae; 103. Erwinia ananas; 104. Erwinia cypripedii; 105. Klebsiella rhinoscleromatis; 106. Erwinia nigrifluens; 107. Alcaligenes faecalis;108. Aeromonas punctata;109. Corynebacterium ilicis; 110. Aeromonas fermicans; 111. Pseudomonas fragii; 112. Vibrio tyrogenes; 113. Vibrio cuneatus; 114. Xanthomonas hederae; 116. Arthrobacter globiformis; 117. Xanthomonas phaseoli; 118. Xanthomonas pisi; 119. Vibrio percolans; 120. Flavobacterium vitarumens; 121. Pseudomonas stulzeri; 122. Pseudomonas putida;123. Microcyclus sp.; 125. Pseudomonas diminuta;126. Pseudomonas maltiphilia; 127. Myxococcus fulvus; 128. Myxococcus virescens; 129. Myxococcus xanthus;130. Flavobacterium falavescens;131. Flavobacterium arborescens, 132. Flavobacterium suaveolens; 133. Flavobacterium esteroaromaticum.

423

TABLE I—Continued

References: Organisms 1–73 (cited in ref. 5); 74–133 (cited in ref. 6).

PROTOZOA: 1. *Tetrahymena pyriformis* 1-A; 2. 1-WH-52; 3. 1-1L-12; 4. 2-1; 5. 3-1; 6. 7-1; 8. 8-2; 9: 9-1; 10. E; 11. GL; 12. *Tetrahymena rostrata*; 13. *Euglena gracilis*; 14. *Isochrysis galbana*; 15. *Prymnesium parvum*; 16. *Crithidia luciliae*; 17. *Crithidia fasciculata*; 18. *Strigomonas oncopelti*; 19. *Leishmania tarentolae*; 20. *Trypanosoma levisi*; 21. *Tetrahymena patula* LFF; 22. *Tetrahymena pyriformis* W; 23. *Paramecium aurelia* 51.7s; 24. *Colpidium colpidium carolina*; 25. *Colpidium colpidium* Burbank; 26. *Colpidium camphylum*; 27. *Colpidium truncatum*; 28. *Glaucoma chattoni*; 29. *Dictyostelium discoideum* NC-4.

FUNGI: 1. *Neurospora crassa*; 2. yeast; 3. *Psalliota campestris*; 4. *Aspergillus niger*.

References: Organisms 1–12 (cited in ref. 18); 13–29 (ref. 19).

References: Organisms 1–2 (cited in ref. 5); 3, 4 (ref. 3).

ALGAE: 1. *Chaetoceros decipiens*; 2. *Rhabdonema adriaticum*; 3. *Thalassiosira Nordenscheldti*; 4. *Scenedesmus acuminatus*; 5. *Scenedesmus quadricauda*; 6. *Ankistrodesmus* sp.; 7. *Hydrodictyon reticulatum*; 8. *Chlamydomonas reinhardi*; 9. *Chlorella ellipsoidea*; 10. *Cystosira barbata*; 11. *Chlamydomonas eugametos*; 12. *Polytoma uvella*; 13. *Chlamydomonas moevusii*; 14. *Monodus subterraneus*; 15. *Polytoma agilis*; 16. *Chlorogonium elongatum*; 17. *Phormidium luridum*; 18. *Astasia longa*; 19. *Ulothrix fimbriata*; 20. *Navicula closterium*; 21. *Navicula pelliculosa*; 22. *Chlamydomonas angulosa*.
* Satellite DNA present.

References: Organisms 1–10 (cited in ref. 5); 11–22 (ref. 20).

HIGHER PLANTS: 1. *Alnus barbata*; 2. *Salix acubifolia*; 3. *Salix caprea*; 4. *Crylus avelana*; 5. *Papaver somniferum*; 6. *Cucurbita pepo*; 7. *Phaseolus vulgaris*; 8. *Arachis hypogaea*; 9. *Triticum vulgare*; 10. *Allium cepa*; 11. *Pinus sibirica*; 12. *Corulus avelana*.

References: Organisms 1–11 (cited in ref. 5); 12. (ref. 21).

INVERTEBRATES: 1. *Cancer borealis* (the major DNA); 2. *Cancer irroratus* (the major DNA); 3. *Carcinus maenas*; 4. *Lumbricas terrestris* (earthworm); 5. *Venus mercenaria* (clam); 6. *Arbacia lixula* (sea urchin); 7. *Arbacia punctulata* (sea urchin); 8. *Echinus esculentus* (sea urchin); 9. *Echinocardium cordatum* (sea urchin); 10. *Paracentrotus lividus* (sea urchin); 12. *Psammechinus miliaris* (sea urchin); 12. *Locusta migratoria* (locust).

References: Organisms 1–12 (cited in ref. 5).

VERTEBRATES: 1. Man (thymus, liver, spleen, sperm); 1 man (kidney, tissue culture); 2. horse (spleen); 3. ox (thymus, spleen, liver, pancreas, kidney, testes, sperm); 4. sheep (thymus, liver, spleen, sperm); 5. pig (thymus, liver, spleen, thyroid); 6. mouse (sarcoma); 6. mouse (testes and spleen); 7. rat (bone marrow); 8. hen (erythrocytes, egg); 9. salmon (sperm); 10. trout (sperm); 11. herring (testes); 12. shad (testes); 13. turtle (erythrocytes); 14. frog (*Rana pipiens*) (testes); 15. alligator (liver, brain, spleen); 16. monkey (rhesus) (liver, brain, spleen); 17. guinea pig (liver, kidney, spleen).

References: Organisms 1–14 (cited in ref. 5); 15–17 (ref. 22).
[b] 3.8–6.4% 5-methylcytosine has been reported.
[c] 0.2–1.8% 5-methylcytosine has been reported.
[d] 1.0–2.8% 5-methylcytosine has been reported.

424

base composition. Marmur and Doty[29] found that the temperature (T_m) at which DNA configuration changes from the double-stranded state to the random coil state measured by the hyperchromic shift in the ultraviolet, is a linear function of the base composition of DNA. DNA's with higher GC-content required higher temperatures for their denaturation. Thus the profile of the hyperchromicity should be indicative of the extent of heterogeneity. Another technique which became available was density gradient centrifugation using cesium chloride as originated by Meselson et al.[30] Using this technique, a positive correlation between density and GC-content of DNA was found independently by Rolfe and Meselson[31] and Sueoka et al.[32] The correlation was studied more extensively later by Schildkraut et al.[33]

1. UNIMODALITY

A wide survey of DNA in CsCl density gradient centrifugation[5, 31-33] revealed that in the majority of cases DNA forms one band, indicating that the distribution of the base composition has an unimodal character. The width of the distribution, however, depends on the organism of origin. In general, higher organisms have a wider distribution than the lower organisms. Since the band profile of a DNA sample is very much affected by both its molecular weight and heterogeneity, an accurate estimation of heterogeneity is not easily obtainable. An approximate picture can be obtained from the results given in Table II. Analyzing distributions of different genetic markers in CsCl density gradient, heterogeneity has been shown in transforming principles of pneumococcus[34, 35] and of Bacillus subtilis.[36] Inactivation of markers by heat denaturation also indicated heterogeneity of base composition,[27, 38] although irreversible denaturation occurs when the most heat-resistant part of the molecule is separated.[38]

There are several cases in which DNA shows a secondary band or bands in relatively small amounts in the density gradient field. These will be discussed in the following section.

2. SATELLITE DNA

The first observation of satellite (or secondary) bands were made in calf thymus, mouse testis and spleen, and crab testis DNA.[5] Since then, numerous cases have been reported (Table III). In most cases, the nature and function of such bands are not clear, but the following are of particular interest. First, Marmur et al.[39] showed that the interspecific transfer of episome F from Escherichia coli to Serratia marcescens[44] was accompanied by the appearance of a satellite band. This satellite band has a density similar to that of E. coli.[44] This finding is important, since it proposes one of mechanism which may account for the origin of satellite bands in general. Second, cases found in higher plants and algae[45] suggest that the satellite bands in these organisms may be connected to some cytoplasmic self-duplicating unit, possibly chloroplast. A third example is the kappa particle in *Paramecia aurelia*.[41] In this case the infectious particle itself has DNA of a different base composition from the host DNA, which may represent a category of intracellular symbiosis. Under this category, a

TABLE II

HETEROGENEITY OF DNA BASE COMPOSITION ESTIMATED BY DENSITY GRADIENT CENTRIFUGATION[a]

Source	2σ (in GC-content, %)	Ref.
Vertebrates		
Human kidney cells	<9.6	
Mouse spleen	<7.6	1
Frog testis	6.2	
Calf thymus	9.6	31
Bacteria		
Diplococcus pneumoniae	3.9	31
Bacillus megaterium		
Bacillus subtilis		
Escherichia coli		
Micrococcus lysodeikticus		
Micrococcus pyogenes aureus	<6.0	4
Serratia marcescens		
Shigella dysenteriae		
Sarcina lutea		
Pseudomonas aeruginosa		

[a] The sign < indicates that the σ (standard deviation) has been calculated from the total variance ($\sigma_T{}^2$) of the DNA distribution in the density gradient field, which gives the maximum estimate of the heterogeneity.

If we take the number-average molecular weight as 5×10^6, we will not be too far from reality. Then, corresponding 2σ expected, is about 1.0.

trypanosomatid flagellate, *Crithidia oncopelti*, contains a bacterial endo-symbiote whose DNA is responsible for the satellite DNA of the flagellate.[45a] A fourth example is found in the recent report by Rolfe[46] on satellite DNA bands in exponentially growing bacteria, *E. coli*, *Bacillus subtilis*, and *Bacillus megaterium*. These findings are important because these satellite bands could be a replicative form of DNA.[46] A fifth example is the satellite DNA which exists in several species of marine crabs both in the Atlantic and in the Pacific[5, 42, 47] (Table III). The density of the satellite band is similar to that of the deoxyadenylate-thymidylate polymer enzymically synthesized.[48] The satellite DNA was isolated[49] by the methylated albumin-kieselguhr column technique.[50] It has double helical characteristics[47] and contains about 3% GC. It can act as a primer for DNA polymerase and the resulting deoxyadenylate and deoxythymidylate residues are found in alternating sequence.[51] The biological significance of the polymer is not clear at the moment. A sixth example is a light satellite DNA of

TABLE III

SATELLITE DNA[a]

Organism	Main DNA		Satellite DNA			Notes	Ref.
	Density	GC (%)	Density	GC (%)	Amt. (%)		
Serratia marscesens with E. coli episome	1.718	58	1.709	50	0.1–0.2	E. coli episome	39
Halobacterium salinarium	1.727	67	1.718	53	20		40
Halobacterium cutirubrum						Small satellite	40
Paramecium aurelia	1.689	29	1.696	36		Kappa particle	41
Cancer borealis	1.702	42	1.681	2.7	30	Analyzed by Swartz et al.[41a]	5
Cancer irroratus	1.700	42	1.000		11		5
Cancer antennaris Stimpson	1.700	42	1.677		26		42
Cancer gracilis Dana	1.700	42	1.680		9		42
Cancer magister Dana	1.701	42	1.677		14		42
Cancer productus Randall	1.701	42	1.679		32		42
Calf thymus	1.704	44	1.715	55			43
Mouse testis and spleen	1.702	43	1.692	33			43
Guinea pig	1.703	44	1.697	38			22
Escherichia coli, Bacillus subtilis, B. megaterium	Rolfe[43] reports that in these bacteria DNA from exponentially growing cells show two satellite bands in CsCl density gradient centrifugation, one heavier than the main band, the other slightly lighter than the average of the main band						
Chlamydomonas reinhardi, Euglena, spinach	Chun et al.[45] find two satellite bands in these organisms, at least one of which may correspond to DNA in chloroplasts. Some species of algae have satellite DNA (see Table I) which are not listed here because of the preliminary nature of the observation						

[a] In order to make the density values of DNA comparable, the system[33] in which the density of E. coli DNA was taken as 1.710 was adopted in this table.

mouse testis and spleen.[5, 22, 52] The density of the satellite band is lighter than the main band ($\Delta\rho = -0.010$) and corresponds to 32% GC. However, the lightness of this DNA may not be due to a lower GC-content. Cheng and Sueoka[43] fractionated mouse testis DNA on a methylated albumin column which can separate nucleic acids by base composition[49] as well as by size.[50] The satellite DNA elutes in a lower concentration of NaCl than the main DNA, which is opposite to the result expected. The narrowness of the satellite band in the density gradient suggests that the elution pattern cannot be explained by a small molecular size. The result indicates, therefore, either that the light satellite band contains a high content of an unusual base, or that it is combined firmly with other material of low density. This is compared with the heavy satellite band of calf thymus DNA which behaves as we expect, i.e., it elutes with a lower concentration of NaCl.

There are several other cases where satellite DNA bands (Table III) exist, but their nature and significance remain to be elucidated.

3. INTERCHAIN BIASES

Although equimolarity of A to T and G to C holds in the Watson-Crick double helical structure of DNA, there can be two orientations of the base pairs, namely, A-T or T-A, and G-C or C-G.[9] If the two orientations are equally frequent for each base pair, each of the two complementary chains of DNA should have four bases of equal frequency. On the other

TABLE IV
UNBALANCED BASE COMPOSITIONS OF NUCLEIC ACIDS

Organism	Nucleic acid	C	G	T(U)	A	Ref.
φX 174	Single-stranded DNA	18.5	24.1	32.7	24.7	54
Phage α	Double-stranded DNA					
	Strand 1	21.3	24.1	24.5	30.1	13
	Strand 2	24.2	19.9	32.1	24.0	
Phage f2	RNA	27	26	25	22	55
Southern bean mosaic virus	RNA	23	26	25	26	56
Tomato bushy stunt virus	RNA	21	28	25	28	56
Cucumber virus	RNA	19	26	30	26	56
Tobacco mosaic virus	RNA	19	26	27	29	56
Turnip yellow virus	RNA	38	17	22	23	56
Poliovirus	RNA	22	24	25	29	57

hand, if there is a bias in the orientation, the A/T and/or G/C of each chain may be different. This point was raised first by Davern.[53] Known cases where DNA and RNA have biased orientations of base pairs are summarized in Table IV. Various phages of *B. subtilis* have different densities for the two chains of their DNA, possibly because of the biased contents of 5-hydroxymethyl-deoxyribouridylic acid between the two complementary chains.[53a] The bias is bound to have biological significance; this will be discussed later.

4. INTRAMOLECULAR HETEROGENEITY

Data on intramolecular heterogeneity of DNA base composition are very scarce. When calf thymus and pneumococcus DNA molecules are fragmented by sonication without breaking hydrogen bonds, the increase of the DNA band width in the CsCl density gradient does not exceed appreciably the value expected from the reduction of the molecular weight.[58] In this case, original DNA samples had molecular weights of 10×10^6 for calf thymus and pneumococcus, and after sonication, 0.8×10^6 and 1.6×10^6, respectively. This indicates that intramolecular base distribution is fairly uniform. However, the technique cannot be applied for smaller molecular weights because of the difficulty of banding small molecules in CsCl density gradient centrifugation. The nearest neighbor frequency analyses of various DNA (Josse et al.[67]) indicate the frequencies of different dinucleotides fairly close to those expected from the frequency of each base in the DNA sample for random sequence of the bases. This indicates that distribution of bases along the DNA chain is rather uniform. Heterogeneity in small regions of the DNA molecule should come from studies on simpler systems, like phage DNA or episomes. In this connection, mention should be made of recent studies on genetics[59] and physicochemical studies of phage λ[60] and of phage T2.[61] Another technique is the isolation of messenger RNA of a particular locus, which should allow us to infer the base composition of the locus. Such a technique is being developed.[62, 63]

5. TISSUE DIFFERENCE

No definite case in which the mean base composition is different among different tissues has been reported to the author's knowledge. On the other hand, there are a number of cases which give similar DNA base compositions of different tissues (see Chargaff's review).[1] More recently, Kit[64, 65, 66] found no difference in DNA base composition between normal tissues and tumors of mice. Kit[22] also examined DNA from different tissues of the mouse, monkey, guinea pig, and alligator by CsCl density gradient centrifugation. Again there was no tissue difference in the DNA profiles. Mice and guinea pig DNA had a satellite DNA, which was found in all tissues examined.

C. SEQUENCE ANALYSIS

The more detailed and direct approach, of course, is to analyze the nucleotide sequence of DNA. At the moment, only indirect methods are available. It should be pointed out, however, that unique information can be provided by indirect methods.

1. NEIGHBOR ANALYSIS

Using the differential cleavage of phosphodiester linkages of DNA, Josse et al.[67] analyzed the frequencies of neighboring nucleotides. The nearest neighbor analysis with a variety of DNA primers yielded results showing a small but significant deviation from the frequencies predicted by a random arrangement of the mononucleotides.[68] This oriented discrepancy could be expected if the code is universal, or partially so. In a universal code, certain dinucleotide sequences may be more frequent than others, if that sequence is found in sensible triplets (for nondegenerate cases) or in more frequent amino acids in the proteins of the organisms (for degenerate cases).[69] Another explanation was given[70] that the nonrandomness may be due to a residual effect of the common origin of organisms. The two theories may be stating the same thing.

The neighbor analysis of DNA[67] illuminates two important issues. The data prove chemically that the two chains of DNA have opposite polarity in the sugar phosphate backbone, and permit a comparison of the template action of DNA in synthesizing RNA. It has been found *in vitro* that RNA synthesized with a DNA primer[71-73] has not only a complementary base composition, but also a complementary sequence of nucleotides with that of the primer DNA as judged by a nearest neighbor analysis.[74, 75]

2. HYBRIDIZATION

The discovery of Marmur and Lane[37] and Doty *et al.*[76] on the renaturation of heat-denatured DNA by slow cooling opened a new possibility of investigating the homology of the base sequence between different samples of DNA. Marmur *et al.*[77] examined the hybridization between DNA's of several species of *Bacillus*. In each combination of two species, the DNA of one species was labeled with deuterium and nitrogen-15, and the DNA of the other species was not labeled. A mixture of the two DNA preparations was heated to 100°C. and cooled slowly. Treatment of the slowly cooled sample with phosphodiesterase of *E. coli* eliminated nonspecific complexes and left the more regular double-strained DNA. They found that only closely related organisms formed hybrid molecules. The hybridization technique was extended to the DNA-RNA complex, which played a critical role in the identification and isolation of the messenger RNA.[78-82] In these experiments, comparison of DNA and RNA base compositions has been the guiding rule.

III. Base Composition of RNA

The compositional relation between DNA and bulk RNA was first examined by Belozersky and Spirin[24] and only a slight correlation, if any, was observed. More recent data on base composition of the three kinds of RNA, ribosomal, soluble, and messenger,[83] are summarized in Tables V, VI, and VII and Figs. 1, 2, and 3.

The base composition of messenger RNA correlates almost perfectly with homologous DNA, whereas soluble and ribosomal RNA do not.

IV. Amino Acid Composition of Protein

Current views on DNA-protein coding assume that the base sequence of DNA has direct correspondence with the amino acid sequence in protein. As we have seen, the base composition of DNA is quite variable from organism to organism, and yet the heterogeneity of the base compo-

TABLE V

BASE COMPOSITIONS OF RIBOSOMAL RNA

Organism	DNA-GC(%)	Comment	C	G	U	A	GC (%)	Pu/Py	Ref.
Bacillus cereus	35		21.9	31.7	21.2	25.2	53.6	1.32	84
Diplococcus pneumoniae	38	Large microsome	19.2	31.1	24.0	25.4	50.3	1.31	85
		Small microsome	18.9	30.7	24.8	25.4	49.6	1.28	
Bacillus subtilis	43		22.8	32.2	20.4	24.6	55.0	1.32	84
Escherichia coli	50	30S	22.8	31.6	21.0	24.6	54.4	1.28	
		50S	20.9	31.4	22.1	25.6	52.3	1.32	86
		70S	22.1	31.5	21.4	25.0	53.6	1.30	
			22.9	32.4	20.8	23.9	55.3	1.30	84
		Large microsome	20.1	32.4	22.6	24.7	52.5	1.33	85
		Small microsome	20.7	31.7	23.2	24.2	52.4	1.25	
Serratia marcescens	59		22.0	32.1	22.0	23.9	54.1	1.27	84
Alkaligenes faecalis	67		22.0	31.9	21.7	24.4	53.9	1.30	84
Sarcina lutea	71		22.6	34.2	21.7	21.5	56.8	1.26	84
Micrococcus lysodeikticus	72	Large microsome	20.8	33.3	22.7	23.0	54.1	1.20	85
		Small microsome	22.1	31.5	24.1	22.2	53.6	1.16	
Pea stem	40		22.3	31.4	22.0	24.3	53.7	1.26	87
Rabbit reticulocytes	—		28.7	34.5	18.2	18.6	63.2	1.14	87
Sheep reticulocytes	43		30.9	32.7	18.2	18.2	63.6	1.03	87

sition of DNA molecules from each species is relatively small. In this connection, comparative analyses of the amino acid composition of protein from organisms with widely different DNA base compositions should be instructive. Such data are available for the total protein of various bacteria (Sueoka, 1961).[97, 98] The protein preparations consist of soluble plus ribosomal protein with the membrane fractions removed. Results reveal several points of interest. In the first place, unknown ninhydrin-positive material constitutes less than 1% of the total amino acids, and none of them is correlated with the GC-content of DNA. Second, the amino acid composition of the total protein is remarkably invariant to environmental changes. For example, minimal versus an enriched medium, stages of growth, and culture temperature do not affect results appreciably. The

TABLE VI
BASE COMPOSITIONS OF SOLUBLE RNA

Organism	DNA-GC (%)	C	G	U	A	ψ^a	GC (%)	Pu/Py	Ref.
Bacillus cereus	35	28.0	31.1	18.8	20.5	1.6	59.1	1.06	84
Diplococcus pneumoniae	38	22.9	29.7	25.0	22.2	—	52.6	1.08	85
Bacillus subtilis	43	26.9	30.8	19.7	21.9	0.7	57.7	1.12	84
Escherichia coli	50	28.6	31.0	18.8	20.4	1.2	59.6	1.06	84
		24.7	32.0	22.5	20.5	—	56.7	1.11	85
Serratia marcescens	59	22.2	32.4	22.8	20.9	1.7	54.6	1.14	84
Alkaligenes faecalis	67	27.6	34.1	17.8	19.3	1.3	61.7	1.14	84
Sarcina lutea	71	27.3	34.6	17.8	19.3	1.0	61.9	1.17	84
Micrococcus lysodeikticus	72	25.1	31.7	23.4	19.6	—	56.8	1.06	85
Yeast	36	28.4	29.2	20.0	18.5	3.9	57.6	0.91	88

^{a} ψ: Pseudouracil.

TABLE VII
BASE COMPOSITIONS OF MESSENGER RNA

Organism	DNA-GC (%)	C	G	U	A	GC (%)	Pu/Py	Ref.
Bacillus megaterium	38	19.7	23.4	29.0	27.9	43.4	1.05	89
Proteus vulgaris	40	19.9	19.1	32.5	28.5	39.0	0.91	90
Escherichia coli	50	24.0	30.2	21.3	24.5	54.2	1.21	90
		24.1	27.1	23.7	25.1	51.2	1.09	91
		24.7	27.7	23.5	24.1	52.4	1.07	89
Pseudomonas aeruginosa	64	31.0	29.0	20.5	19.5	60.0	0.94	90
		29.0	29.5	20.2	21.3	58.5	1.03	89
Bacteriophage T2	35	18.0	18.0	32.0	32.0	36.0	1.00	90
Bacteriophage T7	47	23.7	21.8	27.8	26.7	45.5	0.94	90
Yeast	36	21.7	21.2	28.7	28.6	42.9	0.99	92
Calf thymus	43	19.6	23.8	29.0	27.4	43.4	1.05	93
Rabbit thymus	—	20.4	21.3	29.6	28.7	41.7	1.00	94
Pigeon pancreas	—	22.2	18.5	31.2	28.1	40.7	0.87	95
Rat liver	42	23.6	17.8	28.4	30.2	41.4	0.92	96

amino acid composition of the total protein of any species is obviously an average composition of many kinds of protein. The constancy of the over-all composition suggests that no protein possessing an amino acid composition widely disparate from the average is produced in large proportions under the conditions examined. It will be remembered that the compositional heterogeneity of DNA of a bacterial species is rather small

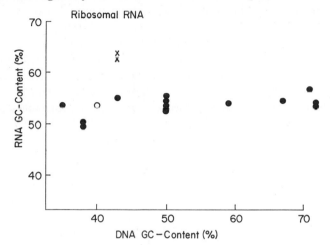

FIG. 1. Compositional relation between ribosomal RNA and DNA. The data listed in Table V are plotted against the GC-content of DNA. Closed circles: bacteria; open circle: pea stem; crosses: rabbit and sheep. The GC content of rabbit DNA was assumed to be 43%.

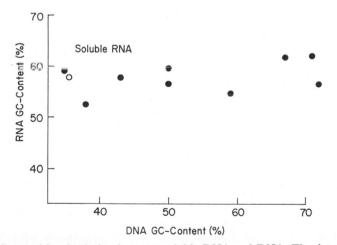

FIG. 2. Compositional relation between soluble RNA and DNA. The data listed in Table VI are plotted against the GC-content of DNA. Closed circles: bacteria; open circle: yeast.

compared with that of higher organisms. The extent of compositional heterogeneity in DNA may reflect that of amino acid composition in protein. For example, histidine, tyrosine, phenylalanine, and methionine are found at distinctly lower levels when compared with other amino acids. Finally, the results indicate that there exist several significant correlations between DNA base composition and the amino acid composition of protein. According to the nature of correlations, we can classify amino acids into three groups. Among 18 amino acids tested, alanine, arginine, glycine, and proline are positively correlated with the GC-content of DNA. Isoleucine, lysine, aspartic acid plus asparagine, glutamic acid plus glutamine, tyrosine, and phenylalanine are negatively correlated. Histidine, valine, leucine, threonine, serine, and possibly methionine are extremely uniform with no detectable evidence of correlation. Correlations become

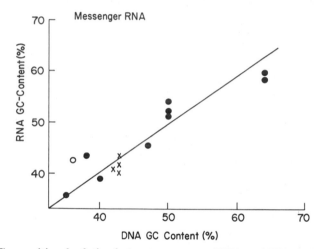

Fig. 3. Compositional relation between messenger RNA and DNA. The data listed in Table VII are plotted against the GC-content of DNA. Closed circles: phages or bacteria; open circle: yeast, crosses: calf thymus, rabbit thymus, pigeon pancreas, and rat liver. DNA GC-contents of rabbit and pigeon are assumed to be 43%.

clearer when we include various strains of *Tetrahymena pyriformis* which have a GC-content of DNA in the range of 24 to 32%.[98] The presence of correlations indicates the universality of the code. Moreover, the shapes of the curve are best interpreted by assuming degeneracy of the code.[98]

V. Discussion

The main features of the variation and heterogeneity of DNA base compositions are:

1. Among bacteria (possibly protozoa and algae also), the mean GC-content of DNA varies approximately from 25 to 75%, and this range extends over the range of the mean GC-content of higher organisms.

2. Phylogenetic relations are reflected in the mean GC-content. Thus, closely related organisms show similar base compositions.

3. Distribution of the GC-content among the DNA molecules-of an organism is unimodal, and the range of heterogeneity is comparatively narrow. Consequently, if the mean GC-content of DNA of two species is different by 10% in bacteria, there are few common DNA molecules of the same GC-content between the two species.

4. When closely related organisms show a difference (usually small) in the mean GC-content, the difference is rather uniform among the molecules.

5. When genetic recombination occurs between two genomes, the DNA base composition of the two organisms is similar. However, the *addition* of a chromosome or chromosomal fragment of one organism to the other does not necessarily require similarity of base composition.

6. Satellite DNA's which have different base compositions from the main DNA have been found in various organisms. The origin and function of the satellite DNA are diverse.

Construction of theoretical pictures accounting for the wide variation and small heterogeneity of DNA base composition has been attempted by Sueoka et al.,[32] Rolfe and Meselson,[31] Lanni,[2] Sueoka,[5] Sueoka,[69] and Freese.[70] Lanni[2] raised the possibility of "genetic factors which may set general species-specific rules of composition within which the individuality [specific fine structure] of the ordinary genes must then be modulated." Sueoka[5, 69] proposed a theory which put special emphasis on differential conversion rates for $AT \rightleftharpoons GC$ by mutation and selection. According to the theory, the average base composition of DNA will approach an equilibrium value which is a function of the ratio of the two over-all conversion rates, $AT \rightarrow GC$ and $GC \rightarrow AT$. The heterogeneity of base composition also can be calculated for the equilibrated condition. Freese[70] gave a similar theory and further emphasized the small but systematic discrepancy of dinucleotide pairs[68] as an indication of evolutionary relationship. When we interpret the over-all features of the variation and heterogeneity of DNA base composition as the result of mutation and selection, it is reasonable to think that the mean GC-content of DNA is a stable character and its shifting is an extremely slow process.[69, 70] There are, however, some reports contradictory to this picture. Spirin et al.[99] reported induced charges of GC-content of *E. coli* from 52 to 42 or 67%, of *Salmonella typhosa* from 53 to 44 or 65%, and of *Shigella dysenteriae* from 53 to 67%. Recently, Weed[99a] reports that by growing *B. subtilis* with 10^{-4} *M* cupric ion in the medium for 3 weeks, a new form of bacteria appeared. The DNA base composition of the new strain had 65% GC instead of 42% GC of the original strain. These reports deserve careful confirmation because of their implication to coding and evolution as well as to the mutagenic effect of cupric ion.

The wide variation and small heterogeneity of the DNA base composition raised some doubts about the universality of the code which had been taken for granted.[100] Rolfe and Meselson[31] pointed out the possibility that the code could be species-specific. However, even if the code is universal, variation and heterogeneity of DNA base composition are possible.

Sueoka et al.[32] raised three other possibilities.

1. "The proteins that perform common functions in bacteria may be structurally quite different in many cases. For example, in enzymes, the active sites may be similar, but the main part of the proteins are different. This is the situation that might be expected if the evolutionary development of bacteria has followed a number of independent paths, each corresponding to the elaboration of a complex genome from a primary deoxyribonucleic acid of a particular composition. In general, this view suggests that the distribution of DNA base composition reflects their phylogenetic relationship."

2. "The proteins that perform common functions in bacteria are very similar structurally. If all the deoxyribonucleic molecules are genetically active and yet unrelated in composition in many cases, the coding between the deoxyribonucleic acid and the protein must be very different from those that have been considered hitherto, that is, it has been customary to assume that the sequence of amino acids in proteins is coded in the sequence of the four nucleotides in deoxyribonucleic acid. Since it has been shown that various triplets of nucleotides are sufficient to specify each amino acid, it follows that similar proteins must be derived from deoxyribonucleic acid molecules of similar composition, unless quite artificial, ad hoc, restrictions are imposed. If the coding concept is to remain, a radical revision is necessary in order to eliminate this dependence on composition. For example, the four-letter alphabet (adenine, cytosine, guanine, and thymine) could be abandoned in favor of a two-letter alphabet in which adenine and cytosine (6 amino-bearing nucleotides) would serve as one letter and guanine and thymine (6 keto-bearing nucleotides)[100a] would serve as the other. In this case, no relation to composition would be expected. Of course, it would be possible to retain the four-letter alphabet if it were assumed that different codes applied to different bacteria, but this alternative is unattractive because it is most unlikely that different codes would yield the same number of amino acids."

3. "The proteins that perform common functions in bacteria are very similar structurally, and the current ideas concerning the coding problem remain acceptable. This could only be true if the major part of the deoxyribonucleic acid could then have a composition in common with the corresponding part of other bacterial deoxyribonucleic acid. It appears that this minor part would have to be less than 10 per cent of the whole to have escaped detection."

As one can see in the following discussion, the first possibility seems to be supported by the current data more than the other two possibilities.

Universality and degeneracy of the code were first supported experimentally from the correlation between DNA base composition and amino acid composition of protein among bacteria and *Tetrahymena*.[18] Universality and degeneracy get further support from the fact that the assignment of codons[101] by the cell-free system[102, 103] has become more consistent with the compositional correlations between DNA and protein[101, 104-107] when the degeneracy has become more extensive.[108, 109] Further support for universality was given by Signer et al.,[110] who showed that the alkaline phosphatase produced in a *Serratia marcescens* carrying an *E. coli* episomic factor with P+ (alkaline phosphatase locus) is almost identical with the *E. coli* alkaline phosphatase. In the same system, a similar result was obtained for β-galactosidase (Jacob).[111]

More direct results supporting universality were given by von Ehrenstein and Lipmann.[112] Hemoglobin was synthesized in an *in vitro* system using rabbit reticulocyte ribosomes and amino acyl-sRNA (soluble RNA) from *E. coli* in which leucine was radioactive. The autoradiograph of the "fingerprints" of the tryptic digests of the product was very similar to that of normal rabbit hemoglobin. A similar situation has also been reported in the *in vitro* synthesis of TMV (tobacco mosaic virus) protein, using TMV RNA and a cell-free system of *E. coli* (Tsugita et al.[113]). In the case of RNA containing bacteriophage f2, the product of the cell-free system using viral RNA and *E. coli* extracts gives an almost identical fingerprint with the phage coat protein (Nathans et al.[114]).

The stimulation of amino acid incorporation into a ribosomal fraction by synthetic polynucleotides provides a relatively simple method to test universality. Some results are available. Thus Arnstein et al.[115] showed that the stimulation of phenylalanine incorporation by poly-U also occurs in a cell-free system from rabbit reticulocytes. Weinstein et al.[116] reported that the cell-free system from *Chlamydomonas reinhardi* has very similar response to synthetic polyribonucleotides as found in *E. coli*.

Assuming universality, attempts to specify the base sequence of each codon have been made, with a certain amount of success. These attempts have employed amino acid replacement data mainly from hemoglobin and TMV protein and from code assignments in the cell-free system of *E. coli*. (Smith[117, 118], Jukes[119, 120]).

It should, however, be remembered that the adaptor hypothesis between the template and polypeptide chain supported by the finding of amino acid transfer RNA (Hoagland)[121] rendered any *a priori* theoretical rules of coding immaterial. Consequently, there is no mechanical reason why the code should be universal. The only conservative force for maintaining a universal coding system is the selection force against random mutation which causes a disturbance of the normal relationship between sRNA and the template and/or amino acid-activating enzymes. There have been several cases where mutation could have changed the code translating mechanism.[122-124] Although universality seems likely, it should not be accepted on the strength of such data as are available at the moment, but its detailed feature should be thoroughly looked into experimentally.

Base compositions of ribosomal and soluble RNA do not mimic the DNA base composition, and the equimolarity of A to U and G to C does not hold particularly in ribosomal RNA. Contrary to the messenger RNA, therefore, it is quite possible that these two species of RNA should be free from DNA control. However, three types of evidence are available which indicate that their synthesis may also be specified by DNA. The first evidence was provided by Zalokar[125] showing that in *Neurospora* hyphae RNA is transferred from the nucleus to cytoplasm and becomes associated with ribosomes.

The second point is that the homologous combinations of DNA and soluble (Giacomoni and Spiegelman[126], Goodman and Rich[127]) and ribosomal RNA (Yankofsky and Spiegelman[128]) seem to form specific hybrids. The third point is a negative one indicating that no RNA-synthesizing system discovered so far uses RNA as the primer, except for the case of RNA-containing coliphage, MS-2 (Weissman *et al.*[129]). The discrepancy in the base composition of soluble and ribosomal RNA suggests that their structural loci are quite unique from other parts of the genome. The significance of this fact is an interesting problem for experimental and theoretical studies because the base composition of soluble and ribosomal RNA must have resisted the leveling effect of mutation. This suggests that the base sequence of soluble and, especially, ribosomal RNA is restricted by their function.

Lanni[2] recognized that genetic recombinations in bacteria and viruses are observed only between species with DNA of similar base composition. The underlying principle is the requirement of homology in the base sequence for pairing and recombination. Detailed information on this point can be found in the appropriate review articles (Lanni,[2] Marmur *et al.*[6]). When base compositions of two DNA molecules are similar, their base sequences are not necessarily similar. On the other hand, if the base compositions are different, the sequences must be different. The relation between genetic interaction, base composition, and sequence became amenable to experimental analysis by the hybridization technique developed by Marmur and Lane,[37] and Doty *et al.*[76] Thus, in the genus *Bacillus*, the similarity of base composition was a necessary condition for transformation, but was not sufficient. Apparently, a base sequence homology is also necessary. In this connection, episomic transfer of a part of the chromosome from one organism to another seems not to require compositional similarity of DNA between these organisms.[44, 130-137] However, since even in these systems there is no case reported where genetic recombination occurs between the foreign and host chromosomes, except in homologous or closely related bacteria, the requirements of base sequence homology for genetic recombination has not been violated.

Interchain biases of base composition of DNA suggest the functional differentiation of the two chains. Robison and Guild[138] presented evidence that there are interchain biases in pneumococcal DNA which can be shown by centrifuging denatured pneumococcal DNA in CsCl at pH 12. They also reported evidence that the phenotypic expression of genetic markers is immediate in one chain, and one generation after in the other chain.

In the case of phage SP8 of *B. subtilis*, where two chains of the DNA molecule can be clearly separated, only one chain seems to be copied for the messenger RNA *in vitro*.[139] Sinsheimer[54] found that coliphage ϕX 174 has a single-stranded DNA, whose base composition is not balanced (equimolarity of A and T, and/or G and C are not held; see Table IV). When the phage DNA penetrates the cells, it becomes a double-stranded form (replicative form).[140] Here again, the question is whether only one chain or both chains are copied for messenger RNA. Again the answer seems to be that only one chain is copied *in vivo*.[141] Since, in the majority of instances, messenger RNA has a balanced base composition, whether or not this one chain-copying mechanism of messenger RNA is a general phenomenon should be examined further. If the unbalanced base composition between the two chains of DNA is the common feature of the functional DNA, and if only one chain is copied, then the balanced base composition of most messenger RNA should come from an average effect of numerous kinds of messenger RNA.

In conclusion, the compositional studies of biological macromolecules, DNA, RNA, and protein, have furnished an essential basis for our understanding of the storing and processing of genetic information. The results of such studies have offered not only an over-all picture of the system, but also suggested many new experiments which have led to several penetrating discoveries. The problems for the future are to examine the detailed feature of DNA base composition in different localities of the chromosome and DNA molecules in relation to the genetic function of different loci and within the locus. The unique base compositions of soluble and ribosomal RNA are still beyond our comprehension. Evolutionary stability of DNA base composition and universality of the code still present some unsettled questions. The functional significance of most satellite DNA's observed should be investigated.

We all understand very well that sequence study gives the ultimate answer to our understanding of the mechanism of information transfer. However, compositional studies often have played an important role in the realization of the problem, and have offered the criteria for judgment. It is also clear that detailed analysis of the sequence is time-consuming, and often misses the whole picture.

REFERENCES

[1] E. Chargaff, in "The Nucleic Acids" (E. Chargaff and J. N. Davidson, eds.), Vol. I, p. 307. Academic Press, New York, 1955.

[2] F. Lanni, Perspectives Biol. Med. 3, 418 (1960).

[3] A. N. Belozersky and A. S. Spirin, in "The Nucleic Acids" (E. Chargaff and J. N. Davidson, eds.), Vol. III, p. 147. Academic Press, New York, 1960.

[4] R. L. Sinsheimer, in "The Nucleic Acids" (E. Chargaff and J. N. Davidson, eds.), Vol. III, p. 187. Academic Press, New York, 1960.

[5] N. Sueoka, J. Mol. Biol. 3, 31 (1961).

[6] J. Marmur, S. Falkow, and M. Mandel, Ann. Rev. Microbiol. 17, 329 (1963).

[7] E. Chargaff, Federation Proc. 10, 654 (1951).

[8] G. R. Wyatt, in "The Chemistry and Physiology of the Nucleus" (V. T. Bowen, ed.), p. 201. Academic Press, New York, 1952.

[9] J. D. Watson and F. H. C. Crick, Cold Spring Harbor Symposia Quant. Biol. 18, 123 (1953).

[10] E. Volkin and L. Astrachan, Virology 2, 149 (1956).

[11] P. Doty, J. Marmur, and N. Sueoka, Brookhaven Symposia in Biol., No. 12, 1, 1959.

[12] I. Takahashi and J. Marmur, Biochem. Biophys. Research Communs. 10, 289 (1963).

[13] S. Cordes, H. T. Epstein, and J. Marmur, Nature 191, 1097 (1961).

[14] W. Schäfer, in "The Viruses" (F. M. Burnet and W. M. Stanley, eds.), Vol. I, p. 475. Academic Press, New York, 1959.

[15] T. Ben-Porat and A. S. Kaplan, Virology 16, 261 (1962).

[16] L. V. Crawford, Virology 19, 279 (1963).

[17] R. G. Kallen, M. Simon, and J. Marmur, J. Mol. Biol. 5, 248 (1962).

[18] N. Sueoka, Cold Spring Harbor Symposia Quant. Biol. 26, 35 (1961).

[19] C. L. Schildkraut, M. Mandel, S. Levisohn, J. E. Smith-Sonneborn, and J. Marmur, Nature 196, 795 (1962).

[20] N. Sueoka, unpublished results.

[21] G. P. Serenkov and M. V. Pachomova, Biologicheskie Nauki 4, 156 (1959).

[22] S. Kit, J. Mol. Biol. 3, 711 (1961).

[23] K. Y. Lee, R. Wahl, and E. Barbu, Ann. inst. Pasteur 91, 212 (1956).

[24] A. N. Belozersky and A. S. Spirin, Nature 182, 111 (1958).

[25] N. Sueoka and D. L. Nanney, in preparation.

[26] E. Chargaff, C. F. Crampton, and R. Lipshitz, Nature 172, 289 (1953).

[27] G. L. Brown and M. Watson, Nature 172, 339 (1953).

[28] C. F. Crampton, R. Lipshitz, and E. Chargaff, J. Biol. Chem. 211, 125 (1954).

[29] J. Marmur and P. Doty, Nature 183, 1427 (1959).

[30] M. Meselson, F. Stahl, and J. Vinograd, Proc. Natl. Acad. Sci. U. S. 43, 581 (1957).

[31] R. Rolfe and M. Meselson, Proc. Natl. Acad. Sci U. S. 45, 1039 (1959).

[32] N. Sueoka, J. Marmur, and P. Doty, Nature 183, 1429 (1959).

[33] C. L. Schildkraut, J. Marmur, and P. Doty, J. Mol. Biol. 4, 430 (1962).

[34] R. Rolfe and H. Ephrussi-Taylor, Proc. Natl. Acad. Sci. U. S. 47, 1450 (1961).

[35] W. R. Guild, *J. Mol. Biol.* **6**, 214 (1963).
[36] H. Yoshikawa and N. Sueoka, *Proc. Natl. Acad. Sci. U. S.* **49**, 559 (1963).
[37] J. Marmur and D. Lane, *Proc. Natl. Acad. Sci. U. S.* **46**, 451 (1960).
[38] M. Roger and R. D. Hotchkiss, *Proc. Natl. Acad. Sci. U. S.* **47**, 653 (1961).
[39] J. Marmur, R. Rownd, S. Falkow, L. S. Baron, C. Schildkraut, and P. Doty, *Proc. Natl. Acad. Sci. U. S.* **47**, 972 (1961).
[40] J. G. Joshi, W. R. Guild, and P. Handler, *J. Mol. Biol.* **6**, 34 (1963).
[41] J. Smith-Sonneborn, L. Green, and J. Marmur, *Nature* **197**, 385 (1963).
[41a] M. N. Swartz, T. A. Trautner, and A. Kornberg, *J. Biol. Chem.* **237**, 1961 (1962).
[42] M. Smith, *Biochem. Biophys. Research Communs.* **10**, 67 (1963).
[43] T. Y. Cheng and N. Sueoka, *Science* **141**, 1194 (1963).
[44] S. Falkow, J. Marmur, W. F. Carey, W. M. Spillman, and L. S. Baron, *Genetics* **46**, 703 (1961).
[45] E. H. L. Chun, M. H. Vaughan, Jr., and A. Rich, *J. Mol. Biol.* **7**, 130 (1963).
[45a] J. Marmur, M. E. Cahoon, Y. Shimura, and H. J. Vogel, *Nature* **197**, 1228 (1963).
[46] R. Rolfe, *Proc. Natl. Acad. Sci. U. S.* **49**, 386 (1963).
[47] N. Sueoka and T. Y. Cheng, *Proc. Natl. Acad. Sci. U. S.* **48**, 1851 (1962).
[48] H. K. Schachman, J. Adler, C. M. Radding, I. R. Lehman, and A. Kornberg, *J. Biol. Chem.* **235**, 3242 (1960).
[49] N. Sueoka and T. Y. Cheng, *J. Mol. Biol.* **4**, 161 (1962).
[50] J. D. Mandell and A. D. Hershey, *Anal. Biochem.* **1**, 66 (1960).
[51] M. N. Swartz, T. A. Trautner, and A. Kornberg, *J. Biol. Chem.* **237**, 1961 (1962).
[52] W. Szybalski, *in* "The Molecular Basis of Neoplasis" (S. Kit, ed.) p. 147. Univ. Texas Press, Austin, 1962.
[53] C. I. Davern, *Nature* **188**, 208 (1960).
[53a] J. Marmur and S. Cordes *in* "Informational Macromolecules" (H. J. Vogel, V. Bryson, and J. O. Lampen, eds.), p. 79. Academic Press, New York, 1963.
[54] R. L. Sinsheimer, *J. Mol. Biol.* **1**, 43 (1959).
[55] T. Loeb and N. D. Zinder, *Proc. Natl. Acad. Sci. U. S.* **47**, 282 (1961).
[56] M. Yčas, *Nature* **188**, 209 (1960).
[57] F. L. Schaffer, H. F. Moore, and C. E. Schwerdt, *Virology* **10**, 530 (1960).
[58] N. Sueoka, *Proc. Natl. Acad. Sci. U. S.* **45**, 1480 (1959).
[59] A. D. Kaiser, *J. Mol. Biol.* **4**, 275 (1962).
[60] A. D. Hershey, E. Burgi, and L. Ingraham, *Proc. Natl. Acad. Sci. U. S.* **49**, 748 (1963).
[61] C. A. Thomas and T. C. Pinkerton, *J. Mol. Biol.* **5**, 356–372 (1962).
[62] E. K. F. Bantz and B. D. Hall, *Proc. Natl. Acad. Sci. U. S.* **48**, 400 (1962).
[63] E. T. Bolton and B. J. McCarthy, *Proc. Natl. Acad. Sci. U. S.* **48**, 1390 (1962).
[64] S. Kit, *Arch. Biochem. Biophys.* **87**, 330 (1960).
[65] S. Kit, *J. Biol. Chem.* **235**, 1756 (1960).
[66] S. Kit, *Biochem. Biophys. Research Communs.* **3**, 361 (1960).
[67] J. Josse, A. D. Kaiser, and A. Kornberg, *J. Biol. Chem.* **236**, 864 (1961).
[68] A. D. Kaiser and R. L. Baldwin, *J. Mol. Biol.* **4**, 418 (1962).
[69] N. Sueoka, *Proc. Natl. Acad. Sci. U. S.* **48**, 582 (1962).
[70] E. Freese, *J. Theoret. Biol.* **3**, 82 (1962).
[71] S. Weiss and L. Gladstone, *J. Am. Chem. Soc.* **81**, 4118 (1959).
[72] A. Steven, *Biochem. Biophys. Research Communs.* **3**, 92 (1960).
[73] J. Hurwitz, A. Bresler, and R. Diringer, *Biochem. Biophys. Research Communs.* **3**, 15 (1960).
[74] S. B. Weiss and T. Nakamoto, *Proc. Natl. Acad. Sci. U. S.* **47**, 1400 (1961).
[75] J. Hurwitz, J. J. Furth, M. Anders, P. J. Ortiz, and J. T. August, *Cold Spring Harbor Symposia Quant. Biol.* **26**, 91 (1961).

[76] P. Doty, J. Marmur, J. Eigner, and C. Schildkraut, *Proc. Natl. Acad. Sci. U. S.* **46**, 461 (1960).

[77] J. Marmur, E. Seaman, and J. Levine, *J. Bacteriol.* **85**, 461 (1963).

[78] B. D. Hall and S. Spiegelman, *Proc. Natl. Acad. Sci. U. S.* **47**, 137 (1961).

[79] S. Spiegelman, B. D. Hall, and R. Storck, *Proc. Natl. Acad. Sci. U. S.* **47**, 1135 (1961).

[80] H. M. Schulman and D. M. Bonner, *Proc. Natl. Acad. Sci. U. S.* **48**, 53 (1962).

[81] E. K. F. Bantz and B. D. Hall, *Proc. Natl. Acad. Sci. U.S.* **48**, 400 (1962).

[82] E. T. Bolton and B. J. McCarthy, *Proc. Natl. Acad. Sci. U.S.* **48**, 1390 (1962).

[83] F. Jacob and J. Monod, *J. Mol. Biol.* **3**, 318 (1961).

[84] K. Miura, *Biochim. et Biophys. Acta*, **55**, 62 (1962).

[85] C. R. Woese, *Nature* **189**, 920 (1961).

[86] P. F. Spahr and A. Tissières, *J. Mol. Biol.* **1**, 237 (1959).

[87] J. M. Wallace and P. O. P. Ts'o, *Biochem. Biophys. Research Communs.* **5**, 125 (1961).

[88] R. Monier, M. L. Stephenson, and P. C. Zamecnik, *Biochim. et Biophys. Acta* **43**, 1 (1960).

[89] M. Hayashi and S. Spiegelman, *Proc. Natl. Acad. Sci. U.S.* **47**, 1564 (1961).

[90] E. Volkin, *Federation Proc.* **21**, 112 (1962).

[91] F. Gros, W. Gilbert, H. H. Hiatt, G. Attardi, P. F. Spahr, and J. D. Watson, *Cold Spring Harbor Symposia Quant. Biol.* **26**, 111 (1961).

[92] Y. Kitazume, M. Yčas, and W. S. Vincent, *Proc. Natl. Acad. Sci. U.S.* **48**, 265 (1962).

[93] A. Sibatani, S. R. deKloet, V. G. Allfrey, and A. E. Mirsky, *Proc. Natl. Acad. Sci. U.S.* **48**, 471 (1962).

[94] R. Logan and J. N. Davidson, *Biochim. et Biophys. Acta* **24**, 196 (1957).

[95] L. E. Hokin and M. R. Hokin, *Biochim. et Biophys. Acta* **13**, 401 (1954).

[96] P. Boulanger and J. Montreuil, *Biochim. et Biophys. Acta* **9**, 619 (1952).

[97] N. Sueoka, *Proc. Natl. Acad. Sci. U.S.* **47**, 1141 (1961).

[98] N. Sueoka, *Cold Spring Harbor Symposia Quant. Biol.* **26**, 35 (1961).

[99] A. S. Spirin, A. N. Belozersky, D. G. Kudlaj, A. G. Skavronskaja, and V. G. Mitereva, *Biokhimiya* **23**, 154 (1958).

[99a] L. Weed, *J. Bacteriol.* **85**, 1003 (1963).

[100] S. Brenner, *Proc. Natl. Acad. Sci. U.S.* **43**, 687 (1957).

[100a] R. L. Sinsheimer, *J. Mol. Biol.* **1**, 218 (1959).

[101] F. H. C. Crick, *in* "Progress in Nucleic Acid Research" (J. N. Davidson and W. E. Cohn, eds.), Vol. 1, p. 164. Academic Press, New York, 1962.

[102] M. W. Nirenberg and J. H. Matthaei, *Proc. Natl. Acad. Sci. U.S.* **47**, 1588 (1961).

[103] P. Lengyel, J. F. Speyer, and S. Ochoa, *Proc. Natl. Acad. Sci. U.S.* **47**, 1936 (1961).

[104] R. B. Roberts, *Proc. Natl. Acad. Sci. U.S.* **48**, 897 (1962).

[105] M. Yčas, *Intern. Rev. Cytol.* **13**, 1 (1962).

[106] F. Lanni, *Proc. Natl. Acad. Sci. U.S.* **48**, 1623 (1962).

[107] L. L. Gatlin and J. C. Davis, *J. Theoretical Biol.* **5**, 249 (1963).

[108] O. W. Jones and M. W. Nirenberg, *Proc. Natl. Acad. Sci. U.S.* **48**, 2115 (1962).

[109] A. J. Wahba, R. S. Gardner, C. Basilio, R. S. Miller, J. F. Speyer, and P. Lengyel, *Proc. Natl. Acad. Sci. U.S.* **49**, 116 (1963).

[110] E. R. Signer, A. Torriani, and C. Levinthal, *Cold Spring Harbor Symposia Quant. Biol.* **26**, 31 (1961).

[111] F. Jacob, *Cold Spring Harbor Symposia Quant. Biol.* **26**, 34 (1961).

[112] G. von Ehrenstein and F. Lipmann, *Proc. Natl. Acad. Sci. U.S.* **47**, 941 (1961).

[113] A. Tsugita, H. Fraenkel-Conrat, M. W. Nirenberg, and J. H. Matthaei, *Proc. Natl. Acad. Sci. U.S.* **48**, 846 (1962).

[114] D. Nathans, G. Notani, J. H. Schwartz, and N. D. Zinder, *Proc. Natl. Acad. Sci. U.S.* **48**, 1424 (1962).

[115] H. R. V. Arnstein, R. A. Cox, and J. A. Hunt, *Nature* **194**, 1042 (1962).

[116] I. B. Weinstein, R. Sager, and J. R. Fresco, *Federation Proc.* **22**, 644 Abstr. (1963).

[117] E. L. Smith, *Proc. Natl. Acad. Sci. U.S.* **48**, 677 (1962).

[118] E. L. Smith, *Proc. Natl. Acad. Sci. U.S.* **48**, 859 (1962).

[119] T. H. Jukes, *Biochem. Biophys. Research Communs.* **7**, 497 (1962).

[120] T. H. Jukes, *Proc. Natl. Acad. Sci. U.S.* **48**, 1809 (1962).

[121] M. B. Hoagland, *Brookhaven Symposia in Biol.* No. **12**, 40 (1959).

[122] S. Benzer and S. P. Champ, *Proc. Natl. Acad. Sci. U.S.* **47**, 1025 (1961).

[123] C. Yanofsky, D. R. Helinski, and B. D. Maling, *Cold Spring Harbor Symposia Quant. Biol.* **26**, 11 (1961).

[124] A. Garen and O. Siddiqi, *Proc. Natl. Acad. Sci. U.S.* **48**, 1121 (1962).

[125] M. Zalokar, *Exptl. Cell Research* **19**, 114 (1960).

[126] D. Giacomoni and S. Spiegelman, *Science* **138**, 1328 (1962).

[127] H. M. Goodman and A. Rich, *Proc. Natl. Acad. Sci. U.S.* **48**, 2101 (1962).

[128] S. A. Yankofsky and S. Spiegelman, *Proc. Natl. Acad. Sci. U.S.* **48**, 1069, 1466 (1962).

[129] C. Weissman, L. Simon, and S. Ochoa, *Proc. Natl. Acad. Sci. U.S.* **49**, 407 (1963).

[130] L. S. Baron and S. Falkow, *Records Genet. Soc. Am.* **30**, 59 (1961).

[131] S. Falkow, J. A. Wohlhieter, R. Citarella, and L. S. Baron, *Bacteriol. Proc. (Soc. Am. Bacteriologists)* p. 31 (1963).

[132] D. Martin and F. Jacob, *Compt. rend. acad. sci.* **254**, 3589 (1962).

[133] P. H. Makela, J. Lederberg, and E. M. Lederberg, *Genetics* **47**, 1427 (1962).

[134] R. Nakaya, A. Nakamura, and Y. Murata, *Biochem. Biophys. Research Communs.* **3**, 654 (1960).

[135] T. Akiba, K. Koyama, Y. Ishiki, and S. Kimura, *J. Microbiol.* **4**, 216 (1960).

[136] T. Watanabe and K. W. Lyang, *J. Bacteriol.* **84**, 422 (1962).

[137] T. Watanabe, *Bacteriol. Revs.* in press (1963).

[138] M. Robison and W. R. Guild, *Federation Proc.* **22**, 643 Abstr. (1963).

[139] J. Marmur and C. M. Greenspan, *Science* **142**, 387 (1963).

[140] R. L. Sinsheimer, B. Starman, C. Nagler, and S. Guthrie, *J. Mol. Biol.* **4**, 142 (1962).

[141] S. Spiegelman, personal communication.

CHAPTER 10

Toward a Definition of the Bacteria

R. Y. STANIER

To conclude this treatise, it seems appropriate to consider the central question of bacteriology: What are the bacteria, biologically speaking? In other words, where do they belong in the hierarchy of life, and to which other biological groups, if any, do they show affinities? Logic would seemingly dictate that an analysis of this problem should have prefaced, rather than terminated, a treatise on the bacteria. In fact, no satisfactory analysis was possible at the time when the treatise was originally planned; only in the last five years has the general framework of an answer become evident.

I. Historical Background of the Problem

The detailed exploration of the microbial world was one of the distinctive accomplishments of nineteenth century biology. As this last frontier of natural history was conquered, biologists came to recognize several major groups of microorganisms: algae, protozoa, fungi, bacteria, and— after the turn of the century—viruses. They were therefore faced with the problem of classifying these groups. The solution adopted was arbitrary and illogical, thanks to reliance on a false axiom and a stubborn refusal to look facts in the face.

The false axiom was the belief, essentially a prescientific judgment of common sense, that the world contains only two, mutually exclusive, categories of living organisms—plants and animals. Since this judgment had been accepted by the biological community as self-evident, the primary question to be decided was, apparently, to which kingdom the various microbial groups should be assigned. By a judicious selective emphasis on certain characters, it proved possible to decree that protozoa were "animals," whereas fungi, algae, and bacteria were "plants." In consequence of the primary taxonomic cleavage of biology that existed in the

445

mid-nineteenth century, the protozoa accordingly became the domain of zoologists, and the algae, fungi, and bacteria, the domain of botanists. Only one major biologist of the time, Haeckel,[1] protested this arbitrary partitioning of the microbial world, and stressed the cardinal fact that at this relatively simple level of biological organization the concepts of "plant" and "animal" lose their clarity. His taxonomic solution, to place all microorganisms in a third major category, the protists, was not adopted, despite its obvious merits.

The recognition of bacteria as important agents of disease led in the late nineteenth century to the establishment of bacteriology as a separate biological field; thereafter, bacteria became the domain of a new kind of biologist, armed with new, specialized techniques and a mental outlook quite unlike that of the scientists who had previously worked with bacteria. Insofar as bacteriologists thought about the matter at all, they tended to accept the dogma that bacteria were non-photosynthetic plants, comprising a group cognate with the fungi. However, the question of bacterial affinities was seldom seriously raised; in practice, it proved very easy to distinguish most bacteria from other microorganisms. The viruses were discovered and explored largely by scientists trained in the bacteriological tradition. At first, it seemed plausible to regard these entities as smaller, nutritionally highly specialized, cellular microorganisms of the bacterial type; this easy assumption was shattered only in 1935, with the crystallization of tobacco mosaic virus.[2]

The world of microbiologists has thus been split for historical reasons into three groups: one, with the prejudices of the zoological tradition, which studies protozoa; a second, with the prejudices of the botanical tradition, which studies algae and fungi; and a third, with the very special prejudices of the bacteriological tradition, which studies bacteria and viruses. It is an unfortunate fact that the world of microorganisms is rather poorly served by this division of professional interest. Most algae, the protozoa, and the fungi—the higher protists—can be construed as belonging to one very large and diverse microbial assemblage, nonetheless united by a number of fundamental properties, and intergrading at many different points, so that in the final analysis no satisfactory and clear-cut distinctions between "algae," "fungi," and "protozoa" can be made. However, it so happens that the intergradations occur between algae and protozoa, and between protozoa and fungi, with the consequence that the fundamental unity of the whole assemblage has never been evident to most botanists and zoologists. The broad affinities among higher protists were first clearly perceived by Pascher[3] in terms of structural characters, and the Pascherian argument was later ably extended by Lwoff[4] in terms of nutritional and physiological characters. However, one group of microorganisms traditionally assigned to the algae, the blue-green algae, stands apart. These organisms do not share the common properties which unite other algal groups with the protozoa and the fungi. We shall consider their affinities after discussing the various groups of organisms traditionally assigned to the bacteria.

The establishment of the bacteria as a special microbial group antedated the foundation of bacteriology as a separate biological science. It was, in essence, the work of one man, the botanist Ferdinand Cohn.[5-7] With a few exceptions, the organisms united by Cohn as bacteria comprised a very homogeneous group: the unicellular non-photosynthetic eubacteria, which multiply by binary fission and show flagellar motility if they are motile. However, as time went on, a whole series of microorganisms differing greatly in their properties from this original bacterial assemblage came, by common consent, to be accepted as bacteria. They included actinomycetes, the myxobacteria, the spirochetes, the photosynthetic bacteria, the rickettsias, and the pleuropneumonia group, with the viruses tentatively accepted (until their peculiar properties were understood) as a marginal addition. The extraordinary diversity of the organisms now generally placed among the bacteria (excluding viruses) is shown by a simple enumeration of the properties which they can possess. They can be unicellular, multicellular, or coenocytic; permanently immotile, or motile by any one of three distinct mechanisms; able to reproduce by binary fission, by budding, or by the formation of special reproductive cells, such as the conidia of actinomycetes; photosynthetic or non-photosynthetic. Despite this diversity, there has been remarkably little dispute among microbiologists about the assignment of any given organism or group of organisms to the bacteria. In practice, an experienced microbiologist has no difficulty in distinguishing bacteria from protozoa, fungi, and most algae, even when (as in the case of actinomycetes and mycelial fungi) there are substantial similarities of gross form. The two groups from which it has appeared difficult to distinguish certain bacteria are the viruses and the blue-green algae.

Some bacteria—the rickettsias, and the psittacosis-lymphogranuloma venereum group—are obligate intracellular parasites, the structural units of which are so small as to be barely resolvable by the light microscope. In these two respects, accordingly, they resemble the larger animal viruses, and the view has often been expressed that they are "transitional" between other bacteria and viruses. It was possible to express such a view, even as recently as 1955,[8] only because the essential properties of viruses had not been clearly grasped. This important logical analysis was undertaken in 1957 by Lwoff,[9] who for the first time formulated the constellation of properties which distinguishes the virus from the cell. The infectious viral particle, or virion, contains only one kind of nucleiͅ acid, enclosed in a coat of protein, formed by the polymerization of identical subunits. It carries few, if any, proteins endowed with enzymic function. It cannot divide. During its replication, which can take place only within a susceptible cell, the only component of the virion that is directly reproduced is its nucleic acid. Once the general properties of viruses had been formulated, it became evident that the differences between viruses and cells are of such a nature that no truly "intermediate" stage of biological organization could be envisaged. The problem presented by the rickettsias and the psittacosis-lymphogranuloma venereum group can now be differently phrased: Do these entities have the fundamental properties of cells, or of viruses? All present evidence (summarized by Moulder[10]) indicates that they are cellular in nature, and hence belong to the bacteria *sensu lato*.

The other diagnostic problem alluded to above—namely, that of distinguishing bacteria from blue-green algae—is not so easily solved. As Ferdinand Cohn[7] was the first to emphasize, there are close structural similarities between bacteria and blue-green algae; many of the nonmotile, coccoid or rod-shaped, unicellular blue-green algae have counterparts among the unicellular bacteria. A clear-cut distinction between these two groups could, however, be made on a physiological basis, by defining blue-green algae in terms of their photosynthetic metabolism, which is of the oxygen-evolving type characteristic of other algae and higher plants, as well as in terms of their characteristic pigment system. More serious difficulties arose through Winogradsky's studies[11] on the sulfur "bacteria" *Beggiatoa* and *Thiothrix*, which though indistinguishable in structure and mode of locomotion from filamentous blue-green algae, lack a photosynthetic pigment system. In more recent years, many other non-photosynthetic, filamentous, gliding organisms have been recognized.[12-17] In every case, these microorganisms could be defined either as blue-green algae (if one wished to emphasize their structural attributes) or as bacteria (if one wished to emphasize their mode of energy-yielding metabolism). In evolutionary terms, there can be little doubt that they represent non-photosynthetic descendants of filamentous blue-green algae, analogous to the leucophytes[4] so commonly found among the various groups of flagellate algae. This very instructive series of examples shows that, unless one invokes biochemical criteria, it is not possible in the last analysis to draw any sharp line of distinction between bacteria and blue-green algae.[17]

Since blue-green algae are the only group of organisms which pose this problem of differentiation from bacteria, it is an obvious inference that the two groups must share some fundamental similarities of cellular construction that set them rather sharply apart from other organisms. Such a view has been put forward at intervals by microbiologists ever since the time of Ferdinand Cohn; but the seemingly intractable problem has always been to characterize the distinctive common features of bacteria and blue-green algae in a biologically meaningful way. Simply to state, as many authors have done, that their cells are "primitive" does not serve any useful purpose; and the first attempts (e.g., Stanier and van Niel[17]) to describe the common group features in more specific terms were not particularly successful.

Since 1950, the development of the electron microscope as an effective instrument for biological research and the introduction of new analytical approaches to cytological problems have revolutionized our understanding of the organization of cells. For the most part, this rapid growth of knowledge has emphasized or brought to light fundamental homologies of cellular construction; the resemblances between the cells of plants, animals, and most microorganisms now seem much greater than the differences. However, the new cytological generalizations cannot be extended to the level of the bacteria and blue-green algae; their cells have proved to be constructed on an organizational plan entirely different from the plan that underlies the construction of the cell in other groups.[18, 19] We shall term the cellular plan characteristic of bacteria and blue-green algae "procaryotic"; and the plan characteristic of other protists, plants and animals, "eucaryotic." It is the procaryotic nature of their cells that unites the bacteria and blue-green algae, and separates them from all other cellular organisms. In the following sections of this chapter, the distinctive properties of this kind of cell will be outlined.

II. Organization of Functional Subunits in Eucaryotic and Procaryotic Cells

One basic difference between the two plans of cellular architecture is the manner in which major subunits of cellular function are housed within the enclosing cytoplasmic membrane. In the eucaryotic cell, the nuclear material (at least during interphase) and the multienzyme systems which perform respiration and photosynthesis are severally enclosed within individual unit membranes, distinct from the cytoplasmic membrane. These internal membranes accordingly serve to isolate physically the genetic system and the enzymic machinery of respiration and photosynthesis from other internal regions of the cell, each in a structurally distinctive organelle. In the procaryotic cell, on the other hand, there is no equivalent structural separation between the major subunits of cellular function; the cytoplasmic membrane itself is the only bounding membranous element in the cell, and within its confines the separation between functional subunits is maintained without the interposition of any obvious physical barriers. The maintenance of separate functional regions in procaryotic cells without an interposed membrane is particularly evident with respect to the nucleus. Cytochemical methods define a discrete nucleus region, the unique site of the cellular DNA (deoxyribonucleic acid).[20] Electron micrographs of thin sections fixed by the procedure of Ryter and Kellenberger[21] show that there is a sharp separation between the nuclear region, densely filled with fibrils of DNA, and the adjacent, ribosome-filled cytoplasm; but at the same time these electron micrographs provide clear evidence for the absence of an interposed membrane. The continuous maintenance of this phase separation between nucleus and cytoplasm in the procaryotic cell is a very curious phenomenon; it is scarcely understandable unless one assumes that the contents of the cell have at all times the properties of a gel. In fact, the immobility of the cytoplasm of procaryotic cells in the living state affords one of the most helpful clues for recognizing bacteria and blue-green algae by examination with the light microscope. Of course, the cytoplasm of some eucaryotic cells shows little if any internal movement; but there are a host of phenomena—ameboid movement, cytoplasmic streaming, the formation, migration, and coalescence of vacuoles, the migration of nuclei, the light-directed orientation of chloroplasts—which all attest to the internal mobility, actual or potential, of the cytoplasm in eucaryotic cells. None of these phenomena has a counterpart in bacteria and blue-green algae.

III. Nuclear Structure and Reproduction in Procaryotic Organisms

A second fundamental difference between the eucaryotic and procaryotic cell lies in the organization of the genetic elements. A clear description in classical cytological terms of the properties of the procaryotic nucleus became possible only 20 years ago, when Robinow[22] developed satisfactory procedures of fixation and staining. Ensuing cytological studies showed that every kind of procaryotic cell contains discrete nuclear elements, the division of which is regularly correlated with cell division. The division of each nuclear element involves a broadening and splitting, unaccompanied by any gross change of form through the divisional cycle. Despite transient dissent,[23] it is now universally agreed by bacterial cytologists that nothing resembling a mitotic apparatus, or an organization of the nuclear substance into discrete chromosomes, can be recognized during the course of division. The electron microscopy of bacterial thin sections (see Robinow[24]) simply confirms these inferences, without adding any further information about the details of the divisional process.

The next step to the understanding of procaryotic nuclear organization came with the genetic analysis of *Escherichia coli* (see Wollman and Jacob[25]). The genetic data could be physically interpreted only by the assumption that the genes are linearly arranged in a single, closed linkage group. In other words, *E. coli* appeared to have a single circular chromosome, if we wish to employ classical cytogenetic terminology.

Recent physicochemical work has invested this model with structural reality. The radioautographic investigation by Cairns[26, 27] on the chromosome of *E. coli* has demonstrated that it consists of a single piece of two-stranded DNA, approximately 1000 μ long, which duplicates by forming a fork, the new limbs of the fork each containing one strand of new material and one strand of old material. Furthermore, physical evidence for the circularity postulated for genetic reasons could be derived from these experiments. Equally striking electron microscopic evidence that the bacterial chromosome comprises a single, continuous molecule of two-stranded DNA has been obtained by Kleinschmidt and Lang[28] for *Micrococcus lysodeikticus*, using the ingenious technique of breaking protoplasts by osmotic shock, and spreading the DNA molecules out with a film-forming protein.

The combined genetic and physical studies on the structure of the bacterial chromosome accord excellently with the grosser picture of procaryotic nuclear structure and behavior established by cytological methods, both classical and modern. What is perceived by the cytologist as the bacterial nucleus actually consists of a single, two-stranded DNA molecule, almost 1 mm. in length, and probably circular. This giant molecule is compressed into a compact mass some 0.2 μ in diameter. It replicates by forking, new strands being laid down in strictly polarized sequence along each strand of the fork.* The physical mechanism for the segregation of the daughter DNA molecules is not yet established. The absence of mitosis in procaryotic cells now becomes fully understandable. Mitosis is an elaborate biological device which permits the equipartition of the replicated genetic material at the time of nuclear division when, as in all eucaryotic cells, the sum of genetic determinants is dispersed over two or more units of structure, the eucaryotic chromosomes. A mitotic machinery could have no reason for existence in a cell where all genetic determinants reside in a single molecule.

Considering its traditional meaning, the word "chromosome" is obviously not a desirable designation for the DNA molecule which carries the genetic determinants of the procaryotic cell. The procaryotic "chromosome" is functionally equivalent to the total chromosome complement of a eucaryotic nucleus; it does not undergo the elaborate secondary structural changes characteristic of eucaryotic chromosomes; and it does not even have the same gross chemical composition, being devoid of the basic proteins which are always associated with DNA in eucaryotic chromo-

* For a genetic confirmation of the mode of replication, see Nagata[28a] and Yoshikawa and Sueoka.[28b]

somes. This terminological difficulty demonstrates in the most effective possible fashion the distinctiveness of the procaryotic cell. Since all our basic concepts about cells were derived historically from the study of eucaryotic cells, we now find ourselves saddled with a cytological terminology which cannot be easily applied to a different kind of cell.

As an appendix to this analysis of procaryotic nuclear structure, we may briefly summarize the consequences of the physical organization of the bacterial genome insofar as mechanisms of genetic transfer are concerned.[25] All modes of gene transfer so far discovered in bacteria have certain common features that distinguish them sharply from sexual and parasexual processes in eucaryotic organisms. Except in rare cases of bacterial conjugation, procaryotic gene transfers involve the introduction of a small fragment of the genome from a donor cell into a recipient cell with a complete genome. The recipient cell is consequently not *genetically* equivalent to a eucaryotic zygote; it becomes a partial diploid, or merozygote. If recombination then takes place, the normal haploid condition is reestablished by the elimination of supernumerary alleles; there is never a production of reciprocal recombinants, a basic feature of the recombinational event in eucaryotic sexual processes. A further difference from the situation in eucaryotic organisms is that modification of the procaryotic genome by genetic transfer does not necessarily require that the introduction of new genetic material into the recipient cell be followed by recombination. In many instances, the newly introduced genetic fragment can maintain itself more or less indefinitely in the autonomous state, as an episome.

IV. The Organization of Respiratory and Photosynthetic Function in Procaryotic Cells

One of the functional consequences of the internal compartmentalization characteristic of eucaryotic cells is that two major energy-generating metabolic unit processes, respiration and photosynthesis, take place entirely within the confines of special organelles, the mitochondrion and the chloroplast, respectively. Each of these organelles is in turn compartmentalized. The systems directly responsible for ATP (adenosine triphosphate) synthesis (oxidative phosphorylation and photosynthetic phosphorylation) are localized in the internal membrane systems of the respective organelles, while associated biochemical processes (reactions of the Krebs cycle in mitochondria, of the Calvin cycle in chloroplasts) take place in the adjacent, less highly structured regions. Thanks to the characteristic dispositions of the internal membrane systems associated with mitochondria and chloroplasts, each of these organelles can be readily identified by its distinctive profile as seen in electron micrographs of thin sections. The electron microscopic studies of the past decade (see Novikoff[29] for a summary) compel us to conclude that despite minor structural variations from group to group, the mitochondrion is a basically homologous cellular element throughout the entire span of eucaryotic cellular organisms (higher protists, plants and animals). It is also a well-nigh universal component of the eucaryotic cell, seemingly absent only in those rare eucaryotic protists that are obligate anaerobes. The chloroplast is, of course, a cellular organelle of less universal occurrence; but over the tremendous organismal span of eucaryotic photosynthetic organisms, when it does occur as a component of the cell, it likewise seems to be basically homologous (see Granick[30] for a summary).

Procaryotic organisms can also use photosynthesis and respiration as major energy-generating metabolic unit processes. Frequently, these processes are *biochemically* almost indistinguishable from the same processes as they occur in eucaryotic cells (e.g., photosynthetic metabolism in blue-green and in eucaryotic algae). However, the structural basis for the performance of respiration and photosynthesis in a procaryotic cell is wholly different. No organelles homologous with mitochondria and chloroplasts exist. In fact, the structural difference can be epitomized by the statement that *no unit of structure more simple than the procaryotic cell as a whole* (exclusive of wall and appendages) *can be recognized as the site of either metabolic unit process.*

A partial analysis of the organization of bacterial respiratory function became possible as a result of Weibull's discovery[31, 32] that the cytoplasmic membrane of certain bacteria can be isolated in a structurally identifiable state, free both from wall material and from the internal constituents of the cell. This isolation is dependent on a total dissolution of the cell wall by lysozyme, followed by gentle osmotic lysis of the protoplast. It can, therefore, be applied only to those relatively few Gram-positive bacteria, the walls of which can be completely stripped from the protoplast by lysozyme treatment. In two such organisms, *Bacillus megaterium* and *Sarcina lutea*, it has been shown[33-35] that the whole machinery of respiratory electron transport is intimately associated with the cytoplasmic membrane, as are also a few enzymes of the Krebs cycle (notably, succinoxidase). If we may generalize from these two cases, it accordingly appears that the cytoplasmic membrane of aerobic bacteria, in addition to fulfilling the universal physiological function of such membranes (namely, regulation of transport), has associated with it the enzymic machinery which, in eucaryotic cells, is built into the internal membranes of the mitochondrion. As a consequence of this organizational pattern, the physical integrity of the cell as a whole cannot be impaired without far-reaching effects on the biochemical integrity of the respiratory system. The "soluble" enzymes required for respiration, located in the cytoplasm proper, flow out of the cell and become dissociated from the electron transport system as soon as the cytoplasmic membrane is breached. The effects with regard to respiration are entirely analogous to those which follow osmotic or mechanical rupture of isolated mitochondria, and explain why bacteria proved unsuitable in the hands of the biochemists as sources of cell-free systems capable of full respiratory activity.

The original assumption of the cytologists, that the cytoplasmic membrane of bacteria is a simple membrane following the contour of the surrounding wall, has recently proved to be an oversimplification. In many aerobic bacteria, the membrane shows a more or less extensive degree of infolding, which may either be localized at certain points in the cell, or else extend over the entire cortical region of the cytoplasm. Localized complex infoldings, characteristically occurring in close association with sites of transverse wall formation, were first observed by electron microscopy of thin sections in Gram-positive bacilli[36, 37] and actinomycetes.[38] These are the structures for which Fitz-James[36] has coined the name of "mesosomes." They have been found in many other groups of Gram-positive bacteria, including *Corynebacterium*,[39] *Mycobacterium*,[40] *Micrococcus*,[40a] and *Listeria*.[41] Mesosomes are, however, not confined to Gram-positive bacteria; typical ones occur in *Caulobacter*.[42] The membranous infoldings may also assume other forms, such as the "simple" intrusions observed by Murray[43] in *Spirillum*. In two nitrifying bacteria, *Nitrosocystis* and *Nitrobacter*, Murray[44] has found extremely elaborate lamellar intrusions, disposed with great regularity in a particular region of the cytoplasm. The lamellar stacks of *Nitrosocystis* form a closely packed band across the cell, of sufficient size to be detectable in stained cells by light microscopy, although of course the fine structure cannot be resolved with the light microscope. In *Nitrobacter*, the lamellae are concentrated at one end of the cell; it is this internal arrangement which appears to determine the characteristically pear-shaped form of *Nitrobacter* cells. A particularly instructive study has been conducted by Pangborn et al.[45] on the internal membrane system of *Azotobacter*. When cells of this bacterium are broken by "gentle" methods (ballistic disintegration, osmotic shock) and washed free of liberated soluble cytoplasmic components, thin sections of the residual cytoskeleton reveal an extremely extensive internal network of tubular and vesicular membranes, connected with the cytoplasmic membrane proper. Further mechanical treatment greatly reduces the internal membrane system, and at the same time liberates a considerable amount of the reduced diphosphopyridine nucleotide oxidase originally present in the cytoskeleton in a form that is no longer readily sedimentable. From this, the authors conclude that the internal membranes are the probable site of the electron transport system in the cell. The internal membrane system can be detected in sections of whole cells, but is not readily visible, as a result of low contrast with the surrounding cytoplasmic materials.

The recent revelation of the structural complexity and variability of the cytoplasmic membrane in aerobic bacteria of course raises at once a new question: is the electron transport system evenly distributed through the cytoplasmic membrane *as a whole,* or is this system localized, as Pangborn et al.[45] imply, in the internal intrusions from the membrane? At present, no clear-cut answer to this question can be given.*

We must now consider the nature of the structures associated with the performance of photosynthesis in the cells of bacteria and blue-green algae. A number of recent electron microscopic studies on thin sections of blue-green algae (e.g., Niklowitz and Drews,[46] Shatkin,[47] Ris and Singh[48]) reveal that much of the cytoplasmic region is traversed by an extended system of paired lamellae. As shown by Ris and Singh,[48] the patterns of these lamellar systems vary considerably in different members of the blue-green algae. The lamellae seem to be structurally analogous to (and conceivably homologous with) the internal lamellae of chloroplasts; however, they are not enclosed within a common membrane which separates them from other regions of the cytoplasm. This point is particularly well shown in the electron micrographs of Ris and Singh,[48] where the ribosomal matrix of the cytoplasm is clearly resolved; in a number of cases it can be seen that this matrix actually extends between adjacent pairs of lamellae. Fragments of the lamellar system have been isolated from broken cells by Petrack and Lipmann[49]; they contain the chlorophyll of the cell, and are endowed with photophosphorylative function.

In photosynthetic bacteria, the picture is a much more variable one. As Vatter and Wolfe[50] first showed, the cytoplasmic region of many nonsulfur purple bacteria grown anaerobically in the light appears to be packed with spherical vesicles, about 500 A. in diameter; these vesicles were absent from cells of facultatively aerobic species grown aerobically in the dark, and thus rendered essentially free of photosynthetic pigments. Cohen-Bazire and Kunisawa[51] have recently made a detailed study of the fine structure of one species, *Rhodospirillum rubrum,* grown under a series of well-defined conditions, the influence of which on the pigment content of the cell was known from previous physiological work.[52] They established that the abundance of vesicles is correlated with the specific chlorophyll content of the cell. Each vesicle is defined by a unit membrane, indistinguishable in cross-section from the cytoplasmic membrane, which encloses a region of very low electron density. In sections of cells with a low content of vesicles, it could be seen that some of the vesicles represent simple

---

* See, however, Vanderwinkel and Murray.[45a]

intrusions of the cytoplasmic membrane, the transparent central region being directly connected with the space between the membrane and the cell wall. These observations suggest that the vesicles characteristic of so many purple bacteria, and shown by isolation[53] to contain the photosynthetic pigments of the cell, may in fact be an extremely extensive internal membrane system formed from the cytoplasmic membrane, and at all times in physical continuity with it.

In at least two purple bacteria[54-56] vesicles are absent, their place being taken by a system of paired lamellae resembling those found in blue-green algae. Just as in blue-green algae, the internal arrangement differs in the two purple bacteria in question. Giesbrecht and Drews[57] have recently shown, by examining thin sections of osmotically lysed cells, that the leaf-shaped lamellar bundles characteristic of *Rhodospirillum molischianum* arise from, and are attached to, the cytoplasmic membrane. There is probably no fundamental difference between the vesicular and lamellar systems of purple bacteria: if flattened, a vesicle would in effect become indistinguishable from a paired lamella. Indeed, Fuller[58] has recently established that the purple sulfur bacterium *Chromatium* may contain either vesicles or lamellae, depending on the conditions of cultivation; and Cohen-Bazire[59] has found that another purple sulfur bacterium, *Thiocapsa*, contains a mixture of vesicular and lamellar elements.

In the case of purple bacteria, a problem analogous to that discussed in connection with aerobic bacteria presents itself: Is the photosynthetic apparatus evenly distributed throughout the cytoplasmic membrane as a whole, or localized in the vesicular and lamellar intrusions? Here also, no final answer can be given at present.

One further point concerning the organization of photosynthetic function in procaryotic cells deserves emphasis. As so conclusively demonstrated by Arnon and his collaborators,[60] the eucaryotic chloroplast is the site not simply of the multienzyme system and pigment system required for photosynthetic energy conversion, but also of the entire array of soluble enzymes responsible for primary photosynthetic carbon assimilation and sugar synthesis. Although there is now abundant evidence that the internal membranes of photosynthetic bacteria and blue-green algae contain the systems necessary for photosynthetic energy conversion,[61] there is no evidence whatsoever that the soluble enzymes responsible for the reactions of primary photosynthetic carbon assimilation are *specifically* associated with the photosynthetic apparatus.

In concluding this analysis of the localization of respiratory and photosynthetic function in procaryotic cells, we must attempt to see what generalizations emerge. In the first place, it seems highly probable that the cytoplasmic membrane of the procaryotic cell is functionally far more complex than the equivalent structure of the eucaryotic cell. It must, of course, regulate the entry and exit of materials, but in addition to this, it (or its extensions) appears to be the sole site within the procaryotic cell of respiratory and photosynthetic ATP synthesis. Since the thickness of this unit membrane is fixed, the only way in which its mass can be varied, relative to that of the cell as a whole, is by a change of area. Since the total volume of the cell is established by its rigid enclosing wall, increase in the area of the membrane can be achieved only by infolding. We would therefore expect to find extensive infolding of the cytoplasmic membrane in any procaryotic cells that have a high specific level of respiratory or photosynthetic activity. The observations of Cohen-Bazire and Kunisawa[51] on *Rhodospirillum rubrum* provide an experimental demonstration of the predicted correlation between photosynthetic activity and the extent of the internal membrane system. It is also no doubt significant that *Azotobacter*, which has the highest respiratory rate of any known organism, likewise has the most extensive internal membrane system so far found in an aerobic bacterium.[45] The particular form which the membranous infoldings take in different procaryotic cells may vary widely, and is probably of secondary importance. From their structure alone, it cannot be deduced with certainty whether such infoldings are associated with a respiratory or a photosynthetic apparatus: the simple intrusions in *Spirillum* look very like the photosynthetic vesicles of *Rhodospirillum rubrum*, and the lamellae of nitrifying bacteria mimic the regular lamellar stacks of *Rhodospirillum molischianum*.

V. Structures Associated with Procaryotic Cellular Movement

One of the greatest achievements of electron microscopy has been to demonstrate the basic structural homology of all eucaryotic contractile locomotor organelles. The flagella of algae, protozoa, and lower fungi, the ciliary apparatus of ciliates, the tails of male gametes, both plant and animal, are all constructed on the same fundamental pattern, and probably share the same ontogeny, although this is less certain.[62, 63] Contractile locomotor organelles also occur in two groups of procaryotic organisms, the true bacteria and the spirochetes, but are not homologous with eucaryotic locomotor organelles. A single bacterial flagellum, which has the approximate dimensions of one of the eleven internal fibrils of the eucaryotic flagellum, can serve as the complete unit of bacterial locomotor function (see Weibull[64] for a general discussion). Until recently, electron microscopy has not revealed any internal structure in the bacterial flagellum; but Kerridge *et al.*[65] have now shown the presence of molecular subunits, and have suggested alternate models, consisting either of three helical or of five parallel strands of subunits. Unlike eucaryotic flagella, bacterial flagella are not surrounded by an extension of the cytoplasmic membrane; instead, they extend through it, and are chemically distinct from it.[65]

The axial filament of spirochetes has been much less closely studied. Electron micrographs by Bradfield and Cater[66] and Swain[67, 68] suggest that it may be structurally equivalent to a bundle of bacterial flagella, wrapped helically about the cell and anchored in its two poles.

Many eucaryotic protists, the cells of which are not enclosed within a wall, can move over solid surfaces by directed cytoplasmic streaming ("ameboid movement"). No procaryotic organism capable of such movement is known.

One other major type of cellular locomotion occurs in procaryotic organisms: the "gliding movement" characteristic of myxobacteria and many blue-green algae. No locomotive organelles have ever been demonstrated on cells capable of gliding movement, and its mechanism is still unknown. Some groups of higher protists (desmids, gregarines, the simpler red algae) also move by mechanisms which have been described as "gliding," but here again the mechanism is as yet unclear. Hence we do not yet know whether the gliding movements of eucaryotic and of procaryotic cells are mechanistically identical.

VI. The Chemical Structure of the Wall in Procaryotic Cells

A wall, structurally distinct from the cytoplasmic membrane, is a well-nigh universal component of procaryotic cells; the pleuropneumonia-like organisms (PPLO) are the only group in which it appears to be absent. The obvious selective value of the wall in bacteria and blue-green algae may be correlated with the fact that they possess no *physiological* mechanism for the maintenance of water balance in a hypotonic environment; in eucaryotic protists without walls, the contractile vacuole provides a device for coping with this problem.[69] Hence, loss of the wall in procaryotic organisms (as exemplified by the PPLO group) restricts possible habitats, by prescribing an osmotically buffered environment.

Although studies on the chemical composition of procaryotic cell walls were initiated little more than ten years ago,[70] a large body of information about them has now accumulated; in fact, far more is known about their structure than about the structure of the walls of eucaryotic protists. Here we shall ignore the structural complexity and diversity of procaryotic walls, which have been ably reviewed elsewhere,[71-73] and discuss only their common chemical properties.

In the Gram-positive bacteria which possess walls of relatively simple chemical composition, electron microscopy of thin sections reveals the wall as consisting of a single, apparently homogeneous layer. The chemical analysis of such walls first revealed the existence of a distinctive class of biological heteropolymers, the bacterial mucopeptides,[74] which in extreme cases are the sole wall constituents of some Gram-positive bacteria. The polysaccharidic backbone of these mucopeptides consists of alternating units of muramic acid and N-acetylglucosamine. The carboxyl group of muramic acid affords a point of attachment, although peptide bonding, of short chains of highly characteristic amino acids. These amino acids invariably include glutamic acid and alanine, both of which have in part the "unnatural" D configuration, together with either lysine or diaminopimelic acid. A few other amino acids (glycine, serine, aspartic acid) may in some cases also be incorporated.[72]

In Gram-negative eubacteria, which have chemically more complex walls, the electron microscopy of thin sections reveals the wall as a multilayered structure, the various layers often differing from one another in thickness and profile. Once the fundamental chemical composition of the mucopeptides from the walls of gram-positive bacteria had been worked out, it became evident that the same key constituents (notably muramic acid and diaminopimelic acid, which occur uniquely in this class of heteropolymers) were also present in the welter of monomeric constituents obtainable by the hydrolysis of walls from Gram negative bacteria. Martin and Frank[75] have recently demonstrated, by an elegant series of fractionations, that in two Gram-negative bacteria the basal layer of the cell wall, adjoining the cytoplasmic membrane, consists of pure mucopeptide. Accordingly, the Gram-negative bacteria have, underlying additional layers of different chemical nature, a wall that is chemically homologous with the simple walls of certain Gram-positive bacteria. Although this basal layer makes a very small contribution in Gram-negative bacteria to the total mass of the wall,[75] it is evidently in large part responsible for maintaining the structural integrity of the cell, as shown by the susceptibility of Gram-negative bacteria to penicillin and lysozyme, which both affect the integrity of the mucopeptide layer.[76, 77]

The discovery of diaminopimelic acid in the cells of blue-green algae[78] provided the first indication that they might possess walls with the same distinctive chemical constituents as those of bacteria. This has been beautifully confirmed by Frank et al.,[79] who have used a combined electron microscopic and chemical approach to the analysis of wall structure in a filamentous blue-green alga, *Phormidium*. They were able to show that each cell in a filament is completely enclosed by a layer of pure mucopeptide; the wall in addition contains a second, outer layer of different composition.

The wall structure of other major procaryotic groups has not yet been studied in detail. It should be noted, however, that mucopeptide constituents have been reported in myxobacteria[80] and in rickettsias.[81] The absence of mucopeptide has been reported for only one procaryotic group, the PPLQ organisms,[82] which appear to be devoid of walls.

There are conceivably other chemical and biochemical properties which may prove distinctive of procaryotic organisms as a whole; but the presence of a unique class of mucopeptides as the principal strengthening element of the wall is as yet by far the best established one.

VII.- The Common Denominators of Eucaryotic and Procaryotic Cells

The foregoing analysis of the organizational peculiarities of procaryotic cells makes it easy to understand in retrospect why the problem of defining concisely the common properties of bacteria and blue-green algae proved so intractable. Apart from the absence of chloroplasts, long recognized to be characteristic of blue-green algae, none of the distinctive features of the procaryotic cell could be fully resolved by the techniques of classical cytology. The difficulties were compounded by the fact that, *at the level of gross structure and function,* eucaryotic and procaryotic cells are very similar to one another. In each case, growth and reproduction bring into play much the same characteristic sequence of events. Grossly considered as units of biochemical function, the two kinds of cells are likewise equivalent; all modern biochemistry attests to this fact. At the gross genetic level, there are likewise far-reaching homologies. Both kinds of cell can enter into the same modes of organismal structure: unicellularity, multicellularity, and the coenocytic state. The differences between them are, accordingly, expressed only to a very minor extent in terms of gross properties. Essentially, the differences now revealed represent two different modes of detailed construction, each of which can serve effectively as a basis for the performance of the universal functions of a cell.

VIII. Evolutionary Implications

Pringsheim[83] has presented convincing arguments for the belief that the bacteria and blue-green algae encompass a number of quite distinct major groups, not closely related to one another, but nonetheless united (as we can now see) by the possession of procaryotic cells. The procaryotic cell has, accordingly, provided a framework for extensive evolutionary diversification. Diversification is expressed in both structural and physiological properties. Among the most important structural features may be noted: organismal structure (unicellular, coenocytic, and simple multicellular groups) ; manner of cell division (binary fission, budding) ; mechanism of cellular movement. The physiological diversification is most strikingly exemplified by the variety of patterns of energy-yielding metabolism: there are three quite distinct photosynthetic groups, each with its unique pigment system, as well as a vast number of specialized chemotrophic groups.

In many of these respects, there are parallel modes of evolutionary diversification among the eucaryotic protists as a whole (protozoa, fungi, and eucaryotic algae). It thus appears that natural selection has operated in much the same ways on the two different lines of protists, eucaryotic and procaryotic, to produce specialized groups in each line which grossly mimic one another. There is a strikingly analogous case, at a much higher level of biological organization. This is the evolutionary diversification of the marsupials on the Australian continent, to produce a whole series of specialized groups which mimicked the adaptive radiations of the placental mammals on other continents. We can, however, infer from the much more restricted development of marsupial lines when they existed in free competition with mammals that the possibility for this parallel evolution in Australia depended on the geological accident of continental isolation. The eucaryotic and procaryotic protists, on the other hand, are at all times in direct competition. The successful survival and diversification of procaryotic organisms in the face of active competition from analogous forms with more highly developed cells are, therefore, at first sight an evolutionary paradox. How can it be explained? In the case of certain physiologically highly specialized groups, the answer is obvious. The photosynthetic bacteria can perform energy conversion with wavelengths in the solar spectrum that are not absorbed by any other phototrophs; the chemolithotrophic bacteria employ chemical energy sources not utilizable by any other living organisms. For the many procaryotic organisms that are not so nutritionally specialized, the occupation of a unique ecological niche cannot, however, be invoked as a solution. In this more general case, it may be surmised that the primary selective advantage has been conferred by the capacity for rapid growth, a consequence of the relative cellular simplicity, and above all of the enormously greater simplicity of the genetic material and its mode of replication.

In the whole span of contemporary living organisms, the gap which separates procaryotic from eucaryotic protists is without doubt the largest single evolutionary discontinuity. So far, we know of no organisms which, in terms of their cellular construction, could be considered transitional between the two. It is, nevertheless, difficult to avoid the conclusion that at some time in the past the transition from procaryotic to eucaryotic forms of life must have taken place; despite the differences, there are too many features shared by both kinds of cells for us to assume completely separate evolution. Above all, the sharing of a distinctive mode of photosynthetic metabolism by blue-green algae and the various groups of eucaryotic algae suggests that this crucial step in the evolution of the cell took place after the emergence of aerobic photosynthesis, and in a line which had acquired this physiological capacity. For the evolutionary biologist, the procaryotic protists thus provide a precious and unexpected body of evidence about one of the earliest stages in biological evolution, the evolution of the cell.

REFERENCES

[1] E. Haeckel, "Generelle Morphologie der Organismen." G. Reimer, Berlin, 1866.

[2] W. M. Stanley, *Science* **81**, 644 (1935).

[3] A. Pascher, *Arch. Protistenk.* **38**, 2 (1917).

[4] A. Lwoff, "L'Evolution Physiologique." Hermann, Paris, 1944.

[5] F. Cohn, *Nov. Act. Leo-Carol.* **24**, 103 (1854).

[6] F. Cohn, *Beitr. Biol. Pflanz.* **2**, 127 (1872).

[7] F. Cohn, *Beitr. Biol. Pflanz.* **3**, 141 (1874).

[8] G. S. Wilson and A. A. Miles, "Principles of Bacteriology and Immunity," 4th ed., p. 1057. Williams & Wilkins, Baltimore, Maryland, 1955.

[9] A. Lwoff, *J. Gen. Microbiol.* **17**, 239 (1957).

[10] J. W. Moulder, "The Biochemistry of Intracellular Parasitism." Univ. of Chicago Press, Chicago, Illinois, 1962.

[11] S. Winogradsky, "Beiträge zur Morphologie und Physiologie der Bacterien." I. Schwefelbacterien. A. Felix, Leipzig, Germany, 1888.

[12] S. Soriano, *Antonie van Leeuwenhoek* **12**, 215 (1947).

[13] E. G. Pringsheim, *J. Gen. Microbiol.* **5**, 124 (1951).

[14] R. Harold and R. Y. Stanier, *Bacteriol. Revs.* **19**, 49 (1955).

[15] J. W. F. Costerton, R. G. E. Murray, and C. F. Robinow, *Can. J. Microbiol.* **7**, 329 (1961).

[16] R. Lewin, *Can. J. Microbiol.* **8**, 555 (1962).

[17] R. Y. Stanier and C. B. van Niel, *J. Bacteriol.* **42**, 437 (1941).

[18] R. G. E. Murray, *Symposium Soc. Gen. Microbiol.* **12**, 119 (1962).

[19] R. Y. Stanier and C. B. van Niel, *Arch. Mikrobiol.* **42**, 17 (1962).

[20] C. F. Robinow, *Bacteriol. Revs.* **20**, 207 (1956).

[21] A. Ryter and E. Kellenberger, *Z. Naturforsch.* **13b**, 597 (1958).

[22] C. F. Robinow, *J. Hyg.* **43**, 413 (1944).

[23] E. D. Delamater, *Symposium Soc. Gen. Microbiol.* **6**, 215 (1956).

[24] C. F. Robinow, *Brit. Med. Bull.* **18**, 31 (1962).

[25] E. L. Wollman and F. Jacob, "Sexuality and the Genetics of Bacteria." Academic Press, New York, 1961.

[26] J. Cairns, *J. Mol. Biol.* **4**, 407 (1962).

[27] J. Cairns, *J. Mol. Biol.* **6**, 208 (1963).

[28] A. Kleinschmidt and D. Lang, *Proc. European Regional Conf. Electron Microscopy*, Delft, **II**, 690 (1960).

[28a] T. Nagata, *Proc. Natl. Acad. Sci. U.S.* **49**, 551 (1963).

[28b] H. Yoshikawa and N. Sueoka, *Proc. Natl. Acad. Sci. U.S.* **49**, 559 (1963).

[29] A. B. Novikoff, *in* "The Cell" (J. Brachet and A. E. Mirsky, eds.), Vol. II, p. 299. Academic Press, New York, 1961.

[30] S. Granick, *in* "The Cell" (J. Brachet and A. E. Mirsky, eds.), Vol. II, p. 489. Academic Press, New York, 1961.

[31] C. Weibull, *J. Bacteriol.* **66**, 688 (1953).

[32] C. Weibull, *J. Bacteriol.* **66**, 696 (1953).

[33] R. Storck and J. Wachsman, *J. Bacteriol.* **73**, 784 (1957).

[34] M. Mathews and W. R. Sistrom, *J. Bacteriol.* **78**, 778 (1959).

[35] C. Weibull, H. Beckman, and L. Bergström, *J. Gen. Microbiol.* **20**, 519 (1959).

[36] P. C. Fitz-James, *J. Biophys. Biochem. Cytol.* **8**, 507 (1960)

[37] W. van Iterson, *J. Biophys. Biochem. Cytol.* **9**, 183 (1961).

[38] A. M. Glauert and D. A. Hopwood, *J. Biophys. Biochem. Cytol.* **6**, 515 (1959).

[39] T. Kawata, *Japan. J. Microbiol.* **5**, 441 (1961).

[40] M. Koike and K. Takeya, *J. Biophys. Biochem. Cytol.* **9**, 597 (1961).

[40a] M. R. J. Salton and J. A. Chapman, *J. Ultrastruct. Research* **6**, 489 (1962).

[41] T. Kawata, *J. Gen. Appl. Microbiol. (Tokyo)* **9**, 1 (1963).

[42] G. Cohen-Bazire and J. L. Stove, unpublished observations.

[43] R. G. E. Murray, "Lectures on Theoretical and Applied Aspects of Modern Microbiology." Department of Bacteriology, University of Maryland, Baltimore, 1960–1961.

[44] R. G. E. Murray, *in* "General Physiology of Cell Specialization" (D. Mazia and A. Tyler, eds.). McGraw-Hill, New York, in press.

[45] J. Pangborn, A. G. Marr, and S. A. Robrish, *J. Bacteriol.* **84**, 669 (1962).

[46] W. Niklowitz and G. Drews, *Arch. Mikrobiol.* **27**, 150 (1957).

[47] A. Shatkin, *J. Biophys. Biochem. Cytol.* **7**, 583 (1960).

[48] H. Ris and R. N. Singh, *J. Biophys. Biochem. Cytol.* **9**, 63 (1961).

[49] B. Petrack and F. Lipmann, *in* "A Symposium on Light and Life" (W. D. McElroy and B. Glass, eds.), p. 21. Johns Hopkins Press, Baltimore, Maryland, 1961.

[50] A. E. Vatter and R. S. Wolfe, *J. Bacteriol.* **75**, 480 (1958).

[51] G. Cohen-Bazire and R. Kunisawa, *J. Cell Biol.* **16**, 401 (1963).

[52] G. Cohen-Bazire, W. R. Sistrom, and R. Y. Stanier, *J. Cellular Comp. Physiol.* **49**, 25 (1957).

[53] H. K. Schachman, A. B. Pardee, and R. Y. Stanier, *Arch. Biochem. Biophys.* **38**, 245 (1952).

[54] A. E. Vatter, H. C. Douglas, and R. S. Wolfe, *J. Bacteriol.* **77**, 821 (1959).

[55] E. S. Boatman and H. C. Douglas, *J. Biophys. Biochem. Cytol.* **11**, 469 (1961).

[56] G. Drews, *Arch. Mikrobiol.* **36**, 99 (1960).

[57] P. Giesbrecht and G. Drews, *Arch. Mikrobiol.* **43**, 152 (1962).

[58] R. C. Fuller, *in* "General Physiology of Cell Specialization" (D. Mazia and A. Tyler, eds.) McGraw-Hill, New York, in press

[59] G. Cohen-Bazire, unpublished observations.

[60] D. I. Arnon, *in* "Enyzmes: Units of Biological Structure and Function" (O. H. Gaebler, ed.), p. 279. Adademic Press, New York, 1956.

[61] D. Geller, *in* "The Bacteria" (I. C. Gunsalus and R. Y. Stanier, eds.), Vol. II, p. 461. Academic Press, New York, 1962.

[62] D. Fawcett, *in* "The Cell" (J. Brachet and A. E. Mirsky, eds.), Vol. II, p. 217. Academic Press, New York, 1961.

[63] E. Fauré-Frémiet, *Biol. Revs.* **36**, 464 (1961).

[64] C. Weibull, *in* "The Bacteria" (I. C. Gunsalus and R. Y. Stanier, eds.), Vol. I, p. 153. Academic Press, New York, 1960.

[65] D. Kerridge, R. W. Horne, and A. Glauert, *J. Mol. Biol.* **4**, 227 (1962).

[66] J. R. C. Bradfield and D. B. Cater, *Nature* **169**, 944 (1952).

[67] R. H. A. Swain, *J. Pathol. Bacteriol.* **69**, 117 (1955).

[68] R. H. A. Swain, *J. Pathol. Bacteriol.* **73**, 155 (1957).

[69] R. R. L. Guillard, *J. Protozool.* **7**, 262 (1960).

[70] M. R. J. Salton and R. W. Horne, *Biochim. et Biophys. Acta* **7**, 177 (1951).

[71] M. R. J. Salton, *in* "The Bacteria" (I. C. Gunsalus and R. Y. Stanier, eds.), Vol. I, p. 97. Academic Press, New York, 1960.

[72] M. R. J. Salton, "Microbial Cell Walls." Wiley, New York, 1960.

[73] C. S. Cummins and H. Harris, *J. Gen. Microbiol.* **14,** 583 (1956).

[74] E. Work, *J. Gen. Microbiol.* **25,** 167 (1961).

[75] H. H. Martin and H. Frank, *Zentr. Bakteriol Parasitenk, Abt. I,* **184,** 306 (1962).

[76] J. Lederberg, *Proc. Natl. Acad. Sci. U.S.* **42,** 574 (1956).

[77] M. R. J. Salton, *Nature* **170,** 746 (1952).

[78] E. Work and D. L. Dewey, *J. Gen. Microbiol.* **9,** 394 (1953).

[79] H. Frank, M. Lefort, and H. H. Martin, *Z. Naturforsch.* **17b,** 262 (1962).

[80] D. J. Mason and D. M. Powelson, *Biochim. et Biophys. Acta* **29,** 1 (1958).

[81] A. C. Allison and H. R. Perkins, *Nature* **188,** 796 (1960).

[82] O. Kandler and C. Zehender, *Z. Naturforsch.* **126,** 725 (1957).

[83] E. G. Pringsheim, *Bacteriol. Revs.* **13,** 47 (1949).

Author Index

Numbers in parentheses are reference numbers and indicate that an author's work is referred to although his name is not cited in the text. Numbers in italic show the page on which the complete reference is listed.

A

Abbo, F. E., 108(194), *148*

Abbott, M. T., 365(176), *371*

Abe, M., 117(291), 139(348, 353a), *151, 152*

Abraham, E. P., 247(51), *251*

Achenbach, N. E., 27(117), *47*

Adams, J. N., 74(29), 75(31), *85*, 165(53), 170(53), 171(53), 211(276), 214(276), *216, 222*

Adams, M. H., 116(279), *150*

Adelberg, E. A., 2(8), 8(8), 9(8), 9(35), 10(34), 11, 11(34), 22(8), 27(118), 29 (118), 33(34), 34(34), 35(135), *44, 45, 52, 84, 85, 156, 175, 177, 178,* 179(147), 180(154), 181, 182(9), 185(148), 187 (170, 171), 188, 189(148, 186), 194 (148), 195, 206, 207(171), 212, *215, 219, 220, 222,* 249(59), *251,* 265(174), 298(174), 299(174), *324*

Adler, J., 265(219), 320(219), *326,* 344 (101), 345(105), 346(112), 347(105, 113), 353(105, 131), 357, *369, 370,* 427(48), *441*

Akiba, T., 200, *221,* 439(135), *443*

Alačević, M., 245, *251*

Alberts, A. W., 405(153), *416*

Alberts, B. M., 338, *368*

Albertson, P. A., 20(87), *46*

Alexander, H. E., 89(17), 90(17, 24, 26), 97(57, 58), 100(58), 101(89, 90), 102 (112), 102(112), 104(17), 108(17), 112 (17), 113(17), 114(17), 116(58, 265), 123, 135(344), *144, 145, 146, 151, 152*

Alfoldi, L., 35(130), *47,* 191(209), 192, 193, *220*

Alikhanian, S. I., 223(7, 10), 244, 245, 247(10, 52), 248(53, 54), *250, 251*

Allen, M. K., 379(63), 380(63), 381(63), 388(63), 409(63), *414*

Allfrey, V. G., 432(93), *442*

Allison, A. C., 459(81), *464*

Allison, W. S., 113(248), *150*

Alloway, J. L., 89(20), 98(15), 108, *144*

Altenbern, R. A., 174(118b), *218*

Amano, T., 209(266), *222*

Ames, B. N., 258(46), 262(54, 54a), 264 (46, 54, 54a, 152, 207), 265(207), 277, 292(152), 299(54), 306(46), 312(54), 313(54), 316(207), 317(207), 318(46, 54, 54a, 152), 320, *321, 324, 325,* 378 (53), 401(53, 136), 402(136), 405(136), *414, 416*

Anagnostopoulos, C., 101(94, 97), 116, 117(94), 128(97), 129(97), 135(97), 141(97), *146,* 273(91), *322*

Anders, M., 329(16), 360(16), 362(16), 365(168), *367, 371,* 430(75), *441*

Anderson, D. L., 237(30), *251*

Anderson, E. S., 172(103), *218*

Anderson, R. L., 265(82), 271(82), 313 (82), 318(82), *322,* 382(89), *414*

Anderson, T. F., 20(96), 24(96, 106, 109), 25(109), 27(96, 106), 28(96, 106), 36 (96), 38(96, 106), 39(96), *46, 47,* 175 (128), 176(128), *218,* 237(31), 249 (55), *251*

Anderson, W. F., 111(228), 112(228), *149*

Anfinsen, C. B., 375(30), 377(41, 42), *413*

Anton, D. N., 35(131), *47,* 193(217b), *220*

Apger, J., 375(24), *413*

Aposhian, H. V., 343(94), 344(94, 95, 99), 354(94, 95), 355(99), 358(94, 95), 359 (95), 360(94, 95), 361(95, 99), 362(95), *369*

Appleyard, R. K., 52(9), *84,* 158(25, 30), *216*

Arber, W., 13(41), 22(41), *45,* 57(17, 19), 58(17), 64(17), 76(17, 33), 80(17), *84, 85,* 126, *151,* 168(68), 171, 172(101), 174(101), 187(172), 207(101, 172), *217, 218, 219,* 362(156a), *371*

Arca, M., 338(56), *368*

Arens, A., 308(193), *325*

H

Haber, E., 375(30), *413*

Haeckel, E., 446, *462*

Hagiwara, A., 22(100), *46*

Hahn, F., 97(58), 100(58), 102(112), 109 (206), 112(206), 113(206), 116(58), 123(58), 135(344), *145, 146, 149, 152*

Hakura, A., 17(74), *46*

Hall, B. D., 121(308, 309), *151, 363*(160), *371*, 399(124, 125), *415*, 429(62), 430 (78, 79, 81), *441, 442*

Hall, C. E., 105(155), 107(187), 111(155), *147, 148*, 351, *370*

Hamilton, L. D., 104(138), *147*, 332(24, 25), 333(183), 334(25), 335(28, 29), *367, 372*

Hamon, Y., 191(213), 195, 196(222, 227), *220, 221*

Hanaoka, M., 209(266), *222*

Hanawalt, P. C., 358(144), *371*

Handler, P., 427(40), *441*

Harada, K., 199(241), 200(245), *221*

Harold, R., 448(14), *462*

Harris, H., 226(20), *250*, 458(73), *464*

Hartman, P. E., 79(41), 81(41), 82(41, 44), 84(49), *85*, 175, *218*, 236(26), 237 (27), *250*, 258(38), 262(38, 52, 54, 54a, 56), 264(38, 52, 53, 54, 54a, 100, 152), 265(56), 273(52, 56), 275, 277, 279, 280(38, 52), 282(38), 283(52), 284 (56), 292(152), 296(53), 299(53, 54), 300(50), 311(38, 50, 56), 313(38, 54, 56), 318(54, 54a, 152), 320, *321, 322, 323, 324*, 378(53), 401(53, 136), 402 (136), 405(136), 406(170), *414, 417*

Hartman, Z., 82(44), *85*, 262(50), 264 (50, 53), 296(53), 299(53), 313(50), *321*, 406(170), *417*

Hartmann, D., 114(268), *150*

Haselkorn, R., 337(47), 339(63), *368*

Hashimoto, H., 200(245), *221*

Hashimoto, K., 141(355), *152*, 258(41), 262(41), 285(41), *321*

Hawthorne, D. C., 411(196), *417*

Hayashi, M., 102(108), 121(108), *146*, 371(163), 371, 402(140), *416*, 432(89), *442*

Hayes, W., 2(4, 6, 7), 3(12, 13, 16), 4(4, 16), 5(4), 7(6), 8(4), 23(6), 26(111), 27(12), 28(12, 13, 111), 29(16, 111), 32(125), 38(111), 43(156), 44(4), *44*,

45, 47, 175(127, 130, 132), 176(132, 139), 184(130), 191(139), 205(257, 258), 214, *218, 221*, 238(33), *251*, 253 (1), *320*

Hecht, L. I., 314(201), *325*

Hede, R., 105(150), *147*, 339(74), *369*

Helinski, D. R., 166(60), *217*, 265(75, 77, 110), 269(75, 77), 270(75, 77), 279 (110), 281(110), 282(110), 283(77), 285(110, 116), 289(110), 292(110), 294(110), 302(77, 110), 307(110), 308(110), 309(110), *322, 323*, 379(68), 381(68), 383(95), 385(95), 386(95), 388(68, 95), 389(103), 395(95), 399 (95, 103), 410(68), *414, 415*, 438(123), *443*

Helling, R. B., 265(83), 271(83), 319(83), *322*

Henning, U., 265(110, 183), 279(110), 281 (110), 282(110), 285(110, 116), 289 (110), 292(110), 294(110), 302(110, 183), 307(110), 308(110), 309(110), *323, 325*, 379(84), 383(96, 97), 385 (96), 386(96), 388(96, 97), 395(96, 97), 396(97), 399(96, 97), *414, 415*

Heppel, L. A., 114(253), *150*, 329(10), *367*

Herman, R. K., 189, 190, *220*

Hermann, R. K., 35(137), *47*

Herrington, K., 111(227), *149*

Herriott, R. M., 104(141, 143), 110(214, 215), 111(229), 113(244), 114(256), 115(278), 116(278, 281), 118, 119(256, 278), 120(256, 278), 128(328), 138 (214, 215), 141(356), *147, 149, 150, 151, 152*, 360(150), *371*

Hershey, A. D., 40(148), *48*, 96(54), 105 (145, 149), 106, *145, 147, 148*, 175 (125), *218, 276, 323*, 339(75, 79), 342, *369*, 427(50), 429(60), *441*

Herzenberg, L. A., 258(46), 264(46), 306 (46), 318(46), *321*

Hiatt, H. H., 314(204), *325*, 432(91), *442*

Hill, R. L., 377(39), 400(39), *413*

Hilmoe, R. J., 329(10), *367*

Hirota, Y., 5(23), 7(28), 9(28), 17(74), 23(23), 34(28), *45, 46*, 156(10, 11), 175(10, 11), 176(11), 180(153), 181, 182(155), 184, 185(155), 201(248), 203, 207, 208(248), *215, 219, 221*

Hirsch, U., 247(50), *251*

Subject Index

A

Acetyl coenzyme A carboxylase, activation of, 405

N-Acetylglucosamine, cell walls and, 459

Acid(s), nucleic acid stability and, 331, 336

Acridine(s),
colicinogenic factors and, 192
deoxyribonucleic acid and, 113
donor ability and, 5, 17
episomes and, 156
F factor and, 175, 176, 179, 181, 184, 186, 190
F_0-lac factor and, 204
intermediate donor strains and, 9
mutability-transfer factor and, 205
mutations and, 290–291, 304–305, 381, 389–391
replicator and, 212–213
resistance transfer factor and, 199, 201, 207, 209
R factor and, 16

Acriflavin, cytoplasmic inheritance and, 246

Actinomyces globisporus,
deoxyribonucleic acid, composition of, 422

Actinomyces griseus,
deoxyribonucleic acid, composition of, 422

Actinomyces viridochromogenes,
deoxyribonucleic acid, composition of, 422

Actinophage(s),
lysogeny and, 246
prototrophs and, 245

Active site region, structure of, 376–377

Adenine,
complex gene loci and, 265
methylation of, 330
nitrous acid and, 112
occurrence of, 329

Adenosine, protonated form of, 330

Adenosine diphosphate, glutamic dehydrogenase and, 406

Adenosine triphosphate, aspartic transcarbamylase and, 405

Adenylosuccinase, suppressor mutation and, 412

Aeration,
competence and, 116
F₋ phenocopies and, 21

Aerobacter aerogenes,
deoxyribonucleic acid, composition of, 422

Aeromonas formicans,
deoxyribonucleic acid, composition of, 422

Aeromonas punctata,
deoxyribonucleic acid, composition of, 422
deoxyribonucleic acid, composition of, 422

Agar, competence and, 116

Agrobacterium tumefaciens,

Alanine,
cell walls and, 459
deoxyribonucleic acid composition and, 434
tryptophan synthetase and, 388

Alanine dehydrogenase, glutamic dehydrogenase and, 406

Albumin, competence and, 116, 120

Alcaligenes faecalis,
deoxyribonucleic acid, composition of, 422
ribonucleic acid,
ribosomal, 431
soluble, 432

Algae,
bacterial affinities and, 446–449
deoxyribonucleic acid, base composition of, 421, 422, 424
diaminopimelic acid in, 459

Alkali(s), nucleic acid stability and, 331, 336

Alkylating agents, transforming activity and, 113

Alleles, nonidentical, 262

Allelism, test for, 93–94

Phosphorylation,
oxidative, factor transfer and, 203
Photosynthesis, procaryotic cells and, 455–457, 461–462
Piliation factor, nature of, 205
Pinus sibirica,
deoxyribonucleic acid, composition of, 422
Plants,
bacterial classification and, 445–446
deoxyribonucleic acid, base composition of, 422, 424
Plaque(s),
formation, transduction and, 58
Plectridium saprogenes,
deoxyribonucleic acid, composition of, 422
Pleuropneumonia-like organisms, osmotic balance and, 458
Pneumococcus, see also *Diplococcus*
competence in, 115–116
complex loci in, 271
deoxyribonucleic acid,
heterogeneity of, 425
interchain biases and, 439
heterologous nucleic acid and, 121
interspecific transformation of, 102
streptomycin dependent, 141
transformation of, 89, 90, 97, 134, 276
Polarity effects, mutations and, 402–403
Poliovirus,
ribonucleic acid, unbalanced composition of, 428
Polynucleotides,
synthetic,
amino acid incorporation and, 437
genetic code and, 308
Polynucleotide phosphorylase, known nucleotide sequences and, 396
Polyoma virus,
deoxyribonucleic acid, 342
composition of, 422
Polypeptide, repressor and, 166–167
Polyphosphate, competence and, 116
Polyribonucleotides,
nitrous acid and, 398
synthetic, amino acid incorporation and, 392–394
Polysaccharide(s),
biosynthesis, capsules and, 135

capsular, tranformation and, 89, 91–92, 97
conjugation and, 22
deoxyribonucleic acid preparation and, 98
resistance transfer factor and, 201
Polytoma agilis,
deoxyribonucleic acid, composition of, 422
Polytoma uvella,
deoxyribonucleic acid, composition of, 422
Polyuridylic acid, code and, 393
Primer, deoxyribonucleic acid synthesis and, 107, 343
Proactinomyces citreus,
deoxyribonucleic acid, composition of, 422
Proflavin, lysogeny and, 170
Proline,
auxotrophs, linked loci and, 313
complex gene loci and, 265
deoxyribonucleic acid composition and, 434
protein structure and, 301
Proline marker, sex factors and, 181
Prophage,
attachment,
mode of, 159–169
site of, 158–159
bacterial chromosome and, 52–53
defective, 53–54
transduction vector, 57–60
deoxyribonucleic acid, transformation and, 103
elimination, F-*lac* and, 208–209
fertility and, 13, 14
host-dependent mutants of, 54
induction, conjugation and, 36
transfer of, 24–26, 29–30, 35
Prophage λ*dg*, transduction and, 58
Protease(s), transforming activity and, 89
Protein,
colicinogenic factors and, 194, 195
competence and, 117
composition, deoxyribonucleic acid and, 431–434, 436
conjugation and, 34, 36